Biochemical Actions of Hormones

VOLUME V

Contributors

VINCENT G. ALLFREY

FRED R. BUTCHER

GRAHAM CARPENTER

STANLEY COHEN

PHILIP FEIGELSON

IRVING B. FRITZ

ROBERT D. IVARIE

EDWARD M. JOHNSON

ALVIN M. KAYE

DAVID T. KURTZ

ANTHONY W. NORMAN

BERT W. O'MALLEY

JANET RING

GORDON M. RINGOLD

WILLIAM T. SCHRADER

MICHAEL R. STALLCUP

J. R. TATA

LOUIS E. UNDERWOOD

JUDSON J. VAN WYK

WAYNE V. VEDECKIS

KEITH R. YAMAMOTO

Biochemical Actions of Hormones

Edited by **GERALD LITWACK**

Fels Research Institute and Department of Biochemistry
Temple University, School of Medicine
Philadelphia, Pennsylvania

VOLUME V

ACADEMIC PRESS New York San Francisco London 1978

A Subsidiary of Harcourt Brace Jovanovich, Publishers

ACADEMIC PRESS, INC.
111 Fifth Avenue, New York, New York 10003

United Kingdom Edition published by
ACADEMIC PRESS, INC. (LONDON) LTD.
24/28 Oval Road, London NW1

Library of Congress Cataloging in Publication Data

Main entry under title:

Biochemical actions of hormones.

Includes bibliographies.
1. Hormones. I. Litwack, Gerald, ed. II. Axelrod,
Julius, Date   [DNLM: 1. Hormones. 2. Physiology.
WK102 B615]
QP571.B56   574.1'927   70-107567
ISBN 0-12-452805-8 (v. 5)

Contents

1. Postsynthetic Modifications of Histone Primary Structure: Phosphorylation and Acetylation as Related to Chromatin Conformation and Function

Edward M. Johnson and Vincent G. Allfrey

2. Regulation of Exocytosis

Fred R. Butcher

7. Biochemical Properties of the Intestinal Receptor System for the Steroid Hormone 1,25-Dihydroxyvitamin D

Anthony W. Norman

8. The Chick Oviduct Progesterone Receptor

Wayne V. Vedeckis, William T. Schrader, and Bert W. O'Malley

9. Integrated Mammary Tumor Virus Genes: Transcriptional Regulation by Glucocorticoids and Specific Effects on Host Gene Expression

Keith R. Yamamoto, Robert D. Ivarie, Janet Ring, Gordon M. Ringold, and Michael R. Stallcup

10.   Induction and Regulation of Vitellogenin Synthesis by Estrogen

J. R. Tata

11.   Multihormonal Control of the Messenger RNA for the Hepatic Protein Globulin

David T. Kurtz and Philip Feigelson

List of Contributors

Numbers in parentheses indicate the pages on which the authors' contributions begin.

Vincent G. Allfrey (1), The Rockefeller University, New York, New York 10021

Fred R. Butcher* (53), Section of Physiological Chemistry, Division of Biology and Medicine, Brown University, Providence, Rhode Island 02912

Graham Carpenter (203), Department of Biochemistry, Vanderbilt University, Nashville, Tennessee 37232

Stanley Cohen (203), Department of Biochemistry, Vanderbilt University, Nashville, Tennessee 37232

Philip Feigelson (433), Institute for Cancer Research and Department of Biochemistry, Columbia University, New York, New York 10032

Irving B. Fritz (249), Banting and Best Department of Medical Research, University of Toronto, Toronto, Ontario, Canada

Robert D. Ivarie (373), Department of Biochemistry and Biophysics, Metabolic Research Unit, University of California, San Francisco, San Francisco, California 94143

Edward M. Johnson (1), The Rockefeller University, New York, New York 10021

Alvin M. Kaye (149), Department of Hormone Research, The Weizmann Institute of Science, Rehovot, Israel

*Present address: Department of Biochemistry, School of Medicine, West Virginia University, Morgantown, West Virginia.

David T. Kurtz (433), Institute for Cancer Research and Department of Biochemistry, Columbia University, New York, New York 10032

Anthony W. Norman (283), Department of Biochemistry, University of California, Riverside, California 92521

Bert W. O'Malley (321), Department of Cell Biology, Baylor College of Medicine, Houston, Texas 77030

Janet Ring (373), Department of Biochemistry and Biophysics, Metabolic Research Unit, University of California, San Francisco, San Francisco, California 94143

Gordon M. Ringold (373), Department of Biochemistry and Biophysics, Metabolic Research Unit, University of California, San Francisco, San Francisco, California 94143

William T. Schrader (321), Department of Cell Biology, Baylor College of Medicine, Houston, Texas 77030

Michael R. Stallcup (373), Department of Biochemistry and Biophysics, University of California, San Francisco, San Francisco, California 94143

J. R. Tata (397), National Institute for Medical Research, Mill Hill, London NW7 1AA, England

Louis E. Underwood (101), Department of Pediatrics, University of North Carolina School of Medicine, Chapel Hill, North Carolina 27514

Judson J. Van Wyk (101), Department of Pediatrics, University of North Carolina School of Medicine, Chapel Hill, North Carolina 27514

Wayne V. Vedeckis (321), Department of Cell Biology, Baylor College of Medicine, Houston, Texas 77030

Keith R. Yamamoto (373), Department of Biochemistry and Biophysics, University of California, San Francisco, San Francisco, California 94143

Preface

Fundamental endocrinology seems to be expanding rapidly on three major fronts: newer understanding of the actions of well-known hormones made possible by progress in biochemistry and molecular biology, the discovery of new hormones, and the nature of interaction of multiple hormones in regulating specific phenotypes. The contributions to Volume V of "Biochemical Actions of Hormones" exemplify these categories. Topics in the first category involve modifications of chromatin structure by hormones by E. M. Johnson and V. Allfrey; regulation of exocytosis by F. Butcher; ontogeny of estrogen receptors by A. M. Kaye; hormonal regulation of cells of the seminiferous tubule by I. B. Fritz; advances on the progesterone receptor by W. V. Vedeckis, W. T. Schrader, and B. O'Malley; the role of glucocorticoids in the integration of mammary tumor virus genes by K. R. Yamamoto, R. K. Ivarie, J. Ring, G. M. Ringold, and M. R. Stallcup; and a model system for estrogen action by J. R. Tata. Under the category of phenomenology of newer hormones there are contributions from J. J. Van Wyk and L. E. Underwood on somatomedins and their actions, from G. Carpenter and S. Cohen on epidermal growth factors, and from A. W. Norman on the specific mode of action of 1,25-dihydroxyvitamin D. Finally, under the nature of interaction of multiple hormones regulating specific phenotypes, there is a contribution from D. T. Kurtz and P. Feigelson on multihormone control of mRNA for a specific hepatic protein.

The expansion of basic endocrinology must be as unlimited as the potential progress of molecular biology, an evident conclusion which will guarantee future volumes in this treatise.

This is an appropriate place in which to thank the contributors to this volume and Academic Press for their continued fine cooperation in the publication of this treatise.

GERALD LITWACK

Contents of Previous Volumes

CHAPTER 1

Postsynthetic Modifications of Histone Primary Structure: Phosphorylation and Acetylation as Related to Chromatin Conformation and Function

Edward M. Johnson and Vincent G. Allfrey

I. INTRODUCTION

It is now well known that individual histones are subject to several distinct biochemical modifications which occur following histone synthesis and which alter the primary structure and, consequently, the physical and chemical properties of the histone molecules. The different types of postsynthetic modifications confer a structural variability which contrasts with the conservation of amino acid sequences of most histones throughout various eukaryotic tissues and species. Changes in postsynthetic modifications of histones, occurring under cellular regulation, may represent a mechanism for altering structural and functional properties of histones in the chromatin. Little is presently known regarding possible biological functions of histone modification, and, for most modifications, possible hormonal influences have not been detailed. In certain instances histone modifications have been correlated with events occurring during hormonal stimulation or in the processes of cell differentiation or proliferation. Numerous studies have been conducted concerning the enzymes regulating histone modification. Amino acid sequences of several histones are known, and examination of modification sites has provided information regarding interactions of specific histone regions with DNA and other chromatin proteins. Such studies are relevant to an eventual assessment of the effect of modifications on histone participation in chromosomal structure and activities.

Since the earliest reports on modification of histones (Phillips, 1963; Allfrey *et al.*, 1964; Murray, 1964; Kleinsmith *et al.*, 1966a,b; Ord and Stocken, 1966), several different reactions involving alterations of histone amino acid residues have been described. These reactions include methylation resulting in modified amino acids ϵ-N-methyllysine in mono-, di-, or trimethyl forms, ω-N-methylarginine, and 3-methylhistidine (Murray, 1964; Paik and Kim, 1967; Gershey *et al.*, 1968; DeLange *et al.*, 1969; Allfrey, 1971). Histones may also be acetylated, resulting in modified amino acids N-acetylserine and N-acetyllysine (for reviews of histone acetylation, see Allfrey, 1971, 1977; Louie *et al.*, 1973; Ruiz-Carrillo *et al.*, 1975). Histone phosphorylation may result in modified amino acids O-phosphoserine, O-phosphothereonine, N-phospholysine, and N-phosphohistidine (for reviews on histone phosphorylation, see Dixon *et al.*, 1975; Bradbury, 1975; Langan and Hohmann, 1975; Johnson, 1977). Recent reports suggest that histones may also incorporate poly(ADP-ribose) (Smith and Stocken, 1973; Dietrich *et al.*, 1973; Ueda *et al.*, 1975; Dixon, 1976), although sites of histone amino acid residues modified by ADP ribosylation have not been identified with the precision seen in localization of acetyl or methyl groups on particular amino acid residues. The present review concerns primarily the phosphorylation and acetylation of histones, the mechanisms through which these modifications are controlled, and the evidence for hormonal intervention in the dynamics of histone side-chain modification.

II. HISTONE PHOSPHORYLATION

Following initial reports on the incorporation of phosphate into lysine-rich histones (Kleinsmith, *et al.*, 1966a; Ord and Stocken, 1966; Langan and Smith, 1967), considerable progress has been made concerning both structural and regulatory aspects of histone phosphorylation. At this time amino acid sequences comprising several histone phosphorylation sites are known, and distinct protein kinases which catalyze phosphorylation of specific sites have been isolated. In at least one case, that involving phosphorylation catalyzed by cyclic AMP-dependent protein kinase, the mechanisms exist whereby hormonal modulation of histone phosphorylation may be implemented. Several reviews and recent papers have dealt with various aspects of histone phosphorylation, including technical aspects of measuring phosphorylation (Hnilica, 1972), histone phosphorylation and chromosome condensation (Bradbury, 1975; Matthews *et al.*, 1975), and the processing of newly synthesized histone molecules (Louie *et al.*, 1973; Dixon *et al.*, 1975; Ruiz-Carrillo *et al.*, 1975). Several recent reports concern biological correlates of histone phosphorylation and may be relevant to an assessment of the possible involvement of such phosphorylation in processes concerned with alterations in chromatin structure and with gene expression and replication.

A. PHOSPHORYLATION OF H1

Histone H1 has been the most thoroughly characterized of the individual histones with respect to sites of phosphorylation as well as to mechanisms regulating phosphate incorporation and turnover. Many of the properties of this lysine-rich histone differ from those of the other histones. H1 is the largest of the five major histone classes, possessing a molecular weight of about 21,000, corresponding to 210–220 amino acids. Unlike the other major histones, H1 displays considerable tissue and species heterogeneity, there being three to five subfractions of H1 in all mammalian sources examined. In part because of success in fractionating this group, sequence analysis of individual H1-types has been possible. Amino acid sequences for the N-terminal half and most of the C-terminal half of rabbit thymus H1 (subfraction 3) have been reported (Jones *et al.*, 1974; cf. Elgin and Weintraub, 1975), as have partial sequences for trout (Dixon *et al.*, 1975) and calf (Rall and Cole, 1971) H1. Recently a complete sequence for rabbit H3 has been presented (Cole, 1977).

Histone H1 was the first histone found to be phosphorylated. Kleinsmith *et al.* (1966a) observed that ^{32}P-phosphate could be incorporated into proteins in isolated lymphocyte nuclei and found that phosphate could be detected esterified to serine residues of the H1 histone fraction. Ord and Stocken (1966) observed lysine-rich (H1) histone phosphorylation *in vivo* in rat liver.

1. Cyclic AMP-Dependent H1 Phosphorylation

Early research on histone kinase activities revealed the ability of cyclic AMP-dependent protein kinase to catalyze H1 phosphorylation. Langan and Smith (1967) found that rat liver contains a histone kinase which catalyzes phosphorylation of histones and protamine. Upon isolation of this enzyme, it was observed that among the histones, H1 was preferentially phosphorylated by the enzyme (Langan and Smith, 1967; Langan, 1968). This histone kinase was found to be dependent upon cyclic AMP and to be similar, if not identical, to the cyclic AMP-dependent protein kinase isolated from other tissues and species (Langan, 1968, 1971a). In addition to the cyclic AMP-dependent histone kinase, a cyclic AMP-independent histone kinase, which phosphorylated histone H1, was also isolated from several different calf tissues (Langan, 1971a,b).

It has been observed that *in vivo* incorporation of ^{32}P-phosphate into H1 of rat liver can be stimulated by injection of certain hormones, such as insulin and glucagon, and by dibutyryl cyclic AMP (Langan, 1969a,b, 1970, 1971a, 1973; Takeda and Ohga, 1973). In experiments performed by Langan and co-workers, histone H1 phosphorylation was measured by isolation of a phosphorylated polypeptide obtained upon trypsin digestion of isolated H1. An 8- to 20-fold enhancement of ^{32}P-phosphate incorporation into the specific H1 fragment was observed upon injection of glucagon or dibutyryl cyclic AMP. Insulin, when injected intraperitoneally, also stimulated ^{32}P-phosphate incorporation into the specific H1 fragment. However, when insulin was perfused through rat livers along with ^{32}P-phosphate, no effect of the hormone upon H1 phosphorylation was observed, indicating that the action of insulin observed upon injection may have been an indirect effect (Mallette *et al.*, 1973). Hydrocortisone and ACTH had no effect upon phosphorylation of liver H1 (Langan, 1969b, 1970, 1971a). In response to glucagon injection, increased phosphorylation of H1 was clearly detectable after 15 minutes and was maximal after about 1 hour. Phosphorylation was not affected by injection of actinomycin D or cycloheximide (Langan, 1969b, 1970, 1971a).

These experiments suggest that phosphorylation of histone H1 in rat liver is under hormonal control. The possibility exists that in these experiments cyclic AMP-mediated phosphorylation of H1 might occur artifactually upon liver homogenization. This possibility was dealt with in subsequent studies by Wicks and co-workers (1975), who extracted H1 directly from cells with sulfuric acid, thereby allowing little opportunity for histone phosphorylation to occur during homogenization. In these studies the ability of various cyclic AMP analogs to induce tyrosine aminotransferase in Reuber H35 hepatoma cells was correlated with the ability of the analogs to stimulate phosphorylation of endogenous H1. All analogs which induced the enzyme also enhanced phosphorylation of a specific serine residue on H1 severalfold, although no causal relationship between these events was established.

Takeda and Ohga (1973) also examined the ability of hormones to stimulate phosphorylated protamine and H1 than on other histones or phosvitin. The of glucagon into rats, these workers measured liver cyclic AMP levels, protein kinase activity (in the absence of cyclic AMP), histone phosphorylation, and tyrosine aminotransferase activity. They found that a rapid increase in intracellular cyclic AMP levels and protein kinase activity preceded incorporation of phosphate into a specific site on histone H1 and an increase in activity of tyrosine aminotransferase. Because the same H1 site was phosphorylated both *in vitro* and *in vivo*, the authors concurred with earlier studies indicating that H1 is a substrate for cyclic AMP-dependent protein kinase *in vivo*.

A histone phosphatase reported to specifically dephosphorylate histones and protamine has been isolated from rat liver (Meisler and Langan, 1969). This enzyme was observed to remove phosphate from histones phosphorylated by cyclic AMP-dependent protein kinase. Activity of the enzyme was about 2-fold greater with phosphorylated H1 as a substrate than with phosphorylated H2B, although activity was greater with phosphorylated forms of protamine than with any of the phosphohistones tested. This enzyme could be isolated from several eukaryotic cell types but was not found in extracts from several prokaryotes. It has been reported that estrogen can induce synthesis of a protein associated with phosphoprotein phosphatase activity in rat uterus (Vokaer *et al.*, 1974). It was found that the phosphatase, when purified, had significant substrate specificity, acting more efficiently on phosphorylated protamine and H1 than on other histones or phosvitin. The phosphatase removed phosphate from H1 and protamine phosphorylated *in vitro* by cyclic AMP-dependent protein kinase. Other workers have reported that the uterine phosphoprotein phosphatase can be separated from an estrogen-induced protein and may not be itself induced by the hormone (Kaye *et al.*, 1975). Liu and Greengard (1974) have observed that aldosterone can induce phosphosphoprotein phosphatase activity of toad bladder. These observations raise the possibility that histone phosphorylation and dephosphorylation may be part of an interlocking control mechanism involving different hormones and cyclic nucleotides. However, until more is known about the natural substrates for phosphoprotein phosphatases, little can be deduced regarding a regulatory role for these enzymes.

The site of phosphorylation of histone H1 by cyclic AMP-dependent protein kinase has been localized to a single serine residue corresponding to position 37 of rabbit thymus H1, or serine 38 of calf thymus H1 (Langan, 1971a; Langan *et al.*, 1971). Recent results of Shlyapnikov and co-workers (1975) agree with the earlier results of Langan (1971a) indicating that isolated cyclic AMP-dependent protein kinase transfers only 1 mole of phosphate per mole of histone H1 *in vitro*, and that the site of phosphorylation of calf H1 is serine 38. The amino acid sequence of the H1 region containing this serine residue is known for both rabbit thymus and calf thymus H1 fractions (Rall and Cole, 1971) (see Fig. 1). It has been reported that histone kinase preparations from several tissues can phosphorylate two distinct sites on the H1 molecule. Separation of kinase enzyme activities from these tissues allowed the determination that cyclic AMP-dependent protein kinase catalyzes phosphorylation specifically of serine 38, while a separate cyclic AMP-independent histone kinase catalyzes phosphorylation of a serine residue (shown in Fig. 1) which corresponds to serine 105 of rabbit thymus H1 (Langan, 1971a,b; Langan and Hohmann, 1975). It should be noted that the substrate specificity of the cyclic AMP-dependent protein kinase *in vitro* is highly dependent on assay conditions, and that it is not yet clear whether or not H1 sites other than serine 38 may be phosphorylated by this enzyme *in vivo*.

It is notable that serine 38 is a site of amino acid heterogeneity in H1 molecules of certain species. For instance, H1 fraction 3 from rabbit thymus has alanine in place of serine at position 37 (analogous to calf thymus serine 38), while H1 fraction 4 from rabbit thymus has serine at position 37 (Langan *et al.*, 1971). This specific substitution of alanine for serine, occurring at a major site of histone phosphorylation, determines the phosphate acceptor capacity of a class of H1 molecules of a particular cell. It is interesting to contemplate the possible biological need for a cell to possess a class of H1 molecules insensitive to stimulation by cyclic AMP.

Serine residue 38 is located near the basic amino terminal region of the H1 molecule, and phosphorylation at this site would thus be expected to reduce

```
Ac-Ser-Glu-Ala-Pro-Ala-Glu-Thr-Ala-Ala-Pro-Ala-Pro-Ala-Glu-Lys-Ser-Pro-Ala-Lys-Lys-Lys-Lys-
 1                          10                                        20
                                                Ser-P*‡
Ala-Ala-Lys-Lys-Pro-Gly-Ala-Gly-Ala-Ala-Lys-Arg-Lys-Ala-Ala-Gly-Pro-Pro-Val-Ser-Glu-Leu-Ile-
                   30                                        40

Thr-Lys-Ala-Val-Ala-Ala-Ser-Lys-Glu-Arg-Asn-Gly-Leu-Ser-Leu-Ala-Ala-Leu-Lys-Lys-Ala-Leu-Ala-
                   50                                        60

Ala-Gly-Gly-Tyr-Asp-Val-Glu-Lys-Asn-Asn-Ser-Arg-Ile-Lys-Leu-Gly-Leu-Lys-Ser-Leu-Val-Ser-Lys-
         70                                  80                                  90
                                                       P‡
Gly-Thr-Leu-Val-Glu-Thr-Lys-Gly-Thr-Gly-Ala-Ser-Gly-Ser-Phe-Lys-Leu-Asn-Lys-Lys-Ala-Ala-Ser-
                        100                                  110

Gly-Glu-Ala-Lys-Pro-Lys-Pro-Lys-Lys-Ala-Gly-Ala-Ala-Lys-Pro-Lys-Lys-Pro-Ala-Gly-Ala-Thr-Pro-
                   120                                  130

Lys-Lys-Pro-Lys-Lys-Ala-Ala-Gly-Ala-Lys-Lys-Ala-Val-Lys-Lys-Thr-Pro-Lys-Lys-Ala-Pro-Lys-Pro-
         140                                  150                                  160

Lys-Ala-Ala-Ala-Lys-Pro-Lys-Val-Ala-Lys-Pro-Lys-Ser-Pro-Ala-Lys-Val-Ala-Lys-Ser-Pro-Lys-Lys-
                        170                                  180

Ala-Lys-Ala-Val-Lys-Pro-Lys-Ala-Ala-Lys-Pro-Lys-Ala-Pro-Lys-Pro-Lys-Ala-Ala-Lys-Ala-Lys-Lys-
                   190                                  200

Thr-Ala-Ala-Lys-Lys-Lys-Lys-OH
         210
```

FIG. 1. Observed biochemical modifications of histone H1 residues. The sequence of rabbit thymus H1 subfraction RTL3 is depicted (Cole, 1977). Serine 37 is a site of amino acid heterogeneity in rabbit H1 fractions (Langan *et al.*, 1971). In calf thymus, phosphorylation of the corresponding site occurs at serine 38. Sequenced sites of several calf thymus serine and threonine residues, not indicated in this figure, phosphorylated by growth-associated histone kinases from Ehrlich ascites cells, have recently been reported by Langan (1976). It has been observed that in trout testis H1 the sequence -Lys-Ser-Pro-Lys- is repeated three times between residues 153 and 200 and may represent a recurrent site of phosphorylation (Dixon *et al.*, 1975). In Figs. 1–5, * indicates that modification of a site has been observed to occur *in vivo*, and † indicates that a modification may be obtained *in vitro*.

the net positive charge of this region of the molecule. Circular dichroic measurements of DNA and histones indicate that histone H1 imposes on DNA bases a characteristic shift in position relative to the helical axis, and that phosphorylation of H1 at serine 38 reduces the ability of the histone to impose such a conformational change (Adler *et al.*, 1971). Watson and Langan (1973) have obtained evidence suggesting that phosphorylation of H1 by cyclic AMP-dependent protein kinase reduces the ability of the histone to block RNA synthesis on reconstituted chromatin templates.

2. H1 Phosphorylation in the Cell Cycle

Several recent experiments concern H1 phosphorylation occurring at particular times in the cell proliferative cycle. Extensive H1 phosphorylation has been shown to occur in rapidly dividing cells (Balhorn *et al.*, 1972; Louie and Dixon, 1972; Lake, 1973; Gurley *et al.*, 1973, 1974; Marks *et al.*, 1973; Hohmann *et al.*, 1975, 1976). In many eukaryotic cells two to four H1 sites are phosphorylated in the late G1 and S phases of the cell cycle (Balhorn *et al.*, 1972; Louie and Dixon, 1972; Marks *et al.*, 1973; Gurley *et al.*, 1975). Additional sites are phosphorylated in M (Lake and Salzman, 1972; Lake, 1973; Bradbury *et al.*, 1973, 1974). The increased phosphorylation during mitosis may be the consequence of a 6- to 10-fold increase in levels of a specific growth-associated histone kinase, as has been reported for certain mammalian cells (Lake and Salzman, 1972).

Several experiments concerning growth-associated H1 phosphorylation have recently been performed using the acellular slime mold *Physarum polycephalum*. The natural synchrony of nuclear division in this organism allows precise timing of events in the proliferative cycle. Bradbury and co-workers have observed that a peak of H1 phosphorylation occurs in late G2 or M, just preceding chromosome condensation and nuclear division (Bradbury *et al.*, 1973, 1974). It was hypothesized that H1 phosphorylation at this point in the cycle may constitute a mechanism for initiating chromosome condensation (Bradbury *et al.*, 1974). It was reported that exogenously added histone kinase, incorporated through the easily permeable outer membrane of the *Physarum* syncytium, could advance the onset of mitosis in synchronously growing nuclei (Inglis *et al.*, 1976). In recent experiments Matthews and co-workers have been able to separate newly synthesized protein kinases from existing protein kinases by exploiting the enhanced density of the new enzymes following growth of *Physarum* in medium containing D_2O. Experiments performed using synchronized *Physarum* plasmodia suggest that the increase in phosphorylation preceding M is likely to be due to activation of existing H1 kinases rather than to synthesis of new kinase molecules (H. R. Matthews, personal communication).

Assessment of the biological function of H1 phosphorylation at mitosis is complicated by recent observations of an apparent absence of H1 from mitotically dividing micronuclei of *Tetrahymena* (Gorovsky and Keevert, 1975; Johmann *et al.*, 1976). *Tetrahymena* contains certain histones not electrophoretically comparable to those of higher eukaryotes, and observations thus far do not preclude the possibility that in the micronucleus another histone or histones have taken over functions performed by H1 in other cells. Jackson and colleagues (1976) have found that inhibition of phosphatase activity with $ZnCl_2$ in metaphase HTC cells prevents the dephosphorylation of H1 which occurs as the cells shift from M into G1. It was observed that chromosomes decondensed normally in G1, although H1 remained phosphorylated. These results argue against involvement of massive H1 phosphorylation in maintenance of the metaphase condensed state but do not rule out the possibility that phosphorylation acts as an initiator of condensation.

Growth-associated phosphorylation of histone H1 predominantly involves sites different from serine 38 (Langan and Hohmann, 1975; Hohmann *et al.*, 1976) and may be catalyzed by histone kinases which are independent of activation by cyclic AMP (Lake, 1973; Comber and Taylor, 1974; Langan and Hohmann, 1975). Ajiro and co-workers (1976) have reported that in HeLa cells during mitosis, as many as six separate H1 amino acid residues may be simultaneously phosphorylated. These workers found that two distinct HeLa H1 subfractions are phosphorylated to different levels at all times during the cell cycle. In contrast to the low percentage of H1 phosphorylation mediated *in vivo* by cyclic AMP, it has been reported that at certain times in dividing cells all H1 molecules of a cell may be simultaneously phosphorylated (Chalkley *et al.*, 1973). Amino acid sequences in the vicinity of four different sites of H1 phosphorylation by a chromatin-bound growth-associated histone kinase have recently been identified (Langan, 1976). These observed sites of H1 phosphorylation by cyclic AMP-independent protein kinases include threonine as well as serine residues.

In developing trout testis, H1 is phosphorylated at up to four different sites. Amino acid sequences for these phosphorylation sites have been described (Dixon *et al.*, 1975). One of these sites contains serine 156 in the sequence -Ala-Ala-Lys-Lys-Ser(P)-Pro-Lys-. Sequences of the other phosphorylated sites are similar to this sequence in that they all contain the sequence -Lys-Ser-Pro-Lys-, which occurs repeatedly in the carboxy-terminal portion of the trout H1 molecule. This H1 phosphorylation occurs during rapid cell division in the early stages of spermatogenesis. Because H1 phosphorylation occurs a considerable time after synthesis of the H1 molecule, it has been speculated that this modification is involved in modulating the physical structure or activity of chromosomes rather than in regulating initial binding of H1 to the DNA (Louie and Dixon, 1973; Dixon *et al.*, 1975).

Experiments have been reported which relate changes in histone phosphorylation to hormonal stimulation in hydrocortisone-stimulated liver cells (Murthy *et al.*, 1970) and in lactating mammary gland cells (Barraclough and Campbell, 1973; Majumder, 1974). Stimulation of livers of adrenalectomized rats with hydrocortisone *in vivo* enhances primarily phosphorylation of the lysine-rich histones (Murthy *et al.*, 1970). In mammary glands of lactating and late pregnant guinea pigs, histone phosphorylation was observed to occur only on histones H1 and H2B (Barraclough and Campbell,

1973). A cyclic AMP-dependent protein kinase has been isolated from bovine lactating mammary glands (Majumder and Turkington, 1972; Chew and MacKinlay, 1974). Activity of this enzyme is induced by prolactin (Majumder and Turkington, 1972). A protein modulator of this protein kinase activity has been observed to specifically stimulate the phosphorylation of H1 and H2b *in vitro* (Majumder, 1974).

There is presently little evidence which would implicate phosphorylation of serine 37 as an event among those chromosomal changes taking place during the cell proliferative cycle, although additional studies in this area are needed. Analyses of levels of cyclic AMP-dependent protein kinase activity throughout the cell cycle of synchronized HeLa cells indicate that specific activity of the enzyme in the cytosol declines steadily throughout the cycle in inverse proportion to the amount of total cellular protein (Karn *et al.*, 1974). Costa and colleagues (1976) have reported that in CHO cells type I cyclic AMP-dependent protein kinase is high in mitosis and constant throughout the cell cycle, while type II cyclic AMP-dependent protein kinase appears to be correlated with initiation of DNA synthesis during S phase. Phosphorylation of serine 37 has been detected upon resumption of growth of serum-deprived Reuber H35 cells (Langan and Hohmann, 1975; Hohmann *et al.*, 1976). Comber and Taylor (1974) have reported that in folate-stimulated rat kidney, a peak level of intracellular cyclic AMP accompanies a peak of H1 phosphorylation shortly before maximum mitotic activity. Rather than mediating massive alterations in chromosomal structure, cyclic AMP-dependent H1 phosphorylation may be involved in altering structure or activity of more discrete chromatin segments in response to intracellular signals. Such a limited role for cyclic AMP-dependent H1 phosphorylation is consistent with results of Langan (1971a, 1973) which indicate that at certain times phosphorylation at serine 37 represents only a small portion of H1 phosphorylation *in vivo*. In rat liver the amount of H1 phosphorylated at serine 37 in response to hormones or cyclic AMP represents about 1% of the total lysine-rich histone. As noted previously, phosphorylation of serine 37 has been observed in rat liver cells as a response to hormonal stimulation (Langan, 1969b; Takeda and Ohga, 1973), and in Reuber hepatoma cells as a correlate to tyrosine transaminase induction by added cyclic AMP analogs (Wicks *et al.*, 1975). In these experiments no enhancement of phosphorylation of sites other than serine 37 was reported. At present, however, the possibility cannot be ruled out that cyclic AMP-mediated phosphorylation of sites other than serine 37 might occur *in vivo* on a small percentage of H1 molecules.

A class of histone kinases which catalyze formation of acid-labile phosphates of H1 and H4 has been observed in several tissues. Phospholysine could be detected in H1, and phosphohistidine in H4. The sites phosphorylated by these kinases have not yet been characterized. Enhancement of this type of kinase activity was correlated with the onset of DNA synthesis in regenerating rat liver (Chen *et al.*, 1974).

3. *H1 Phosphorylation and Chromatin Structure*

The functional significance of phosphorylation at different sites on the H1 molecule remains to be clarified. It is now known that most of the 60 positively charged basic amino acid residues of rabbit thymus H1 are located mainly at the N- and C-terminal ends of the molecule, with the center of the protein relatively depleted in positive charges (Bustin and Cole, 1969). Thus, it is conceivable that placement of a phosphate group near an end of the molecule could reduce ionic interaction of the basic amino acid residues with the negatively charged DNA phosphates. Recently, Fasy *et al.* (1977) have observed that phosphorylation of various species of H1 by the purified C subunit of cyclic AMP-dependent protein kinase reduces the affinity of the histone for DNA, as measured by chromatography on columns containing DNA covalently linked to a solid support. It is now believed that H1 is not a component of the core structure of the monomer nucleosome complex (Kornberg and Thomas, 1974; Bellard *et al.*, 1976), although evidence suggests that H1 may be associated with DNA contiguous to the core structure in the repeating unit (Noll and Kornberg, 1977). Several studies suggest that H1 may be involved in the higher-order folding or supercoiling of chromatin (Littau *et al.*, 1965; cf. Bradbury, 1975). It is possible that phosphorylation of a large percentage of H1 molecules at several sites, as has been observed during the cell proliferative cycle, could result in extensive changes in higher-order chromosome structure. Conversely, phosphorylation of H1 in response to cyclic nucleotides or hormones, occurring on a less extensive scale, could result in relatively localized alterations in chromatin structure, possibly associated with activation of specific regions of the genome.

B. Phosphorylation of H2A

Histone H2A is a lysine-rich histone with a lysine-to-arginine ratio of about 1.2. Calf thymus H2A has 129 amino acid residues and a molecular weight of 14,300. A sequence for calf thymus H2A has been determined (Yeoman *et al.*, 1972). As is the case with H1, the basic amino acid residues of H2A are predominantly located near the N- and C-terminal ends of the molecule, with the central region being dominated by hydrophobic and acidic amino acids. Evidence indicates that H2A, along with equimolar amounts of H2B, H3, and H4, is a constituent of the core complex of the nucleosome repeating unit of chromatin (Kornberg and Thomas, 1974; Simpson and Bustin, 1976). H2A may participate in specific histone–histone interactions within the chromatin subunit (D'Anna and Isenberg, 1974; Weintraub *et al.*, 1975). The precise molecular interactions of H2A with DNA and other histones remain to be elucidated.

An interesting feature of histone H2A, also true of histone H4, is that the N-terminal amino acid of the molecule is a serine residue which is at times both phosphorylated, on its hydroxyl group, and acetylated, on its amino group (Louie *et al.*, 1973; Dixon *et al.*, 1975). These modifications of H2A may be linked to processing of newly, synthesized histone molecules for entry into the nucleus and insertion into the chromatin. Little is presently known regarding mechanisms of regulation of H2A phosphorylation.

Evidence indicates that H2A is phosphorylated *in vivo* in regenerating rat liver (Sung *et al.*, 1971), during spermatid development in trout testis (Marushige *et al.*, 1969), and in synchronously dividing Chinese hamster cells (Gurley *et al.*, 1973). Gurley and colleagues found that phosphorylation of H2A in hamster cells is independent of cell cycle position, occurring in G1, G2, and M when DNA synthesis is absent, as well as in S phase during active DNA synthesis. This H2A phosphorylation is independent of histone synthesis, of DNA synthesis, and of H1 phosphorylation. It was suggested that H2A phosphorylation be considered in models involving activation of DNA template activity (Gurley *et al.*, 1973). Phosphorylation of H2A in maturing avian erythrocytes persists after the phosphorylation of the other major histone classes has ceased (Ruiz-Carrillo *et al.*, 1976).

H2A serves as a substrate for cyclic AMP-dependent protein kinase *in vitro* (Johnson and Allfrey, 1972; Shlyapnikov *et al.*, 1975). Shlyapnikov and co-workers have reported that a cyclic AMP-dependent protein kinase from pig brain has very high substrate specificity and phosphorylates only histones H1, H2A, and H2B. In the case of H2A, the enzyme transfers no more than 1 mole of phosphate to 1 mole of histone. The site of H2A phosphorylation has been identified as serine 19 (Shlyapnikov *et al.*, 1975). This site is near a cluster of basic amino acids at the N-terminal end of the histone, and it might be expected that phosphorylation of H2A at this location would significantly alter the charge density of this portion of the molecule. Cyclic AMP has been reported to enhance H2A phosphorylation in regenerating rat liver *in vivo*, although the sites of cyclic AMP-stimulated phosphorylation have not been identified (Letnansky, 1975).

C. Phosphorylation of H2B

Histone H2B is a lysine-rich histone with a lysine-to-arginine ratio of 1.5. Calf thymus H2B has 125 amino acid residues and a molecular weight of 13,800. An amino acid sequence for calf thymus H2B has been reported

(Iwai *et al.*, 1970). In H2B the basic amino acids are scattered throughout the molecule but are predominantly concentrated in the N-terminal region. H2B possesses 14 serine residues and eight threonine residues, thus presenting a seemingly good target for modification by phosphorylation. H2B is one of the four histones complexed with DNA in the core of the chromatin nucleosome (Kornberg and Thomas, 1974; Weintraub *et al.*, 1975; cf. Elgin and Weintraub, 1975).

Histone H2B has been reported to be phosphorylated in developing trout testis (Louie *et al.*, 1973; Dixon *et al.*, 1975) and in developing erythrocytes (Ruiz-Carrillo *et al.*, 1976). In developing erythrocytes H2B phosphorylation is closely correlated with DNA synthesis and, simultaneously, with synthesis of the histone. In developing trout testis, H2B phosphorylation occurs on serine residue 6 at times of DNA and histone synthesis in spermatogonia and primary spermatocytes (Dixon *et al.*, 1975; Dixon, 1976). Several cell divisions, both mitotic and meiotic, occur during spermatid development, and the relationship of histone phosphorylation to chromosomal events in this system is presently unclear. Because H2B phosphorylation occurs significantly after H2B synthesis (Dixon *et al.*, 1975), it is possible that the phosphorylation may be related to events occurring during cell division rather than to chromatin assembly. In developing trout testis, H2B phosphorylation is at a relatively low level, including only about 5% of the H2B molecules (Louie *et al.*, 1973). There is presently little evidence to indicate that H2B is phosphorylated during the proliferative cycle of mammalian cells. Gurley and colleagues have reported that phosphorylation in HTC cells originally attributed to H2B is most likely due to phosphorylation of an H3 subfraction (Gurley and Walters, 1973; Gurley *et al.*, 1975).

H2B is a good substrate for phosphorylation by cyclic AMP-dependent protein kinase *in vitro* (Chen and Walsh, 1971; Johnson and Allfrey, 1972; Shlyapnikov *et al.*, 1975). Under certain circumstances, H2B gives a higher maximal velocity of phosphorylation than does H1 when employed as a substrate for isolated protein kinase (Chen and Walsh, 1971; Johnson and Allfrey, 1972). Amino acid sequences at sites of phosphorylation of calf thymus H2B by cyclic AMP-dependent protein kinase have been reported by Farago and co-workers (1975), using human lymphocyte protein kinase, by Shlyapnikov and co-workers (1975), using pig brain protein kinase, and by Hashimoto and co-workers (1975), using silkworm protein kinase. Farago *et al.* (1975) isolated a tryptic phosphopeptide from H2B containing serine residues 36 and 38. Both Shlyapnikov *et al.* (1975) and Hashimoto *et al.* (1975) determined that serine 36 of H2B is phosphorylated. Hashimoto and co-workers also reported phosphorylation of serine 32 by the protein kinase. Kuroda and colleagues (1976) found that purified protein kinases from silkworm and bovine cerebellum each phosphorylated sites serine 32 and serine 36 of calf thymus H2B. Serine residue 14 of H2B was reported to be a site of cyclic AMP-mediated phosphorylation by Shlyapnikov and co-workers, but Hashimoto and co-workers did not observe phosphorylation at serine 14 in their experiments.

D. PHOSPHORYLATION OF H3

H3 is an arginine-rich histone which possesses a molecular weight of 15,300 in calf thymus. H3 is a component of the nucleosome core (Kornberg and Thomas, 1974). It interacts specifically with H4 (Camerini-Otero *et al.*, 1976) and, like H4, appears to occur at the 5'-ends of the DNA strands in isolated nucleosomes (Simpson, 1976) although further work is necessary to establish this. Interaction of H3 with other histones has also been described (D'Anna and Isenberg, 1974). Histone H3 is phosphorylated in cultured Chinese hamster cells (Gurley and Walters, 1973), in developing trout testis (Louie *et al.*, 1973; Dixon *et al.*, 1975), and in maturing avian erythroid cells (Ruiz-Carrillo *et al.*, 1975, 1976). Evidence obtained by Dixon and colleagues (1975) indicates that in trout testis, H3 may have one phosphorylation site per molecule. Studies performed using cultured Chinese hamster cells indicate that H3 phosphorylation occurs at low levels throughout interphase, and that, just prior to mitosis, an intense burst of H3 phosphorylation accompanies the previously described phosphorylation of H1 (Gurley *et al.*, 1975). H3 serves as a substrate for cyclic AMP-dependent protein kinase *in vitro* (Chen and Walsh, 1971; Johnson and Allfrey, 1972), although there is little evidence to suggest that this enzyme catalyzes *in vivo* H3 phosphorylation. Recently, Shoemaker and Chalkley (1977) have isolated an H3-specific histone kinase from nuclei of rat and calf thymus. The kinase reportedly phosphorylates H3 at a single site which appears identical to the site phosphorylated during metaphase-associated H3 phosphorylation. Further characterization of H3 phosphorylation sites should aid in assessing possible mediation by regulatory agents.

E. PHOSPHORYLATION OF H4

Histone H4, an arginine-rich histone, is the smallest histone and the histone least subject to evolutionary changes in amino acid sequence (cf. DeLange and Smith, 1972; Elgin and Weintraub, 1975). H4 is one of the four histones comprising the nucleosome protein core (Kornberg and Thomas, 1974; Simpson, 1976; Camerini-Otero *et al.*, 1976). H4 is phosphorylated on its N-terminal serine residue in both trout testis cells (Dixon *et al.*, 1975) and avian erythroid cells (Ruiz-Carrillo *et al.*, 1975). In trout testis, phosphorylation at this residue occurs after a long period following histone synthesis and may be concerned with altering DNA–histone interactions subsequent to insertion of H4 into the chromatin (Louie *et al.*, 1973). It is notable that the N-terminal serine of H4 is subject to two modifications: phosphorylation and acetylation. Histone H4 is a poor substrate for cyclic AMP-dependent protein kinase *in vitro* (Johnson and Allfrey, 1972). It has been reported that arginine-rich histones are effective substrates for cyclic GMP-dependent protein kinases isolated from different tissues (Kuo, 1974). Cyclic GMP-dependent protein kinases have not been localized in nuclei, although stimulatory effects of cyclic GMP upon lymphocyte nuclear proteins have been noted (Johnson and Hadden, 1975). Glucagon has been observed to enhance guanylate cyclase activity in rat liver nuclei through a mechanism possibly mediated by cyclic AMP (Earp *et al.*, 1977). Activities of cyclic GMP-dependent protein kinases have not yet been investigated using purified H3 and H4 histones. Recently, Masaracchia *et al.* (1977) have reported the isolation from murine lymphosarcoma cells of two histone kinases specific for H4. H4-Kinase(I) was found to catalyze formation of 1.02 moles of phosphoserine per mole of H4. The enzyme did not catalyze phosphorylation of a synthetic hepatapeptide corresponding to the N-terminal sequence of H4, but it did catalyze phosphorylation of a synthetic peptide analog corresponding to H4 residues 13–19 at serine 47. H4-Kinase(II) phosphorylated the H4 peptide containing serine 1.

F. Phosphorylation of H5

Histone H5 is a lysine-rich and serine-rich histone found specifically in nucleated avian erythrocytes. As the red blood cells of birds mature, they progressively lose their capacity for RNA synthesis, and a change in the state of the chromatin from a loosely packed, diffuse state to a more compact, condensed state is accompanied by a partial displacement of the lysine-rich histone H1 with H5 (Cameron and Prescott, 1963; Ruiz-Carrillo *et al.*, 1975). Analysis of the N-terminal amino acid sequence of H5 indicates that this histone may be similar to H1 with regard to interspecies sequence variability (Seligy *et al.*, 1976). Recent results of Sung (1977) indicate that H5 is a highly phosphorylated protein, containing up to nine phosphates per histone molecule in immature erythrocytes. During maturation H5 is dephosphorylated, leading to the suggestion that H5 phosphorylation and dephosphorylation may be factors in the timing of erythrocyte chromatin condensation (Sung, 1977). Histone H5 is an effective substrate *in vitro* for cyclic AMP-dependent protein kinase (T. M. Fasy, E. M. Johnson, and V. G. Allfrey, unpublished observations). It was found that under certain conditions H5 is phosphorylated to a greater extent than is H1 when incubated with a purified cyclic AMP-dependent protein kinase from calf thymus. At this point little is known regarding regulation of H5 phosphorylation in intact cells.

G. HISTONE KINASE ACTIVITIES

1. Possibilities for Hormonal Regulation

Numerous protein kinase enzyme activities have been found associated with nuclei of various tissues and species (Kish and Kleinsmith, 1974; Johnson *et al.*, 1975; Jungmann *et al.*, 1974; Johnson, 1977). Among these kinases are apparently a specific H3 histone kinase (Shoemaker and Chalkley, 1977), a specific H4 histone kinase (Masaracchia and Walsh, 1977), and several kinases including cyclic AMP-dependent protein kinases which catalyze phosphorylation of different sites on H1 (cf. Johnson, 1977). Protein kinases have been found which specifically catalyze phosphorylation of nonhistone nuclear proteins (Kish and Kleinsmith, 1974; Ahmed and Wilson, 1975). Recently, cyclic AMP-independent phosphorylation of yeast RNA polymerase has been observed to modulate polymerase activity (Bell *et al.*, 1976). Keller *et al.* (1975) have reported that chromatin protein kinase activity is enriched in the transcriptionally active fraction of chromatin. Certain nuclear protein kinases may be subject to modulation by histones. Changing levels of H1 or H4 in isolated rat liver nuclei alters levels of phosphorylation of specific nonhistone proteins (E. M. Johnson *et al.*, 1973). Both cyclic AMP- (Miyamoto *et al.*, 1973) and cyclic GMP-dependent protein kinases (Kuo *et al.*, 1976) can be dissociated into subunits and activated by histones.

The most extensively studied histone kinase to date has been the cyclic AMP-dependent protein kinase. Phosphorylation catalyzed by this enzyme represents one example of possible hormonal regulation of a histone modification. As cited previously, evidence suggests that this enzyme phosphorylates a specific site on H1 both *in vitro* and *in vivo*. The functional significance of this H1 phosphorylation remains to be elucidated, as does the biological role of cyclic AMP in the cell nucleus. Evidence has been presented that the catalytic subunit of calf thymus cyclic AMP-dependent protein kinase has an affinity for calf DNA in excess of that expected for a simple ionic interaction (Johnson *et al.*, 1975). Such an affinity may be a factor influencing substrate specificity of the kinase in the nucleus. Numerous reports concern the action of this cyclic nucleotide on incorporation of radioactive precursors into RNA (Sharma and Talwar, 1970; Rosenfeld *et al.*, 1972), enhancement of RNA polymerase activities (Martelo *et al.*, 1974; Jungmann *et al.*, 1974), or induction of specific enzyme synthesis (Beck *et al.*, 1972; Russel and Pastan, 1974; Insel *et al.*, 1975). There is currently little evidence to indicate that cyclic AMP functions as a differential regulator of transcription at specific gene sites in eukaryotes, although further work in this area is necessary. Available data are consistent with the possibility that the cyclic nucleotide can regulate rates or levels of expression of regions of the genome in response to extracellular signals. This type of regulation would be compatible with possible effects of cyclic AMP upon chromatin structure, mediated by histone phosphorylation.

2. Site Specificity of Histone Kinases

Several recent reports have concerned the recognition by the protein kinase of amino acid sequences in the vicinity of phosphorylatable serine residues on substrate proteins. From studies on genetic variants of β-casein as substrates for protein kinase, it has been hypothesized that location of an arginine residue in proximity to serine is a specificity determinant (Kemp *et al.*, 1975). These workers observed that the synthetic polypeptide Arg-Gly-Tyr-Ser-Leu-Gly is a substrate for rabbit skeletal muscle protein kinase. Replacement of Arg by Gly, His, or Lys in this polypeptide resulted in a reduction in the V_{max} of phosphorylation. Synthetic polypeptides representing varying lengths of part of the phosphorylatable site of rat liver pyruvate kinase were also examined as substrates for cyclic AMP-dependent protein kinase (Kemp *et al.*, 1976). It was found that the shortest peptide which could be significantly phosphorylated was a pentapeptide with sequence Arg-Arg-Ala-Ser-Val. The most effective synthetic substrate examined thus far has been the heptapeptide (a) Leu-Arg-Arg-Ala-Ser-Leu-Gly, which corresponds to a segment of pig liver pyruvate kinase (Kemp *et al.*, 1976). The affinity of this heptapeptide for the protein kinase is approximately equal to that of the most effective substrate proteins, and the V_{max} of phosphorylation of the heptapeptide is considerably higher than that of most proteins thus far examined.

It can be seen that certain aspects of the heptapeptide substrate (a) resemble the sequence surrounding the site of cyclic AMP-dependent H1 phosphorylation (see Fig. 1). In each case two basic amino acid residues including arginine (-Arg-Lys- or -Arg-Arg-) are in close proximity to the phosphorylated serine residue on the amino-terminal side. In addition, two nonpolar residues are in proximity to the serine on the carboxy-terminal side. H1 is among the best protein substrates for the kinase. Recent work from our laboratory has established that the synthetic peptide sequences (b) Arg-Lys-Ala-Ser-Gly-Pro and (c) Arg-Arg-Lys-Ala-Ser-Gly-Pro, corresponding to the site containing serine 38 of calf thymus H1, can serve as effective substrates for the protein kinase. The inclusion of an extra arginine, as in (c), results in a 5-fold enhancement of the V_{max} of phosphorylation of the synthetic peptide. Whereas the V_{max} of phosphorylation of (b) is 4.1 μmoles/minute/mg under our conditions, the V_{max} for (c) is 22.1 μmoles/minute/mg (Pomerantz *et al.*, 1977). The V_{max} for (a) under our conditions is 50.6 μmoles/minute/mg. The H1 analogs (b) and (c) possess affinities for the protein kinase which are about 20- to 50-fold lower than that of intact H1. Thus it appears that additional structural aspects of H1 are involved in the substrate capacity of the histone. We have determined that substitution of D-serine for L-serine in (a) results in a striking diminution of the ability of the peptide to serve as a substrate for the kinase. Enzyme kinetic studies employing (a) as substrate have provided evidence that phosphorylation involves the formation of an enzyme–peptide–ATP intermediate (Pomerantz *et al.*, 1977).

Several criteria for evaluating the functional significance of protein phosphorylation have previously been described (Johnson, 1977). One important means of assessing the role of phosphorylation at a specific site is to selectively inhibit *in vivo* phosphorylation at that site. Knowledge of sequence specificities of histone phosphorylation should lead to the design of specific inhibitors and to a greater understanding of the biological role of phosphorylation at the individual sites.

III. HISTONE ACETYLATION

A. Enzymatic and Structural Basis

Since the discovery of histone acetylation in 1964 and the coordinate finding that acetylation of the histones diminishes their capacity to inhibit RNA synthesis *in vitro* (Allfrey, 1964; Allfrey *et al.*, 1964), there have been many indications that acetylation of histones H3 and H4 provides a significant index of changing transcriptional patterns *in vivo*. Much of the evidence has been summarized in earlier reviews (Allfrey, 1966, 1970, 1971, 1977; Ruiz-Carillo *et al.*, 1975). The present discussion will reconsider that evidence and some more recent results in the light of more detailed knowledge of the structures of histones, their sites of modification, and the relationships between certain types of acetylation and the transcriptional activity of cells responding to hormonal, mitogenic, or other stimuli.

1. "Terminal" and "Internal" Acetylation

It is now recognized that a clear distinction must be made between two major forms of histone acetylation. The first involves the modification of the NH_2-terminal serine residues of histones H1, H2A, and H4 (Phillips, 1963,

1968; DeLange *et al.*, 1969; Ogawa *et al.*, 1969; Liew *et al.*, 1970; Rall and Cole, 1971). This modification of the amino-terminal serine residue occurs in the cytoplasm at the time of histone synthesis and probably occurs on the nascent polypeptide chains while they are still attached to the polysomes (Liew *et al.*, 1970; Pestana and Pitot, 1975). Terminal acetylation is not commonly observed in nondividing cells, and it appears to be an essentially irreversible modification without the dynamic "turnover" associated with the second major type of histone acetylation, which leads to alteration of the ε-amino groups of lysine residues within the polypeptide chain (Gershey *et al.*, 1968; Vidali *et al.*, 1968).

$$CH_3-\overset{\overset{\text{O}}{\|}}{C}-S-CoA \; + \; -\underset{\underset{\text{H}}{|}}{N}-\overset{\overset{\text{NH}_3^+}{|}}{\underset{\underset{(CH_2)_4}{|}}{C}}-\overset{\overset{\text{O}}{\|}}{\underset{\underset{\text{H}}{|}}{C}}-\underset{\underset{\text{H}}{|}}{N}- \; = \; -\underset{\underset{\text{H}}{|}}{N}-\overset{\overset{CH_3-\overset{\overset{\text{O}}{\|}}{C}-NH}{|}}{\underset{\underset{(CH_2)_4}{|}}{C}}-\overset{\overset{\text{O}}{\|}}{\underset{\underset{\text{H}}{|}}{C}}-\underset{\underset{\text{H}}{|}}{N}- \; + \; CoA-SH \qquad (1)$$

The acetylation of lysine residues (internal acetylation) involves an enzymatically catalyzed transfer of acetyl groups from acetyl coenzyme A, according to the general reaction (1) (Allfrey, 1964; Nohara *et al.*, 1966; Libby, 1968; Gallwitz, 1968, 1970, 1971; Gallwitz and Sekeris, 1969; Gallwitz and Sures, 1972; Pestana *et al.*, 1971; Racey and Byvoet, 1971; Horiuchi and Fujimoto, 1972; Lue *et al.*, 1973; Pestana and Pitot, 1975). The enzymes catalyzing this type of histone modification are complex; they differ in chromatographic properties (Gallwitz, 1971; Gallwitz and Sures, 1972; Lue *et al.*, 1973; Harvey and Libby, 1976), pH optima (Berkovic and Mauritzen, 1977), and in substrate specificity requirements (Gallwitz and Sures, 1972). Such complexity is not unexpected in view of the structural complexity of their substrates and the site specificity of histone acetylation, as described below.

2. *Intracellular Distribution of Acetyltransferases*

Because the acetylation of lysine residues in histones is largely a nuclear phenomenon, emphasis has been placed on enzymes of nuclear origin. Acetyltransferases have been described in nuclei from calf and rat thymus (Allfrey, 1964, 1966; Gallwitz and Sures, 1972), avian erythrocytes (Berkovic and Mauritzen, 1977), pigeon liver (Nohara *et al.*, 1966), and the kidney (Gallwitz, 1971), brain (Bondy *et al.*, 1970) and liver of the rat (Gallwitz, 1968, 1971; Gallwitz and Sekeris, 1969; Lue *et al.*, 1973). From the salt concentrations needed for effective extraction of acetyltransferases from isolated nuclei or chromatin fractions (Racey and Byvoet, 1972; Gallwitz and Sures, 1972; Lue *et al.*, 1973; Harvey and Libby, 1976), one may surmise that the enzymes are tightly bound to chromatin. This conclusion is supported by autoradiographic evidence that histone acetylation occurs along the polytene chromosomes of *Chironomus thummi* (Allfrey *et al.*, 1968) and *Drosophila melanogaster* (Clever and Ellgard, 1970) and in the maternal chromosomes of *Planococcus citrii* (Berlowitz and Pallotta, 1972). There is also evidence that the acetyltransferases remain associated with some of the nucleosomes after staphylococcal nuclease fragmentation of the chromatin (C. C. Liew, personal communication, 1977).

Histone acetylating enzymes also occur in the cytoplasm (Pestana *et al.*, 1971; Horiuchi and Fujimoto, 1972; Ruiz-Carrillo *et al.*, 1975; Jackson *et al.*, 1976). One of these appears to be specific for histone H4 (Horiuchi and Fujimoto, 1972). This is particularly significant because H4 is subject to a transient acetylation of a lysine residue at the time of its biosynthesis (Ruiz-Carrillo *et al.*, 1975; Jackson *et al.*, 1975, 1976). That acetyl group is rapidly lost when the newly synthesized H4 molecule enters the cell nucleus and joins the DNA strand. This rapidly reversible modification of H4 is believed to be a key event in the assembly of the nucleosome (Ruiz-Carrillo *et al.*, 1975). Once incorporated into the nucleosome, histone H4—together with the other histones of the nucleosome "core"—becomes subject to a controlled series of acetylation and deacetylation reactions. The structural basis of many of these reactions will now be considered.

3. Sites of Histone Acetylation

In considering the biological implications of histone acetylation, it is significant that histone H1, which is not a component of the 140-base-pair nucleosome "core," does not contain detectable amounts of ϵ-N-acetyllysine (Sanders *et al.*, 1973; DeLange and Smith, 1975; Dixon *et al.*, 1975). [A nonphysiological acetylation of H1 lysine residues is carried out by acetyltransferases *in vitro* (Nohara *et al.*, 1968; Gallwitz, 1968; Gallwitz and Sures, 1972; Lue *et al.*, 1973; Berkovic and Mauritzen, 1977), but acetylation *in vivo* is coordinate with H1 synthesis (Ruiz-Carrillo *et al.*, 1976) and results in the formation of N-acetylserine at the amino terminus (Fig. 1).]

The "core" histones (H2A, H2B, H3, and H4) are all subject to enzymatic acetylation of their lysine residues, but each histone has characteristic sites of acetylation which differ in their surrounding amino acid residues and in their frequency of substitution. The known sites of acetylation in each of the "core" histones are shown in Figs. 2–5, which summarize information derived from peptide mapping and isotopic labeling of histones from a variety of different cell types.

4. H2A

Histone H2A contains ϵ-N-acetyllysine at position 5 of the polypeptide chain (Candido and Dixon, 1972a; Sautiere *et al.*, 1974; Dixon *et al.*, 1975)

```
      P*              Ac*                                                          P‡
Ac-Ser-Gly-Arg-Gly-Lys-Gln-Gly-Gly-Lys-Ala-Arg-Ala-Lys-Ala-Lys-Thr-Arg-Ser-Ser-Arg-
   1                           10                                    20

-Ala-Gly-Leu-Gln-Phe-Pro-Val-Gly-Arg-Val-His-Arg-Leu-Leu-Arg-Lys-Gly-Asn-Tyr-Ala-Glu-
                         30                                    40

-Arg-Val-Gly-Ala-Gly-Ala-Pro-Val-Tyr-Leu-Ala-Ala-Val-Leu-Glu-Tyr-Leu-Thr-Ala-Glu-Ile-
                      50                                    60

-Leu-Glu-Leu-Ala-Gly-Asn-Ala-Ala-Arg-Asp⁻Asn-Lys-Lys-Thr-Arg-Ile-Ile-Pro-Arg-His-Leu-
                      70                                    80

-Gln-Leu-Ala-Ile-Arg-Asn-Asp-Glu-Glu-Leu-Asn-Lys-Leu-Leu-Gly-Lys-Val-Thr-Ile-Ala-Gln-
                      90                                   100

-Gly-Gly-Val-Leu-Pro-Asn-Ile-Gln-Ala-Val-Leu-Leu-Pro-Lys-Lys-Thr-Glu-Ser-His-His-Lys-
                     110                                   120

⁻Ala-Lys-Gly-Lys-COOH
        129
```

FIG. 2. Observed biochemical modifications of histone H2A residues. The sequence shown is that reported by Yeoman *et al.* (1972) for calf thymus H2A. Phosphorylation and acetylation at serine 1 (Sung and Dixon, 1970) and acetylation at lysine 5 (Candido and Dixon, 1972a) have been observed to occur in trout testis H2A.

(Fig. 2). It is important to stress that in this, and in other cases of histone acetylation to be considered, not every designated site of acetylation is modified in every histone molecule. Each histone class is made up of sets of polypeptide chains of identical amino acid sequence, some of which may be internally acetylated to different degrees, while others are not acetylated at all. Each of these subfractions may then, in addition, differ with regard to other forms of substitution, such as phosphorylation or methylation. [Microheterogeneity in histone sequences, as observed in histone H3, for example (Patthy and Smith, 1975; Marzluff *et al.*, 1972), adds additional complexity.]

5. H2B

Histone H2B has multiple sites of internal acetylation; ϵ-N-acetyllysine may occur at positions 5, 10, 13, and 18 of the polypeptide chain (Candido and Dixon, 1972b; Dixon *et al.*, 1975) (Fig. 3). Because H2B also has multiple sites of phosphorylation (Fig. 3), the potential for varying DNA affinity is likely to be very large.

6. H3

Histone H3 has sites of acetylation at lysine residues in positions 9, 14, 18, and 23 of the polypeptide chain (Candido and Dixon, 1972b; DeLange *et al.*,

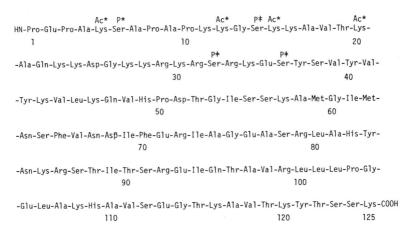

```
              Ac*  P*                    Ac*      P‡ Ac*                    Ac*
    HN-Pro-Glu-Pro-Ala-Lys-Ser-Ala-Pro-Ala-Pro-Lys-Lys-Gly-Ser-Lys-Lys-Ala-Val-Thr-Lys-
      1                               10                              20
                                         P‡          P‡
    -Ala-Gln-Lys-Lys-Asp-Gly-Lys-Lys-Arg-Lys-Ser-Arg-Lys-Glu-Ser-Tyr-Ser-Val-Tyr-Val-
                   30                              40

    -Tyr-Lys-Val-Leu-Lys-Gln-Val-His-Pro-Asp-Thr-Gly-Ile-Ser-Ser-Lys-Ala-Met-Gly-Ile-Met-
                   50                              60

    -Asn-Ser-Phe-Val-Asn-Aspβ-Ile-Phe-Glu-Arg-Ile-Ala-Gly-Glu-Ala-Ser-Arg-Leu-Ala-His-Tyr-
                   70                              80

    -Asn-Lys-Arg-Ser-Thr-Ile-Thr-Ser-Arg-Glu-Ile-Gln-Thr-Ala-Val-Arg-Leu-Leu-Leu-Pro-Gly-
                   90                              100

    -Glu-Leu-Ala-Lys-His-Ala-Val-Ser-Glu-Gly-Thr-Lys-Ala-Val-Thr-Lys-Tyr-Thr-Ser-Ser-Lys-COOH
                   110                             120                 125
```

FIG. 3. Observed biochemical modifications of histone H2B residues. The sequence of calf thymus H2B is depicted (Iwai *et al.*, 1970).

1972; Marzluff and McCarty, 1972; Hooper *et al.*, 1973; Brandt *et al.*, 1974; Dixon *et al.*, 1975; Thwaits *et al.*, 1976a) (Fig. 4). Histone H3 also has multiple sites of phosphorylation (Marzluff and McCarty, 1972; Dixon *et al.*, 1975) and methylation (DeLange *et al.*, 1972; Brandt *et al.*, 1974; Dixon *et al.*, 1975). Each site of methylation, which involves substitution on the ε-amino groups of lysine residues, may contain one, two, or three methyl groups (Hooper *et al.*, 1973).

7. Thiol Groups in H3

The complexity of histone H3 is further compounded by the presence of one or two cysteine residues in different subfractions from the same species. Two forms of H3 occur in calf thymus lymphocytes, one with cysteine residues at positions 96 and 110, and another minor fraction which contains only one cysteine residue in position 110 and a serine substitution in position 96 (Patthy and Smith, 1975). Because of the possibility that disulfide bond formation may play a role in the organization of the nucleosome or in cross-linking histones to other proteins in chromatin, the presence of one or two sulfhydryl residues on different H3 molecules could be a key determinant of chromatin structure. Changes in thiol:disulfide ratio have been observed during the cell cycle and in embryonic development (Ord and Stocken, 1968, 1969; Sadgopal and Bonner, 1970) and in certain echinoderms, in which histone H4 also contains cysteine residues (Subirana, 1971; Strickland

```
                                Ac*
                            Me*    P*                      Ac*              Ac*
H₂N-Ala-Arg-Thr-Lys-Gln-Thr-Ala-Arg-Lys-Ser-Thr-Gly-Gly-Lys-Ala-Pro-Arg-Lys-Gln-Leu-
     1                              10                                     20

             Ac*              Me*   P*
-Ala-Thr-Lys-Ala-Ala-Arg-Lys-Ser-Ala-Pro-Ala-Thr-Gly-Gly-Val-Lys-Lys-Pro-His-Arg-Tyr-
                    30                                            40


-Arg-Pro-Gly-Thr-Val-Ala-Leu-Arg-Glu-Ile-Arg-Arg-Tyr-Gln-Lys-Ser-Thr-Glu-Leu-Leu-Ile-
                         50                                   60


-Arg-Lys-Leu-Pro-Phe-Gln-Arg-Leu-Val-Arg-Glu-Ile-Ala-Gln-Asp-Phe-Lys-Thr-Asp-Leu-Arg-
                    70                                  80


-Phe-Gln-Ser-Ser-Ala-Val-Met-Ala-Leu-Gln-Glu-Ala-Cys-Glu-Ala-Tyr-Leu-Val-Gly-Leu-Phe-
                    90                                  100


-Glu-Asp-Thr-Asn-Leu-Cys-Ala-Ile-His-Ala-Lys-Arg-Val-Thr-Ile-Met-Pro-Lys-Asp-Ile-Gln-
                    110                                 120


-Leu-Ala-Arg-Arg-Ile-Arg-Gly-Glu-Arg-Ala-COOH
                    130
```

FIG. 4. Observed biochemical modifications of histone H3. H3 fractions differing in amino acid sequence are known to exist in certain cells. A sequence reported for calf H3 is shown (DeLange and Smith, 1972; DeLange *et al.*, 1973; Olson *et al.*, 1972). The indicated acetylation sites have been reported to occur in trout testis H3 (Louie *et al.*, 1973). Phosphorylation at serine residues 10 and 28 has been reported for calf thymus H3 (Marzluff and McCarty, 1972). In trout H3 the two methylation sites at lysine residues 9 and 27 have been observed to occur adjacent to phosphorylated serine residues, as shown here.

et al., 1974), a reversible cross-linking of H3 and H4 has been demonstrated (A. Ruiz-Carrillo and V. G. Allfrey, unpublished observation, 1976). The latter observation provides direct evidence that histones H3 and H4 occur in close proximity in the nucleosome. In fact, recent studies of nucleosome structure indicate that histones H3 and H4 can organize DNA segments the length of the nucleosome "core" even in the absence of the other histone classes (Camerini-Otero *et al.*, 1976; Sollner-Webb *et al.*, 1976). Thus, it is all the more significant that histones H3 and H4 are major targets of histone acetylating enzymes *in vivo* (Allfrey *et al.*, 1964; B. G. T. Pogo *et al.*, 1966, 1968; Vidali *et al.*, 1968; Wilhelm and McCarty, 1970; A. W. Johnson *et al.*, 1973; Edwards and Allfrey, 1973).

8. *H4*

The enzymatic acetylation of lysine residues was first detected in histone H4 (Gershey *et al.*, 1968; Vidali *et al.*, 1968), and the major site of this modification was identified as lysine-16 (DeLange *et al.*, 1969; Ogawa *et al.*, 1969). The occurrence of ϵ-N-acetyllysine at positions 5, 8, and 12 of the

```
      P*                Ac*        Ac*               Ac*              Ac*              Me*
  *Ac-Ser-Gly-Arg-Gly-Lys-Gly-Gly-Lys-Gly-Leu-Gly-Lys-Gly-Gly-Ala-Lys-Arg-His-Arg-Lys-
      1                            10                                                  20

  -Val-Leu-Arg-Asp-Asn-Ile-Gln-Gly-Ile-Thr-Lys-Pro-Ala-Ile-Arg-Arg-Leu-Ala-Arg-Arg-Gly-
                                30                                   40

  -Gly-Val-Lys-Arg-Ile-Ser-Gly-Leu-Ile-Tyr-Glu-Glu-Thr-Arg-Gly-Val-Leu-Lys-Val-Phe-Leu-
                                50                                   60

  -Glu-Asn-Val-Ile-Arg-Asp-Ala-Val-Thr-Tyr-Thr-Glu-His-Ala-Lys-Arg-Lys-Thr-Val-Thr-Ala-
                        70                                   80

  -Met-Asp-Val-Val-Tyr-Ala-Leu-Lys-Arg-Gln-Gly-Arg-Thr-Leu-Tyr-Gly-Phe-Gly-Gly-COOH
                                                      100     102
```

FIG. 5. Observed biochemical modifications of histone H4 residues. The sequence shown is that of calf H4 (DeLange *et al.*, 1969, 1972; Ogawa *et al.*, 1969). The indicated acetylation sites and phosphorylation of serine 1 have been reported for H4 from trout testis (Louie *et al.*, 1973) and avian erythrocytes (Ruiz-Carrillo *et al.*, 1975).

polypeptide chain has also been established (Sung and Dixon, 1970; Candido and Dixon, 1971; Dixon *et al.*, 1975; Thwaits *et al.*, 1976b) (Fig. 5).

B. HISTONE ACETYLATION AND DNA CONFORMATION

It should be noted that the distribution of ϵ-N-acetyllysine in histones is not random; all the modifiable lysine residues in H4 occur in the amino-terminal portion of the polypeptide chain, which by virtue of its clustering of the basic amino acids—arginine, lysine, and histidine—carries a high net positive charge. Similar structural considerations apply to histones H3, H2A, and H2B (Figs. 2–4). These positively charged regions of the histone molecule are most likely to interact with the negatively charged phosphate groups of the DNA helix which envelops the nucleosome "core" (Boublik *et al.*, 1971; Li and Bonner, 1971; Ziccardi and Schumaker, 1973; Weintraub and van Lente, 1974; Adler *et al.*, 1974a; Baldwin *et al.*, 1975). Acetylation of one to four lysine residues would diminish the positive charge in the DNA-binding sequences of the histone chain, and would be expected to destabilize the histone–DNA complex. Direct tests of the effects of histone acetylation on the conformation of DNA–histone complexes have become possible with the development of chromatographic and electrophoretic methods for the purification of histone subfractions which differ in their degree of internal acetylation (Wangh *et al.*, 1972; Ruiz-Carrillo *et al.*, 1974). For example, histone H4 from calf thymus lymphocytes has been separated into its naturally occurring nonacetylated, monoacetylated, and multiacetylated subfractions (Wangh *et al.*, 1972). Each of these subfractions was compared with respect to its interactions with double-stranded calf thymus DNA, using circular dichroism to monitor changes in conformation of the complex. The results indicated that the acetylated forms of H4 are far less effective than the nonacetylated forms in altering the conformation of DNA (Adler *et al.*, 1974b). This is the first direct evidence that acetylation of lysine residues in histones, as it occurs naturally, can influence the structure of DNA–histone complexes, a fact which had been surmised from studies of the effects of chemically acetylated histones on RNA synthesis (Allfrey, 1974; Allfrey *et al.*, 1964; Marushige, 1976). The ease of displacement of histones from calf thymus chromatin after acetylation with acetic anhydride (Wong and Marushige, 1976) and the increase in acridine orange binding to DNA after acetylation of lymphocyte nuclei (Killander and Rigler, 1965, 1969) offer additional evidence that this modification of lysine residues has a direct consequence in increased availability of the associated DNA sequences. On the premise that this change in chromatin structure would offer a mechanism for the control of DNA template function, the acetylation of histones has been studied in a variety of cell types during periods of gene activation or repression.

C. Correlations between Acetyl Group "Turnover" and Chromosomal Function

In considering the possible relationships between histone acetylation and gene activity, it is important to recognize the dynamic nature of the acetylation process. Early experiments on the incorporation of radioactive acetate into histones established that the isotopically labeled acetyl groups, once incorporated, are not stable, but are subject to removal without degradation of the polypeptide chains to which they are attached (Allfrey, 1964, 1966; Allfrey *et al.*, 1964; B. G. T. Pogo *et al.*, 1966, 1967, 1968; Marzluff and McCarty, 1970; Wilhelm and McCarty, 1970; Boffa *et al.*, 1971; Edwards and Allfrey, 1973; Sanders *et al.*, 1973; A. W. Johnson *et al.*, 1973; Jackson *et al.*, 1975). The release of previously incorporated acetyl groups is carried out by enzymes which attack the amide linkage between the ϵ-amino group of the modified lysine residue and the carboxy carbon of the acetyl group. Most of the assays for deacetylase activity are based on the kinetics of release of radioactive acetate from histones which had been previously labeled *in vivo* or *in vitro* (Inoue and Fujimoto, 1969, 1970, 1972; Fujimoto and Segawa, 1973; Kaneta and Fujimoto, 1974; Horiuchi and Fujimoto, 1973, 1975; Libby, 1970; Vidali *et al.*, 1972; Krieger *et al.*, 1974, 1977). The specificity of the histone deacetylases has been studied by comparing the rates of deacety-lation of individual histones (Vidali *et al.*, 1972) and by measuring the deacetylation of histone fragments obtained by protease digestion (Horiuchi and Fujimoto, 1973) or prepared by solid-phase peptide synthesis (Krieger *et al.*, 1974, 1977). It has been shown that a calf thymus deacetylase can distin-guish between the natural sites of histone modification and random sites acetylated by [^{14}C]acetic anhydride (Inoue and Fujimoto, 1969, 1970). A highly purified histone deacetylase from calf thymus has been shown to be localized in the nucleus (Vidali *et al.*, 1972). This enzyme can remove acetyl groups from positions 12 and 16 of the histone H4 sequence (Krieger *et al.*, 1977), but it is not yet clear whether removal of all four of the acetyl groups on histones H4 can be accomplished by a single enzyme. There is good evidence for the heterogeneity of the histone deacetylases; some are chromatographically separable (Inoue and Fujimoto, 1972; Kikuchi and Fujimoto, 1973; Kaneta and Fujimoto, 1974) and some preparations are unable to deacetylate chromatin-bound histones, while others have this ability (Kaneta and Fujimoto, 1974). A further complication is the presence of naturally occurring inhibitors of histone deacetylase activity (Inoue and Fujimoto, 1970; Vidali *et al.*, 1972), a finding in accord with numerous observations that the rate of histone deacetylation is under physiological control (Pogo *et al.*, 1967, 1968; Boffa *et al.*, 1971; Candido and Dixon, 1972c; Wangh *et al.*, 1972; Louie *et al.*, 1973; Sanders *et al.*, 1973; Ruiz-Carrillo *et al.*, 1974, 1975, 1976).

The dynamic balance between acetylation and deacetylation reactions de-termines the proportions of the acetylated and nonacetylated histone subfrac-tions present in a given cell type, or in different regions of the chromatin (Allfrey, 1964, 1970, 1977). Those proportions are subject to change during gene activation or repression by hormones, mitogens, drugs, and develop-mental stimuli. Striking temporal correlations between increases in histone acetylation and subsequent increases in transcriptional activity have been noted in organisms as diverse as mammals, birds, echinoderms, myxomy-cetes, and ciliates. Together with autoradiographic and other types of evi-dence for selective localization of the acetylated histones in "active" regions of the chromatin, the significance of this postsynthetic modification of DNA-associated proteins becomes increasingly clear. Some examples of the relationship will now be considered.

1. Histone Acetylation and Gene Activation in Lymphocytes

Human peripheral lymphocytes, which rarely divide in culture, are in-duced to reenter the growth cycle by mitogenic agents such as phytohemagglutinin (PHA). In the presence of PHA, 70–80% of the cells undergo a blastogenic transformation, as indicated by an increase in size, resumption of DNA synthesis, and eventual mitosis (Moorhead *et al.*, 1960). The synthesis of DNA and the "new" histones necessary for cell division is a relatively late event in the transformation process; [2-^{14}C]thymidine incorporation, for example, is negligible for the first 24 hours in culture (B. G. T. Pogo *et al.*, 1966). Changes in RNA and protein synthesis, on the other hand, occur shortly after addition of PHA to the culture medium (B. G. T. Pogo *et al.*, 1966). The lymphocyte response to PHA may be regarded as a triggering of chromosomal functions necessary for cell growth and division, and it provides a useful paradigm for studies of changes in chromosomal proteins at the time of gene activation (B. G. T. Pogo *et al.*, 1966; Kleinsmith *et al.*, 1966a,b; Levy *et al.*, 1973; Johnson *et al.*, 1974).

The kinetics of radioactive acetate uptake into the histones after the addition of PHA are particularly suggestive. Within a few minutes, the "arginine-rich" histones, H3 and H4, show a major increase in their rates of [^{14}C]acetate incorporation. There is no concomitant increase in the rate of histone synthesis at these early times, and the acetylation is internal, not NH$_2$-terminal. The comparative kinetics of change in RNA synthesis and histone acetylation indicate characteristic and suggestive differences in the time courses of the two processes. Pulse-labeling experiments with [2-^{14}C]uridine and [2-^{14}C]acetate as precursors showed that the increase in acetylation of the histones precedes the increase in the rate of nuclear RNA synthesis (B. G. T. Pogo *et al.*, 1966).

The chemistry of histone acetylation, as noted above, strongly suggests that changes in chromosomal ultrastructure would be initiated by the acetylation of lysine residues; the resulting diminution of histone charge would be expected to weaken histone–DNA interactions. That such changes follow PHA treatment of human lymphocytes is indicated by the changing reactivity of the chromatin toward the DNA-binding dye, acridine orange (AO). Killander and Rigler (1965, 1969) have shown that the amount of AO-binding to the nuclei of PHA-treated cells increases rapidly over a time course which is very similar to that observed by B. G. T. Pogo *et al.* (1966) for histone acetylation. Of particular interest is their observation that a chemical acetylation of the proteins in control lymphocytes increases the binding of acridine orange to DNA, while acetylation of the PHA-stimulated cells does not lead to any further increase in DNA dye-binding capacity. The results support the view that a limited enzymatic acetylation of the basic proteins of the nucleus can result in a significant change in the "availability" and potential template activity of the DNA strand. This conclusion is further supported by experiments showing an increased binding of radioactive actinomycin D to the DNA of PHA-stimulated lymphocytes (Darzynkiewicz *et al.*, 1969).

In considering the significance of histone acetylation it is important to point out that acetylation is not, in itself, sufficient cause for the induction of

RNA synthesis at previously repressed gene loci. For example, the blastogenic transformation of PHA-treated lymphocytes can be blocked by the addition of cortisol to the culture medium, and no increase in RNA synthesis is observed (Ono *et al.*, 1969). Under these conditions an increase in histone acetylation is still detectable, and the DNA of the chromatin becomes more accessible to probes such as AO or actinomycin D, but there is no obvious stimulation of transcription. It follows that the change in the physical state of the chromatin is merely a prelude to other, more specific interactions which are needed to initiate RNA synthesis at particular gene loci. In this view, the acetylation of the histones provides an enzymatic mechanism for the "release" of obstructed DNA templates—the first step in a complex chain of events which must be set into motion to modify the patterns of transcription in the cells of higher organisms.

The inhibitory effects of cortisol on blastogenesis are in accord with other observations that lymphoid cells respond to glucocorticoids by a suppression of RNA polymerase activity (Fox and Gabourel, 1967; Makman *et al.*, 1970) and a diminished capacity to synthesize RNA (Kidson, 1965; Wagner, 1970; Darzynkiewicz and Andersson, 1971; Kaiser *et al.*, 1973). Corticosteroids induce a rapid decrease in actinomycin D binding sites on lymphocyte nuclear DNA (Darzynkiewicz and Andersson, 1971; Darzynkiewicz and Jacobson, 1971). The capacity of thymus lymphocyte chromatin to bind AO by intercalation of the dye between DNA bases decreases within 15 minutes after the injection of dexamethasone (Alvarez and Truitt, 1977). This decrease in DNA accessibility is accompanied by an increase in thermal stability, suggesting stronger interactions between DNA and associated proteins. This is the result expected if a decrease in histone acetylation has taken place, and tests of acetate incorporation in thymus lymphocyte nuclei have shown inhibition of histone acetylation by exposure to β-methasone phosphate (Allfrey *et al.*, 1966).

2. PHA-Induced Suppression of RNA Synthesis and Histone Acetylation in Granulocytes

In contrast to the enhanced RNA synthesis seen in the lymphocyte response to phytohemagglutinin, polymorphonuclear leukocytes exposed to PHA curtail RNA synthesis within 15 minutes; histone acetylation is also suppressed under these conditions (Pogo *et al.*, 1967). Moreover, it has been shown that the granulocytes actually increase their rates of histone deacetylation as soon as PHA is added to the culture medium; radioactive acetyl groups which had been incorporated under normal conditions are released as RNA synthesis is suppressed (Pogo *et al.*, 1967). The results suggest that histone deacetylation provides a sensitive and early indication of impaired nuclear function in RNA synthesis. This conclusion is supported by changes occurring during the normal differentiation of erythrocytes and spermatocytes.

D. CHANGING PATTERNS OF HISTONE ACETYLATION DURING DIFFERENTIATION AND DEVELOPMENT

1. Diminished Acetylation of Histones during Maturation of Erythroid Cells

The maturation of the nucleated avian erythrocyte involves a programed series of nuclear and cytoplasmic events that eventually lead to an almost complete cessation of RNA synthesis. The RNA synthetic capacity of isolated erythroblasts and early polychromatic erythrocytes is at least eight times higher than that of mature erythrocytes (Ruiz-Carrillo *et al.*, 1974, 1976). There is a parallel decline in the rate of histone acetylation (Ruiz-Carrillo *et al.*, 1976), and the proportions of the acetylated forms of histones H3 and H4 decrease significantly with age (Wangh *et al.*, 1972; Ruiz-Carrillo *et al.*, 1974). Moreover, it has been shown that histone deacetylase activities for each of the four histones of the nucleosome "core" are considerably higher in mature erythrocytes than in reticulocytes from the same species (Sanders *et al.*, 1973).

As in the case of the lymphocyte responding to PHA, the acetylation of erythroid histones and the act of transcription are not tightly coupled; e.g., inhibitors of RNA synthesis such as rifamycin AF/013 or actinomycin D do not simultaneously block the uptake of radioactive acetate into the histones of erythroid cells. It follows that histone acetylation can proceed independently of RNA polymerase activity, at least for a short time (Ruiz-Carrillo *et al.*, 1976). Yet the analysis of chromatin subfractions by a variety of techniques shows the acetylated histones to be preferentially localized in the transcriptionally active regions, as would be expected if this modification is part of the mechanism for maintaining an "active" conformation of the associated DNA strand (see below).

2. Histone Acetylation during Spermatogenesis

The acetylation of histones during spermatogenesis has been studied in greatest detail in the testis of trout (Candido and Dixon, 1971, 1972a,b; Dixon *et al.*, 1975). The patterns of acetylation are complex during the meiotic and mitotic divisions of the sperm precursor cells, due in part to the synthesis of new histones; in addition, the histones of the spermatid are extensively modified by acetylation prior to their replacement by protamines. Similar observations have been made on histone acetylation in rat (Grimes *et al.*, 1975) and bull testis (Marushige and Marushige, 1975). These findings are consistent with the view that acetylation—by weakening the ionic bonds between histones and DNA—facilitates their removal and eventual replacement by protamines or other sperm-specific basic proteins.

In some species, such as *Arbacia lixula,* histones are retained by the mature sperm cell which has lost its capacity to synthesize RNA. Significantly, all the H3 and H4 molecules of *Arbacia* sperm occur in their nonacetylated forms (Wangh *et al.*, 1972). Similarly, the relative amounts of the acetylated histones are markedly decreased at the late spermatid stage of *Xenopus laevis* (Risley and Eckhardt, 1975). After fertilization, when RNA synthesis resumes at the late blastula stage, the acetylated forms of H3 and H4 are again prominent (Wangh *et al.*, 1972). There is a 2.5-fold increase in the rate of histone acetylation between the blastula and gastrula stages of development in *Arbacia punctulata;* the timing of the increase correlates closely with the activation of new genes at that stage (Burdick and Taylor, 1976).

There are other indications that the acetylation of histones H3 and H4 is altered during embryonic development. In chick embryo muscle, for example, the incorporation of [^{14}C]acetate into ε-N-acetyllysine residues is more than doubled during the period of activation of synthesis of the contractile proteins (Boffa and Vidali, 1971). Histone deacetylase activity is appreciably suppressed during this inductive stage of muscle development (Boffa *et al.*, 1971).

3. Changing Patterns of Histone Acetylation and RNA Synthesis during Regeneration of the Liver

The regenerative response which ensues after partial hepatectomy involves a reprograming of hepatocyte function for DNA synthesis and cell replication. Gene activation is known to be a relatively early event in the first cycle of cell division; it has been demonstrated by increases in the DNA-template activity of isolated hepatocyte nuclei (A. O. Pogo *et al.*, 1966), by the heightened RNA synthetic capacity of isolated chromatin fractions (Tsukada and Lieberman, 1965; Doly *et al.*, 1965; Marushige and Bonner, 1966; Thaler and Villee, 1967), and by the appearance of "new" species of RNA detectable by RNA–DNA hybridization techniques (Church and McCarthy, 1967).

Pogo *et al.* (1968) compared the changes in RNA synthetic capacity of liver nuclei at different times after partial hepatectomy with changes in histone acetylation kinetics during the same interval. Gene activation, as revealed by RNA polymerase assays, begins at 1–2 hours after the operation, and a "plateau" of activity is reached at 6 hours (Fujioka *et al.*, 1963; Thaler and Villee, 1967; Pogo *et al.*, 1968). Acetylation of histones H3 and H4 reaches a peak at 3–4 hours and declines abruptly by 5 hours. The high acetyl content of the histones in the early stages of liver regeneration is due to an increase in the rate of acetate incorporation and also to a decrease in the rate at which the histones are deacetylated (Pogo *et al.*, 1968). The net effect is a peak in the acetyl content of the histones about 2 hours before maximal rates of RNA synthesis are achieved. Thus, as in the case of lymphocytes responding to PHA, gene activation in the regenerating liver involves changes in the level of histone acetylation which precede the increase in RNA synthetic capacity of the nucleus. The change in the proportions of acetylated and nonacetylated histone subfractions is regulated by mechanisms which influence the removal as well as the attachment of acetyl groups to lysine residues in histones H3 and H4 (Pogo *et al.*, 1968).

It is likely that similar mechanisms operate at later stages in the cell cycle to control histone interactions with the newly replicating DNA strands (Sung and Dixon, 1970; Louie *et al.*, 1973). The acetylation of histones during the cell cycle is known to involve complex changes in acetate uptake and release (Shepherd *et al.*, 1971), due in part to the acetylation of the NH_2-terminal serine residues of new histones synthesized during the S phase (Liew *et al.*, 1970), and to a transient acetylation of lysine residues on newly synthesized molecules of histone H4 (Ruiz-Carrillo *et al.*, 1975; Jackson *et al.*, 1975, 1976). These modifications greatly complicate the interpretation of changes in the pattern of histone acetylation at later stages in liver regeneration; but histone synthesis is negligible in the first 16 hours after partial hepatectomy (Holbrook *et al.*, 1962; Butler and Cohn, 1963; Tidwell *et al.*, 1968), and the early changes observed by Pogo *et al.* (1968) are more likely to represent a mechanism for altering the structure of "old" DNA strands prior to the activation of quiescent genes.

E. STEROID HORMONE EFFECTS ON HISTONE ACETYLATION

The effects of hormones upon their target tissues is often expressed at the level of transcription, and there are many indications that the response of the target tissue involves alterations in the composition and metabolism of the nuclear proteins. The suppression of histone acetylation and RNA synthesis in lymphocytes treated with glucocorticoids has already been described; the following examples illustrate some positive correlations between enhanced RNA synthesis in a variety of tissues responding to steroid or peptide hormones and the acetylation of the nuclear basic proteins.

1. Hydrocortisone Effects on Histone Acetylation in the Liver

It is known that hydrocortisone causes an increase in RNA synthesis in the livers of adrenalectomized rats (Feigelson *et al.*, 1962; Kenney and Kull,

1963). This increase occurs prior to the induction of a number of enzyme activities, such as tyrosine aminotransferase, commonly used to monitor the hormone response. Studies of histone acetylation in adrenalectomized rats showed that the uptake of radioactive acetate into hepatic histones increases within 30 minutes after injection of hydrocortisone (Allfrey et al., 1966). The magnitude of the increase (about 26% at 30 minutes) corresponds to estimates of the increase in template activity of the chromatin under similar conditions (Dahmus and Bonner, 1965). Comparisons of the kinetics of acetylation, RNA synthesis, and enzyme induction after hydrocortisone injection showed that histone acetylation precedes the increase in RNA synthesis and the appearance of tyrosine aminotransferase (Graaff and von Holt, 1973).

2. Effects of Estrogens on Histone Acetylation in the Uterus

The administration of estrogens leads to rapid increases in the rates of RNA synthesis in the uterus (Mueller et al., 1958; Hamilton, 1964; Gorski et al., 1965; Means and Hamilton, 1966; Teng and Hamilton, 1968; O'Malley and Means, 1974; Luck and Hamilton, 1975). The changes in DNA template activity are evident in isolated uterine chromatin (Barker and Warren, 1966; Teng and Hamilton, 1968; Glasser et al., 1972) and in isolated rat uterine nucleoli (Nicolette and Babler, 1974).

The effects of estradiol-17β on the acetylation of uterine histones have been studied by Libby (1972), who found an increase in [^{3}H]acetate incorporation into histone H4 within 2–5 minutes after injection of the hormone. (There was no corresponding increase in histone acetylation in the liver of the hormone-treated animals.) In animals pretreated with nafoxidine, a potent antiestrogen known to inhibit the uterine response to estradiol (Jensen et al., 1966), the administration of estradiol-17β did not stimulate acetate incorporation into the histone fraction (Libby, 1972). Other estrogens, such as stilbestrol and estriol, were also found to stimulate histone acetylation in the uterus, but testosterone had no such effect (Libby, 1972). The mechanism of hormonal activation of histone acetylation within 2–5 minutes is not clear, but there is evidence that uterine histone acetyltransferase activity is directly stimulated by estradiol-17β (Libby, 1968).

The response to sex hormones is not limited to the cells of higher organisms; the fungus Achlya ambisexualis responding to sexual steroid (antheridol) acetylates its histones prior to an increase in RNA-synthetic capacity (Horgen and Ball, 1974).

3. Effects of Aldosterone on Histone Acetylation in the Kidney

Mineralocorticoids, such as aldosterone, are known to stimulate RNA synthesis in the kidney (Edelman and Fimognari, 1968). Increases in the RNA polymerase activity of heart and kidney nuclei following the administration of aldosterone to adrenalectomized rats have also been reported (Liew *et al.*, 1972).

A sharp increase in histone acetylation in the kidney of aldosterone-treated animals has been independently observed in several laboratories (Trachewsky and Lawrence, 1972; Libby, 1973; Liew *et al.*, 1973). The acetylation of histone H4 was increased nearly 3-fold within 5 minutes after a physiological dose of aldosterone (Libby, 1973). Other adrenocortical steroids with mineralocorticoid activity, such as deoxycorticosterone, also stimulated histone acetylation in the kidney, but hormones with little or no mineralocorticoid activity, such as progesterone, had no effect. The antimineralocorticoid spironolactone SC14266, when administered to animals 30 minutes before the injection of aldosterone, blocked the increase in acetylation of the histones. The organ specificity of the aldosterone effect is indicated by its failure to increase histone acetylation in the liver (Libby, 1973; Liew *et al.*, 1973), and by the stimulation of histone acetylation and RNA synthesis in another target tissue, cardiac muscle (Liew *et al.*, 1972, 1973). In the kidney response to aldosterone, as well as in the uterine response to estradiol-17β (Libby, 1972), the increase in histone acetylation is a transient phenomenon; the acetylation rate of H4 returns to normal in about 20 minutes. Most of the increase in RNA synthesis occurs after the acetylation has peaked.

F. Peptide Hormone Effects on Histone Acetylation

1. Erythropoietin Stimulation of Histone Acetylation and RNA Synthesis in the Spleen

Erythropoietin, which stimulates RNA synthesis in hematopoietic cells *in vivo* (Pieber-Perretta *et al.*, 1965; Nakao *et al.*, 1966; Rudolf and Perretta, 1967; Takaku *et al.*, 1969) and stimulates the RNA polymerase activity measured *in vitro* (Krantz and Goldwasser, 1965), also stimulates the acetylation of spleen histones (Takaku *et al.*, 1969). The increase in the rate of incorporation of radioactive acetate into the histones preceded the increase in RNA synthesis in the erythropoietin-responsive cells by 4 hours (Takaku *et al.*, 1969).

2. Insulin Stimulation of Histone Acetylation and RNA Synthesis in the Liver

The broad spectrum of insulin effects on hepatocytes includes the induction of tyrosine aminotransferase by a mechanism requiring *de novo* RNA and protein synthesis (Wicks, 1969; Schimke and Doyle, 1970). Insulin has been found to stimulate both the acetylation and phosphorylation of liver histones prior to the rise in RNA synthesis (Graaff and von Holt, 1973). The increase in histone acetylation after insulin injections is even more extensive than that seen in hepatocytes responding to cortisol (Graaff and von Holt, 1973).

3. *Gonadotropin-Induced Modifications of Histone Acetylation and RNA Synthesis*

The action of gonadotropins on the ovary of prepubertal rats includes an early stimulation of nuclear RNA synthesis *in vivo* (Reel and Gorski, 1968; Jungmann and Schweppe, 1972b) and of DNA-dependent RNA polymerase activity measured in isolated ovarian nuclei (Van Dyke and Katzman, 1968). The injection of human chorionic gonadotropin into immature rats has been found to increase the rate of acetylation of histone H4 in the ovary within 10 minutes (Jungmann and Schweppe, 1972a). Although this response is complicated by the multiple forms of acetylation associated with concomitant histone synthesis, the highly selective acetylation of histone H4, relative to that of the other histone fractions, again indicates a modification of the lysine residues associated with chromatin decondensation.

4. *ACTH Effects on Chromatin Structure in the Adrenal*

In the case of the activated lymphocyte, discussed earlier, the acetylation of histones is accompanied by changes in chromatin structure which increase the accessibility of DNA to probes such as acridine orange and [³H]actinomycin D. The response of target cells to peptide hormones also involves an enhancement of AO binding. Cytochemical studies of rat adrenal gland nuclei isolated after stimulation by exogenous ACTH showed significant increases in AO dye binding and decreases in thermal stability of the DNA within 4 hours. A decreased binding of acid dyes to the histones of the stimulated cells was also observed (Alvarez and Lavendar, 1974). All these results are consistent with an increase in acetylation of adrenal histones after ACTH administration; the reduction in charge of the lysine residues would account for the changes in acid dye binding, and the release of associated DNA sequences would permit increased binding of AO.

G. Alterations in Histone Acetylation Induced by Drugs

Drugs that influence RNA synthesis also modify the balance between histone acetylation and deacetylation. Following are three examples.

(a) The administration of phenobarbital or 3-methylcholanthrene to rats leads to a marked elevation in the activity of the hepatic microsomal mixed function oxidase system. The induction of cytochrome P_{450} and other components of the system is dependent upon a prior stimulation of transcription in hepatic chromatin (Gelboin *et al.*, 1967; Madix and Bresnick, 1967; Piper and Bousquet, 1968; Bresnick and Mosse, 1969). The acetylation of histones H3 and H4 is significantly enhanced within 2 hours after the administration of phenobarbital or 3-methylcholanthrene, and in accord with other examples of gene activation, the increase in histone acetylation precedes the enhancement of DNA-template activity (Procaccini and Bresnick, 1975).

(b) The perfusion of the heart with spermine has been shown to result in an increase in RNA synthesis (Caldarera *et al.*, 1975), in agreement with earlier observations of a close relationship between polyamine biosynthesis and increased incorporation of radioactive RNA precursors during cardiac hypertrophy (Caldarera *et al.*, 1974). The rate of acetylation of histone H4 was found to increase by 200% within 5 minutes after the addition of spermine to the perfusion medium. Moreover, drugs that inhibit polyamine or RNA synthesis, such as methylglyoxal bis(guanylhydrazone), cause a decrease in the acetylation of the cardiac histones. Spermine is able to reverse this inhibition (Caldarera *et al.*, 1975).

(c) Intravenous administration of lysergic acid diethylamide (LSD) to rabbits stimulates RNA synthesis in the brain by 54% within 2.5 hours (Brown, 1975); both nucleoplasmic and nucleolar RNA synthesis are increased. Similar doses of LSD increase acetylation of the histones in rabbit cerebral hemispheres and midbrain within 30 minutes. No changes in RNA synthesis or in histone acetylation were detected in the cerebellum of the same animals (Brown and Liew, 1975).

The above examples all illustrate positive temporal correlations between increases in histone acetylation and subsequent increases in RNA synthesis in tissues as diverse as liver, heart, and brain. Further evidence relating histone acetyl content to transcriptional activity arises from studies of drugs that inhibit RNA synthesis. For example, the hepatoxin and carcinogen, aflatoxin B_1, is known to suppress DNA-dependent RNA synthesis in the liver within 15–30 minutes; its mode of action is not simply due to inactivation of the RNA polymerases (LeFarge *et al.*, 1967; Sporn *et al.*, 1966; Clifford and Rees, 1967; Edwards and Wogan, 1970; Pong and Wogan, 1970). It has been shown that the administration of aflatoxin B_1 to rats leads to a sudden increase in the rate at which acetyl groups are released from histones in the liver. The increase in histone deacetylation occurs within 15 minutes and thus is at least as fast as the inhibitory effect of aflatoxin on RNA synthesis (Edwards and Allfrey, 1973). The major loss of acetyl groups occurs in histones H3 and H4. Upon subsequent recovery, the acetylation of these histones appears to precede the restoration of RNA synthetic activity (Edwards and Allfrey, 1973; Pong and Wogan, 1970). The results are consistent with the view that the deacetylation of histones H3 and H4, induced by aflatoxin B_1, leads to a strengthening of the interactions between histones and DNA and to further restriction of the template function of hepatocyte chromatin.

H. Histone Acetylation in Viral Transformation

Increases in histone acetylation have been noted in a variety of cell types transformed by oncogenic viruses: e.g., in WI-38 fibroblasts transformed by SV40 virus (Krause and Stein, 1975) and in human embryonic kidney cells infected with adenovirus-2 or adenovirus-12 (Ledinko, 1970). It is of particular interest that histones associated with the DNA of transforming viruses such as SV40 or polyoma virus are much more acetylated than the corresponding histones of the host cells (Schaffhausen and Benjamin, 1976). The correlation between increased acetyl content of polyoma virus histones and cell transformation is strongly supported by the finding that nontransforming host-range mutants of polyoma virus fail to show a high level of histone acetylation (Schaffhausen and Benjamin, 1976). The results are consistent with the view that cell transformation by viruses (like lymphocyte transformation by mitogens) triggers an increase in the acetylation of host-cell histones which are subsequently incorporated into the viral particle.

I. Spatial Correlations between Histone Acetylation and Transcriptional Activity

In comparisons of different cell types from a given organ, histone acetylation is more active in the more actively transcribing cell types. For example, the acetylation of brain histones H3 and H4 is much greater in isolated neuronal nuclei than in nuclei from glial cells (Sarkander *et al.*, 1975), in accord with the demonstrated differences in their RNA synthetic capacities (Kato and Kurokawa, 1970; Austoker *et al.*, 1972). In addition, a positive correlation was found to exist between the extent of *in vitro* acetylation of chromatin-bound histones and the extent of chromatin-templated UMP incorporation by endogenous RNA polymerases (Sarkander *et al.*, 1975).

The correlations between acetylation and RNA synthetic capacity extend to different regions of the chromatin in a given cell type. The chromatin of calf thymus lymphocytes can be separated by physical techniques to give fractions which differ in their morphology and RNA-synthetic activity (Frenster *et al.*, 1963). The procedure yields clumps of "condensed" chromatin which contain most of the DNA of the nucleus as tightly coiled masses of intertwining nucleoprotein fibrils, and lighter fractions which contain a more "diffuse" state of chromatin made up of loosely extended nucleoprotein fibrils. When such fractionations are carried out after labeling with isotopic RNA precursors, the RNA of the diffuse chromatin is much more radioactive than RNA of the clumped chromatin fraction, whether the incorporation took place in isolated cells or in isolated cell nuclei. The high activity of the chromatin in the diffuse state is not an artifact of isolation because the results have been verified by high-resolution electron microscope autoradiography (Littau *et al.*, 1964). Similar correlations between the diffuse state of chromatin and its activity in RNA synthesis have been observed for mouse cells in tissue culture (Hsu, 1962), in kidney cells (Granboulan and Granboulan, 1965), and in plant tissues (Kemp, 1966).

Comparisons of histone acetylation in the "active" and "inactive" fractions of calf thymus chromatin have shown a direct proportionality with the activity of the fractions in RNA synthesis. The average acetyl content of the histones in the active fraction was estimated to be nearly twice that of the histones in the corresponding compact chromatin fractions (Allfrey, 1964, 1970). Moreover, high-resolution autoradiography of thymus nuclei after incubation with [³H]acetate indicates that much of the acetylation occurred at the boundaries between the compact and diffuse regions of the chromatin, as expected if the modification of histones is related to changes in the physical state of the chromatin (Allfrey, 1970). This conclusion is further supported by observations on the lowered content of ϵ-N-acetyllysine in the chromatin of *Lilium* microsporocytes during periods of meiotic condensation (Nadler, 1976).

Similar observations have been made on insect chromosomes. For example, in *Planococcus citrii*, males preferentially utilize the maternal chromosome set and sequester the paternal chromosomes in a heterochromatic mass. The maternal, transcriptionally active euchromatic chromosome set incorporates about seven times more [³H]acetate than does the heterochromatic and largely inactive paternal set (Berlowitz and Pallotta, 1972).

In multinucleated ciliates such as *Stylonychia mytilus* (Lipps, 1975) and *Tetrahymena pyriformis* (Gorovsky *et al.*, 1973), the transcriptionally active macronucleus and the inactive micronucleus differ in their degree of histone acetylation; in both cases the acetylation is greater in the macronucleus. In *Tetrahymena*, histone H4 occurs in both nuclei, but micronuclear H4 occurs entirely in the nonacetylated form (Gorovsky *et al.*, 1973). The absence of acetylated forms of H4 in the transcriptionally inert micronucleus is reminiscent of the conversion of H4 to its nonacetylated forms during spermatogenesis in *Arbacia lixula* (Wangh *et al.*, 1972).

Further indications that acetylated histones are localized on transcriptionally active regions of the chromatin come from studies of the selective digestion of chromatin by deoxyribonucleases, as is discussed in the following section. It has been shown that a limited digestion of avian erythrocyte chromatin by DNase I leads to a preferential degradation of the globin genes; this is not observed in cell types such as fibroblasts that are not actively engaged in globin synthesis (Weintraub and Groudine, 1976). Similar sensitivity to DNase I digestion has also been demonstrated for the ovalbumin genes in the oviduct (but not in the liver) of the hen (Garel and Axel, 1976). The effect of a limited DNase I digestion on duck erythrocyte chromatin is a selective release of the acetylated forms of histones H3 and H4 (Vidali and Allfrey, 1977). The initial rate of release of chick erythrocyte histones previously labeled with [³H]acetate is three times faster than the rate of DNA release (Wong and Alberts, 1977). The fractionation of *Drosophila melanogaster* chromatin after incubation of cultured cells with [³H]acetate also yields "template-active" and "template-inactive" regions. The acetylation of the histones is higher in the "template-active" fraction (Levy-Wilson *et al.*, 1977). Significantly, the acetylated histones are preferentially released during limited nuclease digestions (with DNase II), as would be expected if they were present in the more "accessible" and transcriptionally active regions of the chromatin (Levy-Wilson *et al.*, 1977).

All the preceding correlations strongly suggest that histone acetylation provides a physiological mechanism for altering the structure of the chromatin, and it is very probable that such modifications are reflected in the organization of the nucleosomes in active and inactive regions of the chromatin. The unfolding of nucleosomes about an axis of symmetry, as suggested, for example, by Weintraub *et al.* (1976), might be facilitated by an acetylation-dependent weakening of histone–DNA interactions. Because the predominant acetylation reactions modify those histones which interact with the ends of nucleosomal DNA (H3 and H4) (Simpson, 1976), they could initiate an unfolding to a more extended configuration. This may account for the increased sensitivity of the associated DNA sequences to DNase I. A further implication is that "active" and "inactive" nucleosomes should differ in their physical properties. Evidence that the mononucleosome population is heterogeneous has been reported for mouse ascites tumor cells (Bakayev *et al.*, 1975) and for *Physarum polycephalum* (Allfrey *et al.*, 1977). It remains to be seen whether the active ribosomal genes of *Physarum* are associated with highly acetylated forms of histone H4, but in view of the diversity of evidence relating acetylation to gene function, the probability seems high.

IV. HISTONE MODIFICATIONS AND CHROMATIN STRUCTURE

Analysis of the fragments produced by micrococcal nuclease digestion of chromatin indicates the existence of significant variability in DNA repeat lengths of chromatin from different sources (cf. Compton *et al.*, 1976). Sizing of subunit DNA repeat lengths from different species has revealed lengths varying from about 165 base pairs in yeast (Thomas and Furber, 1976) to more than 240 base pairs in sea urchin chromatin (Bellard *et al.*, 1976). In general, lower eukaryotes such as *Neurospora* (Noll, 1976), *Aspergillus* (Morris, 1976), and *Physarum* (Johnson *et al.*, 1976) have repeat lengths of approximately 170 base pairs, while most mammalian chromatins have a major repeat length of about 200 base pairs (Bellard *et al.*, 1976). Heterogeneity of DNA repeat lengths within chromatin of a single species has been detected in *Physarum* (Johnson *et al.*, 1976) as well as in yeast (Lohr *et al.*, 1977) and certain higher eukaryotes (Thomas and Thompson, 1977). In *Physarum*, repeat lengths varying from 190 to 173 base pairs could be detected upon treatment of nuclei with staphylococcal nuclease for different lengths of time. It is likely that this variability can be ascribed to differences in internucleosome spacer lengths, with nucleosome monomer DNA lengths remaining constant (Johnson *et al.*, 1976; Lohr *et al.*, 1977). Despite significant evolutionary variability in sequences of certain histones, little variability has been detected in DNA lengths of nucleosome monomers containing these histones. A minimum monomer DNA length of 140 base pairs may be characteristic of most, if not all, chromatin. In addition, a monomer protected DNA segment of 160 base pairs is characteristic of chromatin from *Physarum* (Johnson *et al.*, 1976) and certain mammalian species (Noll and Kornberg, 1977), possibly due to protection by H1 of a 20-base-pair DNA segment adjacent to the monomer core. It is not known whether heterogeneity in chromatin subunit structure reflects differences in states of chromosomal activity. Several recent sudies suggest that changes in nucleosome structure in a given tissue may not result in changes in repeat length, but may instead involve alterations in nucleohistone structure within the repeat.

Weintraub and Groudine (1976) have reported that chromatin containing DNA coding for globin mRNA is preferentially digested by DNase I in avian erythrocytes. It was found that in chromatin from avian tissues in which globin genes are presumed to be inactive, such as liver fibroblasts (but see Humphries *et al.*, 1976), the globin-DNA-chromatin is not preferentially digested by DNase I. The authors have interpreted these results as indicating that chromatin containing active genes is in a different conformation from chromatin containing inactive genes. Similar conclusions have been reported by Garel and Axel (1976) on the basis of experiments involving DNase I treatment of chromatin containing ovalbumin genes. In these studies, precise criteria for defining a gene as active have not been described, and the basis for differential DNase I susceptibility is not known. However, recent studies indicate that nucleosomes containing highly acetylated H3 and H4 are more susceptible to DNase I attack (Vidali *et al.*, 1978). Nonetheless, the conclusions are not inconsistent with observations by several investigators concerning chromatin containing actively transcribing genes. It has long been known from high-resolution electron microscopic autoradiography that RNA synthesis is localized in the diffuse, extended chromatin strands. Electron microscopic observations of spread *Drosophila* ribosomal genes show that DNA in the transcribing region is extended rather than packaged in nucleosome beads (McKnight and Miller, 1976). Foe and co-workers (1976) have observed smooth, unbeaded chromatin on actively transcribing rDNA regions of *Oncopeltus fasciatus,* while spacers between transcribing genes were observed to be in chromatin containing characteristic subunit beads. Woodcock and colleagues (1976) observed that chromatin containing the transcribing matrix of newt ribosomal genes is not in a beaded configuration, but is thicker than would be expected if polymerases were transcribing over free DNA. Weintraub and co-workers (1976) have presented a model whereby activation of chromatin occurs through unfolding of two symmetrically paired half-nucleosomes believed to comprise each nucleosome. This model allows unfolding of nucleohistone complexes for genetic readout without requiring histone displacement. The model is consistent with additional evidence suggesting that histones are present on actively transcribing DNA regions (Lacy and Axel, 1975). Recent studies on ribosomal gene chromatin in *Physarum* provide biochemical evidence for an altered, extended nucleosome structure containing actively transcribing 19 S and 26 S RNA coding regions (Allfrey *et al.,* 1977; Johnson *et al.,* 1977).

The evidence cited indicates that nucleohistone structural characteristics are altered at times of different chromosomal activities. In addition to gene transcription, such activities expected to require nucleosome structural modifications might include processes of DNA replication, chromosome condensation and mitosis, and chromatin reassembly following cell division; these processes are also likely to involve chromatin modifications occurring after histone and DNA syntheses are complete. It is our hypothesis that alterations in nucleosome structure and organization occurring during transitions in chromosomal activities are effected through postsynthetic biochemical modifications of histones.

Histone modifications provide a means for altering chromatin structure, and possibly function, in response to cellular signals. Nucleosome structural changes may occur selectively upon those chromatin regions undergoing alterations in functional activities. For example, electron microscopic evidence indicates that the packing ratio of chromatin comprising actively transcribing ribosomal genes is different from that comprising contiguous nontranscribed spacers, which are organized into nucleosomes (McKnight and Miller, 1976; Foe *et al.,* 1977). Modifications of nucleosomes over active chromatin segments might occur through various mechanisms. Histone modification at one point on a chromatin fiber might induce nucleosome structural changes distal to the modification point along the entire DNA segment to be activated. Such a cooperative mechanism would require some means of distinguishing beginning and end points of chromatin containing an active DNA sequence. Alternatively, each nucleosome upon a DNA segment disposed toward activation could be subject to histone modification, resulting in structural alteration of the active chromatin segment. Such an inclusive mechanism would require a means of distinguishing each nucleosome along an active DNA sequence from those along inactive sequences. Multistep mechanisms for altering chromatin structure on active regions possibly involving more than one type of histone modification can also be envisaged. Nucleosome structural changes may be correlated with changes in chromatin functional activities without being involved in any causal relationship. It is conceivable that selective alterations of nucleosome structure on active DNA regions (Weintraub and Groudine, 1976; Garel and Axel, 1976) require the ability of proteins to recognize potentially active DNA sequences. If histone modifications are involved in such selective structural changes, sequence recognition may be a factor in guiding enzymes catalyzing modifications to their proper sites of action. Clearly, details of the functional role of histone modifications remain to be elucidated.

Knowledge of sites of individual histone modifications allows consideration of the implications of such modifications on nucleosome structure. There is evidence that an H3–H4 complex is an essential component of the nucleosome core (Camerini-Otero *et al.*, 1976; Sollner-Webb *et al.*, 1976; Simpson, 1976). These histones each contain 20–30 basic amino acid residues at the NH_2 termini (see Figs. 4 and 5), which are selectively digested upon treatment of chromatin with trypsin (Weintraub and Van Lente, 1974), suggesting that these ends extend unprotected from the histone complex. Nmr data indicate that these termini are not ordered unless bound to DNA (cf. Bradbury and Crane-Robinson, 1971). Simpson (1976) has presented evidence that H3 and H4 are located at each end of the 140 base-pair core DNA length although further work is necessary to establish this. It is expected that modifications of the basic termini of H3 and H4 would affect the structure of the nucleosome core particle, possibly to the extent of influencing coiling and uncoiling of the DNA within the core segment. It is notable that all *in vivo* H3 and H4 modifications for which sites have been identified, including phosphorylation, acetylation, and methylation, occur within the first 30 residues of the amino terminus of each histone (see Figs. 4 and 5).

Amino terminal ends of H2A and H2B are also thought to be bound to DNA, as suggested by evidence from trypsin digestion (Weintraub and Van Lente, 1974) and nmr (cf. Bradbury and Crane-Robinson, 1971) experiments. These histones are constituents of the nucleosome core (Kornberg and Thomas, 1974; Simpson and Bustin, 1976), although reconstitution of DNA with H2A and H2B alone does not result in formation of an approximately 140 base-pair nuclease-resistant segment as does reconstitution of DNA with H3 and H4 (Camerini-Otero et al., 1976; Sollner-Webb et al., 1976). It can be seen from Figs. 2 and 3 that several known modifications of H2A and H2B occur within the first 40 residues of the amino terminus of each histone. These modifications may affect binding of H2A and H2B to DNA within the nucleosome core and thereby influence core conformation.

Modification of H1 may not influence internal core conformation as H1 is evidently not a core constituent (Kornberg and Thomas, 1974; Oudet et al., 1975). It has been observed that the S values of separated oligomers of repeating chromatin subunits are reduced upon removal of H1, indicating an increase in the axial ratio of the chromatin fragments (Noll and Kornberg, 1977). In H1-depleted chromatin, internucleosome DNA lengths considerably longer than those in native chromatin have been noted (Oudet et al., 1975). Upon addition of H1 to isolated SV40 minichromosomes, a striking reduction in internucleosomal DNA lengths could be obtained (Bellard et al., 1976). These results suggest that H1 may be bound to internucleosome spacer DNA segments, although other possible locations for H1 binding cannot presently be excluded. Several studies suggest that H1 may be involved in the higher-order folding or supercoiling of chromatin (cf. Bradbury and Crane-Robinson, 1971). Experiments performed by Littau and colleagues (1965) indicated that the appearance of chromatin in calf thymus nuclei, examined by electron microscopy, was more significantly altered by selective removal of the lysine-rich histones than by removal of the arginine-rich histones. Brasch and co-workers (1972) found that extraction of H1 from chicken liver nuclei causes the chromatin fibers of 20 nm diameter to be replaced by tightly packed fibers of 10 nm diameter, suggesting that H1 removal causes the supercoiled chromatin to unwind. A bifunctional cross-linking action of H1 is suggested by the H1 amino acid distribution, in which basic amino acids are clustered at the termini of the histone molecule. In contrast to the other histones, the C-terminal region of H1 is more basic than the N-terminal region. Cyclic AMP-dependent phosphorylation of H1 occurs in rat liver near the N-terminal region of H1 (see Fig. 1), and this phosphorylation can influence the binding of H1 to DNA (Adler et al., 1971; Fasy et al., 1977). A cyclic AMP-independent site of phorphorylation is located near the center of the H1 molecule (see Fig. 1). Several sites of growth-associated H1 phosphorylation occur in the C-terminal region of H1 from various sources (not shown in Fig. 1). Cyclic AMP-dependent H1 phosphorylation may be concerned with localized changes in chromosome structure, possibly involving multiple chromatin sites, occurring as a pleiotypic response to certain hormones. Growth-associated phosphorylation may be concerned with more generalized and extensive changes in chromosome structure associated with the process of cell division. Of the major histone fractions, H1 displays the greatest tissue and species heterogeneity, and it is possible that functional activities of H1 are also more diverse than those of the other histones. Analyses of functional aspects of H1 modifications will benefit from a more precise knowledge of the location of H1 relative to the nucleosome core histones.

Postsynthetic biochemical modifications of histones provide an attractive mechanism for the alteration of chromosome structure in response to cellular signals and, very possibly, in response to hormonal signals. Detailed examination of the functional aspects of histone modification as related to hormone action will depend upon further research concerning the ability of specific hormones to affect replicative or transcriptional activity at an individual, well-characterized gene locus, and defining alterations in the nucleohistone structure at such a gene locus during these different states of activity.

ACKNOWLEDGMENTS

This work was supported in part by National Science Foundation Grant PCM76-19926, National Institutes of Health Grant GM 17383, American Cancer Society Grant VC 114F, and the National Leukemia Association.

REFERENCES

Adler, A. J., Schaffhausen, B., Langan, T. A., and Fasman, G. D. (1971). *Biochemistry* **10**, 909.
Adler, A. J., Ross, D. J., Chen, K., Stafford, P. A., Woiszwillo, M. J., and Fasman, G. D. (1974a). *Biochemistry* **13**, 616.
Adler, A. J., Fasman, G. D., Wangh, L. J., and Allfrey, V. G. (1974b). *J. Biol. Chem.* **249**, 2911.
Ahmed, K., and Wilson, M. J. (1975). *J. Biol. Chem.* **250**, 2370.
Ajiro, K., Borun, T. W., and Cohen, L. H. (1976). *Fed. Proc., Fed. Am. Soc. Exp. Biol.* **35**, 1623 (abstr.).
Allfrey, V. G. (1964). *Can. Cancer Conf.* **6**, 313.
Allfrey, V. G. (1966). *Cancer Res.* **26**, 2026.
Allfrey, V. G. (1970). *Fed. Proc., Fed. Am. Soc. Exp. Biol.* **29**, 1447.
Allfrey, V. G. (1971). *In* "Histones and Nucleohistones" (D. M. P. Phillips, ed.), p. 241. Plenum, New York.
Allfrey, V. G. (1977). *In* "Chromatin and Chromosome Structure" (H. J. Li and R. Eckhardt, eds.), p. 167. Academic Press, New York.

Allfrey, V. G., Faulkner, R., and Mirsky, A. E. (1964). *Proc. Natl. Acad. Sci. U.S.A.* **51**, 786.
Allfrey, V. G., Pogo, B. G. T., Pogo, A. O., Kleinsmith, L. J., and Mirsky, A. E. (1966). *Ciba Found. Study Group* **24**, 42.
Allfrey, V. G., Pogo, B. G. T., Littau, V. C., Gershey, E. L., and Mirsky, A. E. (1968). *Science* **159**, 314.
Allfrey, V. G., Johnson, E. M., Sun, I. Y. C., Littau, V. C., Matthews, H. R., and Bradbury, E. M. (1977). *Hum. Mol. Cytogenet., ICN-UCLA Symp. Mol. Cell. Biol., 7th, 1977* (in press).
Alvarez, M. R., and Lavender, K. (1974). *Exp. Cell Res.* **83**, 1.
Alvarez, M. R., and Truitt, A. J. (1977). *Exp. Cell Res.* **106**, 105.
Austoker, J., Cox, D., and Mathias, A. P. (1972). *Biochem. J.* **129**, 1139.
Bakayev, V. V., Melnickov, A. A., Osicka, V. D., and Varshavsky, A. J. (1975). *Nucleic Acids Res.* **2**, 1401.
Baldwin, J. P., Bosely, P. G., Bradbury, E. M., and Ibel, K. (1975). *Nature (London)* **253**, 245.
Balhorn, R., Chalkley, R., and Granner, D. (1972). *Biochemistry* **11**, 1094.
Barker, K. L., and Warren, J. C. (1966). *Proc. Natl. Acad. Sci. U.S.A.* **56**, 1298.
Barraclough, B. R., and Campbell, P. N. (1973). *Biochem. Soc. Trans.* **1**, 601.
Beck, W. T., Bellantone, R. A., and Canellakis, E. S. (1972). *Biochem. Biophys. Res. Commun.* **48**, 1649.
Bell, G. I., Valenzuela, P., and Rutter, W. J. (1976). *Nature (London)* **261**, 429.
Bellard, M., Oudet, P., Germond, J. E., and Chambon, P. (1976). *Dahlem Conf. Life Sci. Res. Rep.* **4**, 253.
Berkovic, S. F., and Mauritzen, C. M. (1977). *Biochim, Biophys. Acta* **475**, 160.
Berlowitz, L., and Pallotta, D. (1972). *Exp. Cell Res.* **71**, 45.
Boffa, L. C., and Vidali, G. (1971). *Biochim, Biophys. Acta* **236**, 259.
Boffa, L. C., Gershey, E. L., and Vidali, G. (1971). *Biochim. Biophys. Acta* **254**, 135.
Bondy, S. C., Roberts, S., and Morelos, S. (1970). *Biochem. J.* **119**, 665.
Boublik, M., Bradbury, E. M., Crane-Robinson, C., and Rattle, H. W. E. (1971). *Nature (London), New Biol.* **299**, 149.
Bradbury, E. M. (1975). *Struct. Funct. Chromatin, Ciba Found. Symp.* No. 28 (New Ser.), p. 131.
Bradbury, E. M., and Crane-Robinson, C. (1971). *In* "Histones and Nucleohistones" (D. M. P. Phillips, ed.), p. 85. Plenum, New York.
Bradbury, E. M., Inglis, R. J., Matthews, H. R., and Sarner, N. (1973). *Eur. J. Biochem.* **33**, 131.
Bradbury, E. M., Inglis, R. J., and Matthews, H. R. (1974). *Nature (London)* **249**, 553.
Brandt, W. F., Strickland, W. N., Morgan, M., and von Holt, C. (1974). *FEBS Lett.* **40**, 167.
Brasch, K., Setterfield, G., and Neelin, J. M. (1972). *Exp. Cell Res.* **74**, 27.
Bresnick, E., and Mosse, H. (1969). *Mol. Pharmacol.* **5**, 219.
Brown, I. R. (1975). *Proc. Natl. Acad. Sci. U.S.A.* **72**, 837.
Brown, I. R., and Liew, C. C. (1975). *Science* **188**, 1122.
Burdick, C. J., and Taylor, B. A. (1976). *Exp. Cell Res.* **100**, 428.
Bustin, M., and Cole, R. D. (1969). *J. Biol. Chem.* **244**, 5286.
Butler, J. A. V., and Cohn, P. (1963). *Biochem. J.* **87**, 330.
Caldarera, C. M., Orlandini, G., Casti, A., and Moruzzi, G. (1974). *J. Mol. Cell. Cardiol.* **6**, 95.
Caldarera, C. M., Casti, A., Guarnieri, C., and Moruzzi, G. (1975). *Biochem. J.* **152**, 91.
Camerini-Otero, R. D., Sollner-Webb, B., and Felsenfeld, G. (1976). *Cell* **8**, 333.
Cameron, J. L., and Prescott, D. M. (1963). *Exp. Cell Res.* **30**, 609.
Candido, E. P. M., and Dixon, G. H. (1971). *J. Biol. Chem.* **246**, 3182.
Candido, E. P. M., and Dixon, G. H (1972a). *J. Biol. Chem.* **247**, 3863.
Candido, E. P. M., and Dixon, G. H. (1972b). *Proc. Natl. Acad. Sci. U.S.A.* **69**, 2015.
Candido, E. P. M., and Dixon, G. H. (1972c). *J. Biol. Chem.* **247**, 5506.

Chalkley, R., Balhorn, R., Oliver, D., and Granner, D. (1973). *In* "Protein Phosphorylation in Control Mechanisms" (F. Huijing and E. Y. C. Lee, eds.), p. 251. Academic Press, New York.

Chen, C. C., Smith, D. L., Bruegger, B. B., Halpern, R. M., and Smith, R. A. (1974). *Biochemistry* 13, 3785.

Chen, L., and Walsh, D. A. (1971). *Biochemistry* 10, 3614.

Chew, L. F., and MacKinlay, A. G. (1974). *Biochim. Biophys. Acta* 359, 73.

Church, R. B., and McCarthy, B. J. (1967). *J. Mol. Biol.* 23, 459.

Clever, U., and Ellgaard, E. G. (1970). *Science* 169, 373.

Clifford, J. I., and Rees, K. R. (1967). *Biochem. J.* 102, 65.

Cole, R. D. (1977). *In* "Molecular Biology of the Mammalian Genetic Apparatus" (P.O.P. T'so, ed.), p. 93. North-Holland Publ., Amsterdam.

Comber, H. J., and Taylor, D. M. (1974). *Biochem. Soc. Trans.* 2, 74.

Compton, J. L., Bellard, M., and Chambon, P. (1976). *Proc. Natl. Acad. Sci. U.S.A.* 73, 4382.

Costa, M., Gerner, E. W., and Russel, D. (1976). *J. Biol. Chem.* 251, 3313.

Dahmus, M., and Bonner, J. (1965). *Proc. Natl. Acad. Sci. U.S.A.* 54, 1370.

D'Anna, J. A., and Isenberg, I. (1974). *Biochemistry* 13, 4992.

Darzynkiewicz, Z., and Andersson, J. (1971). *Exp. Cell Res.* 67, 39.

Darzynkiewicz, Z., and Jacobson, B. (1971). *Exp. Cell Res.* 67, 49.

Darzynkiewicz, Z., Bolund, L., and Ringertz, N. P. (1969). *Exp. Cell Res.* 55, 120.

DeLange, R. J., and Smith, E. L. (1972). *Acc. Chem. Res.* 5, 386.

DeLange, R. J., and Smith, E. L. (1975). *Struct. Funct. Chromatin, Ciba Found. Symp.* No. 28 (New Ser.), p. 57.

DeLange, R. J., Fambrough, D. M., Smith, E. L., and Bonner, J. (1969). *J. Biol. Chem.* 244, 319.

DeLange, R. J., Hooper, J. A., and Smith, E. L. (1973). *J. Biol. Chem.* 248, 3261.

Dietrich, L. S., Jaus, H., and Siebert, G. (1973). *FEBS Lett.* 37, 228.

Dixon, G. H. (1976). *Dahlem Conf. Life Sci. Res. Rep.* 4, 197.

Dixon, G. H., Candido, E. P. M., Honda, B. M., Louie, A. J., MacLeod, A. R., and Sung, M. T. (1975). *Struct. Funct. Chromatin, Ciba Found. Symp.* No. 28 (New Ser.), p. 229.

Doly, J., Ramuz, M., Mandel, P., and Chambon, P. (1965). *Biochim. Biophys. Acta* 108, 521.

Earp, H. S., Smith, P., Ong, S. H., and Steiner, A. L. (1977). *Proc. Natl. Acad. U.S.A.* 74, 946.

Edelman, I. S., and Fimognari, G. M. (1968). *Recent Prog. Horm. Res.* 24, 1.

Edwards, G. S., and Allfrey, V. G. (1973). *Biochim. Biophys. Acta* 299, 354.

Edwards, G. S., and Wogan, G. N. (1970). *Biochim. Biophys. Acta* 224, 597.

Elgin, S. C. R., and Weintraub, H. (1975). *Annu. Rev. Biochem.* 44, 725.

Farago, A., Romhanyi, T., Antoni, F., Takats, A., and Fabian, F. (1975). *Nature (London)* 254, 88.

Fasy, T. M., Johnson, E. M., Inoue, A., and Allfrey, V. G. (1977). *J. Supramol. Struct., Suppl.* 1, 116.

Feigelson, M., Gross, P. R., and Feigelson, P. (1962). *Biochim. Biophys. Acta* 55, 495.

Foe, V. E., Wilkinson, L. E., and Laird, C. D. (1976). *Cell* 9, 131.

Fox, K., and Gabourel, J. (1967). *J. Mol. Pharmacol.* 3, 479.

Frenster, J. H., Allfrey, V. G., and Mirsky, A. E. (1963). *Proc. Natl. Acad. Sci. U.S.A.* 50, 1026.

Fujimoto, D., and Segawa, K. (1973). *FEBS Lett.* 32, 59.

Fujioka, M., Koga, M., and Lieberman, I. (1963). *J. Biol. Chem.* 238, 3401.

Gallwitz, D. (1968). *Biochem. Biophys. Res. Commun.* 32, 117.

Gallwitz, D. (1970). *Biochem. Biophys. Res. Commun.* 40, 236.

Gallwitz, D. (1971). *FEBS Lett.* 13, 306.

Gallwitz, D., and Sekeris, C. E. (1969). *Hoppe-Seyler's Z. Physiol. Chem.* 350, 150.

Gallwitz, D., and Sures, I. (1972). *Biochim. Biophys. Acta* **263**, 315.

Garel, A., and Axel, R. (1976). *Proc. Natl. Acad. Sci. U.S.A.* **73**, 3966.

Gelboin, H. V., Wortham, J. S., and Wilson, R. G. (1967). *Nature (London)* **214**, 281.

Gershey, E. L., Vidali, G., and Allfrey, V. G. (1968). *J. Biol. Chem.* **243**, 5018.

Glasser, S. R., Chytil, F. C., and Spelsberg, T. C. (1972). *Biochem. J.* **130**, 947.

Gorovsky, M. A., and Keevert, J. B. (1975). *Proc. Natl. Acad. Sci. U.S.A.* **72**, 3536.

Gorovsky, M. A., Pleger, G. L., Keevert, J. B., and Johmann, C. A. (1973). *J. Cell Biol.* **57**, 773.

Gorski, J., Noteboom, W. D., and Nicolette, J. A. (1965). *J. Cell. Comp. Physiol.* **66**, 91.

Graaff, G. deV., and von Holt, C. (1973). *Biochim. Biophys. Acta* **299**, 480.

Granboulan, N., and Granboulan, P. (1965). *Exp. Cell Res.* **38**, 604.

Grimes, S. R., Jr., Chae, C. B., and Irvin, J. L. (1975). *Arch. Biochem. Biophys.* **168**, 425.

Gurley, L. R., and Walters, R. A. (1973). *Biochem. Biophys. Res. Commun.* **55**, 697.

Gurley, L. R., Walters, R. A., and Tobey, R. A. (1973). *Arch. Biochem. Biophys.* **154**, 212.

Gurley, L. R., Walters, R. A., and Tobey, R. A. (1974). *J. Cell Biol.* **60**, 356.

Gurley, L. R., Walters, R. A., and Tobey, R. A. (1975). *J. Biol. Chem.* **250**, 3936.

Hamilton, T. H. (1964). *Proc. Natl. Acad. Sci. U.S.A.* **51**, 83.

Harvey, S. R., and Libby, P. R. (1976). *Biochim. Biophys. Acta* **429**, 742.

Hashimoto, E., Takeda, M., and Nishizuka, Y. (1975). *Biochem. Biophys. Res. Commun.* **66**, 547.

Hnilica, L. S. (1972). "The Structure and Biological Functions of Histones." CRC Press, Cleveland, Ohio.

Hohmann, P., Tobey, R. A., and Gurley, L. R. (1975). *Biochem. Biophys. Res. Commun.* **63**, 126.

Hohmann, P., Tobey, R. A., and Gurley, L. R. (1976). *J. Biol. Chem.* **251**, 3685.

Holbrook, D. J., Evans, J. H., and Irvin, J. L. (1962). *Exp. Cell Res.* **28**, 120.

Hooper, J. A., Smith, E. L., Summer, K. R., and Chalkley, R. (1973). *J. Biol. Chem.* **248**, 3275.

Horgen, P. A., and Ball, S. F. (1974). *Cytobios* **10**, 181.

Horiuchi, K., and Fujimoto, D. (1972). *J. Biochem. (Tokyo)* **72**, 433.

Horiuchi, K., and Fujimoto, D. (1973). *J. Biochem. (Tokyo)* **73**, 117.

Horiuchi, K., and Fujimoto, D. (1975). *Anal. Biochem.* **69**, 491.

Hsu, T. C. (1962). *Exp. Cell Res.* **27**, 332.

Humphries, S., Windass, J., and Williamson, R. (1976). *Cell* **7**, 267.

Inglis, R. J., Langan, T. A., Matthews, H. R., Hardie, D. G., and Bradbury, E. M. (1976). *Exp. Cell Res.* **97**, 418.

Inoue, A., and Fujimoto, D. (1969). *Biochem. Biophys. Res. Commun.* **36**, 146.

Inoue, A., and Fujimoto, D. (1970). *Biochim. Biophys. Acta* **220**, 307.

Inoue, A., and Fujimoto, D. (1972). *J. Biochem. (Tokyo)* **72**, 427.

Insel, P. A., Bourne, H. R., Coffino, P., and Tomkins, G. M. (1975). *Science* **190**, 896.

Iwai, K., Ishikawa, K., and Hayashi, H. (1970). *Nature (London)* **226**, 1056.

Jackson, V., Shires, A., Chalkley, R., and Granner, D. K. (1975). *J. Biol. Chem.* **250**, 4856.

Jackson, V., Shires, A., Tanphaichitr, N., and Chalkley, R. (1976). *J. Mol. Biol.* **104**, 471.

Jensen, E. V., Jacobson, H. I., Fleshmer, J. W., Saha, N. N., Gupta, G. N., Smith, S., Colucci, V., Shiplacoff, D., Neumann, H. G., DeSombre, E. R., and Jungblut, P. W. (1966). *In* "S.eroid Dynamics" (G. Pincus, T. Nakao, and J. F. Tait, eds.), p. 133. Academic Press, New York.

Johmann, C. A., and Gorovsky, M. A. (1976). *J. Cell Biol.* **71**, 89.

Johnson, A. W., Wilhelm, J. A., and Hnilica, L. S. (1973). *Biochim. Biophys. Acta* **295**, 150.

Johnson, E. M. (1977). *Adv. Cyclic Nucleotide Res.* **8**, 267.

Johnson, E. M., and Allfrey, V. G. (1972). *Arch. Biochem. Biophys.* **152**, 786.

Johnson, E. M., Vidali, G., Littau, V. C., and Allfrey, V. G. (1973). *J. Biol. Chem.* **248**, 7595.

Johnson, E. M., Karn, J., and Allfrey, V. G. (1974). *J. Biol. Chem.* **249**, 4990.

Johnson, E. M., and Hadden, J. W. (1975). *Science* **187**, 1198.

Johnson, E. M., Littau, V. C., Allfrey, V. G., Bradbury, E. M., and Matthews, H. R. (1976). *Nucleic Acids Res.* **3**, 3313.

Johnson, E. M., Matthews, H. R., Bradbury, E. M., and Allfrey, V. G. (1977). *J. Cell. Biol.* **75**, 129a (abstr.).

Jones, G. M., Rall, S. C., and Cole, R. D. (1974). *J. Biol. Chem.* **249**, 2548.

Jungmann, R. A., and Schweppe, J. S. (1972a). *J. Biol. Chem.* **247**, 5535.

Jungmann, R. A., and Schweppe, J. S. (1972b). *J. Biol. Chem.* **247**, 5543.

Jungmann, R. A., Hiestand, P. C., and Schweppe, J. S. (1974). *Endocrinology* **94**, 168.

Kaiser, N., Milholland, R., and Rosen, F. (1973). *J. Biol. Chem.* **248**, 478.

Kaneta, H., and Fujimoto, D. (1974). *J. Biochem. (Tokyo)* **76**, 905.

Karn, J., Johnson, E. M., Vidali, G., and Allfrey, V. G. (1974). *J. Biol. Chem.* **249**, 667.

Kato, T., and Kurokawa, M. (1970). *Biochem. J.* **116**, 599.

Kaye, A. M., Walker, M. D., and Somjen, D. (1975). *Proc. Natl. Acad. Sci. U.S.A.* **72**, 2631.

Keller, R. K., Socher, S. H., Krall, J. F., Chandra, T., and O'Malley, B. W. (1975). *Biochem. Biophys. Res. Commun.* **66**, 453.

Kemp, B. E., Bylund, D. B., Huang, T. S., and Krebs, E. G. (1975). *Proc. Natl. Acad. Sci. U.S.A.* **72**, 3448.

Kemp, B. E., Benjamini, E., and Krebs, E. G. (1976). *Proc. Natl. Acad. Sci. U.S.A.* **73**, 1038.

Kemp, C. L. (1966). *Chromosoma* **19**, 137.

Kenney, F. T., and Kull, F. J. (1963). *Proc. Natl. Acad. Sci. U.S.A.* **50**, 493.

Kidson, C. (1965). *Biochem. Biophys. Res. Commun.* **21**, 283.

Kikuchi, H., and Fujimoto, D. (1973). *FEBS Lett.* **29**, 280.

Killander, D., and Rigler, R. (1965). *Exp. Cell Res.* **39**, 710.

Killander, D., and Rigler, R. (1969). *Exp. Cell Res.* **54**, 163.

Kish, V. M., and Kleinsmith, L. J. (1974). *J. Biol. Chem.* **249**, 750.

Kleinsmith, L. J., Allfrey, V. G., and Mirsky, A. E. (1966a). *Proc. Natl. Acad. Sci. U.S.A.* **55**, 1182.

Kleinsmith, L. J., Allfrey, V. G., and Mirsky, A. E. (1966b). *Science* **154**, 780.

Kornberg, R. D., and Thomas, J. O. (1974). *Science* **184**, 865.

Krantz, S. B., and Goldwasser, E. (1965). *Biochim. Biophys. Acta* **103**, 325.

Krause, M. V., and Stein, G. S. (1975). *Exp. Cell Res.* **92**, 175.

Krieger, D. E., Levine, R. B., Merrifield, R. B., Vidali, G., and Allfrey, V. G. (1974). *J. Biol. Chem.* **249**, 322.

Krieger, D. E., Merrifield, R. B., Vidali, G., and Allfrey, V. G. (1977). *Proc. Natl. Acad. Sci. U.S.A.* (submitted for publication).

Kuo, J. F. (1974). *Proc. Natl. Acad. Sci. U.S.A.* **71**, 4037.

Kuo, J. F., Patrick, J. G., and Seery, V. L. (1976). *Biochem. Biophys. Res. Commun.* **72**, 996.

Kuroda, Y., Hashimoto, E., Nishizuka, Y., Hamana, K., and Iwai, K. (1976). *Biochem. Biophys. Res. Commun.* **71**, 629.

Lacy, E., and Axel, R. (1975). *Proc. Natl. Acad. Sci. U.S.A.* **72**, 3978.

Lake, R. S. (1973). *In* "Protein Phosphorylation in Control Mechanisms" (F. Huijing and E. Y. C. Lee, eds.), p. 295. Academic Press, New York.

Lake, R. S., and Salzman, N. P. (1972). *Biochemistry* **11**, 4817.

Langan, T. A. (1968). *Science* **162**, 519.

Langan, T. A. (1969a). *Proc. Natl. Acad. Sci. U.S.A.* **64**, 1276.

Langan, T. A. (1969b). *J. Biol. Chem.* **244**, 5763.

Langan, T. A. (1970). *In* "Role of Cyclic AMP in Cell Function" (P. Greengard and E. Costa, eds.), p. 307. Raven, New York.

Langan, T. A. (1971a). *Ann. N.Y. Acad. Sci.* **185,** 166.

Langan, T. A. (1971b). *Fed. Proc., Fed. Am. Soc. Exp. Biol.* **30,** 1089 (abstr.).

Langan, T. A. (1973). *Adv. Cyclic Nucleotide Res.* **3,** 99.

Langan, T. A. (1976). *Fed. Proc., Fed. Am. Soc. Exp. Biol.* **35,** 1623 (abstr.).

Langan, T. A., and Hohmann, P. (1975). *In* "Chromosomal Proteins and Their Role in the Regulation of Gene Expression" (G. S. Stein and L. J. Kleinsmith, eds.), p. 113. Academic Press, New York.

Langan, T. A., and Smith, L. K. (1967). *Fed. Proc., Fed. Am. Soc. Exp. Biol.* **26,** 603 (abstr.).

Langan, T. A., Rall, S. C., and Cole, R. D. (1971). *J. Biol. Chem.* **246,** 1942.

Ledinko, N. (1970). *J. Virol.* **6,** 58.

LeFarge, C., Fraysinnet, C., and deRecondo, A. M. (1967). *Bull. Soc. Chim. Biol.* **47,** 1724.

Letnansky, K. (1975). *Cell Tissue Kinet.* **8,** 423.

Levy, R., Levy, S., Rosenberg, S. A., and Simpson, R. T. (1973). *Biochemistry* **12,** 224.

Levy-Wilson, B., Gjerset, R., and McCarthy, B. J. (1977). *Biochim. Biophys. Acta* **475,** 168.

Li, H. J., and Bonner, J. (1971). *Biochemistry* **10,** 1461.

Libby, P. R. (1968). *Biochem. Biophys. Res. Commun.* **31,** 59.

Libby, P. R. (1970). *Biochim. Biophys. Acta* **213,** 234.

Libby, P. R. (1972). *Biochem. J.* **130,** 663.

Libby, P. R. (1973). *Biochem. J.* **134,** 907.

Liew, C. C., Haslett, G. W., and Allfrey, V. G. (1970). *Nature (London)* **226,** 414.

Liew, C. C., Liu, D. K., and Gornall, A. G. (1972). *Endocrinology* **90,** 488.

Liew, C. C., Suria, D., and Gornall, A. G. (1973). *Endocrinology* **93,** 1025.

Lipps, H. J. (1975). *Cell Differ.* **4,** 123.

Littau, V. C., Allfrey, V. G., Frenster, J. H., and Mirsky, A. E. (1964). *Proc. Natl. Acad. Sci. U.S.A.* **52,** 93.

Littau, V. C., Burdick, C. J., Allfrey, V. G., and Mirsky, A. E. (1965). *Proc. Natl. Acad. Sci. U.S.A.* **54,** 1204.

Liu, A. Y. C., and Greengard, P. (1974). *Proc. Natl. Acad. Sci. U.S.A.* **71,** 3869.

Lohr, D., Corden, J., Tatchell, K., Kovack, R. T., and Van Holde, K. E. (1977). *Proc. Natl. Acad. Sci. U.S.A.* **74,** 79.

Louie, A. J., and Dixon, G. H. (1972). *J. Biol. Chem.* **247,** 5498.

Louie, A. J., and Dixon, G. H. (1973). *Nature New Biol.* **243,** 164.

Louie, A. J., Candido, E. P. M., and Dixon, G. H. (1973). *Cold Spring Harbor Symp. Quant. Biol.* **38,** 803.

Luck, D. N., and Hamilton, T. E. (1975). *Biochim. Biophys. Acta* **383,** 23.

Lue, P., Gornall, A. G., and Liew, C. C. (1973). *Can. J. Biochem.* **51,** 1177.

McKnight, S. L., and Miller, O. L., Jr. (1976). *Cell* **8,** 305.

Madix, J. C., and Bresnick, E. (1967). *Biochem. Biophys. Res. Commun.* **28,** 445.

Majumder, G. C. (1974). *Biochem. Biophys. Res. Commun.* **58,** 756.

Majumder, G. C., and Turkington, R. W. (1972). *J. Biol. Chem.* **247,** 7207.

Makman, M., Nakagawe, S., Dvorkin, D., and White, A. (1970). *J. Biol. Chem.* **245,** 255.

Mallette, L. E., Neblett, M., Exton, J. H., and Langan, T. A. (1973). *J. Biol. Chem.* **248,** 6289.

Marks, D. B., Paik, W. K., and Borun, T. W. (1973). *J. Biol. Chem.* **248,** 5660.

Martelo, O. J., Woo, S. L. C., and Davie, E. W. (1974). *J. Mol. Biol.* **87,** 685.

Marushige, K. (1976). *Proc. Natl. Acad. Sci. U.S.A.* **73,** 3837.

Marushige, K., and Bonner, J. (1966). *J. Mol. Biol.* **15,** 160.

Marushige, K., Ling, V., and Dixon, G. H. (1969). *J. Biol. Chem.* **244,** 5953.

Marushige, Y., and Marushige, K. (1975). *Biochim. Biophys. Acta* **403,** 180.

Marzluff, W. F., Jr., and McCarty, K. S. (1970). *J. Biol. Chem.* **245,** 5635.

Marzluff, W. F., Jr., and McCarty, K. S. (1972). *Biochemistry* 11, 2677.

Marzluff, W. F., Jr., Sanders, L. A., Miller, D. M., and McCarty, K. S. (1972). *J. Biol. Chem.* 247, 2026.

Masaracchia, R. A., Kemp, B. E., and Walsh, D. A. (1977). *J. Biol. Chem.* 252, 7109.

Matthews, H. R., Hardie, D. G., Inglis, R. J., and Bradbury, E. M. (1975). *In* "The Molecular Basis of Circadian Rhythms" (J. W. Hastings and H. G. Schweiger, eds.), p. 395. Dahlem Konferenzen, Berlin.

Means, A. R., and Hamilton, T. H. (1966). *Proc. Natl. Acad. Sci. U.S.A.* 56, 1594.

Meisler, M. H., and Langan, T. A. (1969). *J. Biol. Chem.* 244, 4961.

Miyamoto, E., Petzold, G. L., Kuo, J. F., and Greengard, P. (1973). *J. Biol. Chem.* 248, 7595.

Moorhead, P. J., Nowell, P. C., Mellman, W. J., Battips, D. M., and Hungerford, D. A. (1960). *Exp. Cell Res.* 20, 613.

Morris, R. (1976). *Cell* 8, 357.

Mueller, G. C., Herranen, A. M., and Jervell, K. J. (1958). *Recent Prog. Horm. Res.* 14, 95.

Murray, K. (1964). *Biochemistry* 3, 10.

Murthy, L. D., Pradhan, D. S., and Sreenivasan, A. (1970). *Biochim. Biophys. Acta* 199, 500.

Nadler, K. D. (1976). *Exp. Cell Res.* 101, 283.

Nakao, K., Takaku, F., Fujioka, S., and Sassa, S. (1966). *Blood* 27, 537.

Nicolette, J. A., and Babler, M. (1974). *Arch. Biochem. Biophys.* 163, 263.

Nohara, H., Takahashi, T., and Ogata, K. (1966). *Biochim. Biophys. Acta* 127, 282.

Nohara, H., Takahashi, T., and Ogata, K. (1968). *Biochim. Biophys. Acta* 154, 529.

Noll, M. (1976). *Dahlem Conf. Life Sci. Rep.* 4, 239.

Noll, M., and Kornberg, R. (1977). *J. Mol. Biol.* 109, 393.

Ogawa, Y. (1969). *J. Biol. Chem.* 244, 4387.

Ogawa, Y., Quagliarotti, G., Jordan, J., Taylor, C. W., Starbuck, W. C., and Busch, H. (1969). *J. Biol. Chem.* 244, 4387.

Olson, M. O. J., Jordan, J., and Busch, H. (1972). *Biochem. Biophys. Res. Commun.* 46, 50.

O'Malley, B. W., and Means, A. R. (1974). *Science* 183, 610.

Ono, T., Terayama, H., Takaku, F., and Nakao, K. (1969). *Biochim. Biophys. Acta* 179, 214.

Ord, M. G., and Stocken, L. A. (1966). *Biochem. J.* 98, 888.

Ord, M. G., and Stocken, L. A. (1968). *Biochem. J.* 107, 403.

Ord, M. G., and Stocken, L. A. (1969). *Biochem. J.* 112, 81.

Oudet, P., Gross-Bellard, M., and Chambon, P. (1975). *Cell* 4, 281.

Paik, W. K., and Kim, S. (1967). *Biochem. Biophys. Res. Commun.* 29, 14.

Patthy, L., and Smith, E. L. (1975). *J. Biol. Chem.* 250, 1919.

Pestana, A., and Pitot, H. C. (1975). *Biochemistry* 14, 1404.

Pestana, A., Sudilovsky, O., and Pitot, H. C. (1971). *FEBS Lett.* 19, 83.

Phillips, D. M. P. (1963). *Biochem. J.* 87, 258.

Phillips, D. M. P. (1968). *Biochem. J.* 107, 135.

Pieber-Perretta, M., Rudolf, W., Perretta, M., and Hodgson, G. (1965). *Biochim. Biophys. Acta* 95, 360.

Piper, W. N., and Bousquet, W. F. (1968). *Biochem. Biophys. Res. Commun.* 33, 602.

Pogo, B. G. T., Allfrey, V. G., and Mirsky, A. E. (1966). *Proc. Natl. Acad. Sci. U.S.A.* 55, 805.

Pogo, B. G. T., Allfrey, V. G., and Mirsky, A. E. (1967). *J. Cell Biol.* 35, 477.

Pogo, B. G. T., Pogo, A. O., Allfrey, V. G., and Mirsky, A. E. (1968). *Proc. Natl. Acad. Sci. U.S.A.* 59, 1337.

Pogo, A. O., Allfrey, V. G., and Mirsky, A. E. (1966). *Proc. Natl. Acad. Sci. U.S.A.* 56, 550.

Pomerantz, A. H., Allfrey, V. G., Merrifield, R. B., and Johnson, E. M. (1977). *Proc. Natl. Acad. Sci. U.S.A.* 74, 4261.

Pong. R. S., and Wogan, G. N. (1970). *Cancer Res.* 30, 294.

Procaccini, R. L., and Bresnick, E. (1975). *Chem.-Biol. Interact.* 11, 523.

Racey, L. A., and Byvoet, P. (1971). *Exp. Cell Res.* **64**, 366.
Racey, L. A., and Byvoet, P. (1972). *Exp. Cell Res.* **73**, 329.
Rall, S. C., and Cole, R. D. (1971). *J. Biol. Chem.* **246**, 7175.
Reel, J. R., and Gorski, J. (1968). *Endocrinology* **83**, 1092.
Risley, M. S., and Eckhardt, R. A. (1975). *J. Cell. Biol.* **67**, 362 (abstr.).
Rosenfeld, M. G., Abrass, I. B., Mendelsohn, J., Roos, B. A., Boone, R. F., and Garen, L. D. (1972). *Proc. Natl. Acad. Sci. U.S.A.* **69**, 2306.
Rudolf, W., and Perretta, M. (1967). *Proc. Soc. Exp. Biol. Med.* **124**, 1041.
Ruiz-Carrillo, A., and Palau, J. (1973). *Dev. Biol.* **35**, 115.
Ruiz-Carrillo, A., Wangh, L. J., Littau, V. C., and Allfrey, V. G. (1974). *J. Biol. Chem.* **249**, 7358.
Ruiz-Carrillo, A., Wangh, L. J., and Allfrey, V. G. (1975). *Science* **190**, 117.
Ruiz-Carrillo, A., Wangh, L. J., and Allfrey, V. G. (1976). *Arch. Biochem. Biophys.* **174**, 273.
Russel, T. R., and Pastan, I. H. (1974). *J. Biol. Chem.* **249**, 7764.
Sadgopal, A., and Bonner, J. (1970). *Biochim. Biophys. Acta* **207**, 227.
Sanders, L. A., Schechter, N. M., and McCarty, K. S. (1973). *Biochemistry* **12**, 783.
Sarkander, H. I., Fleischer-Lambropoulos, H., and Brade, W. P. (1975). *FEBS Lett.* **52**, 40.
Sautiere, P., Tyrou, D., Laine, B., Mizon, J., Ruffin, P., and Biserte, G. (1974). *Eur. J. Biochem.* **41**, 563.
Schaffhausen, B. S., and Benjamin, T. I. (1976). *Proc. Natl. Acad. Sci. U.S.A.* **73**, 1092.
Schimke, R. T., and Doyle, D. (1970). *Annu. Rev. Biochem.* **39**, 929.
Seligy, V., Roy, C., Dove, M., and Yaguchi, M. (1976). *Biochem. Biophys. Res. Commun.* **71**, 196.
Sharma, S. K., and Talwar, G. P. (1970). *J. Biol. Chem.* **245**, 1513.
Shepherd, G. R., Noland, B. J., and Harden, J. M. (1971). *Biochim. Biophys. Acta* **228**, 544.
Shlyapnikov, S. V., Arutyunyan, A. A., Kurochkin, S. N., Memlova, L. V., Nesterova, M. V., Sashchenko, L. P., and Severin, E. S. (1975). *FEBS Lett.* **53**, 316.
Shoemaker, C. B., and Chalkley, R. (1977). *Fed. Proc., Fed. Am. Soc. Exp. Biol.* **36**, 784 (abstr.).
Simpson, R. T. (1976). *Proc. Natl. Acad. Sci. U.S.A.* **73**, 4400.
Simpson, R. T., and Bustin, M. B. (1976). *Biochemistry* **15**, 4305.
Smith, J. A., and Stocken, L. A. (1973). *Biochem. Biophys. Res. Commun.* **54**, 297.
Sollner-Webb, B., Camerini-Otero, R. D., and Felsenfeld, G. (1976). *Cell* **9**, 179.
Sporn, M. B., Dingman, C. W., Phelps, H. L., and Wogan, G. N. (1966). *Science* **151**, 1539.
Strickland, M., Strickland, W. N., Brandt, W. F., and von Holt, C. (1974). *FEBS Lett.* **40**, 346.
Subirana, J. A. (1971). *FEBS Lett.* **16**, 133.
Sung, M. T. (1977). *Biochemistry* **16**, 286.
Sung, M. T., and Dixon, G. H. (1970). *Proc. Natl. Acad. Sci. U.S.A.* **67**, 1616.
Sung, M. T., Dixon, G. H., and Smithies, O. (1971). *J. Biol. Chem.* **246**, 1358.
Takaku, F., Nakao, K., Ono, T., and Terayama, H. (1969). *Biochim. Biophys. Acta* **195**, 396.
Takeda, M., and Ohga, Y. (1973). *J. Biochem (Tokyo)* **73**, 621.
Teng, C. S., and Hamilton, T. H. (1968). *Proc. Natl. Acad. Sci. U.S.A.* **60**, 1140.
Thaler, M. M., and Villee, C. A. (1967). *Proc. Natl. Acad. Sci. U.S.A.* **58**, 2055.
Thomas, J. O., and Furber, V. (1976). *FEBS Lett.* **66**, 274.
Thomas, J. O., and Thompson, R. J. (1977). *Cell* **10**, 633.
Thwaits, B. H., Brandt, W. F., and von Holt, C. (1976a). *FEBS Lett.* **71**, 193.
Thwaits, B. H., Brandt, W. F., and von Holt, C. (1976b). *FEBS Lett.* **71**, 197.
Tidwell, T., Allfrey, V. G., and Mirsky, A. E. (1968). *J. Biol. Chem.* **243**, 707.
Trachewsky, D., and Lawrence, S. (1972). *Proc. Soc. Exp. Biol. Med.* **141**, 14.
Tsukada, K., and Lieberman, I. (1965). *J. Biol. Chem.* **240**, 1731.

Ueda, K., Omachi, A., Kawaichi, M., and Hayaishi, O. (1975). *Proc. Natl. Acad. Sci. U.S.A.* **72,** 205.

Van Dyke, K., and Katzman, P. A. (1968). *Endocrinology* **83,** 107.

Vidali, G., and Allfrey, V. G. (1977). *Arch. Biochem. Biophys.* (submitted for publication).

Vidali, G., Gershey, E. L., and Allfrey, V. G. (1968). *J. Biol. Chem.* **243,** 6361.

Vidali, G., Boffa, L. C., and Allfrey, V. G. (1972). *J. Biol. Chem.* **247,** 7365.

Vidali, G., Boffa, L. C., Bradbury, E. M., and Allfrey, V. G. (1978). *Proc. Nat. Acad. Sci.* (in press).

Vokaer, A., Iacobelli, S., and Kram, R. (1974). *Proc. Natl. Acad. Sci. U.S.A.* **71,** 4482.

Wagner, T. (1970). *Biochem. Biophys. Res. Commun.* **38,** 890.

Wangh, L. J., Ruiz-Carrillo, A., and Allfrey, V. G. (1972). *Arch. Biochem. Biophys.* **150,** 44.

Watson, G., and Langan, T. A. (1973). *Fed. Proc., Fed. Am. Soc. Exp. Biol.* **32,** 588 (abstr.).

Weintraub, H., and Groudine, M. (1976). *Science* **193,** 848.

Weintraub, H., and Van Lente, F. (1974). *Proc. Natl. Acad. Sci. U.S.A.* **71,** 4249.

Weintraub, H., Palter, K., and Van Lente, F. (1975). *Cell* **6,** 85.

Weintraub, H., Worcel, A., and Alberts, B. M. (1976). *Cell* **9,** 409.

Wicks, W. D. (1969). *J. Biol. Chem.* **244,** 3941.

Wicks, W. D., Koontz, J., and Wagner, K. (1975). *J. Cyclic Nucleotide Res.* **1,** 49.

Wilhelm, J. A., and McCarty, K. S. (1970). *Cancer Res.* **30,** 418.

Wong, L. J. C., and Alberts, B. M. (1977). *Fed. Proc., Fed. Am. Soc. Exp. Biol.* **36,** 784 (abstr.).

Wong, T. K., and Marushige, K. (1976). *Biochemistry* **15,** 2041.

Woodcock, C. F. L., Frado, L.-L.Y., Hatch, C. L., and Ricciardiello, L. (1976). *Cromosoma* **58,** 33.

Yeoman, L. C., Olson, M. O. J., Sugano, N., Jordan, J. J., Taylor, C. W., Starbuck, W. C., and Busch, H. (1972). *J. Biol. Chem.* **247,** 6018.

Ziccardi, R., and Schumaker, V. (1973). *Biochemistry* **12,** 3231.

CHAPTER 2

Regulation of Exocytosis

Fred R. Butcher

I. INTRODUCTION

It is particularly appropriate that a section on exocytosis be included in a volume concerned with hormone action. Indeed, the hormone release step, which is thought to occur by exocytosis, can be considered as the first step in hormone action, for without this step there can be no effect of the hormone on its target cell. Like other aspects of hormone action, the release step is precisely and specifically controlled. This control has many features in common with hormone action in general since it is thought to involve Ca^{2+} and cyclic nucleotides.

The release of intracellular vesicular contents by exocytosis is not a process unique only to endocrine cell types. Sufficient information is now available which permits the description of several features dealing with the regulation of exocytosis. In the ensuing sections I will deal with many of these features. Because exocytosis has not been fully characterized in any one tissue, I will cite data from a number of tissues as required and will not necessarily cover a particular tissue in depth.

II. STEPS IN THE SECRETORY PROCESS

Based largely on the work of Palade and Jamieson, the synthesis and processing of secretory proteins can be thought of in discrete stages. A diagrammatical sketch of these stages is depicted in Fig. 1. For an analysis more detailed than that presented here, the recent reviews by Palade (1975) and Jamieson (1973) should be consulted.

A. Synthesis and Segregation of Exportable Protein

Proteins made for export are synthesized on polysomes attached to the membrane of the endoplasmic reticulum (Palade, 1975; Jamieson, 1973). Blobel and Sabatini (1970) established that the polypeptide chain synthesized on ribosomes attached to the ER are transferred vectorially into the cisternae of the RER. This observation alone does not account for the specificity inherent in various secretory systems. For example, are there unique classes of ribosomes which have recognition sites on the large ribosomal subunit and the ER membrane? Additionally, is there a specific recognition site between the various mRNA's coding for secretory proteins and ribosomes bound to the ER membrane? Without this element of specificity one would expect to find a high concentration of secretory protein free in the cytosol. These questions may be answered by the recent "signal hypothesis"

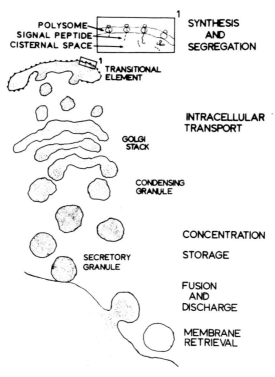

POLYSOME
SIGNAL PEPTIDE
CISTERNAL SPACE

SYNTHESIS
AND
SEGREGATION

TRANSITIONAL
ELEMENT

INTRACELLULAR
TRANSPORT

GOLGI
STACK

CONDENSING
GRANULE

CONCENTRATION

STORAGE

SECRETORY
GRANULE

FUSION
AND
DISCHARGE

MEMBRANE
RETRIEVAL

FIG. 1. The steps involved in the secretory process.

(Blobel and Dobberstein, 1975). According to this hypothesis, a unique sequence of codons, located just to the right of the initiation codon, is common to those mRNA's coding for proteins which will be transferred across the ER membrane. This initial signal sequence of amino acids would provide a specific recognition site for attachment of the large ribosomal subunit to the ER membrane. This hypothesis does not require that initiation of translation of mRNA's coding for the signal peptide be on ribosomes already bound to the ER. To the contrary, translation could be initiated on free ribosomes. After the portion of the nascent peptide chain corresponding to the signal sequence emerged, attachment to ER membrane could occur. An important feature of the model is that a unique class of ribosomes, ribosomal subunits, or a unique recognition between ribosomes and mRNA's coding for export proteins is not required. The polypeptide signal sequence would be recognized by a specific ER-membrane receptor. After attachment and continued translation of the mRNA the signal sequence would be transferred across the ER membrane through a specific pore. Because the

N-terminal sequence of various secretory proteins is different, some mechanism must exist which accounts for the removal of the signal sequence (see Fig. 1). The signal peptide model was based on the observation that translation of the mRNA for the light chain of immunoglobulin by a heterologous protein synthesizing system *in vitro* yielded a product larger than authentic secreted light chain. Devillers-Thiery *et al.* (1975) have presented evidence for the signal hypothesis in the synthesis of pancreatic secretory proteins. That is they found considerable N-terminal sequence homology of the various secretory enzymes of the pancreas. The signal sequence also contained several hydrophobic residues which might aid in the transfer of the polypeptide through the ER membrane.

B. Intracellular Transport

Using a combination of *in vitro* pulse-chase techniques with labeled amino acids and electron microscopic autoradiography, it was observed that labeled secretory proteins were transported from the cisternae of the RER to the transitional elements and subsequently to the peripheral vesicles of Golgi complex (Jamieson, 1973). This transport is an energy-requiring process but does not require continued protein synthesis (Jamieson, 1973). According to Fig. 1, the vesicles bud off the transitional elements and transport the secretory proteins to the Golgi complex. Various protein-modifying reactions take place in the Golgi complex before the proteins emerge on the *trans* side of the Golgi complex in the condensing vacuoles. In contrast to the vesicular transport of the secretory proteins from the transitional elements to the Golgi complex, other authors have proposed that these proteins move through a continuous tubular network which connects the Golgi and transitional elements (Trump, 1975). Because the transport of the secretory proteins from the transitional elements to the Golgi complex requires energy, they must not move through the proposed tubular network by simple diffusion. Perhaps the secretory proteins are moved through the tubular network by an energy-requiring process analogous to peristalsis.

Novikoff (1976) has taken issue with some of the steps as outlined above. He has used enzyme cytochemistry at the light and electron microscope level to differentiate between the Golgi apparatus and a specialized acid-phosphatase-containing region of smooth ER located at the *trans* aspect of the Golgi apparatus. He called this specialized region GERL. According to Novikoff (1976), secretory proteins are processed by GERL and appear to bypass the Golgi apparatus. Using sections of a hamster insulinoma, Novikoff *et al.* (1975) demonstrated that the *trans* elements of the Golgi stained cytochemically for thiamine pyrophosphatase, while staining of GERL was negative. On the other hand, GERL and condensing vacuoles showed acid phosphatase activity and the Golgi did not. From this they concluded that condensing vacuoles and hence secretory granules derive from GERL and not from the Golgi apparatus. The condensing vacuoles were viewed as enlarged cisternal elements of GERL. The exact relationship, if any, between GERL and the Golgi apparatus requires more study before a definitive conclusion can be reached.

C. Concentration

The condensing vacuoles are viewed as dilute solutions of the secretory proteins which become progressively concentrated as the vesicles form mature storage granules. Concentration is not an energy-dependent process, because condensing vacuoles continue to form mature secretory granules after ATP levels are depleted (Jamieson, 1973). Currently, the view that the secretory proteins form osmotically inactive aggregates with a resultant outflow of water is favored. The nature of this aggregation is not understood but presumably involves condensation with some counterion.

D. Intracellular Storage

Once the mature secretory granules are formed they are stored until a specific discharge signal is received. Steps A–D appear to occur uniformly in tissues which release their secretory products by exocytosis. It is interesting that this process is a unidirectional transfer of secretory products through these steps even in the presence of end product (i.e., mature secretory granules) or in the absence of the driving force of continued synthesis of secretory proteins.

In the exocrine pancreas the mature secretory granules have the same digestive enzyme content as the enzyme mixture discharged into the lumen (Scheele and Palade, 1975), supporting the concept of parallel release of the digestive enzymes. Adelson and Rothman (1974) reported selective or non-parallel discharge of the various secretory proteins from the exocrine pancreas. Scheele and Palade (1975) have extensively refuted the above findings of Adelson and Rothman (1974). However, until independent groups compare the exact protocols used in the two laboratories, the parallel vs. non-parallel discharge of pancreatic proteins remains in issue. Rothman (1975, 1976) reports that some of the newly synthesized digestive enzymes exhibit minimal transit times to the extracellular space because they are released from the polysome directly into the cytosol without transfer to ER cisternae.

One important experimental difference between the procedures used by the two laboratories is the method used to label the proteins. In the experiments described by Jamieson (1973), the proteins were pulse labeled with radioactive leucine for 5 minutes; Rothman has radioactive leucine present continuously throughout the experiments. The continuous-labeling technique should enhance the probability of finding a labeled secretory protein with a minimal transit time. The possibility of a secretory protein which is synthesized on ribosomes not bound to membranes is not incompatible with the signal hypothesis of Blobel and Sabatini (1970). According to the signal hypothesis, the translation of mRNA's containing the signal codons begins on "free" ribosomes. It is possible that the mRNA coding for a secretory protein might be translated entirely without becoming bound to the ER membrane and the resulting protein released into the cytosol.

I have some reservations about the ideas presented by Rothman. He has not indicated the quantitative contribution of the nonparallel release pathway to the total amount of enzymes released. Also, it is difficult to rationalize that individual digestive enzyme molecules pass selectively across the cell membrane. Such a selective mechanism must exist because we know that only the digestive enzymes and not the soluble cellular enzymes are released. Thermodynamic considerations suggest that the transfer of large polar molecules such as digestive enzymes across the apolar region of the cell membrane would be very difficult.

It is assumed that newly synthesized exocrine pancreatic secretory granules are mixed homogenously with the older secretory granules. However, if the granule pools were not mixed homogenously, some of the apparently aberrant labeling data of Rothman (see Fig. 5, 1975) could be explained. Using the rat parotid slice system, Sharoni *et al.* (1976) investigated the secretion of old vs. new exportable protein. Proteins were labeled with a 3-minute pulse of [^{3}H]leucine followed by a 90-minute chase. During this time most of the label accumulated in the secretory granules under conditions which assured that 96% of the original amylase content was present (i.e., 96% of that present at the beginning of the pulse phase was present at the end of the chase phase). If submaximal concentrations of isoproterenol were used at the end of the chase phase, unlabeled protein was preferentially released. Saturating concentrations of isoproterenol added at the end of the chase phase caused an initial preferential release of unlabeled protein followed by secretion of a random mixture of new and old exportable protein. Sharoni *et al.* (1976) also obtained evidence for preferential secretion of newly labeled protein over old protein if the secretory granule content of the gland was partially depleted before the pulse-chase experiment. Other agonists (α-adrenergic) caused a random release of labeled and unlabeled protein.

The rate of intracellular transport of the secretory proteins through the various stages is influenced by prior stimulation. Bieger *et al.* (1976a,b) found that infusion of caerulin *in vivo* for 24 hours increased the intracellular transport of secretory proteins up to ten times the transport rate normally observed.

E. DISCHARGE

Secretory granules discharge their content by fusion with the plasma membrane followed by membrane fission of the fused membranes. As a result, the intragranular compartment becomes continuous with the extracellular compartment. This process assures that the release of the secretory products is accomplished without disrupting the barrier between the cytosol and the extracellular space.

F. MEMBRANE RETRIEVAL

It is obvious that continued addition of secretory granule membrane to the plasma membrane would result in tremendous enlargement of the cell. Consequently, some mechanism must exist to retrieve or remove membrane from the plasma membrane in order to maintain a constant cell size. This topic will be taken up again in Section V. This short outline was intended to convey an idea of the overall processing of secretory proteins and some of its complexities. Subsequent portions of this article will deal primarily with topics that are relevant to stages D–F (Fig. 1).

III. POSSIBLE MECHANISMS OF CELL MEMBRANE FUSION

Because fusion between the plasmalemma and secretory granule membrane is a step fundamental to exocytosis, some of the general aspects of membrane fusion will be summarized.

Poste and Allison (1973) have suggested that aggregation of intramembranous particles is an important step in membrane fusion. In support of this notion, several chemical agents (dimethylsulfoxide, glycerol, and the ionophore A-23187) which caused cell fusion also caused aggregation of intramembranous particles as revealed by freeze-fracture (McIntyre *et al.*, 1974; Pinto da Silva and Martinez-Palomo, 1974; Vos *et al.*, 1976). Also, as noted in the next section, unique distribution patterns of intramembranous particles have been observed at exocytotic sites on the plasmalemma surface in several secretory cell types. Aggregation of intramembranous particles around the site of fusion, between isolated Golgi-derived secretory vesicles (Gratzl and Dahl, 1976), isolated secretory vesicles from adrenal medulla (Dahl *et al.*, 1976), and pancreatic β-cells (Dahl *et al.*, 1976; Dahl and Gratzl, 1976), and around fusion sites between membrane vesicles isolated from cultured myoblasts (Schudt *et al.*, 1976) also occur. The requirement for membrane protein aggregation in membrane fusion is not definite. Papahadjopoulos *et al.* (1974) have reported that fusion between protein-free phospholipid vesicles occurs.

Ahkong *et al.* (1975a) have suggested that perturbation of the lipid bilayer fluidity is an important step in membrane fusion. According to their suggestion, changes in cell membrane lipid fluidity allow the aggregation of intramembranous protein particles. According to this hypothesis, aggregation of membrane proteins without a concommitant increase in lipid fluidity would not promote membrane fusion. Conversely, increased membrane lipid fluidity in the absence of membrane protein aggregation might be sufficient to increase cell fusion. Vos *et al.*, (1976) have observed, using hen erythrocytes at 37°, that in the presence of Ca^{2+} the divalent cation ionophore A-23187 caused aggregation of membranous protein particles but only minimal cell fusion (Vos *et al.*, 1976; Ahkong *et al.*, 1975c). Elevating the temperature from 37° to 47° resulted in extensive cell fusion. Vos *et al.* (1976) also noted that the bare regions of the membrane surface observed at 37° no longer excluded the intramembranous proteins when the temperature was elevated to 47°. The implication of their findings is that cell fusion can occur when membrane lipid fluidity is increased sufficiently for intermixing of the membrane lipids between the two lipid bilayers.

Even though alterations in intramembranous protein clustering or lipid fluidity are involved in membrane fusion, this realization does not indicate what proximal signal is responsible for controlling these events. It is perhaps instructive that the presence of calcium (McIntyre *et al.*, 1974; Pinto da Silva and Martinez-Palomo, 1974; Ahkong *et al.*, 1975a; Maggio *et al.*, 1976) is crucial to the action of the chemical fusogenic agents (e.g., DMSO, polyethylne glycol-6000, and glycerol). Also, the ionophores A-23187 and X-537A, which promote passive Ca^{2+} transport, are very good fusogenic agents (Vos *et al.*, 1976; Ahkong *et al.*, 1975c; Hart *et al.*, 1976; Schudt and Pette, 1975). Calcium could interact directly with the membrane phospholipids to alter membrane lipid fluidity. Binding of calcium to membrane phosphatidyl serine results in solid aggregates. This would allow the surrounding phospholipids to form fluid clusters (Ohnishi and Ito, 1974). Phosphatidyl serine binds calcium more tightly than other phospholipids (Hauser and Dawson, 1967). At physiological pH the binding of Ca^{2+} to phosphatidyl serine was three times stronger than that for phosphatidyl ethanolamine (Rojas and Tobias, 1965). The importance of the carboxyl group of phosphatidyl serine is emphasized by the studies of Cook *et al.* (1972). They observed that the action potential recorded from lobster nerve axons was reduced by prior treatment with phosphatidyl serine decarboxylase. The magnitude of the action potential was restored by restoring the carboxyl group. A special role for phosphotidyl serine in histamine release from rat peritoneal mast cells has also been noted (Mongar and Svec, 1972; Foreman and Mongar, 1973), because phosphatidyl serine potentiated anaphylactic histamine release. The potentiation was calcium-dependent, and phosphatidyl ethanolamine would not substitute for phosphatidyl serine (Mongar and Svec, 1972). Phosphatidyl serine also potentiated the contractile response of aortic smooth muscle to submaximal doses of norepinephrine and histamine (Goodman *et al.*, 1976). This effect of phosphatidyl serine appeared to be mediated through a decrease in the efflux of $^{45}Ca^{2+}$ from the smooth muscle. The exact significance of the calcium-dependent effects of phosphatidyl serine is not clear, as these were effects of exogenous phosphatidyl serine. Nevertheless, among several phospholipids, phosphatidyl serine and calcium interact selectively.

The generation of intramembranous lysophospholipids at localized sites has also been suggested as a possible step in cell membrane fusion (Lucy, 1975). Removal of the fatty acid esterified at C-1 of the phospholipid would generate lysophospholipids with an altered configuration which would assume a destabilized micellar arrangement. Lucy (1975) argued that the micellar arrangement of the lysophospholipids would augment fusion between micellar regions of the two lipid bilayers, and lead to cell fusion. Once fusion between the two membranes occurred, membrane stability would be restored through reesterification of fatty acids to C-1 of the lysophospholipid. The lysophospholipid theory would consist of a prefusion deacylation step followed by a postfusion reacylation step. There are several predictions which should hold true if the deacylation–acylation cycle is relevant to membrane fusion. First, lysolecithin or similar detergents should be fusogenic agents. These agents at relatively high concentrations do induce erythrocytes to fuse (Poole *et al.*, 1970; Ahkong *et al.*, 1973). Second, lysophospholipid formation should be enhanced concomitantly with increased fusion. Further, phospholipase A1 and acyl-CoA-lysophospholipid acyl transferase activities should both be detectable within the membranes undergoing fusion. High lysophospholipid content of guinea pig (Meldolesi *et al.*,

1971), ox (White and Hawthorne, 1970), and pig (Rutten *et al.*, 1975) pancreatic zymogen granules has been observed. However, in all cases the formation of lysophospholipids was considered artifactual because the lysophospholipids were formed by endogenous phospholipases during the isolation procedure. Liver-cell plasma membranes contain phospholipase (Victoria *et al.*, 1971) but no acyl-CoA transferase (Eibl *et al.*, 1969) activity. In addition, phospholipase A2 added to liposomes did not induce liposome fusion even though 40–50% of the liposome lecithin was converted to lysolecithin and palmitate (Korn *et al.*, 1974). However, Gullis and Rowe* (1976, 1975a,b,c) have reported that a number of putative transmitters and cyclic nucleotides stimulated the A2-acylation system of isolated synaptic membranes of guinea pig cerebral cortex. It is not clear if these effects are in any way causally related to neurotransmitter release.

Phospholipid turnover in secretory tissues is stimulated by agents which also stimulate secretion (for an extensive review, see Michell, 1975). The effect on turnover is usually most pronounced for inositol phospholipids and phosphatidic acid. Michell (1975) has proposed that not only might the enhanced turnover of phosphatidyl inositol be important for the regulation of various cellular events, but the breakdown products (inositol 1-phosphate, inositol 2-phosphate, and inositol 1,2-cyclic phosphate) might also be important regulators. The relationship of Michell's hypothesis to exocytosis is not clear. For example, in rat parotid tissue those agonists which have the most dramatic effect on amylase release are without effect on phosphatidyl inositol turnover (Oron *et al.*, 1973; Michell and Jones, 1974). Agents which cause little exocytosis in the rat parotid but cause pronounced water and ion efflux have the most dramatic effects on phosphatidyl inositol turnover. On the other hand, cholinergic agents which cause pronounced amylase release from rat pancreas also cause phosphatidyl inositol turnover (Michell, 1975). Hokin-Neaverson *et al.* (1975) have demonstrated that prolonged cholinergic stimulation of exocrine pancreatic secretion also caused the accumulation of *myo*-inositol. High concentrations of extracellular *myo*-inositol have recently been shown to cause a calcium-dependent release of amylase from rat pancreas (Slaby and Bryan, 1976).

Although the information presented is tantalizing, the exact role of phospholipids and phospholipid turnover in exocytosis is not established. It is important to bear in mind that the role of phospholipids in exocytosis might not be the same from tissue to tissue. A finite number of possibilities may exist, and a given tissue may operate via only one or a combination of these.

---

*These data are not based on experimental results but were invented by Gullis. See statement by Gullis in *Nature* **265**, 764.

IV. SITES OF FUSION BETWEEN PLASMA AND
SECRETORY GRANULE MEMBRANES

Because exocytosis involves the fusion of the plasma and secretory granule membranes, it would seem appropriate to consider whether or not there are specific fusion sites. Endocrine cells normally exhibit exocytotic sites at the basement membrane, and exocrine cells exhibit exocytotic sites at the luminal membrane. These observations imply that exocytosis is a highly ordered event. One aspect of this ordering is the existence of an intracellular network which directs the granules undirectionally toward only one cell surface (see Section IX). The asymmetric distribution of unique structures within the plasma membrane and secretory granule membrane which play a role in exocytosis could also account for the specificity of exocytotic sites. In one example of membrane fusion, gap junction formation, a unique distribution of intramembranous proteins (Pappas, 1975) has been identified by a combination of the freeze-fracture and freeze-etch techniques.

Satir *et al.* (1972; Satir, 1974a,b) have extensively studied the details of membrane reorganization during mucocyst discharge in the protozoan *Tetrahymena pyriformis*. This is a particularly good system in that the mucocysts have a specific geometric arrangement with respect to the cilia which serve as external markers. Freeze-fracture studies of *Tetrahymena* plasma membrane revealed the presence of specific internal arrays of intramembranous particles. The particles are arranged in rosettes over the area where mucocysts would be expected. The rosettes consist of nine outer particles and one central particle. As the mucocyst came into close proximity to the plasma membrane a similar rosette of granule membrane particles was observed at the end of the mucocyst nearest the surface membrane. The area of the mucocyst surface membrane encompassed by the rosette was devoid of particles and was the area of fusion between the mucocyst and the plasma membrane. The rosettes appeared to form an annulus around the fusion site and delimited the transition between the plasma membrane and granule membrane. It is assumed that the membrane particles in the rosettes of the plasma membrane and secretory granule membrane interdigitated and defined the circumference of the fusion site. The chemical characteristics of the intramembranous particles are not known.

At the instant the secretory granule and plasma membrane come into apposition there are four layers of lipid at the fusion site: outer and inner lipid layers of the plasma membrane, and outer and inner lipid layers of the secretory granule membrane. Fusion of the lipid layers is thought to occur at the outer circumference of the annulus formed by the intramembranous particles. First the inner lipid layer of the plasma membrane fuses with the outer lipid layer of the secretory granule. Next the outer lipid layer of the plasma membrane fuses with the inner lipid layer of the granule membrane, and the lipids intermix. It should be reiterated that the details of these steps are conjecture and not understood.

The foregoing discussion was based entirely on relevant data on secretion of mucocyst contents from *Tetrahymena*. If the intramembranous particles play a general role in exocytosis, then it should be possible to detect them in other systems. Dreifuss *et al.* (1976) have reported that intramembranous particles appeared in rosette and necklacelike patterns in the plasma membrane of the rat neurohyphophysis. It was not clear whether or not these particle arrangements marked membrane sites for exocytosis. In other tissues, such as the granular cells of the toad urinary bladder (Wade *et al.*, 1975), rat pancreas acinar cells (DeCamilli *et al.*, 1974), and rat parotid acinar cells (DeCamilli *et al.*, 1976), membrane particles were observed in the plasma membrane by freeze-fracture and freeze-etch techniques. No unique pattern such as rosette formation could be detected in either the resting or stimulated states.

Orderly arrangements of membrane particles have been observed in the plasma membrane of intestinal smooth muscle cells (Orci and Perrelet, 1973). The particle distribution correlated with sites of endocytosis because the density of membrane particles was highest in the immediate area of the endocytotic pits. In some cases a necklacelike distribution of membrane particles around the circumference of the endocytotic pit was observed.

V. AN ELECTROSTATIC FUNCTION FOR CALCIUM IN EXOCYTOSIS

The cytoplasmic aspects of the plasma membrane and secretory vesicles carry a net negative charge (Eagles *et al.*, 1976; Matthews and Nordmann, 1976; also see references in Dean, 1975). Therefore, an electrostatic potential energy barrier might retard contact between the secretory vesicles and the plasma membrane. Dean (1975) has observed that contact between the plasma membrane and secretory vesicles would represent a balance between the electrostatic repulsive and London–van der Waals attractive forces in addition to any kinetic energy derived from translational motion of the vesicle. Dean (1975) further points out that the small, electrically charged vesicles behave as lipophobic colloids. Their interactions with charged surfaces can be described by the theories of Derjaguin and Landau (1941) and Verwey and Overbeck (1948). According to Dean's theory, Ca^{2+} ion binding to anionic sites on the colloidal particles or membrane surfaces would diminish the energy barrier between the two surfaces to allow collision to occur. Based on some reasonable assumptions for vesicle and plasma membrane surface potentials, density of calcium binding sites, and equilibrium constants for Ca^{2+} binding to the surface, Dean (1975) demonstrated that the potential energy barrier between the secretory vesicle and membrane could be reduced to zero at 1.5–2.5 mM Ca^{2+}.

Dean also demonstrated that the potential energy barrier could be reduced by decreasing the radius of curvature for the secretory vesicle. Relevant to this later point are the reports which present morphological evidence that stimulus–secretion coupling in some systems was associated with a reduced radius of curvature for a portion of the secretory vesicle membrane (Schramm *et al.*, 1972; Gabbay *et al.*, 1975; Raz and Goldman, 1974). In these systems the areas with the altered radius of curvature took on the appearance of buds of pseudopodia. Recently, Hall and Simon (1976) proposed that the surface energy changes produced by entry and exit of calcium provide the driving force for the changes in the radius of curvature of the membrane. Hall and Simon (1976) suggest that a membrane bilayer has regions over which the monolayers are unconnected. If the surface pressure on one monolayer changes relative to that of the other, the bilayer will curve. According to the ideas of Hall and Simon (1976), which overlap extensively with those of Dean (1975) and Van der Kloot and Kita (1973), the onset of the secretory stimulus results in an influx of Ca^{2+}. The influx of Ca^{2+} screens negative charges on the interior of the plasma membrane and on the exterior of the secretory granule membrane. This would increase the likelihood of close approach between the secretory granule and the plasma membrane.

All the above ideas are valid on a thermodynamic basis and represent some very interesting ideas with respect to the role of Ca^{2+} in exocytosis. I think most of these ideas suffer severely, however, from the standpoint of specificity for the divalent cation and the concentration of Ca^{2+} required to reduce the repulsive forces. The intracellular concentration of Ca^{2+} is normally maintained below 1.0 μM in most cell types. Because concentrations of Ca^{2+} greater than 0.5 mM are required to effect a significant reduction in the potential energy barrier between the cytoplasmic aspects of the plasma membrane and the secretory granule membrane, near equilibration of Ca^{2+} across the plasma membrane would be required to attain the necessary reduction of the potential energy barrier. Matthews and Nordmann (1976) observed that at least 0.5 mM Ca^{2+} was needed to substantially change the electrophoretic mobility of isolated synaptic vesicles.

Dean (1975) recognized that it was essential to postulate a Ca^{2+}-specific step in exocytosis because according to his formulations Mg^{2+} should reduce the repulsive forces as effectively as Ca^{2+}. As mentioned earlier, certain phospholipids bind Ca^{2+} selectively. However, given the observations that intracellular Ca^{2+} concentration is normally maintained below 1.0 μM while the free intracellular divalent cation concentration excluding Ca^{2+} approaches 1.0 mM, it is doubtful that the binding of divalent cations by phospholipids could provide the requisite specificity for Ca^{2+}.

VI. COUPLING OF ENDOCYTOSIS WITH EXOCYTOSIS

If secretory granule membrane were continuously added to the plasma membrane of secretory cells, they would grow to an enormous size. As this does not happen and there is only a temporary increase in cell surface area which accompanies exocytosis, some mechanism must exist for membrane retrieval from the plasma membrane as membrane is contributed by the secretory granule during exocytosis. In cells in which exocytosis occurs, extracellular markers are internalized during membrane retrieval into intracellular vacuolar structures. I prefer to call this process *endocytosis* rather than *micropinocytosis*. The extracellular markers most commonly used are horseradish peroxidase and ferritin (Kalina and Robinovitch, 1975; Garrett and Parsons, 1973; Theodosis *et al.*, 1976), because either the marker or the reaction product can be visualized with the electron microscope.

Douglas (1974, 1975; Douglas *et al.*, 1971) called this scheme "vesiculation coupled to exocytosis." This concept is based largely on observations from ultrastructural studies of neurohypophysial terminals. According to this model, (a) a coating is applied to the granule membrane following extrusion of granule contents, (b) the coating is modified in such a way as to induce invagination and pinching off to form coated microvesicles, (c) the coated vesicles shed their coats to form smooth microvesicles, and (d) the smooth microvesicles are removed. Douglas suggests that the last step is accomplished by lysosomal digestion. This scheme predicts that the granule membrane is specifically retrieved by a mechanism involving the formation of coated vesicles. It also predicts that the granule membrane is not recycled as such but is degraded by lysosomal hydrolysis. Reutilization of membrane constituents formed as a result of degradation of the membrane by the lysosomal hydrolases is not ruled out by this model.

The finding by Douglas (1974) that microvesicles of the neurohypophysis incorporated the extracellular marker horseradish peroxidase is not disputed. However, several very careful studies have questioned the quantitative importance of the microvesicles in membrane retrieval following exocytosis. Neurohypophysial vacuoles larger than the microvesicles and approaching the size of the neurosecretory granules were observed to also take up horseradish peroxidase (Nordmann *et al.*, 1974). The studies of Nordmann and Morris (1976) and Theodosis *et al.* (1976) carefully quantified, by morphometric analysis, the population of neurosecretory granules, vacuoles, and microvesicles before and after a variety of secretory stimuli. In all cases the microvesicle population was constant (i.e., the percent of cell volume occupied by the microvesicles did not increase after stimulation). While the microvesicle population was constant, the neurosecretory granule population decreased and the population of vacuoles increased. Theodosis *et al.* (1976) calculated that 95% of the internalized membrane fragments were present in the vacuoles whereas no more than 5% of the internalized membrane was present as microvesicles. In these studies (Nordmann and Morris, 1976; Theodosis *et al.*, 1976) it should have been possible to detect an increased number of microvesicles, because retrieval of the membrane from each neurosecretory granule would give rise to 10–25 microvesicles. The appearance of large vacuoles following exocytosis has also been observed in a number of other cell types (see Nordmann and Morris, 1976).

Both biochemical and ultrastructural evidence indicates extensive recycling of secretory granule membrane. Meldolesi *et al.* (1975) observed that the various membranes involved in the steps outlined in Fig. 1 are synthesized independently of one another and that they are reutilized for several secretory cycles. They found that the half-life for turnover of membrane constituents, using double-labeling techniques and SDS polyacrylamide electrophoresis, were on the order of days, whereas the half-life of the secretory product was only a few hours. In addition, it appeared that the membrane constituents of the secretory granule were distinct from those of the plasma membrane. The constituents of plasma membrane and secretory granule membrane had widely different turnover characteristics.

Recent ultrastructural studies using freeze-fracture techniques provide additional evidence that the identity of the secretory granule is maintained after fusion (DeCamilli *et al.*, 1976). It was observed that the density of intramembranous particles was different for the lumenal plasma membrane and secretory granule membrane of the parotid acinar cells. Immediately following the stimulation of the exocytotic release of amylase from the parotid acinar cell the distribution of intramembranous particles in the lumenal surface assumes a mosaic appearance. Part of the mosaic resembled the normal pattern observed for the lumenal surface; the other part resembled that observed in the secretory granule membrane. After withdrawal of the secretory stimulus, the mosaic pattern of intramembranous particles in the lumenal membrane disappeared. The area which was originally derived from the secretory granule membrane was removed. These observations suggest that the secretory granule membrane constituents do not intermix with those of the plasma membrane following fusion, and that a mechanism exists for the specific removal of the granule membrane following fusion and emptying of granule contents.

Heuser and Reese (1973), using a different approach, also showed that the membranes from the synaptic vesicles of the frog neuromuscular junction are recycled. They defined the following sequence of events for the neuromuscular junction. Following 1 minute of electrical stimulation there was a 30% depletion of synaptic vesicle membrane which was almost balanced by an increase in surface area of the plasma membrane. After 15 minutes of stimulation 60% of the synaptic vesicles were depleted which was accompanied by the appearance of numerous, irregular cisternae. If the electrical stimulation was stopped the cisternae disappeared within 15 minutes and the synaptic vesicles reappeared. This overall sequence suggested that the synaptic vesicle membranes were recycled via the cisternae which in turn gave rise to synaptic vesicles. Heuser and Reese (1973) corroborated these conclusions by following the intracellular incorporation of horseradish peroxidase over the time course for electrical stimulation outlined above. The horseradish peroxidase first appeared in the cisternae. During the resting phase the horseradish peroxidase appeared in synaptic vesicles. If the muscles containing horseradish peroxidase in the synaptic vesicles were stimulated a second time, the peroxidase disappeared and did not reappear in the cisternae. This strengthened the argument that synaptic vesicles membrane was recycled from the cell surface through cisternae which in turn gave rise to new synaptic vesicles. The work of Heuser and Reese (1973) also suggested that coated vesicles were involved in membrane recycling in a manner similar to the model of Douglas (1974). Electrical stimulation increased the incidence of coated vesicle appearance. The coated vesicles also took up the horseradish peroxidase and were apparent during various stages of coalescence with cisternae. Because the coated vesicles were recognized at different stages of membrane retrieval, the material forming the coat might play a role in the recycling of membrane. Coated vesicles have also been observed in lactating rat mammary epithelial cells (Franke *et al.*, 1976), the exocrine pancreas (Geuze and Kramer, 1976), and in microendocytotic vesicles of human placenta (Ockleford, 1976). The coated vesicles from the various cell types all have a latticelike coat on their cytoplasmic surfaces. The latticelike coats from the coated vesicles isolated from pig brain contained 75% protein and 25% phospholipid by weight. The coats consist of one major polypeptide chain, clathrin (Pearse, 1975), with an apparent molecular weight of 180,000 daltons by SDS–acrylamide gel electrophoresis.

Peptide maps of clathrin from a variety of sources suggest that the amino acid sequence of clathrin is conserved, irrespective of tissue or species origin (Pearse, 1976). Electron micrographs show that the coats are polyhedral lattices made from 12 pentagons plus a variable number of hexagons (Crowther *et al.*, 1976). Although there is a variety of coat sizes, all are thought to have this basic structure. Structure is the only unique property attributed to the coats. It has been speculated that the coats serve a general function in the translocation of membrane within the cell not restricted to recycling secretory granule membrane after exocytosis.

VII. RELEASE OF SECRETORY GRANULE CONTENTS IN
A CELL-FREE SYSTEM

Membrane fusion between cells or between cell organelles can be induced under certain special conditions (see Section III). These systems are useful as general models to study the events of membrane fusion. Studies of the regulation of exocytosis would be greatly faciliated if a defined, reconstituted, cell-free system could be developed. Such a system for insulin release has been reported recently. Davis and Lazarus (1976) and Lazarus *et al.* (1976) have found that a reconstituted system consisting of cod islet plasma membranes and mouse islet granules released insulin in response to appropriate stimuli. Islet membranes were specifically required because plasma membranes from rat pituitary, human fat cells, human liver, mouse liver, and cod livers would not substitute. There was also granule specificity: pituitary granules and chromaffin granules did not release their contents when incubated with islet plasma membranes. These authors also found that when adrenal plasma membranes were mixed with chromaffin granules, epinephrine was released. This release did not occur if plasma membranes other than adrenal membranes were used.

Davis and Lazarus (1976) demonstrated an absolute requirement for Ca^{2+} in the insulin-releasing system. The rate of insulin release was stimulated 6-fold by 2 μM Ca^{2+}. ATP (5 μM) further augmented the rate of release above that observed with Ca^{2+} alone. Neither UTP, GTP, nor 5'-AMP could substitute for ATP. Glucose (17 mM) in combination with 0.5 μM Ca^{2+} and 0.5 μM ATP caused a 20-fold increase in the amount of insulin released in 10 minutes. This amount of insulin was 85% of the insulin present within granules at time zero. Of several phosphorylated glucose metabolites of glucose tested in the presence of ATP and Ca^{2+}, only glucose 6-phosphate and phosphoenolpyruvate augmented the rate of insulin release. The non-phosphorylating analog of ATP, AMP–PNP, substitued for ATP when insulin release was stimulated by glucose. However, glucose 6-phosphate caused insulin release only in the presence of ATP and not AMP–PNP.

Cyclic AMP alone will not increase insulin release from intact pancreatic islet preparations. Cyclic AMP will, however, augment the effect of low concentrations of glucose on insulin release from intact pancreas. Davis and Lazarus (1976) reported that cyclic AMP augmented the rate of Ca^{2+}-dependent insulin release in the reconstituted system, but was without effect when added alone.

Diazoxide, which normally inhibits insulin release from intact islets, also inhibited insulin release in the reconstituted system.

Although the studies by Davis and Lazarus (1976) represent the most complete examination to date of the release of vesicle contents in a reconstituted cell-free system, other authors have examined various reconstituted systems. For example, Ishida *et al.* (1971a) reported studies on the release of amylase from secretory granule isolated from rat parotid glands. They found that ATP, Ca^{2+}, and supernatant factors enhanced amylase release.

Direct effects of ATP on isolated secretory granule structure have also been reported (Ishida *et al.*, 1971b; Pollard *et al.*, 1976). Pollard *et al.* (1976) have reported that ATP not only promotes epinephrine release from isolated chromaffin granules but affects the granule transmembrane potential. Since the $K_{1/2}$ for the effect of ATP on transgranule membrane potential was lower (40 μM) than that for catecholamine release (200 μM), Pollard *et al.* (1976) suggested that changes in transgranule membrane potential were necessary for subsequent events, such as catecholamine release, to take place. The effect of ATP on insulin release (Davis and Lazarus, 1976) was observed at a concentration (5 μM) considerably below that required for an effect on epinephrine release (Pollard *et al.*, 1976) or amylase release (Ishida *et al.*, 1971a). Studies on the release of secretory granule contents in reconstituted cell-free systems must differentiate nonspecific release of vesicle contents unrelated to the physiological release mechanism from an effect on release which is related to the physiological release mechanism.

The studies of Davis and Lazarus (1976) are particularly exciting because they imply a specific interaction between plasma membrane and granule membrane in the release of secretory granule contents. In addition to direct studies of insulin release with the reconstituted system, ultrastructural studies of this system using transmission and scanning electron microscopy as well as freeze-fracture, are also needed. In the studies of Davis and Lazarus (1976) it is not clear whether all the appropriate control studies were performed. For example, in studies of the effects of ATP, Ca^{2+}, and glucose on insulin release from granules in the presence of plasma membrane, it is not clear whether or not they also looked at this same combination of Ca^{2+}, ATP, and glucose with granules alone. Such controls are essential if we are to discern a unique role for the plasma membranes in the cell-free release system. The studies with the isolated system are sufficiently exciting to merit additional studies and should be a powerful tool to explore the details of membrane fusion during exocytosis.

VIII. THE ROLE OF CALCIUM IN SECRETORY PROCESSES

The general importance of Ca^{2+} in a wide range of secretory systems was emphasized by Douglas and Poisner (1963). The subject has been extensively reviewed in a recent monograph by Rubin (1974) and in articles by

Rasmussen (1975) and Berridge (1975). This section will review the approaches used to study the role of Ca^{2+} in secretion.

The simplest approach to the study of the role of calcium in a secretory response is to omit it from the external incubation medium or attempt to deplete internal stores of Ca^{2+}. Both manipulations require the use of a chelating agent such as EGTA which has a higher affinity for Ca^{2+} than for other divalent cations. The EGTA serves as a buffer to maintain the external Ca^{2+} at very low levels. Attempts to deplete internal stores of slowly exchangeable Ca^{2+} normally involve prolonged incubations of the tissue preparation in an EGTA buffer from which Ca^{2+} is omitted. If stimulation of the secretory response is inhibited by either of the above manipulations, this is usually interpreted to indicate a Ca^{2+}-requiring step in some aspect of the secretory response. Although the data obtained using this approach are usually correct as to Ca^{2+} requirements, the interpretation of such data is difficult. For example, if the simple omission of Ca^{2+} from an incubation buffer containing EGTA inhibits the stimulation of a given secretory response, this may mean (a) that external Ca^{2+} is needed for agonist binding to the cell; (b) that Ca^{2+} is a necessary cofactor for signal generation by the agonist at the cell membrane, other than in the agonist binding step; (c) that agonist action stimulates Ca^{2+} uptake into a critical compartment of the cell necessary for activation of the secretory response; or (d) that the critical pool of Ca^{2+} involved in activation of the secretory response comes from a peripheral site in the cell which is in rapid equilibrium with the external medium. A similar number of interpretations can be made about the inhibitory effect which is observed only after prolonged incubation in EGTA-containing buffer without added Ca^{2+}. Consequently, other approaches are needed to obtain a more precise understanding of the role of Ca^{2+} in secretion.

A. Ca^{2+} FLUX MEASUREMENTS DURING ACTIVATION OF THE SECRETORY RESPONSE

$^{45}Ca^{2+}$ may be used to follow changes in Ca^{2+} influx or efflux. The action of agents on $^{45}Ca^{2+}$ uptake can be studied from the standpoint of uptake rate or total amount of uptake at equilibrium. Because the component of Ca^{2+} uptake affected by an agonist might be small in comparison to a large background, this approach might not reveal an effect of an agonist. Another approach often utilized is component analysis of washout curves. The tissues are first incubated with $^{45}Ca^{2+}$ in the presence and absence of agonist. Next the tissues are rinsed and transferred to nonradioactive incubation buffer to follow the efflux of $^{45}Ca^{2+}$ from the tissue. One can then plot the logarithm of the rate of efflux vs. time; this approach usually reveals a minimum of three kinetic components to the washout curve. An extensive mathematical analysis of this approach can be found in an article by Borle (1969). This approach can also be used to study the effect of agonists on $^{45}Ca^{2+}$ efflux. If this is the objective the tissues are first loaded with $^{45}Ca^{2+}$ and then the agonists are added during the efflux phase.

Often the rates of efflux are very rapid and difficult to accurately measure. The use of lanthanum during the efflux phase after first loading the tissue with $^{45}Ca^{2+}$ in the presence and absence of agonist was introduced by Van Breeman *et al.* (1972). Lanthanum inhibits both $^{45}Ca^{2+}$ efflux and exchange of cellular Ca^{2+} with extracellular Ca^{2+}. The washout of $^{45}Ca^{2+}$ occurs over a much longer time course in the presence of lanthanum. The use of these techniques is illustrated in papers by Putney (1976) and Kondo and Schulz (1976).

The kinetic approach using $^{45}Ca^{2+}$ indicates whether or not agonists are affecting the handling of Ca^{2+} by the cell but little more. It does not tell us if the fast "washout" component in the above analysis represents a rapidly exchangeable Ca^{2+} pool on the cell membrane or a rapidly exchangeable pool in some other part of the cell. Often, intuitive interpretations are imposed on the cellular location of the various washout components, but there are no assurances that these interpretations are the correct ones.

It might seem reasonable to study the action of agonists on the subcellular distribution of Ca^{2+} by measuring the level of Ca^{2+} in the subcellular fractions isolated from tissues incubated in the presence and absence of agonists. This approach is fraught with difficulties. Clemente and Meldolesi (1975) have shown that extensive mixing of Ca^{2+} between organelles occurs after homogenization and during the organelle fractionation procedures.

Such cell organelles as plasma membrane, secretory granules, mitochondria, and endoplasmic reticulum can be isolated. The kinetic parameters, regulation, and energy requirements for Ca^{2+} handling by these organelles can be characterized. Tada *et al.* (1975) have shown that cyclic AMP enhanced the uptake of Ca^{2+} by the sarcoplasmic reticulum of skeletal muscle. The increased rate of Ca^{2+} uptake was associated with increased phosphorylation of a sarcoplasmic reticular protein. Phosphorylation of this protein was mediated by a cyclic AMP-dependent protein kinase. The phosphorylated protein found in the presence of protein kinase, ATP, and cyclic AMP was distinguished from the phosphorylated intermediate associated with the Ca^{2+}-ATPase transport protein of the sarcoplasmic reticulum. Borle reported that cyclic AMP enhanced Ca^{2+} loss from isolated mitochondria (1974), but subsequently he (1976) has not been able to reproduce these findings. Similarly, others (Scarpa *et al.*, 1976) were unable to reproduce the original findings of Borle (1974). Because of the tremendous importance of the original report of Borle (1974), I hope more investigators will attempt to corroborate them. Perhaps it is important to consider what was unique about the original conditions which led Borle to his findings. McDonald *et al.* (1976c) have recently characterized the kinetic constants of Ca^{2+} binding to purified plasma membranes isolated from rat adipocytes. They reported two classes of Ca^{2+} binding sites based on binding affinity. Insulin added directly to the isolated plasma membranes caused no alteration in calcium binding, but incubation of intact adipocytes with insulin before isolating the plasma membranes increased calcium binding by 25% (McDonald *et al.*, 1976b). Insulin did not modify the affinity constants but increased the number of binding sites. It was also reported that the exchangeable Ca^{2+} of the isolated plasma membrane accounted for one-third of the calcium bound to the membrane. The other larger pool of calcium did not exchange with $^{45}Ca^{2+}$ and was unaltered by insulin (McDonald *et al.*, 1976b). Mitochondria isolated from rat fat cells have two pools of calcium which can be distinguished on the basis of extraction with EDTA (McDonald *et al.*, 1976a), because only one pool can be removed by EDTA. Treatment of isolated cells with insulin before isolating the mitochondria increased the size of the pool extracted by EDTA and decreased the size of the pool not extracted by EDTA. The total level of mitochondrial calcium was not modified by insulin (McDonald *et al.*, 1976a). These data illustrate that it is possible to detect effects of agonists on the handling of calcium by cell organelles isolated from cells treated with agonists.

Ca^{2+}-activated ATPase activity has been reported for various subcellular fractions isolated from a number of secretory cell types (Formby *et al.*, 1976; Watson *et al.*, 1974; Serck-Hanssen and Christiansen, 1973; Dormer and Ashcroft, 1974; Selinger *et al.*, 1970). Formby *et al.* (1976) reported that the Ca^{2+}-ATPase activity in mitochondrial, granular, and microsomal fractions from mouse isolated pancreatic islets exhibited two K_m activities for activation: a low affinity activity of $7.0 \times 10^{-6}\ M$ and a high affinity activity of $2 \times 10^{-7}\ M$. The low K_m activity of the Ca^{2+}-ATPase in whole homogenates was inhibited by caffeine and theophylline but not by methylisobutyl xanthine. Caffeine also inhibited the low K_m activity in isolated granules, mitochondria, and microsomes. Inhibition was greatest in the microsomal fraction but did not approach that observed for the whole homogenate. This effect of the xanthine derivatives (caffeine and theophylline) is of significance because it suggests a possible effect on intracellular calcium distribution unrelated to their inhibitory effect on cyclic nucleotide phosphodiesterase. A stimulatory effect of theophylline on $^{45}Ca^{2+}$ efflux from pancreatic islets has been reported (Brisson and Malaisse, 1973) which was interpreted as a direct effect of theophylline to induce release of Ca^{2+} from an organelle-bound pool. It will be of interest to see if methylisobutyl xanthine has an effect on $^{45}Ca^{2+}$ efflux from pancreatic islets different from theophylline. It has long been known that caffeine can induce muscle contracture through an effect on intracellular calcium movements (Nayler, 1963) which probably does not involve cyclic nucleotides.

Formby et al. (1976) also reported that 10 μM cyclic AMP caused 25% inhibition of the low K_m Ca^{2+}-ATPase activity in isolated granules, mitochondria, and microsomes. If the Ca^{2+}-ATPase activities studies by Formby et al. (1976) are responsible for sequestration of Ca^{2+} in the pancreatic islets, then inhibition of the Ca^{2+}-ATPase by cyclic AMP could account for an effect of cyclic AMP on pancreatic islet Ca^{2+} homeostasis.

The presence of Ca^{2+}-ATPase activity in subcellular organelles suggests a potential role for these organelles in controlling the concentration of free calcium within the cell. However, it is far from clear how the ability of the organelles to take up and release Ca^{2+} is regulated to achieve the end result needed for the observed precise control of secretory processes.

B. Calcium-Sensitive Light-Emitting Compounds as Probes for "Free Calcium"

The approaches used to study the role of Ca^{2+} in secretion mentioned thus far (i.e., examining the consequences of modifying Ca^{2+} levels, examining Ca^{2+} fluxes, and examining the subcellular distribution of Ca^{2+}) are important but indirect. It is clear that a probe which allows direct *in situ* measurements of alterations in free-ionized levels of calcium within the cell would greatly extend our understanding of how calcium could regulate cellular processes. Such probes are the calcium-sensitive phosphoprotein aequorin and the calcium-sensitive fluorescent dyes arsenazo III and murexide. These probes emit a characteristic fluorescent light in the presence of low concentrations of ionized calcium. Of the two dyes, arsenazo III is superior to murexide (Dipolo et al., 1976). A major drawback to the usefulness of these compounds is the difficulty of getting them into the cell. If the volume of the cell under study is large enough, the compounds (aequorin or fluorescent dye) can be microinjected into the cell. This approach has been used most successfully with the squid axon, for which it was determined that the internal ionized level of calcium under basal conditions, was 20 nM (aequorin) or 50 nM (arsenazo III) (Dipolo et al., 1976). This agrees well with other estimations of the resting concentration of ionized calcium in the squid axon (Baker et al., 1971; Binley et al., 1975). With the squid axon the light-emitting calcium-sensitive probes were used to show that (a) increasing the external calcium concentration from a normal ionized concentration of 4.0 mM to 10 mM increased the ionized calcium concentration in the axoplasm (Dipolo et al., 1976), (b) removal of external Na^+ increased the concentration of ionized axoplasmic calcium but to a smaller extent than predicted from direct measurements of net Ca^{2+} flux (Dipolo *et al.*, 1976), and (c) CN increased the internal ionized calcium concentration but the increase was dependent on external calcium and probably was not due to increased release of mitochondrial calcium. Llinas and Nicholson (1975) have demonstrated, through the use of aequorin injected into the presynaptic terminal of the squid giant synapse, that increased synaptic transmitter release was associated with an increased internal ionized calcium concentration.

Aequorin has been used to demonstrate the tremendous calcium buffering or sequestering capacity of the cytoplasm. During an action potential calcium enters the axon and the level of ionized calcium is increased (Baker *et al.*, 1971), but the increase in ionized calcium is much less than indicated by net uptake. Also, as noted in the preceding paragraph, sodium-free solutions increased the level of ionized axoplasmic calcium to a lesser extent than predicted from net calcium flux. These observations suggest that the axon has a tremendous capacity to prevent large increases in free-ionized calcium. Rose and Loewenstein (1976) have indicated that the diffusion radius of a bolus of microinjected calcium into aequorin-loaded cells was much smaller than the diffusion radius predicted from the known calcium diffusion constants. These findings also emphasize the rapid sequestering capacity of the cytoplasm. The identity of the calcium-sequestering activity is not certain.

If these calcium-sensitive probes are to be of general utility in a wide range of cell types, alternatives to microinjection must be found because the volume of microinjection would too severely distort most secretory cell types. One approach to delivering sufficient probe into the cell might be the use of liposomes containing the probes. The liposomes could then be fused with the secretory cell. If lipid composition of the liposome interfered with the secretory response, perhaps the probes could be incorporated into the cell by fusing the cell with small resealed, secretory-cell plasma membrane vesicles containing the probe. Future developments in the use of calcium-sensitive probes should be very exciting. It must be realized, however, that these probes can only indicate a change in the concentration of free-ionized calcium. Because the resolution provided by these probes is limited to the light microscope, it is not possible to precisely determine where the changes in ionized calcium are taking place or what organelles contribute to the changes.

C. ELECTRON PROBE X-RAY MICROANALYSIS

Because the use of the Ca^{2+}-sensitive fluorescent compounds do not readily permit localization of the subcellular shifts in calcium concentration, another technique for this purpose is required. Electron probe X-ray microanalysis allows elemental analysis of cellular organelles *in situ*. This technique combines the capacity of the electron microscope for ultrastructural analysis with the capacity to obtain compositional information from the interaction of the electrons with the specimen. The limits of sensitivity and several technical aspects of this procedure have been discussed by Shuman *et al.* (1976) and Shuman and Somlyo (1976). Shuman *et al.* (1976) have demonstrated that 10% accuracy and a spatial resolution of 2000 Å can be achieved if a multiple least-squares fitting technique is employed to analyze spectral overlap. Contamination and mass loss are problems which can be overcome by lowering the electron microscope stage temperature to $-110°C$ and by pumping the electron microscope column overnight. Tissue preparation is also an important aspect to this technique. Standard fixation and preparative techniques are not suitable because extensive intermixing of the contents of the various pools can occur. Instead, it is necessary to use such techniques as cryo-ultramicrotomy or freeze-drying cells that were cultured on electron microscope slides (Garfield and Somlyo, 1975). This is a very sophisticated technique and quite clearly is not one to be undertaken lightly, but of the various techniques available it offers the greatest likelihood for success in determining where the changes in intracellular Ca^{2+} are taking place during the secretory process. A note of pessimism is still warranted. It is possible that the net changes in calcium concentration which occur during secretion will be too small to detect by this technique. For example, if the calcium needed for secretion comes from a large pool of sequestered calcium, the net decrease in the sequestered pool of calcium might not be large enough to measure. The term *net decrease* is used because it is possible that calcium coming from a particular pool might be replenished at a rate comparable to the rate at which it is lost.

D. Divalent Cation Ionophores

An alternative approach to the study of the role of calcium in exocytosis was afforded by the introduction of divalent cation ionophores which will transport divalent cations across cell membranes in the direction of the concentration gradient. Two of these, A-23187 and X537A, have been widely used. A list of some of the secretory systems examined using these ionophores is given in Table I.

If the effects of the ionophore are dependent on calcium or if other divalent cations (especially magnesium) do not substitute for calcium, a specific action of the ionophore is assumed. Although the criterion of calcium dependence is an obvious one, it can be somewhat misleading. If buffer calcium is

TABLE I

SURVEY OF THE EFFECTS OF DIVALENT CATION IONOPHORES IN VARIOUS SECRETORY SYSTEMS

Tissue	Response	Ionophore	Ca²⁺ dependent	Reference
Pancreatic islets	Insulin release	A-23187	No	Karl et al., 1975
		X537A	No	Hellman, 1975
	No effect or inhibitory to insulin release			Hellman, 1975
Adrenal (cat)	Catecholamine release	A-23187	Yes	Garcia et al., 1975
Mast cells	Histamine release	A-23187	Yes	Foreman et al., 1973;
				Kagayama and Douglas, 1974;
				Cochrane and Douglas, 1974;
				Diamant and Patkar, 1975
		X537A	Yes	Kagayama and Douglas, 1974;
				Cochrane and Douglas, 1974
		X537A	No	Foreman et al., 1973
Neurohypophysis	Vasopressin release	A-23187	Yes	Robinson et al., 1976
		X537A	Yes, also Na⁺ dependent.	Robinson et al., 1976; Nakazato and Douglas, 1974
Exocrine pancreas	Amylase release	A-23187	Yes	Eimerl et al., 1974; Williams and Lee, 1974
Parotid	Amylase release	A-23187	Yes	Butcher, 1975; Putney et al., 1977
Paramecia	Trichocyst degranulation	A-23187	Yes	Plattner, 1974
Adrenergic neurons	Norepinephrine release	A-23187	Yes	Thoa et al., 1974
		X-537A	No	Thoa et al., 1974
Neuromuscular junction	Acetylcholine release	X537A	Yes	Kita and Van der Kloot, 1974
Blood platelets	Serotonin release	A-23187	Yes	Massini and Luscher, 1974
		X537A	No	Massini and Luscher, 1974

not required for the action of the ionophore, this does not mean that calcium is not involved in the system. Because the ionophore is lipophilic it is certainly possible that it might be taken up into the intracellular space and effect the redistribution of calcium among the intracellular pools. There is ample evidence in the literature that the ionophores can affect the sequestration of calcium by various isolated subcellular organelles. Reed and Lardy (1972a,b) have shown that the ionophore A-23187 can induce a pseudo-uncoupling of mitochondria by causing release of mitochondrial calcium. If A-23187 were taken up by a cell, the mitochondrial pool of calcium would be released into the cytoplasm, and the uncoupling action of the ionophore would lower the ATP concentration. Scarpa *et al.* (1972) have shown that both A-23187 and X537A cause the release of Ca^{2+} from fragments of sarcoplasmic reticulum. Diamant and Patkar (1975) have taken advantage of the ability of A-23187 to release intracellular stores of calcium to show that part of the stimulatory effect of compound 48/80 and antigen on histamine release was dependent on intracellular calcium. Their findings agreed with those of Douglas and Ueda (1973) who reached the same conclusion based on studies involving mast cells incubated 3 hours with EDTA. Consequently, the ability of the ionophores to cause redistribution of calcium among intracellular stores can in some instances account for the lack of an extracellular calcium requirement for ionophore action.

The lack of calcium dependence for ionophore action can also be accounted for on the basis of the ion specificity of the ionophore. The ionophores A-23187 and X537A have only a relative specificity for Ca^{2+}. Both ionophores will also transport Mg^{2+}. In addition, X537A will also transport monovalent cations in the direction of the concentration gradient to an extent sufficient to cause depolarization (Cochrane and Douglas, 1975). Depolarization of frog skeletal muscle fibers was observed with X537A and to a lesser extent with A-23187. This could account for the sodium-dependent actions of X537A listed in Table I. A depolarization-dependent effect of the ionophores does not mean Ca^{2+} independence. There is ample evidence that Na^+ flux might act to regulate intracellular Ca^{2+} stores (see Section VIII,G).

Several compartments, each unique, can exist within a given cell. The level of Ca^{2+} in each of these compartments can be regulated independent of one another. In order for the ionophores to mimic agonist action, the ionophores must increase Ca^{2+} concentration in the same intracellular compartments as the agonist. This consideration can be best appreciated by contrasting the role of Ca^{2+} in the regulation of K^+ release and amylase release from the rat parotid. K^+ release is enhanced by α-adrenergic agonists (Batzri *et al.*, 1971). This release is dependent on buffer Ca^{2+} (Selinger *et al.*, 1973) and is accurately mimicked by A-23187 (Selinger *et al.*, 1974). On the other hand, β-adrenergic agonists cause massive release of amylase (Schramm and Selinger, 1975; Butcher *et al.*, 1975; Leslie *et al.*, 1976), which is also regulated by calcium (Putney *et al.*, 1977; Selinger and Naim, 1970; F. R. Butcher, unpublished). A-23187 does not mimic the action of β-adrenergic agonists on amylase release (Butcher, 1975; Putney *et al.*, 1977; Selinger *et al.*, 1974), nor does it interfere with the action of isoproterenal on amylase release (Putney *et al.*, 1977). In parotid, the indications are that β-adrenergic agonist action requires an intracellular pool of Ca^{2+}, while α-adrenergic agonist action is dependent on an extracellular pool of Ca^{2+}. Only in the latter case can the ionophore mimic agonist action. Rose and Lowenstein (1975, 1976), through the use of aequorin, have shown that a bolus of Ca^{2+} injected into a cell has a very small radius of diffusion, implying that the cell has active mechanisms which sequester calcium and thus restrict it to very limited microdomains within the cell. These observations lend additional support for the concept of separate multiple Ca^{2+} compartments within the same cell. Putney *et al.* (1977) have proposed that two distinctly different pools of Ca^{2+} are involved in the regulation of K^+ efflux and amylase release from rat parotid. The pool controlling K^+ efflux is accessible to that Ca^{2+} introduced by the ionophore; the one involved in regulation of amylase release is not accessible to the Ca^{2+} introduced by A-23187. The restricted accessibility of calcium to the secretory apparatus could be the result of some type of barrier with poor permeability to Ca^{2+}, or it could be the result of active sequestration of Ca^{2+} by various organelles analogous to the phenomena observed by Rose and Lowenstein (1975,1976). It should be pointed out that A-23187 does cause amylase release from rat parotid slices, but the amount of amylase released is very small in comparison to that caused by isoproterenol. This suggests that the separation of Ca^{2+} into two distinct pools each of which regulate different responses may be only relative.

E. Agents That Block Calcium Flux

Agents which block cellular uptake of calcium might help to distinguish between a requirement for extracellular or intracellular calcium in agonist action on secretory processes. The ions Co^{2+}, Ni^{2+}, and Mn^{2+} have been used to block Ca^{2+} flux (Baker, 1972). As indicated in an earlier section, La^{3+} has also been used for this purpose (see Weiss, 1974, for review). Local anesthetics such as tetracaine have also been used to inhibit Ca^{2+} flux (Papahadjopoulos, 1972). Recently, another class of compounds, such as D_{600}, a methoxy derivative of verapamil, with greater selectivity for Ca^{2+} channels than the general anesthetics, was introduced by Fleckenstein (1971). The use of these compounds has been successful in permitting a distinction between intracellular and extracellular requirements for Ca^{2+} in a specific secretory response. Chandler and Williams (1974) reported that La^{3+} did not block the stimulatory effect of bethanecol on amylase release from the exocrine pancreas except at very high concentrations of La^{3+}, which probably had direct inhibitory effects on the secretory mechanisms. They concluded that an intracellular pool of Ca^{2+} was required in the exocrine pancreas for amylase release. This finding is also supported by the observation that D_{600}, like La^{3+}, did not block agonist effects on amylase release (Schreurs *et al.*, 1976). In some secretory tissues which are regulated by multiple agonists, these agents have made it possible to demonstrate that some of the agonists require extracellular Ca^{2+} whereas others require an intracellular source of Ca^{2+}. Thus Devis *et al.* (1975) have demonstrated that D_{600} blocked glucose- and sulfonylurea-induced insulin release, whereas Somers *et al.* (1976) have shown that D_{600} did not inhibit insulin release caused by theophylline. It may be that glucose and the sulfonylureas act in a manner dependent on Ca^{2+} uptake while theophylline acts to mobilize intracellular Ca^{2+}. Similarly, Berridge and Prince (1975) have shown that tetracaine blocked the secretory response of the salivary gland from the adult blowfly to 5-hydroxytryptamine but not to exogenous cyclic AMP. In our laboratory we have shown that cholinergic and α-adrenergic stimulation of K^+ and amylase release from the rat parotid is blocked by tetracaine and by D_{600} (F. R. Butcher, unpublished). On the other hand, stimulation of amylase release from the rat parotid by isoproterenal is not blocked by tetracaine or D_{600}. These results suggest that extracellular Ca^{2+} is more important in the former case and that intracellular Ca^{2+} is more important in the latter (F. R. Butcher, unpublished).

It should be cautioned that interpretation of the results with agents which interfere with Ca^{2+} flux is best coupled with $^{45}Ca^{2+}$ flux measurements. Langer *et al.* (1975) demonstrated that Mn^{2+} diminished dP/dt of the first heart contraction following a quiescent period, whereas verapamil did not. This difference was placed in perspective when $^{45}Ca^{2+}$ flux was studied. Verapamil inhibited $^{45}Ca^{2+}$ influx, as did Mn^{2+}. In contrast, Mn^{2+} induced displacement of a rapidly exchangeable component of calcium from the heart cell and verapamil did not. It was concluded that this rapidly exchangeable pool of Ca^{2+} was the immediate source for contraction of heart muscle. Thus the agents listed above which interfere with Ca^{2+} influx do not always allow a clear-cut distinction between a requirement for a truly extracellular pool of Ca^{2+} and a requirement for one in rapid equilibrium with the extracellular pool of Ca^{2+} as the source of Ca^{2+} in a secretory process.

F. ω-(N,N-Diethylamino)alkyl-3,4,5-trimethoxybenzoates as Calcium Antagonists

A series of ω-(N,N-diethylamino)alkyl-3,4,5-trimethoxybenzoates has been studied as smooth-muscle relaxants (Lindner *et al.*, 1963; Sharma, 1962).

Malagodi and Chiou (1974) and Chiou and Malagodi (1975) have synthesized 8-(N,N-diethylamino)octyl-3,4,5-trimethoxybenzoate (TMB-8) and suggested that it acts as a smooth-muscle relaxant by blocking Ca^{2+} release from intracellular stores, thereby interfering with the availability of Ca^{2+} for muscle contraction. TMB-8 noncompetively inhibited the contractile response of guinea pig ileum to epinephrine and KCl. The inhibitory effect of TMB-8 on KCl-induced contraction was antagonized by raising the bathing medium Ca^{2+} concentration from 1.35 to 5.4 mM. TMB-8 inhibited both efflux and influx of $^{45}Ca^{2+}$ in guinea pig ileum. Using rabbit skeletal muscle sarcoplasmic reticulum, Chiou and Malagodi (1975) found that TMB-8 inhibited caffeine-induced Ca^{2+} efflux but not the basal Ca^{2+} uptake in this sarcoplasmic preparation.

Charo *et al.* (1976) have recently reported an inhibitory effect of TMB-8 on platelet secretion induced by thrombin and A-23187. The inhibitory effect of TMB on secretion caused by A-23187 was reversed by increasing the concentration of Ca^{2+} in the indubation buffer.

Charo *et al.* (1976) have called TMB-8 a specific antagonist of the intracellular actions of Ca^{2+}. I feel that such a conclusion about the specific nature of TMB-8 action is premature although such a reagent is highly desirable. For example, Chiou and Malagodi (1975) observed that TMB-8 inhibited both efflux and influx of $^{45}Ca^{2+}$ in guinea pig ileum. Consequently, any agonist action on guinea pig ileum which required increased Ca^{2+} influx might be inhibited, because TMB-8 blocked uptake. TMB-8 may inhibit the intracellular action of Ca^{2+} but it may have other actions as well.

G. Coupling of Ca^{2+} Flux with Na^+ Flux

Blaustein (1974) has recently written a very lucid review which draws attention to the regulation of Ca^{2+} efflux by Na^+ influx. Most of the experiments which examine the relationship between Ca^{2+} flux and Na^+ flux are with axons, but there are also data for various types of muscle in addition to several secretory systems. The main characteristics of the relationship between Ca^{2+} and Na^+ fluxes are summarized below.

In squid axon and synaptosomes from rat brain (Blaustein and Ector, 1976), a portion of Ca^{2+} efflux is dependent on the external Na^+ concentration. Lowering the external Na^+ concentration to 50 mM almost completely blocked the efflux component of Ca^{2+} which was dependent on external Na^+. The stoichiometry for the Na^+–Ca^{2+} exchange is $3Na^+$:$1Ca^{2+}$. Consequently, decreasing the inward Na^+ concentration gradient would decrease Ca^{2+} efflux and lead to an increased intracellular concentration of Ca^{2+}. It also appears that Ca^{2+} influx may be enhanced by a high internal concentration of Na^+ (Baker *et al.*, 1969) or by an outwardly directed Na^+ concentration gradient. A residual component of Ca^{2+} efflux is dependent on both external Ca^{2+} and Na^+ or some other suitable alkali metal instead of Na^+. That is, Ca^{2+} efflux was partially inhibited by the complete removal of external Ca^{2+}, even in the presence of external Na^+ (Blaustein, 1976, Blaustein and Russell, 1975).

It is well established that an alteration in membrane polarity is an early event of stimulus–secretion coupling in many cells (Petersen, 1976). The change in Na^+ concentration across the plasma membrane which results from alterations of membrane potential might influence sequestration of Ca^{2+} by cell organelles as well as alter Ca^{2+} fluxes as described above. Carafoli (1974) has observed that Na^+ caused a rapid loss of Ca^{2+} from isolated mitochondria.

Vasopressin release from isolated neural lobes by electrical stimulation was potentiated in Na^+ free buffer (Douglas and Sorimachi, 1971). The response was not blocked by tetrodotoxin but was blocked by omission of external Ca^{2+}. Lowering external Na^+ also potentiated the release of vasopressin induced by high external K^+ (Douglas and Poisner, 1964). Dreifuss and Nordmann (1974) have described $^{45}Ca^{2+}$ efflux from the rat neurohypophysis which was dependent on external Na^+. Low external Na^+ also caused calcium-dependent release of histamine from mast cells (Cochrane and Douglas, 1976). In addition, stimulation of secretion by low external sodium was observed for parotid (Putney, 1977) and endocrine pancreas (Hellman *et al.*, 1974a). Removal of extracellular Na^+ inhibited amylase release from the exocrine pancreas (Williams, 1975). Although removal of Na^+ increased insulin release from the endocrine pancreas, additional stimulation of insulin release by glucose was inhibited (Lambert *et al.*, 1974). Veratridine, which increases intracellular Na^+ by activating the Na^+ channels, increased insulin release independent of extracellular Ca^{2+} (Lowe *et al.*, 1976). It was suggested that Na^+ increased insulin release by causing the release of Ca^{2+} from intracellular bound stores (Lowe *et al.*, 1976).

According to the model elaborated for the squid axon, the data for the secretory systems just summarized are compatible with the idea that lowered external Na^+ lowers Ca^{2+} efflux, leading to increased ionized intracellular Ca^{2+}. The increased intracellular Ca^{2+} in turn causes increased exocytosis. If the effect of lowering external Na^+ is mediated solely by an effect on decreased Ca^{2+} efflux, then the effect should not be dependent on external Ca^{2+}. By lowering the external Na^+ concentration the ratio of internal Na^+ to external Na^+ is increased. This situation favors enhanced Ca^{2+} influx, and perhaps this mechanism is important in the calcium-dependent stimulation of secretion observed at low external Na^+ concentrations. Even though an alteration in external or internal Na^+ concentrations results in alterations of secretory rate, it does not mean that Na^+ is an important physiological regulator of Ca^{2+} flux in all the secretory systems mentioned above. Additional work will be needed to clarify this point. Manipulating Na^+ concentration may, however, be an approach to studying the involvement of Ca^{2+} in various secretory responses.

IX. MICROTUBULES AND CONTRACTILE PROTEINS

A. MICROTUBULE ASSEMBLY

Several recent reviews have appeared which cover the physical and chemical characteristics of microtubules (Snyder and McIntosh, 1976; Garland and Teller, 1975; Wilson and Bryan, 1974; Samson, 1976; Amos, 1975; Wilson, 1976). The potential role of microtubules in secretory processes has also been reviewed (Allison and Davies, 1974). This section will review selected aspects of microtubule assembly and regulatory aspects of the *in vivo* assembly process.

The assembly of microtubules *in vitro* was first demonstrated by Weisenberg (1972). GTP and Mg^{2+} are required for microtubule assembly (for review, see Kirschner and Williams, 1974; Olmstead *et al.*, 1974). The assembly reaction can be written

$$6 \text{ S subunits} \rightleftarrows 36 \text{ S rings or disks} \rightleftarrows \text{microtubules}$$

The *in vitro* assembly of microtubules is an equilibrium process which occurs through a 36 S intermediate (Kirschner and Williams, 1974; Olmstead *et al.*, 1974). The isolated 36 S rings can polymerize whereas the 6 S subunits separated from the 36 S rings cannot polymerize to form microtubules. Both the 6 S and the 36 S rings are important in polymerization reaction because both the 6 S and 36 S components disappear as the amount of polymerized tubulin increases.

During the purification of microtubule protein, two high molecular weight (HMW) components copurified with tubulin (Borisy *et al.*, 1975; Murphy and Borisy, 1975; Weingarten *et al.*, 1975; Dentler *et al.*, 1975). The HMW components accelerate the polymerization reaction (Murphy and Borisy, 1975; Weingarten *et al.*, 1975). The HMW components might act on the 6 S components to convert them to the 36 S ring structure which is considered an essential intermediate in microtubule assembly. Ultrastructural studies suggest that the HMW components are structural components of the microtubules projecting from the outer surface of the microtubule wall

(Murphy and Borisy, 1975; Behnke, 1975). These structures may be identical to similar projections reported for cytoplasmic microtubules in nerves (Smith *et al.*, 1975) and spindle apparatus (Hepler *et al.*, 1970).

Polyanions such as RNA or synthetic polynucleotides inhibit *in vitro* assembly of microtubules (Bryan *et al.*, 1975). The polyanions act by removing HMW components essential for polymerization, thereby indicating that HMW components are highly cationic. Several polycationic compounds have been found which nonspecifically substitute for the HMW components in the polymerization reaction (Erickson and Voter, 1976). Possibly the HMW components serve an electrostatic role to neutralize anionic sites on tubulin to permit polymerization.

Microtubule assembly in the absence of GTP or ATP was reported (Shelanski *et al.*, 1973). The nucleotide-independent assembly occurred in the presence of 1 M sucrose or 4 M glycerol and at a slower rate than assembly in the presence of nucleotides. Detrich *et al.* (1976) have shown that glycerol interacts very strongly with tubulin and is not removed by chromatography over Sephadex.

B. Effect of Ca^{2+} on Microtubule Assembly

Several reports have suggested that calcium regulates various secretory processes by an effect on microtubule assembly. This suggestion is largely based on the observation that Ca^{2+} inhibited *in vitro* polymerization of tubulin (Weisenberg, 1972). Conditions which should elevate cytoplasmic Ca^{2+} levels led to the loss of cytoplasmic microtubules (Fuller *et al.*, 1975, 1976; Schliwa, 1976). According to this hypothesis, the assembly of microtubules could be regulated by controlling the cytoplasmic level of Ca^{2+}.

Unlike the original report of Weisenberg (1972), Olmstead *et al.*, (1974) were unable to show that low concentrations of Ca^{2+} inhibited assembly of brain microtubules *in vitro*. They found that millimolar concentrations of Ca^{2+} substituted for Mg^{2+} in the assembly reaction (Olmstead *et al.*, 1974). Because millimolar concentrations of cytoplasmic Ca^{2+} are never reached, the observations by Olmstead *et al.* (1974), if correct, cast doubt on a direct regulatory role for Ca^{2+} in control of microtubule assembly. If calcium inhibits microtubule assembly at micromolar concentrations, the inhibition might require a factor which was present in the studies of Weisenberg (1972) but absent in the studies of Olmstead *et al.* (1974). Such a factor could be analogous to the calcium-binding protein which is discussed in Section XII. If this possibility were true it might explain the contradictory effects of Ca^{2+} on microtubule assembly and offer a mechanism for the inhibitory effect of Ca^{2+}. Additional detailed studies on the effect of Ca^{2+} on microtubule assembly are needed before this critical point can be resolved.

C. Cyclic Nucleotides and Microtubule Assembly

Cyclic AMP was also suggested as an important regulator of microtubule assembly (Willingham and Pastan, 1975; Gillespie, 1975). Goodman *et al.* (1970) reported that cyclic AMP stimulated the phosphorylation of isolated neurotubule subunits. Perhaps cyclic AMP regulates microtubule assembly by a protein phosphorylation mechanism. Phosphorylation of tubulin from anterior pituitary (Sheterline and Schofield, 1975), HeLa cells (Piras and Piras, 1975), *Chlamydomas reinhardtii* (Piperno and Luck, 1976), embryonic chicken muscle (Piras and Piras, 1974), and brain (Goodman *et al.*, 1970; Soifer, 1975; Sloboda *et al.*, 1975) have been reported. Sloboda *et al.* (1975) reported that the HMW components which copurify the tubulin are better substrates for protein kinase than tubulin. Because the HMW components influence microtubule assembly phosphorylation of HMW components could alter their ability to influence microtubule assembly. No functional consequence of phosphorylating either tubulin or HMW components has been found. The increased phosphorylation of brain tubulin caused by cyclic AMP was opposed by cyclic GMP (Sandoval and Cuatrecases, 1976), perhaps by enhancing the activity of a phosphoprotein phosphatase. If phosphorylation of tubulin or microtubule-associated proteins has any functional consequences, then the latter observation offers interesting possibilities for reciprocal regulation of microtubule functions.

A functional role for microtubules in the secretory process is usually assessed by using agents such as colchicine to disrupt the microtubules. If these agents inhibit the secretory process, then it is inferred that microtubules are required for the normal function of the secretory process. Ultrastructural studies have shown secretory vesicles in close apposition with microtubules (Smith, 1971; Smith *et al.*, 1970; Gray, 1975) which were directed toward the presynaptic membrane (Gray, 1975). Rat brain synaptosomes contain a large amount of tubulin (Blitz and Fine, 1974). Allen (1975) has also shown that cytoplasmic vesicles in *P. caudatum* were bound to microtubules. The close relationship observed between vesicles and microtubules may imply a functional relationship between the two, but it does not indicate how microtubules regulate vesicle mobility. It is possible that the microtubules act to carry the vesicles to the cell surface by a contractile mechanism, or they may form channels to direct the vesicles to a specific portion of the plasma membrane.

D. Contractile Proteins in the Secretory Process

The contractile proteins actin and myosin have been found in a number of tissues, some of which exhibit a secretory function (see Pollard and Weihing,

1974, for review). Actin (Gurenstein *et al.*, 1975) or actin binding protein (Boxer *et al.*, 1976) has been demonstrated in the plasma membrane of 3T3 mouse fibroblasts, HeLa cells, and polymorphonuclear leukocytes. Actin and/or myosin have been found associated with adrenal chromaffin granule membranes (Burridge and Philips, 1975), frog retinal pigment granules (Murray and Dubin, 1975), and brain synaptosomes (Blitz and Fine, 1974). A functional role for actin and myosin in secretory tissues has been inferred from the structural organization of these compounds within the secretory tissues. Alternatively, cytochalasin B has been used to infer a functional role for actin and myosin in the secretory response (Allison and Davies, 1974). Cytochalsin B prevents interaction of actin and myosin (Weihing, 1976; Hartwig and Stossel, 1976).

Microtubules and the contractile proteins actin and myosin may all be required for the normal functioning of secretory process. Microtubules could provide a structural framework to define the direction of secretory granule movement, and the myosin and actin could provide the contractile force for secretory granule movement. According to this model, the regulatory role of Ca^{2+} in the secretory process would be mediated through an effect on the interaction of actin and myosin or through an effect on the structural integrity of microtubules. Calcium activation of an actomyosin–ATPase from the smooth muscle of procine aorta (Frederiksen, 1976) and calcium control of an actin-activated myosin–ATPase from *D. discoideum* (Mockrin and Spudich, 1976) have been reported. Similar observations have not been made for secretory systems.

It is now apparent that the distribution of proteins in the plane of the plasma membrane is regulated by structures in the cytoplasm. An increasing body of evidence indicates that the microtubules and microfilaments regulate the mobility of membrane proteins (for an extensive review, see Nicolson, 1976). Therefore, regulatory signals which influence microtubule and microfilament function will also affect the distribution of membrane proteins. In Section IV the evidence for a discrete organizational pattern of membrane proteins around exocytotic or membrane fusion sites was reviewed. Besides providing direction and motive force for secretory granule movement, the microtubules and microfilaments could also play an important regulatory role in exocytosis by controlling the distribution of the membrane proteins involved at the sites of membrane fusion in exocytosis.

A role for Ca^{2+} in exocytosis mediated through an effect on the distribution membrane proteins is also a possibility. Local anesthetics (e.g., tetracaine) which block Ca^{2+} flux enhance the agglutination of fibroblasts by lectins (Poste *et al.*, 1975a,b,c). This effect of local anesthetics on agglutination was also accompanied by an enhancement of lectin-induced redistribution of concanavalin A receptor sites (Poste *et al.*, 1975a,b). If the intracellular Ca^{2+}

concentration was increased with either A-23187 or X537A, the effects on cell-surface protein mobility were the same as that caused by colchicine (Poste and Nicolson, 1976). These data provide additional support for a regulatory role of Ca^{2+} in microtubule and microfilament function.

E. Quantification of Polymerized and Depolymerized Tubulin

As already noted, an intact microtubule system is needed for the normal functioning of a number of secretory systems. In order to study the involvement of the microtubule system more thoroughly it is essential to correlate changes in the amount of polymerized and depolymerized tubulin with changes in secretion. In order to accomplish this a procedure to quantify the amounts of polymerized and depolymerized tubulin under the different conditions is essential.

One approach used with good results is quantitative morphometric analysis of microtubules appearing in electron micrographs. Using this approach, Taylor *et al.* (1975) demonstrated that colchicine lowers the number of cytoplasmic microtubules in the granular epithelial cells of toad bladder. Rubin and Weiss (1975) also used this approach to show that the level of polymerized tubulin in Chinese hamster ovary cells grown in tissue culture increases at confluency and is also increased by dibutyryl cyclic AMP. Analysis by this procedure also demonstrated a similar effect of dibutyryl cyclic AMP on the amount of polymerized tubulin in cultivated Greene melanoma cells (DiPasquale *et al.*, 1976).

The observation that a number of agents such as DMSO (Filner and Behnke, 1973) and glycols (Forer and Zimmerman, 1975) stabilize polymerized tubulin was used as the basis of a procedure to separate polymerized from depolymerized tubulin (Pipeleers *et al.*, 1976; Patzelt *et al.*, 1975). After separating the depolymerized and polymerized tubulin by centrifugation, the amount of tubulin in each fraction was calculated by measuring the [³H]colchicine binding capacity. Using this approach it was found that (a) 40% of hepatic tubulin was polymerized (Patzelt *et al.*, 1975), (b) conditions leading to increased insulin release were associated with an increased amount of polymerized tubulin (Pipeleers *et al.*, 1976), and (c) increased cyclic AMP levels in Greene melanoma cells increased the amount of polymerized tubulin (DiPasquale *et al.*, 1976). Several criticisms can be applied to the use of the latter approach to quantify the amounts of polymerized and depolymerized tubulin. Wilson and Bryan (1974) have emphasized that the high-affinity colchicine binding activity of tubulin is unstable and decays with time. In order to accurately measure colchicine binding activity it is thus essential to make measurements at several times and extrapolate the colchicine binding capacity back to time zero from this decay curve. In addition, assay conditions should be selected to minimize the decay of the colchicine binding activity. No acknowledgment of this problem was made in either of the two methods using this approach to determine polymerized and depolymerized tubulin (Pipeleers *et al.*, 1976; Patzelt *et al.*, 1975). We have recently found that glycerol or DMSO, which are used to stabilize the polymerized tubulin, greatly lowered the binding of colchicine by tubulin in brain and parotid extracts (King and Butcher, 1977). The methods used by Pipeleers *et al.* (1976) and Patzelt *et al.* (1975) stabilized polymerized tubulin with a combination of glycerol and DMSO, or glycerol, respectively. Polymerized tubulin was collected by centrifugation and the depolymerized tubulin remained in the solution containing the microtubule stabilizing agent. Consequently, when the amount of depolymerized tubulin in the stabilizing solution was calculated by measuring the colchicine binding capacity, it was underestimated. Underestimation of the amount of depolymerized tubulin will give artifactually high values for the percent polymerized tubulin.

In order to quantify the amounts of polymerized and depolymerized tubulin by measuring the [^{3}H]colchicine binding capacity, it is clear that the stabilizing agent (i.e., glycerol or DMSO) must be removed before assaying colchicine binding. Also, it is essential to optimize assay conditions to retard decay of high-affinity colchicine binding activity and to extrapolate the amount of binding to t_0 from decay curves.

X. ABNORMALITIES IN EXOCYTOSIS

Exocytosis is a complex process which is precisely regulated to give the appropriate end result. However, there are examples of exocytosis in various cell types which are defective in at least one step or exocytosis.

Exocytosis normally occurs at only specific sites on the cell surface. Horvath and Kovacs (1974) have presented ultrastructural evidence for misplaced exocytosis in some human pituitary adenomas. They observed a number of exocytotic sites on the lateral aspects of cells which were distant from either perivascular spaces or from intercellular extensions of basement membranes. Malaisse-Lagae *et al.* (1975) have reported a decrease rate of insulin release from the β-cells isolated from the pancreas of spiny mice (*Acomy cahirinums*) which was associated with very low levels of microtubules. They analyzed the microtubule content of the β-cells from normal mice, a strain of diabetes mutant mice, and the spiny mice by ultrastructural morphometry. This procedure involved prior exposure of the β-cells to vincristine, which induced the formation of paracystalline deposits of microtubules. With this approach they found that the microtubule level in the β-cells from the spiny mice was four times lower than in the normal controls or the diabetes mutant mice. The reason for the reduced microtubule content was not identified, but might have resulted from a defect in tubulin synthesis or a defect in the polymerization of functional microtubules.

The importance of microtubules in the regulation of secretion and mobility of intramembranous particles was beautifully shown by the work of Oliver *et al.* (1975, 1976a) and Oliver (1975) using cells from beige mice which are an animal model for the human disease, Chediak-Higashi. Oliver *et al.* (1975) observed that only 11% of the Con-A receptor sites on normal C57/6J mouse polymorphonuclear leukocytes (PMN) were capped under control conditions. However, 44% of the Con-A receptor sites on the PMN's from peripheral blood of the beige mice were capped. Agents which disrupt microtubules will lead to capping of occupied Con-A receptors, and this was observed for the PMN's from normal mice. Colchicine added to normal PMN's increased the number of caps from 11 to 55%. The number of caps observed with the PMN's from the beige mice was not affected by colchicine. The distribution of Con-A receptors on the PMN's of beige mice could be made to resemble the normal situation by addition of exogenous cyclic GMP or agents which should elevate intracellular levels of cyclic GMP. Furthermore, the induction of increased cap formation in the beige PMN's by cyclic GMP was antagonized by the same agents which antagonized cap formation in PMN's from normal mice. These studies suggest that cyclic GMP can act in some manner to regulate microtubule formation. However, the mechanism is not known.

Fibroblasts cultured from the beige mice accumulate giant lysosomal granules (Oliver *et al.*, 1976a). A normal lysosomal granule morphology was observed in the fibroblasts if they were cultured in the presence of agents which elevated cyclic GMP levels.

Animal models which display defects in the release of exocytotic products might prove useful as tools to study the details of the various steps involved in exocytosis and also as models for analogous human disorders.

XI. SULFHYDRYL GROUPS AND SECRETORY PROCESSES

Several reports of stimulatory effects of poorly permeating sulfhydryl reagents on secretory responses have appeared. Hellman *et al.* (1974a,b) found that chloromercuribenzene-*p*-sulfonic acid and 5',5'-dithiobis-2-nitrobenzoic acid enhanced insulin release. Sulfhydryl reagents also stimulated amylase release from the rat parotid (Dormer *et al.*, 1973; F. R. Butcher unpublished).

The mechanism for this effect is not known. Possibly the sulfhydryl reagents raise intracellular levels of Ca^{2+} by inhibiting Ca^{2+} efflux (Russell *et al.*, 1974). In pancreatic islets some of the reagents elevated cyclic AMP levels in the presence of methyl isobutyl xanthine, while others did not (Hellman *et al.*, 1974b). The sulfhydryl reagents do not elevate cyclic AMP levels in rat parotid even in the presence of phosphodiesterase inhibitors (F. R. Butcher, unpublished).

Another possible mechanism to explain the effects of sulfhydryl reagents on exocytosis involves tubulin. Kuriyama and Sakai (1974) and Mellon and Rebhun (1976) found 7 moles of —SH groups per 55,000 gm of porcine brain tubulin. Their results also suggested that 2 moles of —SH groups were required for *in vitro* assembly of tubulin. Mellon and Rebhun (1976) reported that diamide which inhibited *in vitro* polymerization of brain tubulin also reduced the number of the free —SH groups of tubulin and destroyed the characteristic 450 Å ring structure of tubulin. Diamide also inhibited *in vivo* assembly of tubulin in human neutrophils (Oliver *et al.*, 1976b) and caused disolution of mitotic spindles in fertilized sea urchin eggs (Nath and Rebhun, 1976). In addition to direct interaction between diamide and tubulin–SH groups, diamide also oxidized glutathione (Kosower *et al.*, 1972). Oliver *et al.* (1976b) observed that diamide inhibited *in vivo* microtubule assembly in neutrophils and lowered reduced glutathione levels. In view of these results, Oliver *et al.* (1976b) suggested that reduced glutathione maintained the sulfhydryl titer of tubulin essential for microtubule polymerization. If polymerized microtubules normally restrain the movement of secretory granules to the cell surface, then depolymerization of tubulin by sulfhydryl reagents would remove this restraint and allow fusion of the secretory granules with the plasma membrane.

XII. A POSSIBLE MECHANISM FOR THE REGULATORY ROLE OF CALCIUM IN EXOCYTOSIS

A possible model to study the regulatory role of Ca^{2+} in secretory processes is afforded by the regulation of cyclic nucleotide phosphodiesterase and adenylate cyclase activity. Ca^{2+} enhances the activity of phosphodiesterase. This activating effect is mediated by a calcium-binding protein (Kakiuchi *et al.*, 1970; Cheung, 1970, 1971). Binding of the activator to the phosphodiesterase is dependent on the presence of Ca^{2+} (Teo *et al.*, 1973; Lin *et al.*, 1974; Teo and Wang, 1973). It has also been shown that the same activator protein stimulates the activity of brain adenylate cyclase (Brostrom *et al.*, 1975; Cheung *et al.*, 1975). The mechanism for Ca^{2+} activation of the brain adenylate cyclase is similar to that for Ca^{2+} activation of phosphodiesterase (Cheung *et al.*, 1975).

Recently it was shown that the calcium-binding protein which mediates the activation of phosphodiesterase and adenylate cyclase is very similar to rabbit muscle troponin C (Stevens *et al.*, 1976; Watterson *et al.*, 1976). Their amino acid composition, molecular weight, isoelectric point, and ultraviolet spectra are alike (Stevens *et al.*, 1976; Watterson *et al.*, 1976). The effect of Ca^{2+} on the conformation of the calcium-binding protein which regulates phosphodiesterase and adenylate cyclase activity (Liu and Cheung, 1976) is similar to the effect of Ca^{2+} on the conformation of muscle troponin C (Murray and Kay, 1972). In all cases, Ca^{2+} binding confers a more helical conformation to the protein. If the effects of Ca^{2+} are mediated by structurally similar Ca^{2+} binding proteins, this concept might serve as a general model to explain the effects of Ca^{2+}. The specificity for Ca^{2+} action would be a function of the structural properties of the Ca^{2+} binding protein. The extensive similarities between the calcium-binding protein, which regulates phosphodiesterase and adenylate cyclase activity, and troponin C provides strong support for such a model.

It will be very interesting to determine if a Ca^{2+}-binding protein such as described in the preceding paragraph mediates an effect of Ca^{2+} on microtubule assembly. I suggest in Section IX,B that the discrepancy between the findings of Olmstead *et al.* (1974), who did not find a deleterious effect of low Ca^{2+} concentrations on microtubule assembly, and Weisenberg (1972), who did, could be due to the loss of a Ca^{2+}-binding protein in the former case.

A protein resembling troponin C has been purified from bovine adrenal medulla (Kuo and Coffee, 1976a,b). It remains to be shown that this troponin-C-like protein from adrenal medulla confers Ca^{2+}-specific regulation on adrenal medullary contractile proteins which might be important in the release of epinephrine from chromaffin granules. Troponin C regulates the Ca^{2+}-sensitive ATPase activity of muscle actomyosin (Ebashi and Endo, 1968), and it was reported that Ca^{2+}–ATPase activity is found in adrenal medulla (see Poisner, 1970). It is not known if the Ca^{2+}–ATPase activity is part of a contractile mechanism in the adrenal medullary cells.

XIII. SUMMARY

My bias in favor of a primary role for Ca^{2+} in the regulation of exocytosis is evident throughout this chapter. I favor a primary role for Ca^{2+} because it greatly simplifies the control elements needed to effect the regulation of exocytosis.

The immediate source of Ca^{2+} in a secretory response or the way Ca^{2+} is handled is a function of the secretory cell type. Two possibilities for the source of Ca^{2+} during the secretory response are Ca^{2+} entering the cell from the extracellular space or Ca^{2+} coming from an intracellular pool, such as mitochondra.

The regulatory role of Ca^{2+} in exocytosis might be mediated by an effect on one or more components of the secretory apparatus. Calcium could alter the function of microtubules, the function of a network of contractile proteins, or the physicochemical properties of the membranes involved in fusion during exocytosis. Possibly, the diverse effects of Ca^{2+} are mediated by Ca^{2+}-binding proteins which impart specificity for the locus of Ca^{2+} action.

I have not treated the role of cyclic nucleotides in exocytosis extensively because there is no indication that cyclic nucleotides are universally involved in exocytosis. In some tissues, elevated cyclic AMP levels are associated with increased exocytosis. In others, elevated cyclic GMP levels are associated with increased exocytosis. In still a third group of tissues, increased exocytosis is not associated with altered levels of either cyclic nucleotide. Regardless of the diverse response pattern for changes in cyclic nucleotide levels during increased exocytosis in various tissues, all require Ca^{2+} in the secretory process. The cyclic nucleotides may have two functions in the regulation of exocytosis. First, they may regulate the availability of Ca^{2+}, perhaps by a protein phosphorylation mechanism analogous to regulation of Ca^{2+} uptake by sarcoplasmic reticulum. Second, they might alter the sensitivity of the components involved in the secretory response to Ca^{2+}. Agonists could regulate the availability of Ca^{2+} by altering cyclic nucleotide levels, by altering Na^+ flux which in turn modifies intracellular Ca^{2+} levels, by directly altering the permeability of organelle membranes to Ca^{2+}, or by a combination of these processes.

Several possible roles for Ca^{2+} and cyclic nucleotides have been delineated, but it is clear that these roles are still only possibilities. Much additional work is needed before we can understand the intricacies involved in the role of cyclic nucleotides and calcium in the secretory response.

ACKNOWLEDGMENTS

Financial support for work described from the author's laboratory was provided by research grants from the Cystic Fibrosis Foundation, NIAMDD, and a USPHS Research Career Development Award.

REFERENCES

Adelson, J. W., and Rothman, S. S. (1974). *Science* **183**, 1087.
Ahkong, Q. F., Fisher, D., Tampion, W., and Lucy, J. A. (1973). *Biochem. J.* **136**, 147.

Ahkong, Q. F., Fisher, D., Tampion, W., and Lucy, J. A. (1975a) *Nature (London)* **253**, 194.

Ahkong, Q. F., Howell, J. I., and Lucy, J. A. (1975b). *Nature (London)* **255**, 66.

Ahkong, Q. F., Tampion, W., and Lucy, J. A. (1975c). *Nature (London)* **256**, 208.

Allen, R. D. (1975). *J. Cell Biol.* **64**, 497.

Allison, A. C., and Davies, P. (1974). *Adv. Cytopharmacol.* **2**, 237.

Amos, L. A. (1975). *In* "Microtubules and Microtubule Inhibitors" (M. Borgers and M. de Brabander, eds.), p. 21. North-Holland Publ., Amsterdam.

Baker, P. F. (1972). *Prog. Biophys. Mol. Biol.* **24**, 177.

Baker, P. F., Blaustein, M. P., Hodgkin, A. L., and Steinhardt, R. A. (1969). *J. Physiol. (London)* **200**, 431.

Baker, P. F., Hodgkin, A. L., and Ridgway, E. B. (1971). *J. Physiol. (London)* **218**, 709.

Batzri, S., Selinger, Z., and Schramm, M. (1971). *Science* **174**, 1029.

Behnke, O. (1975). *Nature (London)* **257**, 709.

Berridge, M. J. (1975). *Adv. Cyclic Nucleotide Res.* **5**, 1.

Berridge, M. J., and Prince, W. T. (1975). *J. Cyclic Nucleotide Res.* **1**, 169.

Bieger, W., Martin-Achard, A., Bassler, M., and Kern, H. F. (1976a). *Cell Tissue Res.* **165**, 435.

Bieger, W., Seybold, J., and Kern, H. F. (1976b). *Cell Tissue Res.* **170**, 203.

Binley, F. J., Jr., Spangler, S. G., and Mullins, L. J. (1975). *J. Gen. Physiol.* **66**, 233.

Blaustein, M. P. (1974). *Ergeb. Physiol., Biol. Chem. Exp. Pharmakol.* **70**, 33.

Blaustein, M. P. (1976). *Fed. Proc., Fed. Am. Soc. Exp. Biol.* **35**, 2574.

Blaustein, M. P., and Ector, A. C. (1976). *Biochim. Biophys. Acta* **419**, 295.

Blaustein, M. P., and Russell, J. M. (1975). *J. Membr. Biol.* **22**, 285.

Blitz, A. L., and Fine, R. E. (1974). *Proc. Natl. Acad. Sci. U.S.A.* **71**, 4472.

Blobel, G., and Dobberstein, B. (1975). *J. Cell Biol.* **67**, 835.

Blobel, G., and Sabatini, D. D. (1970). *J. Cell Biol.* **45**, 146.

Borisy, G. G., Marcum, J. M., Olmsted, J. B., Murphy D. B., and Johnson, K. A. (1975). *Ann. N.Y. Acad. Sci.* **253**, 107.

Borle, A. B. (1969). *J. Gen. Physiol.* **55**, 163.

Borle, A. B. (1974). *J. Membr. Biol.* **16**, 221.

Borle, A. B. (1976). *J. Membr. Biol.* **29**, 209.

Boxer, L. A., Richardson, S., and Floyd, A. (1976). *Nature (London)* **263**, 249.

Brisson, G. R., and Malaisse, W. (1973). *Metab., Clin. Exp.* **22**, 455.

Brostrom, C. O., Hwang, Y. C., Breckenridge, B. M., and Wolff, D. J. (1975). *Proc. Natl. Acad. Sci. U.S.A.* **72**, 64.

Bryan, J., Nagle, B. W., and Doenges, K. H. (1975). *Proc. Natl. Acad. Sci. U.S.A.* **72**, 3570.

Burridge, K., and Phillips, J. H. (1975). *Nature (London)* **254**, 526.

Butcher, F. R. (1975). *Metab., Clin. Exp.* **24**, 409.

Butcher, F. R., Goldman, J. A., and Nemerovski, M. (1975). *Biochim. Biophys. Acta* **392**, 82.

Carafoli, E. (1974). *Biochem. Soc. Symp.* **39**, 89.

Chandler, D. E., and Williams, J. A. (1974). *J. Physiol. (London)* **243**, 831.

Charo, L. F., Feinman, R. D., and Detwiler, T. C. (1976). *Biochem. Biophy. Res. Commun.* **72**, 450.

Cheung, W. Y. (1970). *Biochem. Biophys. Res. Commun.* **38**, 533.

Cheung, W. Y. (1971). *J. Biol. Chem.* **246**, 2859.

Cheung, W. Y., Bradham, L. S., Lynch, T. J., Lin, Y. M., and Tallant, E. A. (1975). *Biochem. Biophys. Res. Commun.* **66**, 1055.

Chiou, C. Y., and Malagodi, M. H. (1975). *J. Pharmacol.* **53**, 279.

Clemente, F., and Meldolesi, J. (1975). *J. Cell Biol.* **65**, 88.

Cochrane, D. E., and Douglas, W. W. (1974). *Proc. Natl. Acad. Sci. U.S.A.* **71**, 408.

Cochrane, D. E., and Douglas, W. W. (1975). *Br. J. Pharmacol.* **54**, 400.

Cochrane, D. E., and Douglas, W. W. (1976). *J. Physiol. (London)* **257**, 433.

Cook, A. M., Low, E., and Ishijimi, M. (1972). *Nature (London)* **239**, 150.

Crowther, R. A., Finch, J. T., and Pearse, B. M. F. (1976). *J. Mol. Biol.* **103**, 785.

Dahl, G., and Gratzl, M. (1976). *Cytobiologie* **12**, 344.

Dahl, G., Gratzl, M., and Ekerdt, R. (1976). *J. Cell Biol.* **70**, 180a.

Davis, B., and Lazarus, N. R. (1976). *J. Physiol. (London)* **256**, 709.

Dean, P. M. (1975). *J. Theor. Biol.* **54**, 289.

DeCamilli, P., Peluchetti, D., and Meldolesi, J. (1974). *Nature (London)* **248**, 245.

DeCamilli, P., Peluchetti, D., and Meldolesi, J. (1976). *J. Cell Biol.* **70**, 59.

Dentler, W. L., Granett, S., and Rosenbaum, J. L. (1975). *J. Cell Biol.* **65**, 237.

Derjaguin, B. V., and Landau, L. D. (1941). *J. Exp. Theor. Phys.* **11**, 802.

Detrich, H. W., III, Berkowitz, S. A., Kim, H., and Williams, R. C. (1976). *Biochem. Biophys. Res. Commun.* **68**, 961.

Devillers-Thiery, A., Kindt, T., Scheele, G., and Blobel, G. (1975). *Proc. Natl. Acad. Sci. U.S.A.* **72**, 5016.

Devis, G., Somers, G., Van Obberghen, E., and Malaisse, W. J. (1975). *Diabetes* **24**, 547.

Diamant, D., and Patkar, S. A. (1975). *Int. Arch. Allergy Appl. Immunol.* **49**, 183.

DiPasquale, A. M., McGuire, J., Moellmann, G., and Wasserman, S. J. (1976). *J. Cell Biol.* **71**, 735.

Dipolo, R., Requena, J., Brinley, Jr., F. R., Mullins, L. J., Scarpa, A., and Tiffert, T. (1976). *J. Gen. Physiol.* **67**, 433.

Dormer, R. L., and Ashcroft, S. J. H. (1974). *Biochem. J.* **144**, 543.

Dormer, R. L., Kerbey, A. L., McPherson, M., Manley, S., Ashcroft, J. H., Schofield, J. G., and Randle, J. P. (1973). *Biochem. J.* **140**, 135.

Douglas, W. W. (1974). *Handb. Physiol., Sect. 7: Endocrinol.* **4**, Part I, 191.

Douglas, W. W. (1975). *In* "Secretory Mechanisms of Exocrine Glands" (N. A. Thorn and O. H. Peterson, eds.), p. 116. Academic Press, New York.

Douglas, W. W., and Poisner, A. M. (1963). *J. Physiol. (London)* **165**, 528.

Douglas, W. W., and Poisner, A. M. (1964). *J. Physiol. (London)* **172**, 1.

Douglas, W. W., and Sorimachi, M. (1971). *Br. J. Pharmacol.* **42**, 647P.

Douglas, W. W., and Ueda, Y. (1973). *J. Physiol. (London)* **234**, 98P.

Douglas W. W., Nagasaw, J., and Schulz, R. A. (1971). *Mem. Soc. Endocrinol.* **19**, 353.

Dreifuss, J. J., and Nordmann, J. J. (1974). *J. Physiol. (London)* **240**, 46P.

Dreifuss, J. J., Akert, K., Sandri, C., and Moor, H. (1976). *Cell Tissue Res.* **165**, 317.

Eagles, P. A. M., Johnson, L. N., and Van Horn, C. (1976). *J. Ultrastruct. Res.* **55**, 87.

Ebashi, S., and Endo, M. (1968). *Prog. Biophys. Mol. Biol.* **18**, 125.

Eibl, H., Hill, E. E., and Lands, W. E. M. (1969). *Eur. J. Biochem.* **9**, 250.

Eimerl, S., Savion, N., Heichal, O., and Selinger, Z. (1974). *J. Biol. Chem.* **249**, 3991.

Erickson, H. P., and Voter, W. A. (1976). *Proc. Natl. Acad. Sci. U.S.A.* **73**, 2813.

Filner, P., and Behnke, O. (1973). *J. Cell Biol.* **59**, 99a.

Fleckenstein, A. (1971). *In* "Calcium and the Heat" (P. Harris and L. Opie, eds.), p. 135. Academic Press, New York.

Foreman, J. C., and Mongar, J. L. (1973). *J. Physiol. (London)* **230**, 493.

Foreman, J. C., Mongar, J. L., and Gomperts, B. D. (1973). *Nature (London)*, **245**, 249.

Forer, A., and Zimmerman, A. M. (1975). *Ann. N.Y. Acad. Sci.* **253**, 378.

Formby, B., Capito, K., Egeberg, J., and Hedeskov, C. J. (1976). *Am. J. Physiol.* **230**, 441.

Franke, W. W., Luder, M. R., Kartenbeck, J., Zerban, H., and Kennan, T. W. (1976). *J. Cell Biol.* **69**, 173.

Frederiksen, D. W. (1976). *Proc. Natl. Acad. Sci. U.S.A.* **73**, 2706.

Fuller, G. M., Ellison, J. J., McGill, M., Sordahl, L. A., and Brinkley, B. R. (1975). *In*

"Microtubules and Microtubule Inhibitors" (M. Borgers and M. de Brabander, eds.), p. 379. North-Holland Publ., Amsterdam.

Fuller, G. M., Artus, C. S., and Ellison, J. J. (1976). *J. Cell Biol.* **70**, 68a.

Gabbay, K. H., Korff, J., and Schneeberger, E. E. (1975). *Science* **187**, 177.

Garcia, A. G., Kirpekar, S. M., and Prat, J. C. (1975). *J. Physiol. (London)* **244**, 253.

Garfield, R. E., and Somylo, A. P. (1975). *Proc. 33rd Annu. Elect. Micro. Soc. Am. Meet.* p. 558.

Garland, D., and Teller, D. C. (1975). *Ann. N.Y. Acad. Sci.* **253**, 232.

Garrett, J. R., and Parsons, P. A., (1973). *J. Physiol. (London)* **237**, 3P.

Geuze, J. J., and Kramer, M. F. (1976). *Cell Tissue Res.* **156**, 1.

Gillespie, E. (1975). *Ann. N.Y. Acad. Sci.* **253**, 771.

Goodman, D. B. P., Rasmussen, H., DiBella, F., and Guthrow, C. E., Jr. (1970). *Proc. Natl. Acad. Sci. U.S.A.* **67**, 652.

Goodman, F. R., Weiss, G. B., and Goth, A. (1976). *J. Pharmacol. Exp. Ther.* **198**, 168.

Gratzl, M., and Dahl, G. (1976). *FEBS Lett.* **62**, 142.

Gray, E. G. (1975). *Proc. R. Soc. London, Ser. B* **190**, 369.

Gullis, R. J., and Rowe, C. E. (1975a). *Biochem. J.* **148**, 197.

Gullis, R. J., and Rowe, C. E. (1975b). *Biochem. J.* **148**, 557.

Gullis, R. J., and Rowe, C. E. (1975c). *Biochem. J.* **148**, 567.

Gullis, R. J., and Rowe, C. E. (1976). *FEBS Lett.* **67**, 256.

Gurenstein, E., Rich, A., and Weihing, R. (1975). *J. Cell. Biol.* **64**, 223.

Hall, J. E., and Simon, S. A. (1976). *Biochim. Biophys. Acta* **436**, 613.

Hart, C. A., Fisher, D., Hallinan, T., and Lucy, J. A. (1976). *Biochem. J.* **158**, 141.

Hartwig, J. H., and Stossel, T. P. (1976). *J. Cell Biol.* **71**, 295.

Hauser, H., and Dawson, R. M. C. (1967). *Eur. J. Biochem.* **1**, 61.

Hellman, B. (1975). *Biochim. Biophys. Acta* **399**, 157.

Hellman, B., Idahl, L., Lernmark, Å., and Taljedal, I. (1974a). *Biochim. Biophys. Acta.* **372**, 127.

Hellman, B., Idahl, L., Lernmark, Å., Sehlin, J., and Taljedal, I. (1974b). *Mol. Pharmacol.* **9**, 792.

Hellman, B., Idahl, L. Å., Lernmark, Å., Sehlin, J., and Taljedal, J. B. (1974c). *Biochem. J.* **138**, 33.

Hepler, P. K., McIntosh, J. R., and Cleland, S. (1970). *J. Cell Biol.* **45**, 438.

Heuser, J. E., and Reese, T. S. (1973). *J. Cell Biol.* **57**, 315.

Hokin-Neaverson, M., Sadeghian, K., Majumder, A. L., and Eisenberg, F. (1975). *Biochem. Biophys. Res. Commun.* **67**, 1537.

Horvath, E., and Kovacs, K. (1974). *Arch. Pathol.* **97**, 221.

Ishida, H., Miki, N., and Yoshida, H. (1971a). *Jpn. J. Pharmacol.* **21**, 227.

Ishida, H., Miki, N., Hata, F., and Yoshida, Y. (1971b). *Jpn. J. Pharmacol.* **21**, 239.

Jamieson, J. D. (1973). *Curr. Top. Membr. Transp.* **4**, 271.

Kagayama, M., and Douglas, W. W. (1974). *J. Cell Biol.* **62**, 519.

Kakiuchi, S., Yamazaki, R., and Nakajima, H., (1970). *Proc. Jpn. Acad.* **46**, 589.

Kalina M., and Robinovitch, R. (1975). *Cell Tissue Res.* **163**, 373.

Karl, R. C., Zawalich, W. S., Ferrendelli, J. A., and Matschinsky, F. M. (1975). *J. Biol. Chem.* **250**, 4575.

King, K. T., and Butcher, F. R. (1978). In preparation.

Kirschner, M. W., and Williams, R. C. (1974). *J. Supramol. Struct.* **2**, 412.

Kita, H., and Van der Kloot, W. (1974). *Nature (London)* **250**, 658.

Kondo, S., and Schulz, I. (1976). *J. Membr. Biol.* **29**, 185.

Korn, E. D., Bowers, B., Batzri, S., Simmons, S. R., and Victoria, E. J. (1974). *J. Supramol. Struct.* **2**, 517.

Kosower, E. M., Correa, W., Kinon, B. J., and Kosower, N. (1972). *Biochim. Biophys. Acta* **264**, 39.

Kuo, I. C. Y., and Coffee, C. J. (1976a). *J. Biol. Chem.* **251**, 315.

Kuo, I. C. Y., and Coffee, C. J. (1976b). *J. Biol. Chem.* **251**, 1603.

Kuriyama, R., Sakai, H. (1974). *J. Biochem. (Tokyo)* **76**, 651.

Lambert, A. E., Henquin, J. C., and Malvaux, P. (1974). *Endocrinology* **95**, 1069.

Langer, G. A., Serena, S. D., and Nudd, L. M. (1975). *Am. J. Physiol.* **229**, 1003.

Lazarus, N. R., Davis, B., and O'Connor, K. J. (1976). *J. Physiol. (Paris)* **72**, 787.

Leslie, B. A., Putney, J. W., Jr., and Sherman, J. M. (1976). *J. Physiol. (London)* **260**, 351.

Lin, Y. M., Liu, Y. P., and Cheung, W. Y. (1974). *J. Biol. Chem.* **249**, 4943.

Lindner, A., Claasen, V., Hendriksen, R. W. J., and Krolt, R. (1963). *J. Med. Chem.* **6**, 97.

Liu, Y. P., and Cheung, W. Y. (1976). *J. Biol. Chem.* **251**, 4193.

Llinas, R., and Nicholson, C. (1975). *Proc. Natl. Acad. Sci. U.S.A.* **72**, 187.

Lowe, D. A., Richardson, B. P., Taylor, P., and Donatsch, P. (1976). *Nature (London)* **260**, 337.

Lucy, J. A. (1975). *In* "Cell Membranes" (G. Weissmann and R. Claiborne, eds.), p. 75. H. P. Publishing Co., New York.

McDonald, J. M., Bruns, D. E., and Jarett, L. (1976a). *Biochem. Biophys. Res. Commun.* **71**, 114.

McDonald, J. M., Bruns, D. E., and Jarett, L. (1976b). *Proc. Natl. Acad. Sci. U.S.A.* **73**, 1542.

McDonald, J. M., Bruns, D. E., and Jarett, L. (1976c). *J. Biol. Chem.* **251**, 5345.

McIntyre, J. A., Gilula, N. B., and Karnovsky, M. J. (1974). *J. Cell Biol.* **60**, 192.

Maggio, B., Ahkong, Q. F., and Lucy, J. A. (1976). *Biochem. J.* **158**, 647.

Malagodi, H., and Chiou, C. Y. (1974). *Eur. J. Pharmacol.* **27**, 25.

Malaisse-Lagae, F., Ravazzola, M., Amherdt, M., Gutzeit, A., Stauffacher, W., Malaisse, W. J., and Orci, J. (1975). *Diabetologia* **10**, 71.

Massini, P., and Luscher, E. F. (1974). *Biochim. Biophys. Acta* **372**, 109.

Matthews, E. K., and Nordman, J. J. (1976). *Mol. Pharmacol.* **12**, 778.

Meldolesi, J., Jamieson, J. D., and Palade, G. E. (1971). *J. Cell Biol.* **49**, 130.

Meldolesi, J., DeCamilli, P., and Peluchetti, D. (1975). *In* "Secretory Mechanisms of Exocrine Glands" (N. A. Thorn and O. H. Peterson, eds.), p. 137. Academic Press, New York.

Mellon, M. G., and Rebhun, L. I. (1976). *J. Cell Biol.* **70**, 226.

Michell, R. H. (1975). *Biochim. Biophys. Acta* **415**, 81.

Michell, R. H., and Jones, L. M. (1974). *Biochem. J.* **138**, 47.

Mockrin, S. C., and Spudich, J. A. (1976). *Proc. Natl. Acad. Sci. U.S.A.* **73**, 2321.

Mongar, J. L., and Svec, P. (1972). *Br. J. Pharmacol.* **46**, 741.

Murphy, D. B., and Borisy, G. C. (1975). *Proc. Natl. Acad. Sci. U.S.A.* **72**, 2696.

Murray, A. C., and Kay, C. M. (1972). *Biochemistry* **11**, 2622.

Murray, R. L., and Dubin, M. W. (1975). *J. Cell Biol.* **64**, 705.

Nakazato, Y., and Douglas, W. W. (1974). *Nature (London)* **249**, 479.

Nath, J., and Rebhun, L. I. (1976). *J. Cell Biol.* **68**, 440.

Nayler, W. G. (1963). *Am. J. Physiol.* **204**, 969.

Nicolson, G. I. (1976). *Biochim. Biophys. Acta* **457**, 57.

Nordmann, J. J., and Morris, J. F. (1976). *Nature (London)* **261**, 723.

Nordmann, J. J., Dreifuss, J. J., Baker, P. F., Ravazzola, M., Malaisse-Lagae, F., and Orci, L. (1974). *Nature (London)* **250**, 155.

Novikoff, A. B. (1976). *Proc. Natl. Acad. Sci. U.S.A.* **73**, 2781.

Novikoff, A. B., Yam, A., and Novikoff, P. M. (1975). *Proc. Natl. Acad. Sci. U.S.A.* **72**, 4501.

Ockleford, C. D. (1976). *J. Cell Biol.* **70**, 344a.

Ohnishi, S. I., and Ito, T. (1974). *Biochemistry* **13**, 881.

Oliver, J. M. (1975). *In* "Microtubules and Microtubule Inhibitions" (M. Borgers and M. de Brabander, eds.), p. 341. North-Holland Publ., Amsterdam.

Oliver, J. M., Zurier, R. B., and Berlin, R. D. (1975). *Nature (London)* **253**, 471.

Oliver, J. M., Krawiec, J. A., and Berlin, R. D. (1976a). *J. Cell Biol.* **69**, 205.

Oliver, J. M., Albertini, D. F., and Berlin, R. D. (1976b). *J. Cell Biol.* **71**, 921.

Olmsted, J. B., Marcum, J. M., Johnson, K. A., Allen, C., and Borisy, G. G. (1974). *J. Supramol. Struct.* **2**, 429.

Orci, L., and Perrelet, A. (1973). *Science* **181**, 868.

Oron, Y., Lowe, M., and Selinger, Z. (1973). *FEBS Lett.* **34**, 198.

Palade, G. (1975). *Science* **189**, 347.

Papahadjopoulos, D. (1972). *Biochim. Biophys. Acta* **265**, 169.

Papahadjopoulos, D., Poste, G., Schaeffer, B. E., and Vail, W. J. (1974). *Biochim. Biophys. Acta* **352**, 10.

Pappas, G. D. (1975). *In* "Cell Membranes" (G. Weissman and R. Claiborne, eds.), p. 87. H. P. Publishing Co., New York.

Patzelt, C., Singh, A., Le Marchand, Y., and Jeanrenaud, B. (1975). *In* "Microtubules and Microtubule Inhibitors" (M. Borgers and M. de Brabander, eds.), p. 165. North-Holland Publ., Amsterdam.

Pearse, B. M. F. (1975). *J. Mol. Biol.* **97**, 93.

Pearse, B. M. F. (1976). *Proc. Natl. Acad. Sci. U.S.A.* **73**, 1255.

Petersen, O. H. (1976). *Physiol. Rev.* **56**, 535.

Pinto da Silva, P., and Martinez-Palomo, A. (1974). *Nature (London)* **249**, 170.

Pipeleers, D. G., Pipeleers-Marichal, M. A., and Kipnis, D. M. (1976). *Science* **191**, 88.

Piperno, G., and Luck, D. J. (1976). *J. Biol. Chem.* **251**, 2161.

Piras, M. M., and Piras, R. (1974). *Eur. J. Biochem.* **47**, 443.

Piras, R., and Piras, M. M. (1975). *Proc. Natl. Acad. Sci. U.S.A.* **72**, 1161.

Plattner, H. (1974). *Nature (London)* **252**, 222.

Poisner, A. M. (1970). *Adv. Biochem. Psychopharmacol.* **2**, 95.

Pollard, H. B., Zinder, O., Hoffman, P. G., and Nikodejevic, O. (1976). *J. Biol. Chem.* **251**, 4544.

Pollard, T. D., and Weihing, R. R. (1974). *Crit. Rev. Biochem.* **2**, 1.

Poole, A. R., Howell, J. I., and Lucy, J. A. (1970). *Nature (London)* **227**, 810.

Poste, G., and Allison, A. C. (1973). *Biochim. Biophys. Acta* **300**, 421.

Poste, G., and Nicolson, G. (1976). *Biochim. Biophys. Acta* **426**, 148.

Poste, G., Papahadjopoulos, D., Jacobson, K., and Vail, W. J. (1975a). *Nature (London)* **253**, 552.

Poste, G., Papahadjopoulos, D., Jacobson, K., and Vail, W. J. (1975b). *Biochim. Biophys. Acta* **394**, 520.

Poste, G., Papahadjopoulos, D., and Nicolson, G. (1975c). *Proc. Natl. Acad. Sci. U.S.A.* **72**, 4430.

Putney, J. W. (1976). *J. Pharmacol. Exp. Ther.* **199**, 526.

Putney, J. W., Jr., Weiss, S. J., Leslie, B. A., and Marier, S. H. (1977). *J. Pharmacol. Exp. Ther.* **203**, 144.

Rasmussen, H. (1975). *In* "Cell Membranes" (G. Weissmann and R. Claiborne, eds.), p. 203. H. P. Publishing Co., New York.

Raz, A., and Goldman, R. (1974). *Nature (London)* **247**, 206.

Reed, P. W., and Lardy, H. A. (1972a). *J. Biol. Chem.* **247**, 6970.

Reed, P. W., and Lardy, H. A. (1972b). *In* "The Role of Membranes in Metabolic Regulation" (M. A. Mehlman and R. W. Hanson, eds.), p. 111. Academic Press, New York.

Robinson, I. C. A. F., Russell, J. T., and Thorn, N. A. (1976). *Acta Endocrinol. (Copenhagen)* **83**, 36.

Rojas, E., and Tobias, J. M. (1965). *Biochim. Biophys. Acta* **94**, 394.

Rose, B., and Loewenstein, W. R. (1975). *Nature (London)* **254**, 250.

Rose, B., and Loewenstein, W. R. (1976). *J. Membr. Biol.* **28**, 87.

Rothman, S. S. (1975). *Science* **190**, 747.

Rothman, S. S. (1976). *Am. J. Physiol.* **20**, 1499.

Rubin, R. P. (1974). "Calcium and the Secretory Process." Plenum, New York.

Rubin, R. W., and Weiss, G. D. (1975). *J. Cell Biol.* **64**, 42.

Russell, J. T., Thorn, N. A., and Warberg, J. (1974). *Acta Endocrinol. (Copenhagen)* **77**, 691.

Rutten, W. J., DePont, J. J. H. H. M., Bonting, S. L., and Daemen, F. J. M. (1975). *Eur. J. Biochem.* **54**, 259.

Samson, F. (1976). *Annu. Rev. Pharmacol. Toxicol.* **16**, 143.

Sandoval, I. V., and Cuatrecasas, P. (1976). *Nature (London)* **262**, 511.

Satir, B. (1974a). *Symp. Soc. Exp. Biol.* **28**, 399.

Satir, B. (1974b). *J. Supramol. Struct.* **2**, 529.

Satir, B., Schooley, C., and Satir, P. (1972). *Nature (London)* **235**, 53.

Scarpa, A., Baldassare, J., and Inesi, G. (1972). *J. Gen. Physiol.* **60**, 735.

Scarpa, A., Malmstrom, K., Chiesi, M., and Carafoli, E. (1976). *J. Membr. Biol.* **29**, 205.

Scheele, G. A., and Palade, G. E. (1975). *J. Biol. Chem.* **250**, 2660.

Schliwa, M. (1976). *J. Cell Biol.* **70**, 527.

Schramm, M., and Selinger, Z. (1975). *J. Cyclic Nucleotide Res.* **1**, 186.

Schramm, M., Selinger, Z., Salomon, Y., Eytan, E., and Batzri, S. (1972). *Nature (London), New Biol.* **240**, 203.

Schreurs, V. V. A. M., Swarts, H. G. P., DePont, J. J. H. H. M., and Bonting, S. L. (1976). *Biochim. Biophys. Acta* **419**, 320.

Schudt, C., and Pette, D. (1975). *FEBS Lett.* **59**, 36.

Schudt, C., Dahl, G., and Gratzl, M. (1976). *Cytobiologie* **13**, 211.

Selinger, Z., and Naim, E. (1970). *Biochim. Biophys. Acta* **203**, 335.

Selinger, Z., Naim, E., and Lasser, M. (1970). *Biochim. Biophys. Acta* **203**, 326.

Selinger, Z., Batzri, S., Eimerl, S., and Schramm, M. (1973). *J. Biol. Chem.* **248**, 369.

Selinger, Z., Eimerl, A., and Schramm, M. (1974). *Proc. Natl. Acad. Sci. U.S.A.* **71**, 128.

Serck-Hanssen and Christiansen, E. N. (1973). *Biochim. Biophys. Acta* **307**, 404.

Sharma, V. N. (1962). *Arch. Int. Pharmacodyn. Ther.* **137**, 140.

Sharoni, Y., Eimerl, S., and Schramm, M. (1976). *J. Cell Biol.* **71**, 107.

Shelanski, M. L., Gaskin, F., and Cantor, C. R. (1973). *Proc. Natl. Acad. Sci. U.S.A.* **70**, 765.

Sheterline, P., and Schofield, J. G. (1975). *FEBS Lett.* **56**, 297.

Shuman, H., and Somlyo, A. P. (1976). *Proc. Natl. Acad. Sci. U.S.A.* **73**, 1193.

Shuman, H., Somlyo, A. V., and Somlyo, A. P. (1976). *Ultramicroscopy* **1**, 317.

Slaby, F., and Bryan, J. (1976). *J. Biol. Chem.* **251**, 5078.

Sloboda, R. D., Rudolph, S. A., Rosenbaum, J. L., and Greengard, P. (1975). *Proc. Natl. Acad. Sci. U.S.A.* **72**, 177.

Smith, D. S. (1971). *Philos. Trans. R. Soc. London, Ser. B* **261**, 395.

Smith, D. S., Jarlfors, U., and Berinek, R. (1970). *J. Cell Biol.* **46**, 199.

Smith, D. S., Jarlfors, U., and Cameron, B. F. (1975). *Ann. N.Y. Acad. Sci.* **253**, 472.

Snyder, J. A., and McIntosh, J. R. (1976). *Annu. Rev. Biochem.* **45**, 699.

Soifer, D. (1975). *J. Neurochem.* **24**, 21.

Somers, G., Devis, G., Van Obberghen, E., and Malaisse, W. J. (1976). *Endocrinology* **99**, 114.

Stevens, F. C., Walsh, M., Ho, H. C., Teo, T. S., and Wang, J. H. (1976). *J. Biol. Chem.* **251**, 4495.

Tada, M., Kirchberger, M. A., and Katz, A. M. (1975). *J. Biol. Chem.* **250**, 2640.

Taylor, A., Maffly, R., Wilson, L., and Reaven, E. (1975). *Ann. N.Y. Acad. Sci.* **253**, 723.

Teo, T. S., and Wang, T. H. (1973). *J. Biol. Chem.* **248**, 5950.

Teo, T. S., Wang, T. H., and Wang, J. H. (1973). *J. Biol. Chem.* **248**, 588.

Theodosis, D. T., Dreifuss, J. J., Harris, M. C., and Orci, L. (1976). *J. Cell Biol.* **70**, 294.

Thoa, N. B., Costa, J. L., Moss, J., and Kapin, I. J. (1974). *Life Sci.* **14**, 1795.

Trump, B. F. (1975). *In* "Cell Membranes" (G. Weissmann and R. Claiborne, eds.), p. 123. H. P. Publishing Co., New York.

Van Breeman, C., Farinas, B. R., Gerba, R., and McNaughton, E. D. (1972). *Circ. Res.* **30**, 44.

Van der Kloot, W., and Kita, H. (1973). *J. Membr. Biol.* **14**, 365.

Verwey, E. J. W., and Overbeck, P. T. G. (1948). "The Theory of Stability of Lyophobic Colloid." Elsevier, Amsterdam.

Victoria, E. J., Van Golde, L. M. G., Hosteller, K. Y., Scherphof, G. L., and Van Deenen, L. L. M. (1971). *Biochim. Biophys. Acta* **239**, 443.

Vos, J., Ahkong, Q. F., Bothman, G. M., Quirk, S. J., and Lucy, J. A. (1976). *Biochem. J.* **158**, 651.

Wade, J. B., DiScala, V. A., and Karnovsky, M. J. (1975). *J. Membr. Biol.* **22**, 385.

Watson, E. L., Siegel, I. A., and Robinovitch, M. R. (1974). *Experientia* **30**, 876.

Watterson, D. M., Harrelson, W. G., Jr., Keller, P. M., Sharief, F., and Vanaman, T. C. (1976). *J. Biol. Chem.* **251**, 4501.

Weihing, R. R. (1976). *J. Cell Biol.* **71**, 303.

Weingarten, M. D., Lockwood, A. H., Hwo, S. Y., and Kirschner, M. W. (1975). *Proc. Natl. Acad. Sci. U.S.A.* **72**, 1858.

Weisenberg, R. C. (1972). *Science* **177**, 1104.

Weiss, G. B. (1974). *Annu. Rev. Pharmacol.* **14**, 343.

White, D. W., and Hawthorne, J. N. (1970). *Biochem. J.* **120**, 533.

Williams, J. A. (1975). *Am. J. Physiol.* **229**, 1023.

Williams, J. A., and Lee, M. (1974). *Biochem. Biophys. Res. Commun.* **60**, 542.

Willingham, M. C., and Pastan, I. (1975). *J. Cell Biol.* **67**, 146.

Wilson, L. (1976). *Life Sci.* **17**, 303.

Wilson, L., and Bryan, J. (1974). *Adv. Cell Mol. Biol.* **3**, 21.

CHAPTER 3

The Somatomedins and Their Actions

Judson J. Van Wyk and Louis E. Underwood

I. INTRODUCTION

The somatomedins are a family of insulin-like peptides which are potent mitogens for a variety of cell lines. Their growth-hormone dependency and ability to stimulate sulfate incorporation into proteoglycans of cartilage led to the original, but as yet unproven, hypothesis that they mediate the actions of somatotropin on skeletal growth (Salmon and Daughaday, 1957).

Although the somatomedins have been the subject of intense interest since their existence was first postulated two decades ago, it is still not known how these substances are produced, how many of them may exist, or what their precise role may be, either in normal physiology or in pathological states. The supplies of these peptides have been so limited that it has not yet been possible to carry out significant *in vivo* studies; furthermore, many of the *in vitro* studies reported have been carried out with highly impure preparations. For these reasons, inferences that these substances may play a critical role in somatic growth (and possibly also in tissue differentiation, wound healing, organ regeneration, aging, and neoplastic growth) are at the present time only speculative in nature. Substance for such speculations, however, is provided by documentation that purified somatomedins possess powerful mitogenic properties in isolated cell systems, and by certain impressive correlations which have been established between growth rates in children and their serum somatomedin levels.

The slow progress in establishing the chemical structure of these substances and obtaining sufficient quantities of pure material for adequate biological studies stems from the fact that no organ has been identified in which somatomedins are stored. For this reason, large quantities of blood have been required for their purification.

It is now generally agreed that to belong in the somatomedin group of peptides, a substance must fulfill three criteria: its concentration in serum must be growth-hormone dependent, it must possess insulin-like actions in extraskeletal tissues, and it must promote the incorporation of sulfate into proteoglycans of cartilage. Four peptides which meet these three criteria have been described: somatomedin A (Hall, 1972; Uthne, 1973), somatomedin C (Van Wyk *et al.*, 1974), nonsuppressible insulin-like activity (NSILA-s) (Froesch *et al.*, 1967; Jakob *et al.*, 1968), and multiplication stimulating activity (MSA) (Pierson and Temin, 1972). Although it is possible that one or more of these substances may ultimately prove to be the same molecular species, each of them has slightly different reported chemical properties. In this review the generic term *somatomedin* will be used when describing properties believed to be shared by all these substances, and the names of the specific somatomedins will be used where required to avoid ambiguity.

II. HISTORY OF THE SOMATOMEDINS

Bioassay systems based on three different phenomena were utilized to isolate the four somatomedins enumerated above and only later was the kinship between these substances recognized. An appreciation of these historical origins is necessary to understand the confusing nomenclature currently in use.

A. THE SULFATION FACTOR PHENOMENON: SOMATOMEDIN A AND SOMATOMEDIN C

The cardinal effect of growth-hormone administration is stimulation of skeletal growth. The classic assay for growth hormone is based on the observation that narrowing of the cartilaginous plates at the epiphyses of the long bones follows hypophysectomy, whereas widening occurs in response to growth-hormone administration (Greenspan *et al.*, 1949). Following growth-hormone administration, all cartilaginous tissues share in a generalized metabolic response. One of the earliest of these responses to be studied was the stimulation of radioactive sulfate incorporation into proteoglycans of cartilage (Ellis *et al.*, 1953). It was subsequently shown that growth-hormone administration also stimulates the synthesis of new DNA, RNA, collagen, and other proteins in this tissue (Section V,A).

In the course of attempts to devise a more sensitive bioassay for growth hormone, Salmon and Daughaday (1957) made their classic observation that the incorporation of $^{35}SO_4$ into cartilage explants is not increased by *in vitro* incubation with growth hormone itself, but is increased by the addition of either normal serum or serum from hypophysectomized rats which had been treated with growth hormone. Serum from untreated hypophysectomized animals had little or no effect on sulfate incorporation in this test system. Because growth hormone is itself inactive in this assay, it was postulated that the growth-promoting actions of growth hormone on the skeleton are mediated through a "sulfation factor" which is either derived from growth hormone itself or induced *in vivo* by growth-hormone action. These workers subsequently showed that a growth-hormone-dependent factor in serum could replicate *in vitro* all the metabolic effects on cartilage observed *in vivo* when growth hormone is administered to the living animal (Section V,A). Because of the possibility that the factor stimulating the growth of cellular matrix might be different from the factor stimulating cell proliferation, several workers introduced the term "thymidine factor" (Van den Brande *et al.*, 1971; Raben *et al.*, 1972) to differentiate the serum component(s) responsible for initiating DNA synthesis in cartilage from that component (or components) responsible for stimulating the synthesis of mature cell products. During the purification of serum, however, it has proven impossible to separate "thymidine factor" activity from "sulfation factor" activity (Van Wyk *et al.*, 1971, 1974); furthermore, it was shown by Hall and Uthne (1971) that the "insulin-like" activity of serum, as measured in the epididymal fat pad, also parallels the "sulfation factor" activity of serum. As a result of these and other studies, the original provisional designations became entirely too constrictive and the more open-ended term "somatomedin" was introduced as a generic designation for these biological activities (Daughaday *et al.*, 1972).

Somatomedin A was initially isolated as a sulfation factor using as an assay the incorporation of $^{35}SO_4$ into pelvic rudiments of chick embryos (Hall, 1972). The isolation of somatomedin C was monitored by a dual isotope assay which depends on the simulation of both $^{35}SO_4$ and [^{3}H]thymidine into costal cartilage segments from young hypophysectomized rats (Van Wyk *et al.*, 1974).

B. Nonsuppressible Insulin-Like Activity (NSILA)

Prior to the introduction of the radioimmunoassay for measuring insulin concentrations in plasma, a variety of sensitive *in vitro* biological assays had been introduced for this purpose. The most sensitive of these assays was the oxidation of [^{14}C]glucose to $^{14}CO_2$ in rat adipose tissue (Winegrad *et al.*, 1959). In 1959, Leonards called attention to the fact that less than 10% of the total insulin-like activity of serum, as measured by this bioassay, could be neutralized by antibodies to insulin itself (Leonards, 1959). That portion of the serum insulin-like activity which could not be inhibited by insulin antibodies *in vitro* was designated "bound" insulin by Antoniades (1961), "atypical" insulin by Samaan *et al.* (1962), and "nonsuppressible insulin-like" activity (NSILA) by Froesch *et al.* (1963).

Starting with a Cohn fraction of outdated human plasma, the group working with Froesch in Zurich showed that a small portion of the insulin-like activity could be extracted into cold acid ethanol (NSILA-s), whereas a majority of this activity was precipitated by this treatment and remained insoluble (NSILA-p) (Jakob *et al.*, 1968). NSILA-s was found to be a single-chain peptide of 7500 daltons containing one or more intrachain disulfide bridges (Humbel *et al.*, 1970). In 1972 Raben *et al.* reported that NSILA-s is a powerful stimulant of $^{35}SO_4$ and [^{3}H]thymidine uptake by cartilage. This finding was later confirmed by Schlumpf *et al.* (1976), who also showed that serum concentrations of NSILA-s are growth-hormone dependent, thus fulfilling all the requirements of a somatomedin.

C. Multiplication Stimulating Activity (MSA)

1. Serum MSA

Under usual conditions of cell culture, most animal cell lines will not proliferate unless the medium is fortified with macromolecular components usually supplied by calf serum or fetal calf serum (Temin *et al.*, 1972). Multiplication stimulating activity (MSA) is the term applied by Pierson and Temin (1972) to describe the mitogenic activity of calf serum. They reported a 6000-fold purification of MSA over native calf serum as judged by potency in stimulating [^{3}H]thymidine incorporation by chick fibroblasts. Although not fully isolated, this preparation possessed nonsuppressible insulin-like activity for rat adipose cells and was likewise active in stimulating radioactive sulfate uptake by hypophysectomized rat cartilage. Cohen *et al.* (1975) subsequently found that the MSA activity of rat serum, as judged by the chick embryo fibroblast assay, was diminished following hypophysectomy and at least partially restored by the administration of growth hormone. Thus, serum MSA likewise fulfills all the requirements of a somatomedin.

2. CRL-MSA

In 1973, Dulak and Temin (1973a,b) reported that peptides with multiplication stimulating activity could be recovered from serum-free culture medium in which a certain strain of rat hepatocytes had been grown. These cells had originally been cloned by Dr. Hayden Coon on the basis of their ability to proliferate in the total absence of serum. Peptides isolated from conditioned rat liver medium have been designated CRL-MSA to distinguish them from serum MSA. CRL-MSA has been found to possess insulin-like activity, to stimulate sulfate incorporation in cartilage, and to cross-react with cell membrane receptors for the other somatomedins (Nissley and Rechler, 1977). Thus, CRL-MSA likewise seems to fit into the family of somatomedins.

D. Related Peptides Not Qualifying as Somatomedins

1. Somatomedin B

Somatomedin B is the designation given a serum peptide which induces thymidine incorporation in cultures of human glial-like cells, but which is inactive in sulfation factor assays (Uthne, 1973; Westermark *et al.*, 1975). This peptide was discovered during the purification of human plasma for sulfation factor activity and was found to have a molecular weight of 5400 daltons and to be more acidic than insulin (Fryklund *et al.*, 1974a). Uthne showed by bioassay (1973) and Yalow by immunoassay (Yalow *et al.*, 1975) that this peptide is partially growth-hormone dependent. Although it thus qualified as a somatomedin under the broad definition in use at the time, the designation of this peptide as a somatomedin is unfortunate as it lacks any activity in cartilage explants and fails to cross-react with other members of the somatomedin family in radioligand assays.

2. *Nonsuppressible Insulin-Like Protein (NSILP)*

Using nondenaturing systems of purification, Poffenbarger (1975) has been successful in isolating an insulin-like protein of approximately 90,000 daltons from normal human serum. This protein possesses about $1/10$ the specific activity of NSILA-s in epididymal fat pad assays, and it is devoid of activity in sulfation factor assays. Although NSILP may represent a bound form of NSILA-s or of another somatomedin, its apparent lack of activity in cartilage assays militates against this possiblity. Final judgment on the relationship, if any, of NSILP to the somatomedins must be reserved, however, until this protein has been tested more rigorously in a variety of test systems.

III. ISOLATION AND CHEMISTRY OF THE SOMATOMEDINS

A. METHODS OF ASSAY

Until recently, purification of the somatomedins required monitoring by cumbersome and imprecise bioassay techniques utilizing cartilage, adipose tissue, or fibroblast cultures (Section II). Following the demonstration that somatomedin C cross-reacts with the insulin receptor on cell membranes (Hintz *et al.*, 1972) and also has its own specific cell membrane receptor (Marshall *et al.*, 1974), it has been possible to monitor purification either by a radioreceptor assay for insulin-like activity or by a much more sensitive and specific radioreceptor assay for somatomedin C itself. All the somatomedins have subsequently been found to cross-react with the insulin receptor as well as with their own more specific receptors (Sections V,C and VI). The radioimmunoassay for somatomedin, recently described by Furlanetto *et al.* (1977), is the first and so far the only immunoassay for one of the somatomedins.[*]

Serum concentrations of somatomedin are expressed as units/ml relative to a reference standard. Traditionally, the standard consists of a pool of

---

[*]Yalow *et al.* (1975) have described an immunoassay for somatomedin B. The reasons for not including this peptide in the somatomedin family as currently defined are given in Section II, D.

serum obtained from healthy young adult males and arbitrarily assigned a potency of 1 unit/ml. The actual potency of such standards varies enormously among laboratories and even from batch to batch in the same laboratory.

B. STARTING MATERIAL AND INITIAL CONCENTRATING STEPS

The isolation of the somatomedins in pure form has depended on access to large volumes of outdated plasma as starting material. Somatomedin is remarkably stable in plasma. The activity is retained for a considerable period of time at 4°C and is not affected by freezing and thawing or by lyophilization. It is also stable to boiling (Koumans and Daughaday, 1963; Salmon and DuVall, 1970b). It retains biological activity after storage at pH 3 but is less stable in highly alkaline solutions. When human plasma is applied at neutral pH to Sephadex gels of different cross-linkage, the somatomedin activity is recovered in fractions with molecular sizes greater than growth hormone (Daughaday and Kipnis, 1966; Bürgi et al., 1966; Van den Brande et al., 1971; Bala et al., 1976). Under the same conditions, plasma somatomedin activity is excluded by Amicon XM 100 ultrafiltration membranes (Van Wyk et al., 1971). After extraction by acid–ethanol or by acid alone, somatomedin activity is recovered after gel filtration in the peptide fractions between 5000 and 10,000 daltons (Bürgi et al., 1966; Jakob et al., 1968; Van Wyk et al., 1971; Hall, 1972).

The most common starting material for the isolation of the somatomedins has been Cohn fraction IV (or its equivalent) rather than whole plasma. The content of somatomedin in the various Cohn fractions as measured by the radioreceptor assay for somatomedin C is shown in Table I. In the case of

TABLE I

ANALYSIS OF COHN FRACTIONS OF OUTDATED PLASMA BY
SOMATOMEDIN C RADIORECEPTOR ASSAY[a]

Preparation	Somatomedin (units/liter)	Recovery (%)
Original plasma	504	100
Cohn fraction I	27.3	5.4
Cohn fraction II	0.5	0.01
Cohn fraction III	44.5	8.8
Cohn fraction IV-4	423.0	83.9
Cohn fraction V	29.1	5.7

[a] The Cohn fractions were a gift of Dr. Joseph P. Dailey, Armour Pharmaceutical Company. (From Van Wyk et al., 1975.)

somatomedin A, somatomedin C, and NSILA-s, the starting Cohn fraction was initially extracted with cold acid–ethanol. Following removal of the bulky isoelectric precipitate which formed during neutralization, the proteins and peptides remaining in the supernatant fraction were precipitated at $-20°C$ with a mixture of acetone and ethanol. Although these initial procedures result in a 100-fold purification or greater, the losses of activity have been substantial and the possibility of chemical alteration has not been excluded. For these reasons, the initial acid–ethanol step has now been abandoned by some laboratories in favor of simple extraction of the starting Cohn fraction by acid (Rinderknecht and Humbel, 1976; Van Wyk *et al.*, to be published).

C. ISOLATION AND CHEMICAL CHARACTERISTICS OF THE INDIVIDUAL SOMATOMEDINS

1. *Somatomedin A₁ and A₂*

Somatomedin A was initially isolated by Hall (1972) and later by Uthne (1973) from acid–ethanol extracts of Cohn fraction IV. These extracts were further purified on Sephadex G-75 and Dowex 50 followed by sequential high-voltage electrophoresis at pH 6.5, pH 3.6, and pH 2.0. Although these procedures yielded high degrees of purification (reported as 2×10^5 to 2×10^6-fold), insufficient material was obtained for further chemical characterization. Fryklund *et al.* (1974a,b) modified the procedure by eliminating the Dowex step and substituting preparative cellulose column electrophoresis at pH 7.5 and pH 5 for the high-voltage electrophoresis steps used by Uthne and Hall. By this procedure, two closely similar peptides were isolated, somatomedin A₁ and somatomedin A₂, each having 60–63 amino acid residues (Fryklund *et al.*, 1974b). Both are neutral peptides with an asparagine at the amino terminus. Each contains only a single half-cystine. This finding is unique for somatomedin A because all the other somatomedins contain at least one disulfide bond.

2. *Somatomedin C*

Somatomedin C was initially isolated from acid–ethanol extracts of Cohn fraction IV of outdated human plasma (Van Wyk *et al.*, 1974).* This procedure was subsequently modified by substituting phosphoric acid as the extractant followed by concentration of the extracts by chromatography on SP

---

*We are indebted to Professor Bertil Aberg, Vice-President and Director of Research, AB Kabi Laboratories, Stockholm, Sweden, for providing acid ethanol extracts of Cohn fraction IV.

Sephadex.* Subsequent isoelectrofocusing reveals that the somatomedin activity in these extracts is accounted for by two major components, one of which is distributed over a broad band in the pH range 6.3–8.0 and another which focuses in the basic region between pH 8.2 and 8.8. Both of these components are detected in cartilage bioassays for "sulfation factor" and "thymidine factor" activity and by a radioreceptor assay for somatomedin C (Van Wyk *et al.*, 1975). Because the largest portion of the biological activity in the rat cartilage assay is found in the basic region, this component was further purified by a combination of narrow-range isoelectric focusing, high pressure liquid chromatography, and by a final chromatographic step on Sephadex G-50 in 1 *M* acetic acid or 0.2 *M* formic acid. Preparative electrophoresis on polyacrylamide gel, as described in earlier preparative schemes, has proven unnecessary to achieve homogeneity.

Somatomedin C is a basic peptide of about 63 amino acid residues and contains one or more disulfide bridges which are required for its biological activity. The modified purification scheme, amino acid composition, and partial amino acid sequence will be published elsewhere (Van Wyk *et al.*, in preparation).

Phosphoric acid extracts of Cohn fraction IV yield somewhat higher quantities of neutral components, as detected by the somatomedin C radioreceptor assay, than reported previously in acid–ethanol extracts of the same material (Van Wyk *et al.*, 1974, 1975). By both methods of extraction, however, the neutral fractions contain considerably more insulin-like activity (as defined by reactivity in an insulin radioreceptor assay) than do the basic fractions (Fig. 1). Conversely, nearly all the somatomedin C activity detectable by a specific radioimmunoassay for somatomedin C is found between pH 8.2 and 8.8. Additional evidence for two naturally occurring somatomedins was obtained by passing extracts of Cohn fraction IV over an affinity column of Sepharose 4B complexed with antibodies raised against somatomedin C. Subsequent isofocusing of the nonadsorbed and adsorbed material demonstrated that the somatomedin recognized by the antibody is exclusively basic, whereas that not adsorbed to the column has an isoelectric point near neutrality.

Efforts to convert neutral somatomedin into basic somatomedin have so far not been successful. These findings suggest that extracts of Cohn fraction IV contain at least two natively occurring somatomedins: neutral somatomedin, which is richer in insulin-like activity, and basic somatomedin, which is

*We are indebted to Dr. Joseph P. Dailey, Vice-President and Director of Research, Armour Laboratories, Kankakee, Illinois, and to Dr. Robert Schlueter, Department of Biochemical Research, for providing Cohn fraction IV and carrying out the initial purification steps.

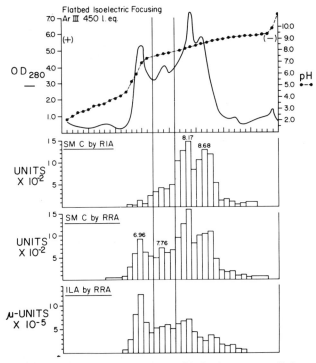

FIG. 1. Isoelectric focusing profile of an extract of Cohn fraction IV. All the acidic fraction and a large portion of the neutral fraction (containing most of the substances detected by the insulin receptor assay) had been removed in a prior step. The somatomedin (SM) content of each fraction was measured by radioimmunoassay (top bar graph) and by a radioreceptor assay (middle bar graph) using a particulate fraction of human placental membranes as receptor and [^{125}I]somatomedin C as radioligand. Insulin-like activity (bottom bar graph) was measured by an insulin radioreceptor assay using porcine insulin as standard. (From Van Wyk *et al.*, 1977.)

richer in growth-promoting activity in cartilage. These substances must have a high degree of similarity, however, because both components are recognized by the somatomedin C receptor, even though only the basic component is recognized by the more specific radioimmunoassay for somatomedin C.

The suggestion in Fig. 1 that there are several forms of basic somatomedin with slightly differing isoelectric points has been a consistent finding. We believe this represents microheterogeneity involving a few amino acid residues rather than completely different forms of somatomedin. Similar microheterogeneity has been described for somatomedin A, CRL-MSA, and NSILA. This has created major difficulties in isolating sufficient quantities of homogenous peptides for sequence analysis.

Liberti (1975) has found that in bovine serum most of the somatomedin activity by bioassay in rat cartilage isofocuses in a manner similar to human somatomedin C, with only 2% focusing between pH 6.0 and 6.7. G. H. Sato (personal communication) has found a similar pattern in bovine blood meal. Chochinov *et al.* (1977) found only basic somatomedin in the serum from rats bearing growth-hormone-producing tumors. These rats had very high somatomedin levels, virtually all of which was induced by growth hormone. This finding suggests that in the rat, growth-hormone-dependent somatomedin has a molecular size similar to that of human somatomedin C.

3. *NSILA-s, NSILA I (IGF I), and NSILA II (IGF II)*

In 1970, Humbel *et al.* reported the details of a procedure for isolating NSILA-s from acid–ethanol extracts of Cohn fraction B of outdated plasma (Humbel *et al.*, 1970). Provisional compositional studies suggested that NSILA-s is a single chain peptide of 7500 daltons. After reduction and alkylation, it was found to contain seven half-cystine residues.

Using a revised scheme of purification, this group reported in 1976 the isolation of two closely related peptides: NSILA I, with a calculated molecular weight of 5757, and NSILA II, with a calculated molecular weight of 5904 (Rinderknecht and Humbel, 1976a). After reduction and alkylation, both peptides were found to contain 4 half-cystine residues but no free SH groups in the native peptides. These findings suggest two disulfide bridges, one or more of which appear to be essential for biological activity. Preliminary data on the amino acid sequences of the two peptides suggest that the two forms of NSILA are homologs. Twenty-two of the first 31 residues are identical in NSILA I and NSILA II (Rinderknecht and Humbel, 1976b). Furthermore, approxmately half of the amino acids in these segments are homologous with the B chain of insulin. The two NSILA peptides are equally active in stimulating [^{3}H]thymidine DNA of chick embryo fibroblasts and in stimulating [^{14}C]glucose into $^{14}CO_2$ in rat epididymal fat pad assays.

It is perhaps significant that the procedures used for the isolation of NSILA I and NSILA II differ considerably from the procedures described earlier for the isolation of NSILA-s. The acid–ethanol extraction procedure was eliminated in favor of simple extraction into 0.5 M acetic acid. This crude extract was further purified by a series of separations based on size using Sephadex G-75 and G-50. Separations based on charge were then accomplished by preparative SDS polyacrylamide gel electrophoresis and cation-exchange chromatography on SE Sephadex. Analytical isofocusing revealed the isoelectric point to be 8.2 ± 0.4. It is noteworthy that the Zurich group has now dropped the designations NSILA-s and NSILA-p from their nomenclature and now refer to their two peptides as insulin-like growth factor I (IGF I) and insulin-like growth factor II (IGF II).

4. MSA

Procedures developed by Pierson and Temin (1972) to isolate MSA from calf serum were based on methods previously used to isolate "bound insulin" and NSILA from serum (Antoniades, 1961; Búrgi et al., 1966). Whole calf serum was passed over Dowex 50 at neutral pH, and a fraction which was eluted at pH 11 was further purified by gel filtration on Bio-Gel P-100 and preparative polyacrylamide gel electrophoresis in an acid–urea system. As judged by potency in initiating DNA synthesis in stationary chick embryo fibroblasts, this preparation was 6000 times more potent than native calf serum/mg protein. The active principle was a small peptide of about 6000 daltons which was inactivated by dithiothreitol and periodate. The peptide had pronounced insulin-like activity and was active in sulfation factor assays. Further chemical characterization of this peptide fraction was not attempted.

The isolation of CRL-MSA (Dulak and Temin, 1973a) was based on the observation that certain strains of rat liver cells, which had been cloned on the basis of their ability to multiply in the absence of serum, produce one or more peptides with multiplication stimulating activity. The MSA concentration in such media is several times greater than in calf serum yet contains only 0.5% as much protein, 90% of which is contributed by tryptose contained in the culture media. Dulak and Temin utilized essentially the same steps which have been employed in purifying MSA from calf serum. One of the fractions eluted from preparative polyacrylamide gel was about four times more active (units/mg protein) in stimulating DNA synthesis in chick fibroblasts than the best preparation obtained from calf serum. Further analysis of this fraction by isoelectric focusing and SDS polyacrylamide gel electrophoresis revealed that MSA activity resides in a family of at least four polypeptides, all about 10,000 daltons in size (Dulak and Temin, 1973b). These peptides had isoelectric points of 5.7 (minor component), 6.2, and 7.0. These peptides were active in cartilage sulfation factor assays and in bioassays for nonsuppressible insulin-like activity, but were inactivated by mercaptoethanol and dithiothreitol, thus suggesting that intact disulfide bonds are required for biological activity.

Nissley and Rechler (1977) have recently confirmed the findings of Dulak and Temin and obtained a preparation of CRL-MSA in essentially pure form. This peptide, with an estimated molecular weight of 8700, is stable to boiling for 15 minutes at pH 5.5 and is inactivated by reduction and alkylation. Two or three cysteic acid residues were identified after performic acid oxidation. Preliminary amino acid composition revealed 1–2 tyrosine residues, 1 histidine, and no methionine or methionine sulfone. In a variety of test systems, this preparation of CRL-MSA did not differ from NSILA-s or somatomedin A in its biological activities and furthermore cross-reacted with cellular receptors for somatomedin A and NSILA.

D. Transport of Somatomedin in Serum

The concentration of somatomedin C in normal serum is probably in the range of 75–200 ng/ml (R. W. Furlanetto and J. J. Van Wyk, unpublished data), and similar estimates have been made for serum concentrations of NSILA-s (Froesch *et al.*, 1975) and somatomedin A (Hall, 1972). These concentrations are several orders of magnitude higher than the concentrations which are characteristic of most peptide hormones. Another difference between somatomedin and other peptide hormones is the much longer disappearance rate of the former group from serum: following intravenous administration or following hypophysectomy in the rat, the $t_{1/2}$ in plasma is about 2–4 hours (Daughaday *et al.*, 1968; Cohen and Nissley, 1976), whereas the $t_{1/2}$ for growth hormone, insulin, and other peptide hormones is about 20 minutes. These findings are compatible with the presence of a binding protein for somatomedin in native serum.

In native serum at neutral pH, the somatomedins are eluted in the void volume of Sephadex G-75, but if the same chromatographic procedure is carried out in acid, somatomedins can be identified only in the fractions containing peptides between 5000 and 9000 daltons in size. The molecular weights of these small peptides remain stable when rechromatographed at neutral pH in the absence of the large proteins (Jakob *et al.*, 1968; Hintz *et al.*, 1974a). Hintz *et al.* (1974a) showed that the large molecular weight fractions, which have been stripped of somatomedin activity by chromatography in acid, regain their ability to bind "small" somatomedin after neutralization.

On Sephadex G-200 at neutral pH, the endogenous somatomedin C in native serum elutes in two distinct peaks, with a major component corresponding in size to the gamma globulins or slightly smaller proteins and a minor component which elutes with the albumin fraction. Under these conditions, virtually no somatomedin activity (<2% of total activity) can be identified in the small molecular weight region (Fig. 2). Under similar chromatographic conditions, the elution pattern of NSILA in whole serum is similar to that of somatomedin C (Burgi *et al.*, 1966).

When serum is preincubated with [^{125}I]somatomedin C and chromatographed in a similar manner (Fig. 2), radioactivity is segregated into three peaks: a first small peak of radioactivity corresponding to the small peak of endogenous somatomedins; a second large peak corresponding to the secondary peak of endogenous somatomedin in the albumin region; and a third peak corresponding to free somatomedin. Binding of [^{125}I]somatomedin C to the two macromolecular peaks is both specific and saturable, because coincubation of [^{125}I]somatomedin C with small amounts of unlabeled somatomedin results in displacement of virtually all the radioactivity into the

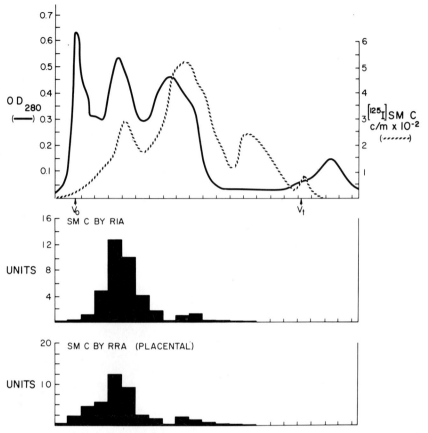

FIG. 2. Gel permeation chromatography of 40 ml of normal male serum on Sephadex G-200 (5 × 95 cm) in phosphate buffer. A preparation of [^{125}I]somatomedin C was freshly purified on an affinity column of somatomedin C antibody coupled to Sepharose 4-B and then incubated with the serum for 6 hours at 5°C before chromatography. Upper panel: protein profile (OD$_{280}$), and distribution of [^{125}I]somatomedin C (cpm/ml). Middle panel: somatomedin C by radioimmunoassay. Lower panel: radioreceptor assay for somatomedin C. (From Van Wyk *et al.*, 1977).

region of free somatomedin. Similar results have been described for the binding of [^{125}I]NSILA-s (Zapf *et al.*, 1975b). Zapf capitalized on the specificity of [^{125}I]NSILA-s binding to serum proteins by using this phenomenon as the basis for a sensitive competitive binding assay for NSILA.

Moses *et al.* (1976) have presented data that binding of [^{125}I]MSA to the γ-globulin fraction is totally lacking in the serum of hypophysectomized rats but is restored by the administration of growth hormone. Cohen and Nissley have further demonstrated that the $t_{1/2}$ of injected MSA into hypophysectomized rats is shortened to 8 minutes, whereas in normal or hypophysectomized rats treated with growth hormone it is more nearly 3 hours. These authors, therefore, suggested that it is the binding protein rather than the active small peptide which is under growth-hormone control.

Although the existence of specific saturable binding proteins for the somatomedins is unique among peptide hormones, specific carrier proteins for thyroxine and steroid hormones are well established. Total blood levels of the latter hormones are more dependent on the concentration of the binding proteins than on the secretory rates of the hormones themselves. Because this may also prove to be the case for the somatomedins, extreme caution should be used in ascribing alterations in total blood concentrations to changes in production rates of the active peptides.

IV. ORIGIN AND DEGRADATION OF THE SOMATOMEDINS

A. MECHANISM AND SITE OF PRODUCTION OF THE SOMATOMEDINS

Almost nothing is known about the mechanisms by which the somatomedins are produced or the role of growth hormone in their production. There is now considerable evidence, however, that the liver plays an important role in somatomedin production, although it is far from certain that this is the only source. Extracts of many tissues, including liver, contain only small amounts of somatomedin-like activity, thus suggesting that this hormone is either not stored, or is stored in the form of a biologically inactive prohormone. Following the administration of growth hormone to hypophysectomized rats or to hypopituitary patients, there is a 3- to 6-hour lag before any elevation of the serum somatomedin level can be detected (Hall, 1971), and normalization of serum levels may not occur for several days (Daughaday, 1975). The suggestion that growth hormone stimulates the formation of a binding hormone rather than somatomedin itself (Moses *et al.*, 1976) may provide a partial explanation for this lag. This explanation, however, still leaves unresolved the mechanism by which somatomedin itself is produced.

Because growth hormone is rapidly concentrated in the liver (Mayberry *et al.*, 1971) and the liver is one of the few organs which has been shown to respond to growth hormone *in vitro* (Jefferson and Korner, 1967), considerable attention has been directed to this organ as a potential site of somatomedin production. McConaghey and Sledge (1970) demonstrated that there was an increase in sulfation factor activity of Waymouth's medium which had been enriched with high concentrations of bovine growth hormone (10 μg/ml) and perfused through isolated rat liver. Control perfusates lacking growth hormone were considerably less active. Phillips *et al.* (1976) have repeated these studies with more quantitative bioassay techniques and found much smaller differences between perfusates containing or lacking growth hormone. McConaghey (1972) showed that somatomedin production in liver slices is enhanced by incubation in the presence of growth hormone.

None of the above incubation and perfusion studies clarifies the physiological role of growth hormone on somatomedin generation because the concentrations of growth hormone required to demonstrate an effect are two or three orders of magnitude greater than physiological levels. It is thus possible that the effects observed could be secondary to a nonspecific increase in the rate of protein synthesis. It is noteworthy that both insulin (Daughaday *et al.*, 1976) and ovine prolactin (Francis and Hill, 1975) have effects similar to growth hormone in liver perfusion experiments, and these effects are observed with more nearly physiological dosages of the latter two hormones than those required in the case of growth hormone.

Although the hormonal control mechanisms remain obscure, *in vivo* studies have provided additional evidence that the liver is indeed a major source of somatomedin production. Uthne and Uthne (1972) found a 75% reduction in serum somatomedin levels 6 hours after partial hepatectomy in the rat. These levels rose again in parallel with liver regeneration. Blood somatomedin levels are also depressed in humans with cirrhosis of the liver (Wu *et al.*, 1974; Giordano *et al.*, 1975).

Schimpff *et al.* (1976) have found that the content of somatomedin in the hepatic vein of dogs is significantly higher than the content in portal vein and peripheral vessels. Using Fick's principle based on hepatic blood flow, Schimpff calculated that hepatic somatomedin production in a dog could reach several milligrams daily. Similar arteriovenous differences across the liver have been obtained in studies on human subjects (Girard *et al.*, 1975).

Attempts to link the kidney with somatomedin generation have been inconclusive. Perfusates from normal rat kidneys are richer in somatomedin activity than perfusates from hypophysectomized rats, and in both groups of animals the somatomedin content of perfusates is higher if the medium is enriched with very high levels of bovine growth hormone (McConaghey and Dehnel, 1972). Reports of serum somatomedin levels in nephrectomized patients or in patients with advanced renal disease have been inconclusive and have not contributed to our understanding of the role of the kidney (Section VII, D).

B. Degradation of the Somatomedins

Daughaday *et al.* (1968) followed the disappearance of sulfation factor activity from the serum of rats following hypophysectomy and estimated the serum half-life to be about three hours. A. J. D'Ercole (unpublished) found that [^{125}I]somatomedin C has a $t_{1/2}$ of 120 minutes in both the pregnant dog and normal rat. Cohen and Nissley (1976) also found a 2- to 4-hour half-life for serum multiplication activity in hypophysectomized rats injected with normal rat serum, but a half-life of less than 20 minutes when hypophysectomized rats were injected with serum lacking the binding protein (Section III,D).

D'Ercole *et al.* (1977a) have studied the degradation of somatomedin C by membrane preparations from various tissues and found the kidney to be many times richer in this activity than any other tissue. In rat kidney, somatomedin C degrading activity takes two forms: the first, thought to be a sulfhydryl protease, is associated with the plasma membrane fraction and is highly specific for somatomedin C ($K_m = 1.6 \times 10^{-8}\ M$); the second form is found in cytosol and can degrade somatomedin C only after reduction ($K_m = 6.3 \times 10^{-8}\ M$). Comparative studies with insulin degradation suggest that the somatomedin C degrading activity in cytosol is attributable to the insulin–glucagon protease. In cytosol, somatomedin C acts as a competitive inhibitor of insulin degradation with a K_i of $6 \times 10^{-9}\ M$, and insulin also inhibits somatomedin degradation. In kidney plasma membranes, insulin does not appear to inhibit somatomedin degrading activity. NSILA-s has been reported to be an inhibitor of the insulin degradation by a liver mem-

TABLE II

Inhibition of Insulin Degradation by Chemically Modified Somatomedin C[a]

Preparation	K_i (nM)	Activity in somatomedin C radioreceptor assay (%)
Intact somatomedin C	5.9	100
Performic acid oxidized	8.3	0
Reduced and aminoethylated	11.9	0
Reduced and aminoethylated + CnBR treated	37.8	0
Reduced and aminoethylated + trypsinized	52.8	0

[a] The rate of insulin degradation by rat kidney cytosol was determined in the presence of intact somatomedin C or one of the somatomedin C preparations listed. K_i was determined from Lineweaver–Burk plots. Activity in somatomedin C radioreceptor assays was determined by inhibition of the specific binding of [^{125}I]somatomedin C to human placental membranes. (From D'Ercole *et al.*, 1977b.)

brane preparation (Kahn *et al.*, 1976) and by preparations of insulin–glucagon protease (Duckworth, 1976; Burghen *et al.*, 1976).

Studies of chemically modified somatomedin C suggest that the active sites on the molecule required for binding to cell membranes (and presumably, therefore, for biological activity) are different from those portions of the molecule required for inhibiting insulin degradation (D'Ercole *et al.*, 1977a). Activity in radioreceptor assays was abolished by performic acid oxidation and by reduction and aminoethylation, whereas the capacity to inhibit insulin degradation was only moderately decreased by these procedures. Some insulin degrading activity of aminoethylated somatomedin C was even preserved after cleavage with trypsin or cyanogen bromide (Table II).

V. *IN VITRO* BIOLOGICAL EFFECTS OF THE SOMATOMEDINS

A. BIOLOGICAL EFFECTS IN CARTILAGE

The mechanisms by which hormones regulate cartilage growth continue to be of particular interest because linear growth of the skeleton is dependent on proliferation of cartilage in the epiphyseal plate. Fortunately, cartilage offers several unique features which facilitate its study *in vitro*. In addition to having no intrinsic blood supply, it contains only one cell type. Cartilage can survive for days on atmospheric oxygen because of its efficient anaerobic glycolysis. Finally, abundant sources of cartilage are readily accessible.

The now classic studies of Salmon and Daughaday (1957), in which the "sulfation factor" phenomenon was first brought into focus (Section II,A), were followed by a series of studies showing that a growth-hormone-dependent serum factor also controls the rate of synthesis of collagen in cartilage (Daughaday and Mariz, 1962) and the incorporation of [³H]thymidine into DNA (Daughaday and Reeder, 1967). Salmon and DuVall (1970a) subsequently showed that a serum fraction with sulfation factor activity also stimulates the incorporation of uridine into RNA and leucine into cartilage protein–polysaccharide complexes. Although all these biochemical responses in cartilage have not been studied with pure preparations of somatomedin, it has been conclusively shown that a single pure peptide stimulates in a dose-dependent manner incorporation of both sulfate into proteoglycans and thymidine into DNA (Fig. 3).

1. Mechanism of Somatomedin Action on Cartilage

Using cartilaginous pelvic rudiments from 10-day-old chick embryos, Adamson and Anast (1966) confirmed the growth-hormone dependency of

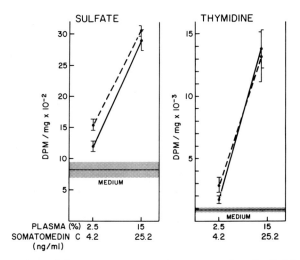

FIG. 3. Comparison of dose–response curves to pure somatomedin C (●- - -●) and to pooled plasma from normal adult males (●———●) in standard cartilage assay for somatomedin activity. The uptakes of $^{35}SO_4$ per mg and [^{3}H]thymidine per mg (± SEM) are plotted on the ordinates of the left- and right-hand panels, respectively, and the test concentrations of plasma and somatomedin C on the abscissas. Uptakes were measured in costal cartilage explants from hypophysectomized rats. (From Van Wyk *et al.*, 1977.)

the sulfate-incorporating activity in rat serum. They further observed that sulfate incorporation into proteoglycans is dependent on protein synthesis, because both sulfate incorporation and protein synthesis are inhibited by either puromycin or actinomycin D. Depletion of the incubation medium of Na^+ or K^+, or the addition of ouabain, also caused a striking diminution of sulfate uptake. It was suggested from these studies that the stimulatory effect of the serum sulfation factor on the incorporation of sulfate by cartilage is the end result of a cascade of intracellular events that begins with the stimulation of potassium-dependent amino acid transport, goes on to include stimulation of amino acid incorporation into protein, and is culminated in the stimulation of sulfate incorporation (Adamson *et al.*, 1964).

Studies by Salmon and his associates also suggested that RNA synthesis is required for sustained synthesis of cartilage protein–polysaccharide complexes (Salmon *et al.*, 1967; Salmon and DuVall, 1970a). They observed that prolonged (24-hour) incubation of cartilage with actinomycin D caused a parallel decrement in the incorporation of leucine and sulfate; with shorter exposures to actinomycin, however, incorporation of [^{3}H]uridine into RNA was inhibited to a greater extent than the incorporation of [^{14}C]leucine into protein. The least effect of actinomycin was observed on sulfate incorporation. This order of inhibition produced by actinomycin suggests that inhibition of sulfate incorporation is secondary to inhibition of protein and polysaccharide synthesis, which in turn results from the primary inhibition of RNA synthesis.

The possibility that nonhormonal mechanisms might modulate the incorporation of sulfate into cartilage comes from the work of Lebovitz and associates (Delcher *et al.*, 1973; Eisenbarth *et al.*, 1973). These investigators showed that the fatty acids butyrate and octonoate inhibit serum-stimulated incorporation of [³H]leucine, [¹⁴C]uridine, and $^{35}SO_4$ into embryonic chicken cartilage. They proposed that fatty acids may in this way regulate proteoglycan synthesis and thereby dissociate the growth-promoting actions of growth hormone from its lipolytic and glucose mobilizing effect.

Conflicting data have been reported on the possible role of cyclic AMP in cartilage growth and its relationship to somatomedin. Tell *et al.* (1973) reported that a partially purified preparation of somatomedin inhibited basal and parathyroid hormone-stimulated adenylate cyclase activity in cell membranes from embryonic chicken cartilage. Similar inhibition of adenylate cyclase was observed in rat liver membranes stimulated with glucagon, and in spleen lymphocyte and adipose cell membranes stimulated with epinphrine. Although these effects were observed only at unphysiologically high concentrations of somatomedin, the results were interpreted as evidence that the growth process may be enhanced by the lowering of adenylate cyclase. Such a relationship would be in line with observations that there is an inverse relationship between the rate of cell proliferation *in vitro* and the production of cAMP; furthermore, cell proliferation is severely inhibited by adding cAMP or its long-acting derivatives to the culture medium (Sheppard, 1971; Johnson *et al.*, 1971; Pastan, 1975).

Conflicting findings have been reported on the relationships between somatomedin and cAMP in intact cartilage. Using whole serum as a source of somatomedin, Lebovitz and his associates found that maximal stimulation of sulfate uptake by cartilage was associated with no changes of cAMP, whereas theophylline increased tissue cAMP levels and decreased $^{35}SO_4$ uptake (Rendall *et al.*, 1972; Birch *et al.*, 1973). In later studies, however, this group found that serum stimulation of cartilage sulfate uptake was associated with increased tissue levels of cAMP (Drezner *et al.*, 1975) and that the addition of 0.1–0.5 mM theophylline also increased the incorporation of uridine, leucine, and sulfate into cartilage (Lebovitz *et al.*, 1976).

Difficulties in assessing the effect of somatomedin on cyclic nucleotides are reminiscent of similar confusion which existed concerning the effects of insulin. This was clarified when Illiano and Cuatrecasas (1972) showed in liver and fat cell membranes that at very low concentrations of insulin (10^{-11} M), adenylate cyclase was inhibited; however, as the dosage of insulin was progressively increased, this effect was abolished and enzyme synthesis was eventually stimulated at unphysiologically high concentrations of insulin (10^{-9} *M*). Similar careful dose-response studies remain to be done with somatomedin preparations of unquestioned purity.

2. *Bioassays for Somatomedin in Cartilage*

Most of the bioassays which have been used to measure somatomedin have been dependent either on the incorporation of $^{35}SO_4$ into chondroitin sulfate of cartilage or the incorporation of [^{3}H]thymidine into DNA. Daughaday's original assay (Daughaday *et al.*, 1959), which utilized costal cartilage from hypophysectomized rats, has been modified by many investigators in attempts to improve reproducibility and precision. These modifications have included variations in assay design (Almquist, 1961), use of cartilage from a single hypophysectomized rat (Weidemann and Schwartz, 1972), and use of cartilage segments from fasted immature rats (Yde, 1968; Alford *et al.*, 1972). The latter modification results in loss of assay sensitivity because of higher basal sulfate uptakes than in cartilage from hypophysectomized animals (Daughaday and Kipnis, 1966).

The variability and expense of the rat cartilage assay led Hall (1970) to substitute pelvic leaflets from 11-day chick embryos for rat cartilage. While this assay is somewhat less sensitive than the rat assay, it has been widely used in many laboratories because of its simplicity and precision. One of the disadvantages of this assay is that, unlike rat cartilage, optimal stimulation of $^{35}SO_4$ incorporation by purified NSILA-s (and presumably other somatomedins) is dependent on the presence of thyroid hormone and an unidentified serum factor which is not under growth-hormone control (Froesch *et al.*, 1976). This disadvantage should not impair the utility of the chick cartilage assay for measuring levels in whole serum.

Van den Brande and DuCaju (1974a) developed an assay using uniform pieces of pig costal cartilage. Although the pig assay sacrifices sensitivity, it is the most precise and reproducible of the various sulfation factor assays and, in addition, it seems to be less subject to the effect of serum inhibitors of sulfate uptake. Phillips *et al.* (1974a) stressed the importance of acquiring cartilage from pigs less than 9 months of age.

Whereas most sera stimulate at most a 3- to 4-fold increase in $^{35}SO_4$ incorporation into cartilage (when contrasted with basal rates of incorporation in serum-free medium), the incorporation of [^{3}H]thymidine into DNA in the presence of sera may be stimulated as much as 8- to 12-fold. The incorporation of [^{3}H]thymidine into cartilage DNA has, therefore, served as the basis for several bioassays for somatomedin (Van den Brande *et al.*, 1971; Raben *et al.*, 1972). These assays are more subject to inhibition at high serum concentrations than are sulfation factor assays. An assay for serum somatomedin activity based on the incorporation of [^{3}H]thymidine into cultured chondrocytes has been described by Garland *et al.* (1976).

One of the major disadvantages of all cartilage bioassays is that a variety of substances may exert inhibitory effects on sulfate and thymidine incorporation. Salmon (1972, 1974, 1975) has studied the nature of these substances both in the serum of hypophysectomized and in starved rats and has found that at least part of the inhibitory material is heat labile, nondialyzable, and destroyed by trypsin digestion. These observations strongly suggest that the inhibitor has a peptide structure. Salmon postulated that the physiological role of the inhibitor is to serve as a means for faster and potentially greater restraint on cartilage growth than might result from a decrease in the level of somatomedin alone. It would thereby serve to limit anabolic events under conditions of restricted nutrient uptake. Inhibitors of the bioassay have also been identified in starved human subjects (Van den Brande and DuCaju, 1974b).

B. MITOGENIC ACTIONS OF THE SOMATOMEDINS

Although the concentration of serum required for the propagation of animal cells *in vitro* can be drastically reduced by providing optimal concentrations of nutrients and known hormones (McKeehan *et al.*, 1976), less well-defined macromolecular substances are still required to serve specific roles in cell survival, attachment to substrate, and promoting cell division (Temin *et al.*, 1972; Holly and Kiernan, 1974). In recent years considerable attention has been focused on the possibility that the somatomedins and certain other peptide growth factors might account for a portion of the growth-promoting activity of serum (Gospodarowicz and Moran, 1976). The fact that in complex organisms the growth rate of different tissues varies enormously with age and changing physiological circumstances suggests that biologically relevant growth-promoting substances in serum should likewise be subject to strict physiological regulation and possess a certain degree of selectivity for different kinds of cells. The somatomedins, along with some of the other recently described peptide growth factors, possess such properties and therefore are attractive candidates for a regulatory role on cell proliferation in the intact organism.

1. Insulin, Insulin-Like Activity, and the Somatomedins

For many years insulin was the only peptide known to stimulate the growth of cells *in vitro*. This effect, first described more than 50 years ago by Gey and Thalheimer (1924), has served as a focus of numerous subsequent investigations. After studying the effect of insulin on normal and virus-transformed avian embryo fibroblasts, Temin (1967) concluded that the concentration of insulin itself is too low to explain the mitogenic properties of serum; he therefore suggested that this activity might be derived from the insulin-like substances which are present in much higher concentrations. His subsequent partial purification of MSA from calf serum and isolation of CRL-MSA was, accordingly, patterned after procedures previously used to isolate these substances from serum (see Section III,C,4).

Salmon and Hosse (1971) were the first to demonstrate that a serum fraction rich in sulfation factor activity could partially substitute for serum in stimulating cell proliferation. The possibility that the sulfation factor might mimic the mitogenic actions of insulin on cell growth was suggested by the marked parallelism between the actions of the sulfation factor and insulin in muscle (Salmon and DuVall, 1970b). All the somatomedins have subsequently been shown to initiate DNA synthesis and stimulate mitosis in chick embryo and human fibroblasts (Morell and Froesch, 1973; Smith and Temin, 1974; Van Wyk *et al.*, 1975; Nissley and Rechler, 1977) (Figs. 4 and

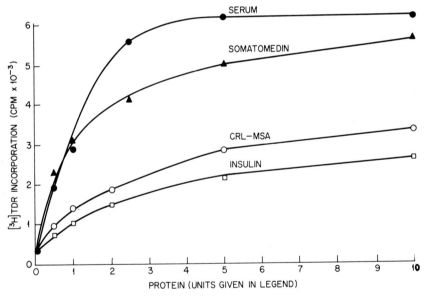

FIG. 4. Dose–response curves of calf serum, somatomedin, purified CRL-MSA, and insulin on the incorporation of [³H]thymidine into stationary chick fibroblasts during a 1-hour pulse 12 hours after the addition of the test substances. The amount of protein in 3 ml of medium (indicated on the abscissa) are in the following units: calf serum (●) mg; somatomedin (▲) mg × 10⁻³; purified CRL-MSA (○) mg × 10⁻⁵; porcine insulin (■) mg × 10⁻⁵. The somatomedin was a partially purified preparation obtained from Dr. Knut Uthne. (From Smith and Temin, 1974, courtesy of the authors.)

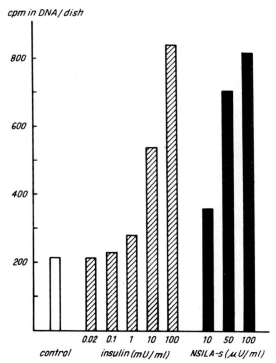

FIG. 5. Incorporation of [³H]thymidine into DNA of secondary cultures of chicken embryo fibroblasts eight hours after stimulation by whole insulin or NSILA-s. 100 mU of insulin represents about 4.2 μg of insulin; 100 μU of NSILA-s represents about 0.22 μg of pure NSILA-s based on a specific activity of 450 mU/mg for the pure peptide. (From Morell and Froesch, 1973, courtesy of the authors.)

5). In a recent study, somatomedin C, in a concentration of 7 ng/ml, was found to be 74% as active as dialyzed serum from a normal adult male in stimulating [³H]thymidine incorporation in serum-starved, fourth passage human foreskin fibroblasts (A. S. Plet and J. J. Van Wyk, unpublished). Somatomedin C has also been found to be active in stimulating DNA synthesis in ovarian tumor cells, rat fetal liver cells, rat myoblasts, pituitary tumor (GH₃) cells, and in maintaining clonal growth of human foreskin fibroblasts.*

Despite the unquestioned mitogenicity of the somatomedins for several cell types, it remains far from clear how much of the mitogenic action of whole serum is due to the somatomedins or under what circumstances the

*Tests in these cell types were carried out, respectively, by Drs. Denis Gospodarowitz and Hyam Leffert of the Salk Institute, Dr. James Florini of New York Upstate Medical Center, Dr. Gordon Sato of the University of California, San Diego, and Dr. W. L. McKeehan of the University of Colorado.

somatomedin concentration might be rate-limiting in cell proliferation. The effect of the somatomedins on the initiation of DNA synthesis, although usually greater than the effect of insulin, is considerably less than the maximal effect obtained with serum. In nuclear labeling studies the somatomedins usually stimulate a smaller percentage of the cell population to undergo mitosis than does serum. Groelke and Baseman (1976) found that following a 6- to 8-hour period during which protein synthesis was inhibited by cyclohexamide, chick embryo fibroblasts completely lost their ability to respond to somatomedin C or insulin, whereas they were fully responsive to the mitogenic effects of serum. This suggested that inhibition of protein synthesis placed chick cells in a stage of the cell cycle in which some factor in serum other than somatomedin or insulin was required to activate DNA synthesis and cell cycle transit.

This inability of the somatomedins to fully replicate the action of serum under artificial culture conditions may simply be due to the absence of other hormones from the artificial culture medium. Hayashi and Sato (1976) have found that a mixture of somatomedins, transferrin, triiodothyroxine, thyrotropin releasing hormone, and parathyroid hormone quantitatively replicates the effect of serum on the growth of the GH_3 rat pituitary cell line. Similar detailed investigations of the hormonal requirements for other cell types are required to evaluate the relative importance of the somatomedins, established hormones, and other peptide growth factors in the total mitogenic effect of serum.

2. Relationship of Somatomedin to Other Peptide Growth Factors

a. *Platelet Growth Factor (PGF), Fibroblast Growth Factor (FGF), and Epidermal Growth Factor (EGF).* The somatomedins are by no means the most powerful mitogens in serum, nor do they possess the greatest degree of specificity. Rutherford and Ross (1976) have demonstrated that during blood coagulation, platelets release a powerful mitogen for primate arterial smooth muscle cells and for dermal fibroblasts. This platelet growth factor satisfactorily explains why serum is often much more effective than plasma in stimulating cell growth *in vitro*. The platelet growth factor is a basic (pI=9.5) peptide of about 13,000 daltons which appears to be very similar or identical to the fibroblast growth factor isolated by Gospodarowicz from bovine pituitary and brain extracts (Gospodarowicz *et al.*, 1975; Ross, 1977). Antoniades and his associates (Antoniades *et al.*, 1975; Antoniades and Scher, 1977) have independently purified this substance from human serum and have confirmed by radioimmunoassay that this basic peptide is higher in human serum from whole clotted blood than in serum from platelet poor plasma. They also found that human pituitary glands contain a substance, presumably the fibroblast growth factor, which cross-reacts immunologically with their serum factor.

The epidermal growth factor, isolated from mouse submandibular gland by Stanley Cohen (Cohen and Taylor, 1974), is apparently also more effective than the somatomedins in stimulating mitosis in certain cell types (Hollenberg and Cuatrecasas, 1975). The disclosure that human EGF isolated from human pregnancy urine (Cohen and Carpenter, 1975) is identical to urogastrone isolated from the same source (Gregory, 1975) suggests that this substance may likewise prove to be a physiologically important component of the mitogens found in human serum.

b. More Specialized Peptide Growth Factors. In addition to the somatomedins and the broad-spectrum mitogens described in the preceding section, serum contains a rapidly expanding list of peptide growth factors with much more limited and specialized actions, but which are responsive to the classic anabolic hormones. Several examples illustrate the diversity of this group of peptides.

Erythropoeitin (Goldwasser, 1975) is a peptide which acts on proerythrocytes to undergo mitosis and differentiate into hemoglobin-synthesizing cells which then lack the capacity for further division. Although anoxia is the primary stimulus for erythropoeitin production, its formation is also partially regulated by growth hormone and androgenic steroids (Jepson and McGarry, 1972).

Nerve growth factor (NGF) exercises its primary role during embryonic development on the differentiation of the sympathetic ganglia. It also serves a maintenance function on the sensory and sympathetic ganglia postnatally. The concentration of NGF in salivary glands, like that of EGF, is highly responsive to androgenic hormones. NGF has a high degree of structural homology with proinsulin (Bradshaw *et al.*, 1974), thus suggesting an ancestral relationship similar to that postulated between somatomedins and insulin.

Thymosin is an acidic peptide of 15,500 daltons which is formed in the thymus and which stimulates lymphoid stem cells to differentiate into the mature T cells required for cell-mediated immune reactions. Although not rigorously studied, there is evidence to suggest that thymosin levels are responsive to pituitary growth hormone and TSH (White and Goldstein, 1975).

Although the above listing of peptide growth factors is by no means complete, it is sufficient to suggest that these peptides collectively constitute an "infrahormonal" mechanism by which the classic hormones and other physiological control mechanisms may selectively regulate cell growth *in vivo*. A comprehensive and critical review of the current status of peptide growth factors has recently been published (Gospodarowicz and Moran, 1976).

C. Insulin-Like Actions of the Somatomedins

1. Biological Effects

The kinship between the insulin-like activity and the "sulfation factor" activity of serum was not appreciated until some years had elapsed after the discovery of each. The use of cold acid–ethanol to extract the sulfation/thymidine factor from serum (Van Wyk *et al.*, 1969) was prompted, however, by the successful use of this technique by Bürgi *et al.* (1966) to extract NSILA-s from serum.* Salmon likewise concluded that the sulfation factor might be related to NSILA after noting the striking parallelism between the effects of insulin and a partially purified preparation of rat somatomedin on protein synthesis in muscle (Salmon and DuVall, 1970b). Direct evidence that the sulfation factor is very similar or identical to NSILA was provided by Hall and Uthne (1971) when they reported that throughout a 10,000-fold purification of human serum the sulfation factor activity, as measured in Hall's chick cartilage assay, could not be dissociated from nonsuppressible insulin-like activity, as measured in epididymal fat pads. Almost simultaneously, Raben *et al.* (1972) reported that a preparation of NSILA-s prepared by Froesch stimulated $^{35}SO_4$ and [^{3}H]thymidine uptake by rat cartilage.

a. *Effects of Somatomedin in Adipose Tissue.* In rat adipose tissue the various somatomedins stimulate [^{14}C]glucose incorporation into $^{14}CO_2$, [^{14}C]fatty acids, [^{14}C]lipids, and [^{14}C]glycogen (Froesch *et al.*, 1966; Oelz *et al.*, 1970; Hall and Uthne, 1971; Clemmons *et al.*, 1974). Clemmons *et al.* (1974) showed that somatomedin and insulin produce parallel dose–response curves both on the degradation of glucose to CO_2 and on the conversion of glucose to lipid; furthermore, the effects of the two hormones are additive when present together at subsaturating concentrations. This was interpreted as evidence that the two hormones act through a common cellular mechanism on these metabolic processes. Schwartz and Goodman (1976) examined the time course of the effect of somatomedin on glucose degradation by adipose tissue to determine whether somatomedin might have the same biphasic effect on adipose tissue as that observed after the administration of growth hormone. They concluded that the early insulin-like effects of growth hormone are probably not mediated through somatomedin because the rate of glucose degradation stimulated by somatomedin remained linear for the entire four hours of incubation. In addition, somatomedin failed to exert the delayed lipolytic effects produced by growth hormone in conjunction with glucocorticoids.

*The use of this procedure to extract sulfation factor was initially suggested by Dr. Kerstin Hall on the basis of reports that serum ILA, like the sulfation factor, is diminished in rat serum by hypophysectomy and is responsive to growth hormone (Randle and Young, 1956).

An additional insulin-like effect of somatomedin in fat is the inhibition of epinephrine-stimulated lipolysis, as measured by liberation of glycerol (Froesch *et al.*, 1966; Underwood *et al.*, 1972). Werner *et al.* (1974) found that somatomedin A produced a dose-dependent depression of glycerol release in rat epididymal fat pad during light stimulation of the adenylate cyclase system by low dosages of ACTH; at higher dosages of ACTH, however, glycerol release was potentiated in a dose-dependent manner by somatomedin A. These workers were unable to consistently demonstrate inhibition of adenylate cyclase activity in fat cell ghosts by somatomedin A. Inhibition of epinephrine-stimulated adenylate cyclase in adipose tissue membranes was, however, demonstrated by Tell *et al.* (1973) and by Renner *et al.* (1973) using crude preparations of somatomedin and NSILA, respectively.

b. Effect of the Somatomedins on Muscle. The first description of an insulin-like effect of one of the somatomedins on muscle was the incorporation of [^{14}C]glucose into [^{14}C]glycogen in rat diaphragm following the administration of a partially purified preparation of NSILA (Froesch *et al.*, 1966). Salmon and DuVall (1970b) demonstrated that a partially purified preparation of somatomedin stimulated the incorporation of [^{3}H]leucine into protein. Uthne *et al.* (1974), working with preparations containing significantly less impurities than used previously, demonstrated that the insulin-like effects of somatomedin on isolated rat diaphragm included not only stimulation of protein synthesis but also the transport of glucose and amino acids into the cell. The latter effects were not inhibited by either puromycin or theophylline, thus suggesting that neither protein synthesis nor changes in cAMP are involved in this particular effect of somatomedin.

The effect of NSILA on glucose utilization by the perfused rat heart was studied by Meuli and Froesch (1975). These workers found that mole for mole, insulin and NSILA were equipotent in the stimulation of glucose uptake, lactate production and the efflux of 3-O-methyl glucose from heart cells.

2. Cross Reactions of the Somatomedins with the Insulin Receptor

A rational explanation for the insulin-like actions of somatomedin was provided by the observation that somatomedin competes with [^{125}I]insulin for binding to the insulin receptor on cell membranes (Hintz *et al.*, 1972). This was the first demonstration that a hormone other than insulin, proinsulin, or various insulin derivatives has the capacity to actively compete for the insulin receptor. In competitive binding assays one unit of somatomedin produces the same inhibitory effect on the binding of [^{125}I]insulin to cell membrane receptors as 100–350 μU of crystalline porcine insulin.

Marshall *et al.* (1974) took advantage of the abundance of insulin receptors in human placental cell membranes (Posner, 1974) to develop a radioreceptor assay capable of detecting both insulin and somatomedin. This was the first quantitative method for the measurement of somatomedin which did not depend on bioassay methodology and was successfully exploited in the original isolation of somatomedin C (Van Wyk *et al.*, 1974).

VI. INTERACTIONS OF THE SOMATOMEDINS WITH SPECIFIC SOMATOMEDIN RECEPTORS

The discovery that somatomedin is recognized by the insulin receptor raised the question whether or not all the actions of somatomedin might be mediated through this receptor interaction. There were, however, great difficulties in accepting this interpretation. Most important, insulin itself has little effect on the *in vitro* stimulation of cartilage growth and stimulates the growth of cells in culture only when present in high, unphysiological concentrations. Therefore, if somatomedin acted only through the insulin receptor, it would have to produce a greater stimulus than insulin itself. The second objection to the insulin-like hypothesis of somatomedin action was that the relatively normal concentrations of somatomedin which are present in the serum of diabetic subjects apparently afford little protection against hyperglycemia and ketosis. Finally, because the predominant metabolic effect of growth hormone is antagonistic to that of insulin, this hypothesis did not explain the paradox of how an insulin-like peptide could be the instrument of growth-hormone action. For these reasons, it was surmised that the insulin-like effects of somatomedin are secondary phenomena and that the primary growth-promoting effects must be mediated through another mechanism.

When somatomedin C of sufficient purity to permit labeling with radioactive iodine became avilable it was, therefore, not surprising to find that somatomedin has its own primary cell membrane receptor which is clearly distinct from the insulin receptor (Van Wyk *et al.*, 1974; Marshall *et al.*, 1974). This observation was followed by reports that each of the other radiolabeled somatomedins bind to cell receptors different from the insulin receptors (Hall *et al.*, 1974; Zapf *et al.*, 1975a; Megyesi *et al.*, 1974a; Rechler *et al.*, 1976). Although the available data suggest that the receptors for the different somatomedins have similar properties, distribution, and hormonal specificities (Megyesi *et al.*, 1976; Zapf *et al.*, 1975a; Takano *et al.*, 1976b; D'Ercole *et al.*, 1976a), insufficient cross-testing with individual pure somatomedins has been carried out to judge whether or not these receptors are identical.

A. Correlation between Biological Actions and
Receptor Interactions

Human placental cell membrane preparations are a particularly rich source of receptors, for both insulin and somatomedin C (Marshall *et al.*, 1974). The quantitative relationship between the interactions of insulin and somatomedin C, with the two receptors in this tissue, shown in Table III, are, in general, representative of the relationships reported for the other somatomedins. At concentrations of about $1 \times 10^{-9} M$ (6–7 ng/ml) both somatomedin C and insulin inhibit specific binding of their own radioligands by 50%, whereas higher concentrations are required to inhibit binding of the other radioligand. On a weight basis, insulin is about 1000 times less active than somatomedin C in inhibiting [^{125}I]somatomedin C binding, whereas somatomedin C is about 50 times less effective than insulin in inhibiting [^{125}I]insulin binding. The potency ratio between the two hormones in inhibiting [^{125}I]insulin binding to the insulin receptor agrees well with the biological potency ratios of the two hormones in the rat fat pad and diaphragm bioassays for insulin; moreover, the relative biological potencies of these two hormones in cell growth and cartilage assays agrees with their relative affinities for the somatomedin C receptor. In the latter systems, exceedingly high dosages of insulin are required to replicate the action of the somatomedins.

These relationships can be interpreted to mean that somatomedin and insulin have an ancestral kinship and retain sufficient structural similarity to be recognized to some degree by their respective receptors. In particular, these studies reveal that the active sites on the somatomedin molecules

TABLE III
Quantitative Relationship between Interactions of Insulin and
Somatomedin C with Human Placental Cell Membrane[a]

	Somatomedin C receptor ([^{125}I]somatomedin C)	Insulin receptor ([^{125}I]insulin)
Somatomedin C	7 ng/ml	350 ng/ml
Porcine insulin	8100 ng/ml	6.5 ng/ml

[a] A particulate fraction containing plasma membrane from human placenta was incubated with either [^{125}I]insulin or [^{125}I]somatomedin C in the presence of graded concentrations of the unlabeled pure hormones. The numbers shown are the concentrations of the unlabeled hormones required to produce 50% inhibition in specific binding of the respective labeled hormones. (From Van Wyk *et al.*, 1977.)

which trigger a growth response are quite different from those responsible for their insulin-like actions.

A discrepant result from the above was reported by Rechler *et al.* (1976), who found that in chick embryo fibroblasts, insulin was nearly as effective as CRL-MSA in stimulating DNA synthesis, and likewise was nearly as effective as CRL-MSA in competing with [^{125}I]CRL-MSA for binding to these cells. The significance of this finding is obscure because similar findings have been observed neither in any mammalian tissues nor in chick fibroblasts with NSILA-s (Morell and Froesch, 1973; Zapf *et al.*, 1975a).

The correspondence between biological actions and receptor interactions makes it possible to hazard some interpretation of the physiological roles of insulin and the somatomedins. Our interpretation is that at physiological concentrations insulin is a growth-promoting hormone only to the extent that it is necessary to preserve metabolic homeostasis; only at exceedingly high levels does insulin act as a primary growth stimulant. Similarly, somatomedin probably has very little effect on carbohydrate homeostasis *in vivo* unless the concentrations are vastly elevated. Megyesi *et al.* (1974b) have shown that in some patients with mesenchymal tumors associated with hypoglycemia, plasma NSILA-s levels, as measured by a radioreceptor assay, are extraordinarily high as a result of ectopic production. This finding, however, has not been confirmed with a radioreceptor assay for somatomedin C.

B. Distribution and Ontogeny of Somatomedin Receptors

Specific binding sites for [^{125}I]somatomedin A (Takano *et al.*, 1976b) and [^{125}I]somatomedin C (D'Ercole *et al.*, 1976a) are widely distributed in mammalian tissues, and in most tissues somatomedin receptors appear to be more abundant than those for insulin. A possible exception is in mature fat cells. In an attempt to determine whether the metabolic actions of somatomedin in adipose tissue (see Section V,C,1) are mediated through the insulin receptor or through the somatomedin receptor, D'Ercole *et al.* (1976a) prepared cell membranes from mature rat adipocytes isolated with crude collagenase. These membranes failed to bind somatomedin but bound insulin in proportion to the concentration of membrane protein. On the other hand, J. Zapf (personal communication) and Takano *et al.* (1976b) have been able to demonstrate specific fat cell receptors for NSILA and somatomedin A, respectively. It remains to be determined whether this discrepancy is derived from differences in the radiolabled hormones or the result of selective destruction of somatomedin receptors by some preparations of crude collagenase.

To explore the possible role of somatomedin in fetal growth, D'Ercole *et al.* (1976b) made a systematic search for somatomedin C receptors in cell membranes prepared from organs of the fetal pig. In most tissues binding of [^{125}I]somatomedin C exceeded that of [^{125}I]insulin binding. In liver, kidney, heart, and the maternal portion of the placenta, apparent binding affinities for somatomedin were relatively constant throughout gestation and were the same for membranes from fetal and adult animals. In the fetal portion of the placenta, however, specific somatomedin C binding and apparent binding affinity increased as gestation progressed. The changes in this tissue correlate temporally with the acceleration of growth of the pig fetus. Membranes prepared from fetal lungs exhibited higher specific binding of somatomedin and higher affinity constants than adult lung membranes. While these results do not prove that the somatomedins play a primary role in fetal growth, they suggest that, at least in certain tissues and at specific times of gestation, this hormone may be physiologically important. It may perhaps be of significance that serum somatomedin C levels in infants who are small for gestational age are significantly lower than in either normal full-term or premature infants (D'Ercole *et al.*, 1976b).

VII. PHYSIOLOGICAL REGULATION OF THE SOMATOMEDINS

Over the past two decades, serum somatomedin concentrations in a wide variety of diseases and in altered physiological circumstances have been reported from many different laboratories. Most of these results have been obtained with various modifications of the original cartilage sulfation factor assay (Section V,A,2). More recently, membrane binding assays have been developed for each of the four somatomedins (Section VI) as well as a specific radioimmunoassay for somatomedin C. Thus, evolving concepts of somatomedin physiology have been derived from a wide assortment of assays which have varied greatly in their precision, sensitivity, specificity, and susceptibility to interference by inhibitors. Furthermore, comparison of results from different laboratories is still being impeded by the lack of any internationally recognized reference standard. The local pools of normal adult serum traditionally employed for this purpose have been known to differ as much as 3-fold in their potencies! In the light of these methodological difficulties, discrepancies in results from different laboratories are hardly surprising; nevertheless, from the mass of published data clear trends have emerged which shed important insights into somatomedin physiology. Some of the present conclusions will undoubtedly require revision, however, when these problems are restudied with more specific and accurate methods.

A. SOMATOMEDIN CONCENTRATIONS IN NORMAL INDIVIDUALS

1 . Relationship between Somatomedin Concentration and Age

The preponderance of available evidence now suggests that somatomedin concentrations are low in cord blood, rise rapidly during the first year or two of life, but do not reach adult levels until early in the adolescent years. The greatest discordance between laboratories has been in the levels of somatomedin in the neonate. As measured by bioassay, somatomedin levels in cord sera have been reported as normal (Anderson *et al.*, 1974), slightly reduced (Chesley, 1962), reduced but subject to wide variation (Tato *et al.*, 1975), and low (Giordano *et al.*, 1976; Hintz *et al.*, 1974b). Using the somatomedin C competitive membrane binding assay, d'Ercole *et al.* (1976b) found the mean somatomedin concentration in 25 newborn cord sera to be 0.33 + 0.017 (SEM) units/ml. Similarly low results have been found with the specific somatomedin C radioimmunoassay.

In the period between birth and approximately 2 years of age, the mean serum somatomedin concentration ranges between 0.4 and 0.5 units/ml (Almquist and Rune, 1961; Van den Brande and DuCaju, 1974b; Takano *et al.*, 1976a; D'Ercole *et al.*, 1977b). These concentrations then rise steadily through childhood and reach adult levels around the age of 10 years (Almquist and Rune, 1961; Van Den Brande and DuCaju, 1974b; D'Ercole *et al.*, 1977b). No sex differences have been reported (Giordano *et al.*, 1976).

There is as yet no clear explanation for the relatively low serum somatomedin concentrations during infancy and early childhood, when linear growth is most rapid. This apparent paradox might be accounted for by lower concentrations of the somatomedin binding protein in the serum of young children, but techniques to determine this possibility are not yet available. From a teleological viewpoint, lower serum concentrations would be understandable if rapidly growing cartilage were shown to be particularly sensitive to somatomedin. Supporting this possibility is the finding of Heins *et al.* (1970) that as rats age their cartilage decreases in its sensitivity to the stimulatory effects of somatomedin. Similar findings have been reported for rabbit cartilage (Beaton and Singh, 1975) and porcine cartilage (Phillips *et al.*, 1974a).

2. Diurnal Variation and Stability of Somatomedin Concentrations in Serum

Two limited studies of normal adult subjects have uncovered no evidence of a diurnal fluctuation in serum somatomedin levels (Daughaday *et al.*, 1959; Giordano *et al.*, 1976). Van den Brande *et al.* (1975), using the pig cartilage bioassay, measured plasma somatomedin concentrations in 67 school children between 9 and 12 years of age. Samples obtained in the morning had significantly lower somatomedin levels (1.20 ± 0.41 units/ml;

SD) than samples obtained in the afternoon (1.45±0.44 units/ml). The very striking negative correlation observed between the concentrations of somatomedin and cortisol in these specimens led these investigators to attribute the lower morning somatomedin concentrations to a direct inhibitory effect of cortisol on their assay.

Although the short-term influences of sleep, acute stress, food intake, and periods of limited fasting appear to exercise a negligible influence on serum somatomedin concentrations, the possibility of small changes requires further investigation with more specific and accurate techniques of measurement.

B. Hormonal Control of Somatomedin

1. Growth Hormone

All investigators are apparently in agreement that growth hormone exercises the single most important influence on serum somatomedin concentrations. In growth-hormone-deficient patients, bioassayable somatomedin generally ranges between 0.1 and 0.8 units/ml, with a mean for most studies of 0.5 units/ml (Daughaday et al., 1959; Almquist, 1961; Giordano et al., 1976; Benet et al., 1974). Similar findings have been reported using placental membrane receptor assays (Marshall et al., 1974; Megyesi et al., 1975; Takano et al., 1976a).

Using a highly specific and sensitive radioimmunoassay for somatomedin C, Furlanetto et al. (1977) found that the concentrations of this peptide in the serum of 17 out of 19 children with hypopituitary dwarfism were 0.1 unit/ml or less, a value which approached the limits of sensitivity of this assay. Because these concentrations are considerably lower than those found with bioassay or radioreceptor techniques, it may be inferred that the latter techniques detect substances other than somatomedin C and that the latter substances are under less stringent growth-hormone control. A comparison of clinical values obtained by the radioreceptor assay and radioimmunoassay for somatomedin C is shown in Fig. 6.

Following the parenternal administration of growth hormone to hypopituitary patients, little increase in somatomedin is observed for 6–12 hours. Normal levels can sometimes be achieved, however, within two to three days (Daughaday et al., 1969; Hall, 1971; Van den Brande, 1973). Typical responses are shown in Fig. 7. In a study of the relationships among changes in somatomedin concentration, metabolic responses, and linear growth rates following the administration of growth hormone, Van den Brande (1973) found that there are limits to the magnitude of the rise in somatomedin during the first few days of growth-hormone therapy. At the initiation of

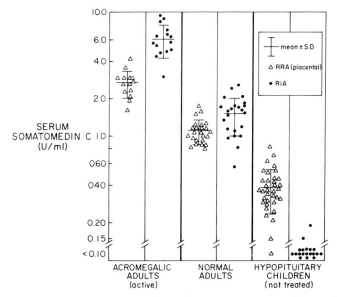

FIG. 6. Comparison of serum somatomedin concentrations as measured by a radioreceptor assay for somatomedin C (△) and by a specific radioimmunoassay (●) for this substance in adults with active acromegaly, normal adults, and hypopituitary children. All the sera measured by radioimmunoassay are included in the larger group of sera measured by the radioreceptor assay. The same serum pool was used as the standard for both assays and was assigned an arbitrary value of 1 unit/ml for each test system. Values are plotted as units/ml on a logarithmic scale. (From Van Wyk *et al.*, 1977.)

treatment, it required dosages of human growth hormone four to five times higher than usual replacement dosages to attain somatomedin levels comparable to those found after a period of chronic treatment. These results could be interpreted either as evidence for impaired somatomedin generation in newly treated growth-hormone-deficient patients or for more rapid turnover of somatomedin in patients previously deficient. There is abundant precedent for impaired responses to other pituitary hormones in hypopituitarism.

During the long-term treatment of hypopituitary children with human growth hormone, a positive correlation has been observed between somatomedin concentrations and linear growth rates. Hall and Olin (1972) used the chick cartilage bioassay to show that somatomedin levels declined concurrently as growth rate decreased during long-term treatment with growth hormone. D'Ercole *et al.* (1977b), using a placental membrane binding assay, confirmed these findings in a group of 31 hypopituitary patients on long-term growth-hormone therapy (Fig. 8); they further pointed out that these correlations were even stronger when analyzed by individual patients.

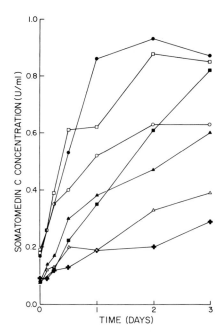

FIG. 7. Rise in serum somatomedin C concentration following parenteral human growth hormone administration to seven hypopituitary children. Each patient was given 1 unit of human growth hormone intravenously at time zero, followed by 1 unit intramuscularly at 6, 24, 48, and 72 hours. Serum somatomedin C concentrations were measured by radioimmunoassay. The standard is a pooled adult human serum sample arbitrarily defined as containing 1 unit of somatomedin C activity/ml. (From Furlanetto *et al.*, 1977.)

In active acromegaly, the concentration of somatomedin, as measured by bioassay, is usually two to four times greater than normal (Daughaday *et al.*, 1959; Almquist *et al.*, 1961) and correlates better with the clinical activity of the disease than with the degree of elevation of immunoreactive growth hormone (Hall, 1972). Somewhat higher values for serum somatomedin levels in acromegalic patients have been found by competitive membrane binding assays for somatomedin C (Marshall *et al.*, 1974) and for somatomedin A (Hall *et al.*, 1974). Even higher concentrations of somatomedin relative to normal patients are found by a specific radioimmunoassay for somatomedin C (Fig. 6) (Furlanetto *et al.*, 1977). Conversely, Megyesi *et al.* have been unable to detect elevated levels in acromegalic patients with a radioreceptor assay for NSILA-s (Megyesi *et al.*, 1975).

2. Thyroid Hormone

The production of somatomedin is probably not significantly impaired in hypothyroid states, because serum concentrations of somatomedin in such

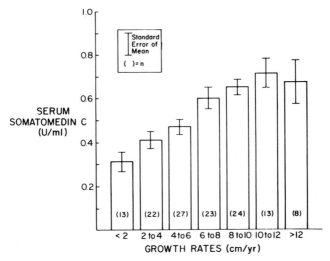

FIG. 8. Correlation between somatomedin C concentrations and linear growth rates in 130 serum samples from 31 hypopituitary children. The samples were assembled into groups according to the linear growth rates in cm/yr extrapolated from accurate height measurements before and after the end of the preceding 3–4 month interval. The number in parentheses in each bar is the number of samples assayed in each group. A significant level of $p < 0.01$ (one tailed T test) between mean somatomedin concentrations in these groups is reached when the growth rate of <2 cm/yr is compared to that of 4–6 cm/yr or greater, when the 2–4 cm/yr group is compared to 6–8 cm/yr or greater, and when the 4–6 cm/yr group is compared to the 8–10 cm/yr group or greater. (From D'Ercole *et al.*, 1977b.)

patients are normal by bioassay in pig or rat cartilage (Van den Brande and DuCaju, 1974b; Giordano *et al.*, 1976) and by membrane receptor assay (Takano *et al.*, 1976a; D'Ercole *et al.*, 1977b). On clinical and experimental grounds, however, the evidence is clear that thyroid hormone plays a permissive role in the action of somatomedin on cartilage. Stimulation of sulfate uptake by pure NSILA in chick embryo cartilage is enhanced by the addition of supraphysiological (5×10^{-8} M) quantities of triiodothyronine (Froesch *et al.*, 1976). Further studies are clearly required to precisely define how thyroid hormone interacts with somatomedin in cartilage from different species and in different tissues.

3. *Glucocorticoids*

The mechanisms proposed to account for the retardation of growth in states of glucocorticoid excess include impaired somatomedin generation and a direct inhibitory effect on cartilage growth. As judged by bioassay techniques, somatomedin concentrations are low in states of cortisol excess (Van den Brande and DuCaju, 1974b; Lecornu, 1973). Glucocorticoid treatment of children causes a dose-related fall in bioassayable serum somatomedin activity (Elders *et al.*, 1975a). Phillips *et al.* (1974b) showed that high dosages of cortisone acetate blunt the rise of serum somatomedin in hypophysectomized rats treated with bovine growth hormone.

Contrary to conclusions based on bioassay data, D'Ercole *et al.* (1977b) found by a competitive membrane binding assay that children with growth arrest due to Cushing's syndrome have normal levels of somatomedin. This finding favors the interpretation that high cortisol levels inhibit linear growth by a direct effect on cartilage. The apparent suppressive effect of cortisol on somatomedin blood levels may therefore be artifactual as a result of interference by cortisol in cartilage bioassays. Such an interpretation was favored by Van den Brande *et al.* (1975) to explain the inverse correlation between apparent somatomedin activity and plasma cortisol concentrations in normal children. High dosages of glucocorticoids have been shown to exercise a direct inhibitory effect on the synthesis of enzymes concerned in the synthesis of glycosaminoglycans (Elders *et al.*, 1975b). Furthermore, Mosier and his associates found that high dosages of cortisol inhibit *in vitro* sulfate uptake and induce a variety of severe ultrastructural changes in chondrocytes and extracellular matrix (Dearden and Mosier, 1972; Mosier *et al.*, 1976).

4. Estrogens

Administration of estradiol to experimental animals decreases linear growth rate, causes narrowing of epiphyseal cartilage width, and causes an *in vivo* decline in sulfate incorporation by cartilage (Berntsen, 1968; Day and Follis, 1941; Herbai, 1970). In addition, estrogen treatment has been shown to inhibit growth-hormone-induced increases in serum levels of somatomedin in hypophysectomized rats and hypopituitary humans (Phillips *et al.*, 1974b; Wiedemann and Schwartz, 1972). Estrogens also cause suppression of serum somatomedin activity in patients with Turner's syndrome (Saenger *et al.*, 1976). The limited success which has been reported in the treatment of acromegaly with high dosages of estrogens (Schwartz *et al.*, 1969) probably depends on the capacity of estrogens to inhibit somatomedin generation, because moderately supraphysiological concentrations of estradiol added to the incubation medium do not suppress sulfate uptake (Phillips *et al.*, 1975; Wiedemann and Schwartz, 1972). Von Puttkamer *et al.* (1977) showed that the suppression of growth in very tall girls treated with high dosages of estrogen is correlated with the inhibition of somatomedin generation.

5. Testosterone

Testosterone has no apparent effect on the somatomedin activity in human serum (Van den Brande and DuCaju, 1974b) or in the serum from hypophysectomized rats (Phillips *et al.*, 1974b). The addition of testosterone to incubates of cartilage has no influence on sulfate uptake (Salmon *et al.*, 1963; Phillips *et al.*, 1975).

6. Placental Lactogen and Fragments of Growth Hormone

Human placental lactogen has less than 10% of the growth-promoting activity of human growth hormone. Treatment of hypophysectomized rats with this substance increases epiphyseal width and stimulates the incorporation of [^{3}H]thymidine into DNA of cartilage in adipose tissue (Murakawa and Raben, 1968; Neri *et al.*, 1972). Studies of serum somatomedin levels following the administration of human placental lactogen have not, insofar as we are aware, been reported. Ovine placental lactogen, a substance with a considerably higher ratio between growth-promoting and lactogenic activity, has recently been found to induce somatomedin in hypophysectomized rats (Hurley *et al.*, 1977).

A variety of methods have been utilized to cleave growth-hormone preparations in attempts to potentiate their growth-promoting effect in humans. Although the potency of certain of these preparations has been enhanced severalfold as judged by standard *in vivo* weight gain and tibial width growth-hormone assays (Lewis *et al.*, 1976), in most cases no direct measurements of somatomedin activity have been reported. Fragments of bovine growth hormone obtained by cyanogen bromide cleavage have been shown not to stimulate serum somatomedin activity nor to increase the *in vitro* thymidine incorporation of cartilage obtained from treated rats (Nutting *et al.*, 1972).

C. Relationship between Nutritional Status and Somatomedin Levels

Studies in malnourished children and starved animals suggest that nutritional factors, as well as growth hormone, modulate somatomedin activity in serum. Phillips and Young (1976) showed that serum somatomedin activity of young rats declined significantly after 24 hours of fasting and fell to hypopituitary levels after 72 hours. This decline in somatomedin was not attributed to growth-hormone deficiency because treatment with growth hormone did not prevent the fall in somatomedin. Addition of fasted rat serum to normal rat serum did not inhibit the somatomedin activity of normal serum, suggesting that the apparent decline in somatomedin was not due to inhibitors affecting the bioassay.

In children with kwashiorkor, growth-hormone levels are markedly elevated (Pimstone *et al.*, 1967), but serum somatomedin concentrations are low (Grant *et al.*, 1973; Van den Brande and DuCaju, 1974b). With refeeding and restoration of serum proteins, the elevated growth-hormone levels decline to normal while somatomedin levels rise (Grant *et al.*, 1973). Concurrent with the rise in the serum concentration of somatomedin, there is an increase in serum levels of albumin and transferrin, both of which are synthesized by the liver. As yet it is not clear whether the low levels of somatomedin in protein–calorie malnutrition reflect a nonspecific breakdown in protein synthesis or whether they represent a well-tuned adaptive process in which low somatomedin and its accompanying growth failure have a protein-sparing effect while excessive concentrations of growth hormone continue to exert lipolytic effects.

Although it has been suggested that the apparent reduction in serum somatomedin concentrations in protein–calorie malnutrition are the result of inhibitors which affect cartilage bioassay systems (Salmon, 1974, 1975; Van den Brande *et al.*, 1975), similarly low concentrations are also found by radioreceptor and radioimmunoassay techniques in which inhibitors would have little or no influence (unpublished data of the authors).

D. SOMATOMEDIN AND CHRONIC RENAL INSUFFICIENCY

The effect of renal insufficiency on serum somatomedin concentration is of particular interest as the kidney is a major site of somatomedin degradation (D'Ercole *et al.*, 1977a) and also has been implicated in somatomedin generation (Section IV,A). Furthermore, children with chronic renal insufficiency often have concurrent failure of linear growth. By bioassay, somatomedin concentrations are low in patients with uremia (Saenger *et al.*, 1974), but concentrations of somatomedin A by placental radioreceptor assay are normal to slightly elevated (Takano *et al.*, 1976a). The discrepancy between these two assay methods again raises the possibility of inhibitors in the bioassay. In particular, the marked increases in serum sulfate concentration which occur in uremia would inhibit the incorporation of radiolabeled sulfate into cartilage *in vitro* (Saenger *et al.*, 1974). For this reason, correction of bioassay results must be made when serum sulfate concentrations are high (Audhya and Gibson, 1974). Increases in somatomedin activity occur with amelioration of uremia by renal transplantation, but normalization of somatomedin does not always correlate with restoration of a normal growth rate (Saenger *et al.*, 1974). It is apparent that comparative studies using bioassays, radioreceptor assays, and radioimmunoassays will be needed to clarify the role of somatomedin in the growth failure of chronic renal insufficiency.

E. LARON DWARFISM

Laron and associates (1966, 1972) described a familial, autosomal recessive form of dwarfism in which the clinical features of affected patients are remarkably similar to the findings in patients with severe growth-hormone deficiency. The unique feature of the syndome, however, is the finding that the serum growth-hormone concentration is increased. In spite of elevated levels of growth hormone, the serum concentration of somatomedin is low and does not rise with the administration of growth hormone (Laron *et al.*, 1971; New *et al.*, 1972; Van den Brande *et al.*, 1974; Kastrup *et al.*, 1975). In addition to their apparent inability to generate somatomedin in response to growth-hormone treatment, affected patients are also unable to retain nitrogen, to increase their blood glucose and fatty acid levels, or to increase their urinary excretion of calcium and hydroxyproline (Van den Brande *et al.*, 1974). On the basis of these findings, it is believed that the defect in these patients rests with the inability of their tissues to respond to growth hormone.

These patients may also provide insight into one of the control mechanisms for growth-hormone secretion. The elevated levels of growth hormone suggest that in normal individuals, the serum concentrations of somatomedin may exert a negative feedback on pituitary growth-hormone secretion. Support for this possibility is also provided by the paradoxical elevation of serum growth-hormone levels in somatomedin-deficient subjects with protein–calorie malnutrition.

VIII. CONCLUDING REMARKS

Our present concepts of the somatomedins have emerged from several different disciplines, as shown in Fig. 9. Although recognition of the kinship between these substances has greatly accelerated progress in unraveling their physiological significance, it remains to be determined where these substances are made and what are the molecular relationships among them. Nature is usually too parsimonious to produce multiple substances to serve exactly the same function.

At the present time, it is unlikely that sufficient quantities of pure somatomedins can be isolated from natural sources to fully meet even the needs of investigators working with *in vitro* systems. The size of these peptides is such, however, that chemical synthesis may be possible when the amino acid structures are fully known. Only then will it be possible to carry out extensive studies of the physiological effects and possible therapeutic uses of these growth factors in experimental animals and human subjects.

ACKNOWLEDGMENTS

This research was supported by USPHS Research Grants AM01022 and HD08299. JVW is a NIH Career Research Awardee No. 4 K06 AM14115, LEU is a Jefferson Pilot Fellow in Academic Medicine.

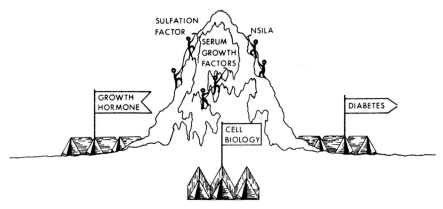

FIG. 9. Different pathways to the same summit?

REFERENCES

Adamson, L. F., and Anast, C. S. (1966). *Biochim. Biophys. Acta* **121**, 10–20.

Adamson, L. F., Gleason, S., and Anast, S. (1964). *Biochim. Biophys. Acta* **83**, 262–271.

Alford, F. P., Bellair, J. T., Burger, H. G., and Lovett, N. (1972). *J. Endocrinol.* **54**, 365–366.

Almqvist, S. (1961). *Acta Endocrinol. (Copenhagen)* **36**, 31–50.

Almqvist, S., and Rune, I (1961). *Acta Endocrinol. (Copenhagen)* **36**, 566–576.

Almqvist, S., Ikkos, D., and Luft, R. (1961). *Acta Endocrinol. (Copenhagen)* **36**, 577–595.

Anderson, H. J., Kastrup, K. W., and Lebech, K. W. (1974). *Acta Paediatr. Scand.* **63**, 328–329.

Antoniades, H. N. (1961). *Endocrinology* **68**, 7–16.

Antoniades, H. N., and Scher, C. D. (1977). *In* "Decennial Review Conference on Cell, Tissue, and Organ Culture" (K. Sanford, ed.) (in press).

Antoniades, H. N., Stathakos, D., and Scher, C. (1975). *Proc. Natl. Acad. Sci. U.S.A.* **72**, 2635–2639.

Audhya, T. K., and Gibson, K. D. (1974). *Endocrinology* **95**, 1614–1620.

Bala, R. M., Blakeley, E. D., and Smith, G. R. (1976). *J. Clin. Endocrinol. Metab.* **43**, 1110–1121.

Beaton, G. R., and Singh, V. (1975). *Pediatr. Res.* **9**, 683.

Benet, E., Schlumberger, A., Chaussain, J. L., and Job, J. C. (1974). *Arch. Fr. Pediatr.* **31**, 339–346.

Berntsen, E. (1968). *Acta Endocrinol. (Copenhagen)* **57**, 69–80.

Birch, M. B., Delcher, H. K., Rendall, J. L., Eisenbarth, G. S., and Lebovitz, H. E. (1973). *Biochem. Biophys. Res. Commun.* **52**, 1184.

Bradshaw, R. A., Hogue-Angeletti, R. A., and Frazier, W. A. (1974). *Recent Prog. Horm. Res.* **30**, 575–596.

Burghen, G. A., Duckworth, W. C., Kitabchi, A. E., Solomon, S. S., and Poffenbarger, P. L. (1976). *J. Clin. Invest.* **57**, 1089–1092.

Bürgi, H., Müller, W. A., Humbel, R. E., Labhart, A., and Froesch, E. R. (1966). *Biochim. Biophys. Acta* **121**, 349–359.

Chesley, L. C. (1962). *Am. J. Obstet. Gynecol.* **84**, 1075–1080.

Chochinov, R. H., Mariz, I. K., and Daughaday, W. H. (1977). *Endocrinology* **100**, 549–556.

Clemmons, D. R., Hintz, R. L., Underwood, L. E., and Van Wyk, J. J. (1974). *Isr. J. Med. Sci.* **10**, 1254–1262.

Cohen, K. L., and Nissley, S. P. (1976). *Acta Endocrinol. (Copenhagen)* **83**, 243–258.

Cohen, K. L., Short, P. A., and Nissley, S. P. (1975). *Endocrinology* **96**, 193–198.

Cohen, S., and Carpenter, G. (1975). *Proc. Natl. Acad. Sci. U.S.A.* **72**, 1317–1321.

Cohen, S., and Taylor, J. D. (1974). *Recent Prog. Horm. Res.* **30**, 533–550.

Daughaday, W. H. (1975). *Adv. Metab. Disord.* **8**, 159–170.

Daughaday, W. H., and Kipnis, D. M. (1966). *Recent Prog. Horm. Res.* **22**, 49–99.

Daughaday, W. H., and Mariz, I. K. (1962). *J. Lab. Clin. Med.* **59**, 741–752.

Daughaday, W. H., and Reeder, C. J. (1967). *J. Lab. Clin. Med.* **68**, 357–368.

Daughaday, W. H., Salmon, W. D., Jr., and Alexander, F. (1959). *J. Clin. Endocrinol. Metab.* **19**, 743–758.

Daughaday, W. H., Heins, J. N., Srivastava, L., and Hammer, C. (1968). *J. Lab. Clin. Med.* **72**, 803–812.

Daughaday, W. H., Laron, Z., Pertzelan, A., and Heins, J. N. (1969). *Trans. Assoc. Am. Physicians* **82**, 129–138.

Daughaday, W. H., Hall, K., Raben, M., Salmon, W. D., Van den Brande, J. L., and Van Wyk, J. J. (1972). *Nature (London)* **235**, 107.

Daughaday, W. H., Phillips, L. S., and Mueller, M. C. (1976). *Endocrinology* **98**, 1214–1219.

Day, H. G., and Follis, R. H., Jr. (1941). *Endocrinology* **28**, 83–93.

Dearden, L. C., and Mosier, H. D., Jr. (1972) *Clin. Orthop. Relat. Res.* **87**, 322–331.

Delcher, H. K., Eisenbarth, G. S., and Lebovitz, H. E. (1973). *J. Biol. Chem.* **248**, 1901–1905.

D'Ercole, A. J., Underwood, L. E., Van Wyk, J. J., Decedue, C. J., and Foushee, D. B. (1976a). *In* "Growth Hormone and Related Peptides" (A. Pecile and E. E. Müller, eds.), pp. 190–201. Excerpta Med. Found., Amsterdam.

D'Ercole, A. J., Foushee, D. B., and Underwood, L. E. (1976b). *J. Clin. Endocrinol. Metab.* **43**, 1069–1077.

D'Ercole, A. J., Decedue, C. J., Furlanetto, R. W., Underwood, L. E., and Van Wyk, J. J. (1977a). *Endocrinology* **101**, 577–586.

D'Ercole, A. J., Underwood, L. E., and Van Wyk, J. J. (1977b). *J. Pediatr.* **90**, 375–381.

Drezner, M. K., Eisenbarth, G. S., Neelon, F. A., and Lebovitz, H. E. (1975). *Biochim. Biophys. Acta* **381**, 384–396.

Duckworth, W. C. (1976). *Biochim. Biophys. Acta* **437**, 531–543.

Dulak, N. C., and Temin, H. M. (1973a). *J. Cell. Physiol.* **81**, 153–160.

Dulak, N. C., and Temin, H. M. (1973b). *J. Cell. Physiol.* **81**, 161–170.

Eisenbarth, G. S., Beuttel, S. C., and Lebovitz, H. E. (1973). *Biochim. Biophys. Acta* **331**, 397–409.

Elders, J. M., Wingfield, B. S., McNatt, M. L., Clarke, J. S., and Hughes, E. R. (1975a). *Am. J. Dis. Child.* **129**, 1391–1396.

Elders, J. M., Wingfield, B. S., McNatt, M. L., Lee, J. A., and Hughes, E. R. (1975b). *Ann. Clin. Lab. Sci.* **5**, 440–451.

Ellis, S., Hublé, J., and Simpson, M. E. (1953). *Proc. Soc. Exp. Biol. Med.* **84**, 603–605.

Francis, M. J. O., and Hill, D. J. (1975). *Nature (London)* **255**, 167–168.

Froesch, E. R., Bürgi, H., Ramseier, E. B., Bally, P., and Labhart, A. (1963). *J. Clin. Invest.* **42**, 1816–1834.

Froesch, E. R., Müller, W. A., Bürgi, H., Waldvogel, M., and Labhart, A. (1966). *Biochim. Biophys. Acta* **121**, 360–374.

Froesch, E. R., Bürgi, H., Müller, W. A., Humbel, R. E., Jakob, A., and Labhart, A. (1967). *Recent Prog. Horm. Res.* **23**, 565–616.

Froesch, E. R., Zapf, J., Meuli, C., Mäder, M., Waldvogel, M., Kaufman, U., and Morell, B. (1975). *Adv. Metab. Disord.* **8**, 211–236.

Froesch, E. R., Zapf, J., Audhya, T. K., Ben-Porath, E., Segen, B. J., and Gibson, K. D. (1976). *Proc. Natl. Acad. Sci. U.S.A.* **73**, 2904–2908.

Fryklund, L., Uthne, K., and Sievertsson, H. (1974a). *Biochem. Biophys. Res. Commun.* **61**, 950–956.

Fryklund, L., Uthne, K., and Sievertsson, H. (1974b). *Biochem. Biophys. Res. Commun.* **61**, 957–962.

Furlanetto, R. W., Underwood, L. E., Van Wyk, J. J., and D'Ercole, A. J. (1977). *J. Clin. Invest.* **60**, 648–657.

Garland, J. T., Jennings, J., Levitsky, L. L., and Buchanan, F. (1976). *J. Clin. Endocrinol. Metab.* **43**, 847–851.

Gey, G. O., and Thalheimer, W. (1924). *J. Am. Med. Assoc.* **82**, 1609.

Giordano, G., Foppiani, E., Minuto, F., Perroni, D., and DiCicco, M. (1975). *Acta Endocrinol. (Copenhagen), Suppl.* **199**, 262.

Giordano, G., Foppiani, E., Perroni, D., and Minuto, F. (1976). *Proc. Natl. Congr. Ital. Endocr. Soc., 16th, 1976*, pp. 175–199.

Girard, F., Schimpff, R. M., Lassare, C., and Donnadieu, M. (1975). *Pediatr. Res.* **9**, 683.

Goldwasser, E. (1975). *Fed. Proc., Fed. Am. Soc. Exp. Biol.* **34**, 2285–2292.

Gospodarowicz, D., and Moran, J. S. (1976). *Annu. Rev. Biochem.* **45**, 531–558.

Gospodarowicz, D., Greene, G., and Moran, J. (1975). *Biochem. Biophys. Res. Commun.* **65**, 779–787.

Grant, D. B., Hambley, J., Becker, D., and Pimstone, B. L. (1973). *Arch. Dis. Child.* **48**, 596–600.

Greenspan, F. S., Li, C. H., Simpson, M. E., and Evans, H. M. (1949). *Endocrinology* **45**, 455–463.

Gregory, H. (1975). *Nature (London)* **257**, 325–327.

Groelke, J., and Baseman, J. B. (1976). *Nature (London)* **263**, 140–142.

Hall, K. (1970). *Acta Endocrinol. (Copenhagen)* **63**, 338–350.

Hall, K. (1971). *Acta Endocrinol. (Copenhagen)* **66**, 491–497.

Hall, K. (1972). *Acta Endocrinol. (Copenhagen), Suppl.* **163**, 1–52.

Hall, K., and Olin, P. (1972). *Acta Endocrinol. (Copenhagen)* **69**, 417–433.

Hall, K., and Uthne, K. (1971). *Acta Med. Scand.* **190**, 137–143.

Hall, K., Takano, K., and Fryklund, L. (1974). *J. Clin. Endocrinol. Metab.* **39**, 973–976.

Hayashi, I., and Sato, G. H. (1976). *Nature (London)* **259**, 132–134.

Heins, J. N., Garland, J. T., and Daughaday, W. H. (1970). *Endocrinology* **87**, 688–692.

Herbai, G. (1970). *Acta Soc. Med. Ups.* **75**, 209–228.

Hintz, R. L., Clemmons, D. R., Underwood, L. E., and Van Wyk, J. J. (1972). *Proc. Natl. Acad. Sci. U.S.A.* **69**, 2351–2353.

Hintz, R. L., Orsini, E. M., and Van Camp, M. G. (1974a). *Program, 56th Annu. Meet. Endocr. Soc.* Abstract No. 31.

Hintz, R. L., Seeds, J. M., and Johnsonbaugh, R. E. (1974b). *Pediatr. Res.* **8**, 369.

Hollenberg, M. D., and Cuatrecasas, P. (1975). *J. Biol. Chem.* **250**, 3845–3853.

Holley, R. W., and Kiernan, J. A. (1974). *Proc. Natl. Acad. Sci. U.S.A.* **71**, 2908–2911.

Humbel, R. E., Bünzli, H., Mülly, K., Oelz, O., Froesch, E. R., and Ritschard, W. J. (1970). *Diabetes, Proc. Congr. Int. Diabetes Fed., 7th, 1971* Excerpta Med. Found. Int. Congr. Ser. No. 231, pp. 306–317.

Hurley, T., D'Ercole, A. J., Handwerger, S., Underwood, L. E., Furlanetto, R. W., and Fellows, R. E. *Endocrinology* **101**, 1635–1638.

Illiano, G., and Cuatrecasas, P. (1972). *Science* **175**, 906–908.

Jakob, A., Hauri, C., and Froesch, E. R. (1968). *J. Clin. Invest.* **47**, 2678-2688.
Jefferson, L. S., and Korner, A. (1967). *Biochem. J.* **104**, 826-832.
Jepson, J. H., and McGarry, E. E. (1972). *Blood* **39**, 238-248.
Johnson, G. S., Friedman, R. M., and Pastan, I. (1971). *Proc. Natl. Acad. Sci. U.S.A.* **68**, 425-429.
Kahn, C. R., Megyesi, K., and Roth, J. (1976). *J. Clin. Invest.* **57**, 526-529.
Kastrup, K. W., Andersen, H., and Hanssen, K. F. (1975). *Acta Paediatr. Scand.* **64**, 613-618.
Koumans, J., and Daughaday, W. H. (1963). *Trans. Assoc. Am. Physicians* **76**, 152-172.
Laron, Z., Pertzelan, A., and Mannheimer, S. (1966). *Isr. J. Med. Sci.* **2**, 152-155.
Laron, Z., Pertzelan, A., Karp, M., Kowadlo-Silbergeld, A., and Daughaday, W. H. (1971). *J. Clin. Endocrinol. Metab.* **33**, 332-342.
Laron, Z., Karp, M., Pertzelan, A., Kauli, R., Keret, R., and Doron, M. (1972). *Growth Growth Horm. Proc. Int. Symp.*, *2nd, 1971* Excerpta Med. Found. Int. Congr. Ser. No. 244, pp. 458-482.
Lebovitz, H. E., Drezner, M. K., and Neelon, F. A. (1976). *In* "Growth Hormone and Related Peptides" (A. Pecile and E. E. Müller, eds.), pp. 202-215. Excerpta Med. Found., Amsterdam.
Lecornu, M. (1973). *Arch. Fr. Pediatr.* **30**, 595-608.
Leonards, J. R. (1959). *Fed. Proc., Fed. Am. Soc. Exp. Biol.* **18**, 272.
Lewis, U. J., Singh, R. N. P., Peterson, S. M., and Vanderlaan, W. P. (1976). *In* "Growth Hormone and Related Peptides" (A. Pecile and E. E. Müller, eds.), pp. 64-74. Excerpta Med. Found., Amsterdam.
Liberti, J. P. (1975). *Biochem. Biophys. Res. Commun.* **67**, 1226-1233.
McConaghey, P. (1972). *J. Endocrinol.* **52**, 1-9.
McConaghey, P., and Dehnel, J. (1972). *J. Endocrinol.* **52**, 587-588.
McConaghey, P., and Sledge, C. B. (1970). *Nature (London)* **225**, 1249-1250.
McKeehan, W. L., McKeehan, K. A., Hammond, S. L., and Ham, R. G. (1977). *In Vitro* **13**, 399-416.
Marshall, R. N., Underwood, L. E., Viona, S. J., Foushee, D. B., and Van Wyk, J. J. (1974). *J. Clin. Endocrinol. Metab.* **39**, 283-292.
Mayberry, H. E., Van den Brande, J. L., Van Wyk, J. J., and Waddell, W. J. (1971). *Endocrinology* **88**, 1309-1317.
Megyesi, K., Kahn, C. R., Roth, J., Froesch, E. R., Humbel, R. E., Zapf, J., and Neville, D. M., Jr. (1974a). *Biochem. Biophys. Res. Commun.* **57**, 307-315.
Megyesi, K., Kahn, C. R., Roth, J., and Gorden, P. (1974b). *J. Clin. Endocrinol. Metab.* **38**, 931-934.
Megyesi, K., Kahn, C. R., Roth, J., and Gorden, P. (1975). *J. Clin. Endocrinol. Metabl.* **41**, 475-484.
Megyesi, K., Kahn, C. R., Roth, J., Neville, D. M., Jr., Nissley, S. P., Humbel, R. E., and Froesch, E. R. (1976). *J. Biol. Chem.* **250**, 8990-8996.
Meuli, C., and Froesch, E. R. (1975). *Eur. J. Clin. Invest.* **5**, 93-99.
Morell, B., and Froesch, E. R. (1973). *Eur. J. Clin. Invest.* **3**, 119-123.
Moses, A. C., Nissley, S. P., Cohen, K. L., and Rechler, M. M. (1976). *Nature (London)* **263**, 137-140.
Mosier, H. D., Jr., Janson, R. A., Hill, R. R., and Dearden, L. C. (1976). *Endocrinology* **99**, 580-589.
Murakawa, S., and Raben, M. S. (1968). *Endocrinology* **83**, 645-650.
Neri, P., Arezzini, C., Canali, G., Cocola, F., and Tarli, P. (1972). *Growth Growth Hor., Proc. Int. Symp.*, *2nd, 1971* Excerpta Med. Found. Int. Congr. Ser. No. 244, pp. 199-208.

New, M. I., Schwartz, E., Parks, G. A., Landey, S., and Wiedemann, E. (1972). *J. Pediatr.* **80**, 620–626.

Nissley, S. P., and Rechler, M. M. (1977). *In* "Decennial Review Conference on Cell, Tissue, and Organ Culture" (K. Sanford, ed.) (in press).

Nutting, D. F., Kostyo, J. L., Mills, J. B., and Wilhelmi, A. E. (1972). *Endocrinology* **90**, 1202–1213.

Oelz, O., Jakob, A., and Froesch, E. R. (1970). *Eur. J. Clin. Invest.* **1**, 48–53.

Pastan, I. (1975). *Adv. Metab. Disord.* **8**, 7–16.

Phillips, L. S., and Young, H. S. (1976). *Endocrinology* **99**, 304–314.

Phillips, L. S., Herington, A. C., and Daughaday, W. H. (1974a). *Endocrinology* **94**, 856–863.

Phillips, L. S., Herington, A. C., and Daughaday, W. H. (1974b). *In* "Advances in Human Growth Hormone Research" (S. Raiti, ed.), DHEW Publ. No. NIH 74-612, pp. 50–75. U.S. Govt. Printing Office, Washington, D.C.

Phillips, L. S., Herington, A. C., and Daughaday, W. H. (1975). *Endocrinology* **97**, 780–785.

Phillips, L. S., Herington, A. C., and Daughaday, W. H. (1976). *Endocrinology* **98**, 606–614.

Pierson, R. W., Jr., and Temin, H. M. (1972). *J. Cell. Physiol.* **79**, 319–329.

Pimstone, B., Barbezat, G., Hansen, J. D. L., and Murray, P. (1967). *Lancet* **2**, 1333–1334.

Poffenbarger, P. L. (1975). *J. Clin. Invest.* **56**, 1455–1463.

Posner, B. I. (1974). *Diabetes* **23**, 209–217.

Raben, M. S., Murakawa, S., and Matute, M. (1972). *Growth Growth Horm., Proc. Int. Symp., 2nd, 1971* Excerpta Med. Found. Int. Congr. Ser. No. 244, pp. 124–131.

Randle, P. J., and Young, F. G. (1956). *J. Endocrinol.* **13**, 335–348.

Rechler, M. M., Podskalny, J. M., and Nissley, S. P. (1976). *Nature (London)* **259**, 134–136.

Rendall, J. L., Delcher, H. K., and Lebovitz, H. E. (1972). *Biochem. Biophys. Res. Commun.* **46**, 1425–1429.

Renner, R., Hepp, K. D., Humbel, R. E., and Froesch, E. R. (1973). *Horm. Metab. Res.* **5**, 56–57.

Rinderknecht, E., and Humbel, R. E. (1976a). *Proc. Natl. Acad. Sci. U.S.A.* **73**, 2365–2369.

Rinderknecht, E., and Humble, R. E. (1976b). *Proc. Natl. Acad. Sci. U.S.A.* **73**, 4379–4381.

Ross, R. (1977). *In* "Decennial Review Conference on Cell, Tissue, and Organ Culture" (K. Sanford, ed.) (in press).

Rutherford, R. B., and Ross, R. (1976). *J. Cell Biol.* **69**, 196–203.

Saenger, P., Wiedemann, E., Schwartz, E., Korth-Schutz, S., Lewy, J. E., Riggio, R. R., Rubin, A. L., Stenzel, K. H., and New, M. I. (1974). *Pediatr. Res.* **8**, 163–169.

Saenger, P., Schwartz, E., Wiedemann, E., Levine, L. S., Tsai, M., and New, M. I. (1976). *Acta Endocrinol. (Copenhagen)* **81**, 9–18.

Salmon, W. D., Jr. (1972). *Growth Growth Horm., Proc. Int. Symp., 2nd, 1971* Excerpta Med. Found. Int. Congr. Ser. No. 244, p. 180.

Salmon, W. D., Jr. (1974). *In* "Advances in Human Growth Hormone Research" (S. Raiti, ed.), DHEW Publ. No. NIH 74-612, pp. 76–94. U.S. Govt. Printing Office, Washington, D.C.

Salmon, W. D., Jr. (1975). *Adv. Metab. Disord.* **8**, 183–199.

Salmon, W. D., Jr., and Daughaday, W. H. (1957). *J. Lab. Clin. Med.* **49**, 825–836.

Salmon, W. D., Jr., and DuVall, M. R. (1970a). *Endocrinology* **86**, 721–727.

Salmon, W. D., Jr., and DuVall, M. R. (1970b). *Endocrinology* **87**, 1168–1180.

Salmon, W. D., Jr., and Hosse, B. R. (1971). *Proc. Soc. Exp. Biol. Med.* **136**, 805–808.

Salmon, W. D., Jr., Bowers, P. H., and Thompson, E. Y. (1963). *J. Lab. Clin. Med.* **61**, 120–128.

Salmon, W. D., Jr., von Hagen, M. J., and Thompson, E. Y. (1967). *Endocrinilogy* **80**, 999–1005.

Samaan, N. A., Dempster, W. J., Fraser, R., Please, M. W., and Stillman, D. (1962). *J. Endocrinol.* **24**, 263–277.

Schimpff, R. M., Donnadieu, M., Glasinovic, J. C., Warnet, J. M., and Girard, F. (1976). *Acta Endocrinol. (Copenhagen)* **83**, 365–372.

Schlumpf, U., Heimann, R., Zapf, J., and Froesch, E. R. (1976). *Acta Endocrinol. (Copenhagen)* **81**, 28–42.

Schwartz, E., Echemendia, E., Schiffer, M., and Panariello, V. A. (1969). *J. Clin. Invest.* **48**, 260–270.

Schwartz, J., and Goodman, H. M. (1976). *Endocrinology* **98**, 730–737.

Sheppard, J. R. (1971). *Proc. Natl. Acad. Sci. U.S.A.* **68**, 1316–1320.

Smith, G. L., and Temin, H. M. (1974). *J. Cell. Physiol.* **84**, 181–192.

Takano, K., Hall, K., Ritzen, M., Iselius, L., and Sievertsson, H. (1976a). *Acta Endocrinol.*

Takano, K., Hall, K., Fryklund, L., and Sievertsson, H. (1976b). *Horm. Metab. Res.* **8**, 16–24.

Tato, L., DuCaju, M. V. L., Prévôt, C., and Rappaport, R. (1975). *J. Clin. Endocrinol. Metab.* **40**, 534–536.

Tell, G. P. E., Cuatrecasas, P., Van Wyk, J. J., and Hintz, R. L. (1973). *Science* **180**, 312–315.

Temin, H. M. (1967). *J. Cell Physiol.* **69**, 377.

Temin, H. M., Pierson, R. W., Jr., and Dulak, N. C. (1972). *In* "Growth, Nutrition and Metabolism of Cells in Culture" (G. H. Rothblat and V. J. Cristofalo, eds.), Vol. 1, pp. 49–81. Academic Press, New York.

Underwood, L. E., Hintz, R. L., Voina, S. J., and Van Wyk, J. J. (1972). *J. Clin. Endocrinol. Metabl.* **35**, 194–198.

Uthne, K. (1973). *Acta Endocrinol. (Copenhagen)* **175**, 1–35.

Uthne, K., and Uthne, T. (1972). *Acta Endocrinol. (Copenhagen)* **71**, 255–264.

Uthne, K., Reagan, C. R., Gimpel, L. P., and Kostyo, J. L. (1974). *J. Clin. Endocrinol. Metab.* **39**, 548–554.

Van den Brande, J. L. (1973). Ph.D. Thesis, Erasmus Universiteit te Rotterdam, The Netherlands.

Van den Brande, J. L., and DuCaju, M. V. L. (1974a). *Acta Endocrinol. (Copenhagen)* **75**, 233–242.

Van den Brande, J. L., and DuCaju, M. L. V. (1974b). *In* "Advances in Human Growth Hormone Research" (S. Raiti, ed.), DHEW Publ. No. NIH 74-612, pp. 98–115. U.S. Govt. Printing Office, Washington, D.C.

Van den Brande, J. L., Van Wyk, J. J., Weaver, R. P., and Mayberry, H. E. (1971). *Acta Endocrinol. (Copenhagen)* **66**, 65–81.

Van den Brande, J. L., DuCaju, M. V. L., Visser, H. K. A., Schopman, W., Hackeng, W. H. L., and Degenhart, H. J. (1974). *Arch. Dis. Child.* **49**, 297–304.

Van den Brande, J. L., Van Buul, S., Heinrich, U., Van Roon, F., Zurcher, T., and Van Steirtegem, A. C. (1975). *Adv. Metab. Disord.* **8**, 171–181.

Van Wyk, J. J., Hall, K., and Weaver, R. P. (1969). *Biochim. Biophys. Acta* **192**, 560–562.

Van Wyk, J. J., Hall, K., Van den Brande, J. L., and Weaver, R. P. (1971). *J. Clin. Endocrinol. Metab.* **32**, 389–403.

Van Wyk, J. J., Underwood, L. E., Hintz, R. L., Clemmons, D. R., Voina, S. J., and Weaver, R. P. (1974). *Recent Prog. Horm. Res.* **30**, 259–318.

Van Wyk, J. J., Underwood, L. E., Baseman, J. B., Hintz, R. L., Clemmons, D. R., and Marshall, R. N. (1975). *Adv. Metab. Disord.* **8**, 127–50.

Van Wyk, J. J., Furlanetto, R. W., Plet, A. S., D'Ercole, A. J., and Underwood, L. E. (1977). *In* "Decennial Review Conference on Cell, Tissue, and Organ Culture" (K. Sanford, ed.) (in press).

von Puttkamer, K., Bierich, J. R., Brugger, F., Hirche, W., and Schönberg, D. (1977). *Deutsch. Med. Wschr.* **102**, 983–994.

Werner, S., Hall, K., and Löw, H. (1974). *Horm. Metab. Res.* **6**, 319–325.

White, A., and Goldstein, A. L. (1975). *Adv. Metab. Disord.* **8**, 359–370.

Wiedemann, E., and Schwartz, E. (1972). *J. Clin. Endocrinol. Metab.* **34**, 51–58.

Winegrad, A. J., Shaw, W. N., Lukens, F. D. W., Stady, W. C., and Renold, A. E. (1959). *J. Biol. Chem.* **234**, 1922–1928.

Wu, A., Grant, D. B., Hambley, J., and Levi, A. J. (1974). *Clin. Sci. Mol. Med.* **47**, 359–366.

Yalow, R. S., Hall, K., and Luft, R. (1975). *J. Clin. Invest.* **55**, 127–137.

Yde, H. (1968). *Acta Endocrinol. (Copenhagen)* **57**, 557–564.

Zapf, J., Mäder, M., Waldvogel, M., Schalch, D. S., and Froesch, E. R. (1975a). *Arch. Biochem. Biophys.* **168**, 630–637.

Zapf, J., Waldovogel, M., and Froesch, E. R. (1975b). *Arch. Biochem. Biophys.* **168**, 638–645.

CHAPTER 4

The Ontogeny of Estrogen Receptors

Alvin M. Kaye

I. INTRODUCTION

The characterization of cytoplasmic and nuclear binding proteins (receptors) for steroid hormones has revealed a general pattern of interactions, which seems common to all steroid hormones, involving the translocation into the nucleus of a steroid–protein complex which in turn binds to chromatin at loci termed acceptor sites and initiates the synthesis of mRNA for proteins characteristic of the hormone. The current picture has been summarized in several excellent recent general reviews; among them are those by Baulieu *et al.* (1975), Chan and O'Malley (1976), Edelman (1975), King

149

(1976), Liao (1975), Yamamoto and Alberts (1976), and the comprehensive book of King and Mainwaring (1974).

The natural development of the field of steroid hormone receptors involved an initial concentration on problems of mechanism of action which resulted in the scheme briefly mentioned above. However, the parallel growth of interest in the effects of steroid hormones in differentiation [see "Hormones in Development," edited by Hamburgh and Barrington (1971)] and age-dependent responses to hormones led an increasing number of investigators to wonder about the extent to which a change in responsiveness of a cell type to a steroid hormone is due to a change in the concentration of receptor molecules available for interaction with the steroid. In the extreme case they sought to find the time of earliest appearance of a receptor in ontogeny which thereby sets a lower limit on the age at which a response can occur. More generally, one can now ask if there is any evidence for a regulatory mechanism in which the concentration of receptor sets a limit on the action of a steroid hormone.

However, the presence of specific protein receptors for a steroid hormone in a cell is only a necessary but not sufficient condition for the response of that cell to the hormone. Study of the ontogeny of steroid receptors has revealed situations in which both cytoplasmic and nuclear receptors were normal by all available criteria and yet the full range of responses to the appropriate steroid hormone failed to be elicited (cf. Yamamoto *et al.*, 1975).

A more general limitation to be kept in mind in all the following considerations results from the plausible prediction (Rosen and O'Malley, 1975; Yamamoto and Alberts, 1975) that there are a small number of undetected specific sites on chromatin (effector sites) at which estrogen is bound at a higher affinity than shown by the many thousands of nuclear acceptor sites now demonstrable. Thus, quantification of the nuclear binding sites may still be at least one step away from dealing with the true "effector" site on the chromatin [see the model of Rosen and O'Malley (1975) in a previous volume of this treatise]. On the other hand, it may also make a reasonable model to assume that "effector" sites are a fairly constant proportion of total nuclear binding sites, so that the concentration of "acceptor" sites now being determined may still turn out to be a useful indicator for the number of "effector" sites, when relative values are compared, as in studies on ontogeny.

In this review, the term *estrogen receptor* will be used in the sense of a protein with a high-affinity specific binding capacity for estrogen, because the identification of any molecular species as the one which actually mediates the action of estrogen has yet to be accomplished. In order to standardize reference to ages of immature animals, the day on which the young were found with their mother will be called day 1. Wherever possible, the ages reported by authors who call this day 0 will be changed to conform to the above convention.

Techniques for the measurement of estradiol receptors are detailed in several highly recommended articles in a recent volume of "Methods in Enzymology" (O'Malley and Hardman, 1975) which should be consulted for the clear distinction between occupied and unoccupied sites and other pitfalls in interpretation of data on receptors.

Because of the classical use of the immature rat uterus for studying the mechanism of action of estrogens (Mueller *et al.*, 1958), we will consider first the ontogeny of estrogen receptors in the uterus. The macromolecular responses to estrogen in rat uterus have been critically reviewed by Katzenellenbogen and Gorski (1975a) in a previous volume of this series.

II. MAMMALIAN REPRODUCTIVE TRACT

The first demonstration of the selective uptake and retention of a steroid hormone by its responsive organs (Glascock and Hoekstra, 1959) was in immature female sheep and goats. Physiological doses of [³H]hexestrol were found in higher concentration in uterus and vagina than in any other organ tested. Subsequently, the pioneering investigations of Jensen and his collaborators utilized the immature (22- to 24-day-old) rat uterus for the study of [³H]estradiol uptake (Jensen and Jacobson, 1960, 1962). The crucial demonstration by Toft and Gorski (1966) of a cytoplasmic estrogen receptor molecule, by sucrose density-gradient centrifugation, also utilized uteri from 20- to 23-day-old rats. The rat uterus, therefore, became a classical source of material for the study of steroid-hormone receptors, and estrogen continued to be a favorite hormone for receptor studies. By 1972, King, in his bibliography on cellular estrogen binding proteins, listed 212 references; however, only four of these papers (Clark and Gorski, 1970; Feherty *et al.*, 1970; Kato *et al.*, 1971a; Lee and Jacobson, 1971) referred to the developmental aspects of estrogen receptors.

A. THE DEVELOPING RAT UTERUS

1. Nuclear and Cytoplasmic Receptors

Clark and Gorski (1970) compared the properties of the cytoplasmic estrogen receptor in rats of several ages between 2 and 24 days after birth, using a glass-binding method (Clark and Gorski, 1969) to obtain the data shown in Fig. 1. The concentration of cytosol receptor found at 2 days was 1.4 fmoles* per μg of DNA, which provides approximately 5000 sites per cell when the value of 6.6 pg DNA per nucleus is taken. The concentration of cytosol

---

*fmoles = femtomoles = 10^{-15} moles.

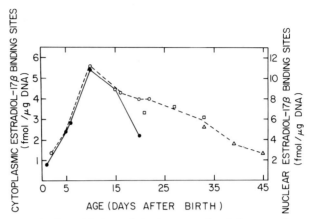

FIG. 1. Ontogeny of binding of [³H]estradiol-17β to cytosol and chromatin from rat uterus. O- - -O, cytosol, average of 3–4 pooled samples (redrawn from Clark and Gorski, 1970); ●——●, nuclei, average of 5–8 pooled samples (redrawn from Sömjen *et al.*, 1973a); □- - -□, cytosol from uteri of rats with closed vaginas, or △- - -△, open vaginas, average of 5–7 pooled samples (drawn from data of Lee and Jacobson, 1971).

receptor rises to a peak at 10 days and then declines to a plateau value between 15 and 22 days, which represents approximately three times the value at 2 days. Feherty *et al.* (1970), as part of a broader study of changes in the concentration of estradiol receptors in uterine cytosol (using a dextran–charcoal method to eliminate low-affinity and nonspecific binding), followed the decline in concentration of receptor from a value of 16 fmoles per μg DNA at 1.5 weeks after birth (rats weighing 20 gm) to an average plateau value of 2.5 fmols per μg DNA in mature rats weighing 70–180 gm.

The subsequent study of nuclear receptors during postnatal development of the rat uterus (Sömjen *et al.*, 1973a) by means of the exchange-binding method of Anderson *et al.* (1972) showed changes in the concentration of nuclear receptors parallel to those in the cytoplasm. Sucrose density-gradient profiles of nuclear 5 S receptors (Luck *et al.*, 1973) showed a smaller peak at 7 days than at 13 or 20 days; within the limitations that these authors point out, i.e., the quantitative reliability of comparing the areas of peaks in density gradients, their results agree with the data presented in Fig. 1. The parallel development of cytoplasmic and nuclear receptors was predictable on the basis of the findings of Williams and Gorski (1972) that, over the entire range of fractional saturation of estrogen binding sites, 85% of the bound estradiol is found in the nucleus. The discrepancy in the absolute values for receptor concentrations among studies on cytoplasmic and nuclear receptors (Fig. 1) is probably due to the different methods used in the assays: e.g., the exchange binding assay was shown by Anderson *et al.* (1972) to give a value for total nuclear receptors which is twice the value for cytoplasmic receptors revealed by the glass-binding assay (Clark and Gorski, 1970).

The values found for cytoplasmic receptor at its peak concentration at 10 days after birth were not significantly different in normal rats and in rats ovariectomized when 2 days old (Clark and Gorski, 1970); the uteri of these two groups of rats also showed no difference in wet weight or in protein or DNA content. These data led to the conclusion that ovarian estrogen is not necessary for the 4-fold increase in estrogen receptor concentration (Fig. 1) between days 2 and 10. The dissociation constant of approximately 3×10^{-9} M of the cytoplasmic receptor in 2- to 10-day-old rats and its sedimentation coefficient of approximately 8 S, as well as the 5 S sedimentation coefficient of the nuclear receptor, are all indistinguishable from the properties of the corresponding receptors found in uteri of 20-day-old or mature rats (cf. Jensen and De Sombre, 1972). By the use of an elegant dry-mount autoradiographic technique, reviewed by Stumpf and Sar (1975a; Stumpf, 1971), these authors demonstrated nuclear concentration of [³H]estradiol in uteri of 2-day-old rats in epithelial, stromal, and myometrial cells (Sheridan *et al.*, 1974a) similar to the previous demonstration (Stumpf, 1968) of nuclear concentration of [³H]estradiol in all the cell types of uteri from 24-day-old rats. This was shown by both the percentage of silver grains over nuclei (68%) and the number of silver grains per 10 μm^3 area, which was 7.5–16 times higher in nuclei than outside the nuclear area.

Available cytoplasmic receptor sites during pubescence were studied by Lee and Jacobson (1971), who found a decrease in receptor concentration in uteri during the period from 21 to 45 days (Fig. 1) correlated with puberty. At 33 days, one-fourth of the rat population was found with open vaginas (and an average uterine weight of 179 mg) and with a receptor concentration of 13 fmoles/mg wet weight uterus. Compared to these, rats with closed vaginas (whose uteri averaged 67 mg wet weight) had a receptor concentration of 26 fmoles/mg uterus.

Because both the technique used above, a modification of the cytosol-binding technique of Puca and Bresciani (1969), and the glass-binding method previously cited measure only unoccupied receptor sites, the above data must be considered in conjunction with the recently available information on the high estrogen concentration in plasma during development, to be described in the following section.

2. Receptors and Changes in Concentration of Circulating Estrogens during Development

The data obtained by Döhler and Wuttke (1975) (Fig. 2) when using anti-estradiol-carbomethoxime BSA immune sera, which did not cross-react more than 0.01% with any other steroid, showed the highest estradiol con-

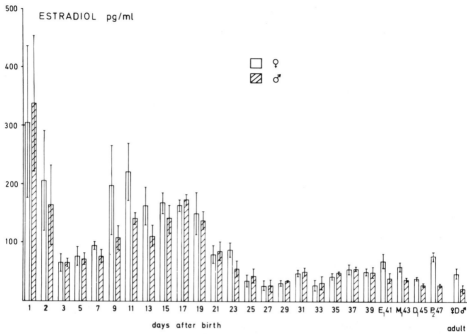

FIG. 2. Concentration of estradiol-17β in serum of developing rats. The days of the first estrous cycle are shown: E_1 = day of vaginal opening, M_1 = 1st metestrus, D_1 = 1st diestrus, P_2 = following proestrus, D = adult diestrus. Vertical lines indicate the standard error of the mean (from Döhler and Wuttke, 1975).

centration measured at any age in the serum of 1-day-old rats (~300 pg/ml in females). By the second day after birth, the estradiol concentration in serum had fallen to near 200 pg/ml in female rats, comparable to the peak concentration seen at 9 and 11 days (Fig. 2). A previous study by Meijs-Roelofs *et al.* (1973), in which plasma estradiol concentration was measured between days 5 and 35 after birth by radioimmunoassay using an antibody against an estradiol-17β-6 (*O*-carboxylmethyl) oxime bovine serum albumin complex, showed a peak value of 55–60 pg/ml between days 10 and 15 after a 10-fold lower value on day 5, and even lower to undetectable values between days 25 and 35. High estrogen values at 10 days were found using a protein binding assay and by a double-isotope-derivative method as well as by radioimmunoassay by Weisz and Gunsalus (1973), who first applied radioimmunoassay techniques to the measurement of estrogen concentrations in plasma from prepuberal rats. They found even higher values for estradiol by radioimmunoassay than by the other two methods used, and concluded from experiments on ovariectomized rats that the adrenal glands were the source of a "spurious" estradiol as well as an "astronomical" quantity of estrone (~1 ng/ml at 10 days). A drop in concentration of serum estradiol from 150 to 19 pg/ml during the period from 10 to 30 days after birth was measured by Cheng and Johnson (1973/1974) by radioimmunoassay using sheep antiserum against bovine serum albumin estradiol-17β conjugate. Employing a more specific and sensitive antibody for estradiol (capable of measuring 0.5 pg of estradiol with a final antibody dilution of 1:10^5), Cheng and Johnson (1974) confirmed the conclusion that the concentration of circulating estradiol drops during this period. The absolute values they obtained, however, were lower; 43 and 22 pg/ml at 11 and 21 days after birth, respectively.

It is striking that the peak estradiol concentrations found at approximately 10 days are significantly higher than the values measured in the same laboratories at the time of the preovulatory estrogen surge in cycling rats.

A peak in estrogen synthesis by rat ovarian homogenates *in vitro* (63 pg/mg tissue/hour) was also found at 10 days after birth by Smeaton *et al.* (1975); this was one order of magnitude higher than the rate at 6 days (6 pg/ml/hour). The rate declined to 19 pg/ml/hour at day 14.

In contrast to the high concentration of circulating estrogen, the concentration of estrogen receptors is at a nadir at 1–2 days after birth (Fig. 1). Following the estrogen peak at 9–19 days (Fig. 2), its concentration declines more steeply than the concentration of cytoplasmic receptors.

Therefore, comparison of the curves in Fig. 1 and the data in Fig. 2, plus the lack of influence of ovariectomy on receptor concentration at 10 days (see above, Clark and Gorski, 1970) leads to the conclusion that there is no direct correlation between the concentration of circulating estradiol and the concentration of estrogen receptors in developing rat uterus. Clark and Gorski (1970) have also questioned whether prior exposure to estradiol is necessary for the initial appearance of estrogen receptors during ontogeny. In the rat uterus, nuclear 5 S receptors have been detected in 1-day-old animals (Sömjen *et al.*, 1973a) and cytoplasmic receptors have been detected in the Müllerian duct of 21-day-old fetuses (Sömjen *et al.*, 1976). Because receptors are therefore present in fetal life (cf. Sections II,A,4, IV, and V for comparable data on younger fetuses, other mammals, and birds) the influence of maternoplacental hormones on the first appearance of receptors remains to be evaluated.

3. Cellular Receptors and Estrogen Binding in Plasma (α_1-Fetoprotein)

The quantitative analysis of estrogen receptors in cytosol of fetal, neonatal, and immature rodents is complicated by the presence of plasma proteins, with a high affinity and binding capacity for estrogens, which are found among the soluble proteins in preparations of cytosol.

During gestation and postnatal life, there are drastic changes in the concentrations of circulating steroid-binding proteins. It was noted first by Wooley *et al.* (1969) that following injection of [^{3}H]estradiol, its concentration in plasma of 4-day-old rats was two orders of magnitude greater than in plasma of intact adult female rats. In plasma from pregnant rats, Soloff *et al.* (1971) found a protein able to bind estradiol-17β and estrone with equally high affinity. Other affinity properties (e.g., lack of displacement by a 9-fold concentration of diethylstilbestrol and a stability of several weeks at 4°C, as compared to several hours for uterine cytosol receptor) distinguished the binding of estradiol by the plasma protein from that by uterine cytosol. Nunez *et al.* (1971a,b,c) found a similar globulin of high binding capacity in serum from 5- to 28-day-old rats of both sexes, and suggested that it was α-fetoprotein. Physiocochemical parameters for this protein were supplied by Raynaud *et al.*, (1971) who called it estradiol-binding plasma protein (EBP) and found a dissociation constant for estradiol of 10^{-8} M at 4°C, a sedimentation coefficient of 4.5 S, stable binding at 60°C, and a concentration of 80 μM in plasma of 20-day-old fetuses of either sex. α-Fetoprotein from both rat and mouse was shown to bind [^{14}C]estradiol and also [^{14}C]estrone (Uriel *et al.*, 1972). Subsequently, Aussel *et al.* (1973) purified α-fetoprotein from rat amniotic fluid, where it is present in concentrations as high as 1 mg/ml, and showed that its characteristics were close to those measured in plasma as described above. Dissociation constants, measured by equilibrium dialysis at 4°C, were 2×10^{-8} M for estradiol and 1×10^{-8} M for estrone. A sedimentation constant of 4 S was found and a molecular weight of 72,000. The group of Nunez purified α-fetoprotein from serum of 18- to 20-day-old rat embryos (Cittanova *et al.*, 1974) and found that it bound 88 pmoles of estradiol per mg (Nunez *et al.*, 1974). The concentration of α-fetoprotein (Fig. 3) falls from a concentration of 60–80 μM in 20-day-old fetuses, with a half-life of 3.9 days, to undetectable levels by the age of 29 days (Raynaud, 1973). A recent review by Sell *et al.* (1976) summarized current knowledge concerning rat and human α-fetoprotein. Partial sequence data are available for α-fetoprotein which show sequence homology with serum albumin (Ruoslahti and Terry, 1976). Serum album in itself, which has a moderate affinity for estradiol and is present in blood at a concentration of 0.7 nM, also is a highly significant serum-binding agent for estrogens (Sandberg *et al.*, 1957).

The presence of such a high and rapidly changing concentration of estrogen-binding protein in rat plasma, which could contribute to the 4 S estradiol-binding peak, led to reinvestigation of the cytoplasmic binding of estradiol during postnatal development (Michel *et al.*, 1974; Sömjen *et al.*, 1974). Both these groups concluded that the 4 S binding peak, which decreased in size with advancing age (Clark and Gorski, 1970) in parallel with

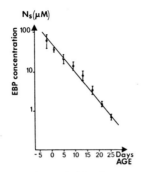

FIG. 3. Decline in concentration of estradiol binding protein (EBP = α-fetoprotein) in rat plasma. The number of binding sites N_s is presented as a function of perinatal age (from Raynaud, 1973).

the decrease in concentration of α-fetoprotein in the plasma, was indeed composed predominantly of a plasma protein which showed a behavior toward diethylstilbestrol (Sömjen *et al.*, 1974) and [³H]estrone (Michel *et al.*, 1974) characteristic of α-fetoprotein. The latter group also showed that antibodies against α-fetoprotein almost eliminated the binding of [³H]estradiol to a protein sedimenting at 4 S, and confirmed that the concentration of the 8 S cytosol estradiol receptor increases rapidly between 6 and 8 days after birth, reaches a peak at 10 days, and declines slightly by day 21. Thus, the refinement of eliminating interference by α-fetoprotein in determining cytosol estrogen receptor led to the same general picture as described in Sections II,A,1 and II,A,2—a peak concentration of cytosol receptor at 10 days coinciding with a peak in the concentration of circulating estrogens. It was a similar use of [³H]diethylstilbestrol by Sömjen *et al.* (1976) to minimize binding to α-fetoprotein which enabled them to demonstrate the presence of an 8 S cytosol receptor for estrogens in the Müllerian ducts of 20-day-old rat fetuses.

4. Estrogen Receptors in the Whole Fetus and in Placenta

Studies of rat fetuses younger than 21 days old are based on analysis of the entire fetus rather than isoalted Müllerian duct (Feherty *et al.*, 1970) and show no detectable binding in fetuses obtained on day 13 of pregnancy, a barely detectable amount (0.05 fmoles/μg DNA) in the younger fetus and in the membranes on the 10th day of pregnancy, and higher values on days 9 and 7 of pregnancy (2.7 fmoles/μg DNA), the earliest time tested for the fetus itself. On the 10th day of pregnancy, a value of 2.3 fmoles/μg DNA was also found for estrogen binding in the placenta; receptors in the placenta declined rapidly with development, disappearing completely in the fetal placenta by the 13th day of pregnancy when only 0.6 fmoles/μg DNA was found in the maternal placenta, a value equal to the concentration in the uterine wall.

The recent study by McCormack and Glasser (1976) demonstrated both cytoplasmic and nuclear estrogen-binding proteins in the basal zone trophoblast of the rat placenta on day 11 of pregnancy, but no detectable receptors in cytosol when tested on day 14 or in nuclei on day 15. The receptors showed the expected high affinity (0.1–0.2 nM), but only a 4 S form was found in cytosol and in the nucleus. KCl extracted a 2 S receptor from the nucleus in poor yield, while trypsin extraction revealed a 4 S receptor. The number of sites per "cell" (based on nuclear counts in this syncytial tissue) is within the range of the reports cited above for uterus and provides another example of an apparently higher number of receptor sites found for estrogen in the nucleus than in the cytoplasm of the same cell.

Because estrogen receptors in the cytoplasm are believed to be the precursors of receptors in the nucleus, it has been tacitly accepted that the absolute values obtained for estrogen receptors, which show a larger number of binding sites in the nucleus than can be accounted for by sites in cytoplasm, are due to methodological inadequacies. However, in regard to other systems, mammalian liver, for example, reports have appeared (Section IV,A) of nuclear binding without the prior necessity for cytoplasmic binding. As pointed out in the introduction (Yamamoto and Alberts, 1975), only a fraction of the nuclear binding observed may be directly related to a response to estrogen. Therefore, it is necessary to consider the range of responses to estradiol before one can attempt to correlate estrogen occupancy of nuclear receptors with response and, in addition, consider suggestions of α-fetoprotein interference with (Raynaud, 1973) or identity with (Uriel *et al.*, 1976) cytoplasmic estrogen receptors.

5. Sequential Acquisition of Responsiveness to Estrogen during Postnatal Development of the Rat Uterus

While both cytoplasmic and nuclear receptors for estrogen are present from birth (see Section II,A,1 above), not all the biosynthetic responses to estrogen which have been observed in 20-day-old or in ovariectomized adult rats are exhibited by rats during the first weeks of life (Kaye *et al.*, 1972, 1974), nor are they all expressed at their maximum capacity (Luck *et al.*, 1973; Katzenellenbogen and Greger, 1974). The earliest biosynthetic response to estrogen as yet reported in this system is the induction in uteri from 2-day-old rats of the first enzyme in the pathway of polyamine biosynthesis, ornithine decarboxylase, to a specific activity (per unit protein) similar to the level attained in the uteri from 21-day-old rats (Kaye *et al.*, 1973). At this age, there is no increase in the concentration of DNA in the uterus 24 hours after injection of estradiol-17β (Luck *et al.*, 1973). DNA concentration is apparently the only other macromolecular parameter which has been measured in uteri of 2-day-old rats.

Tests for other biosynthetic responses which have been made in uteri from 5-day-old Wistar-derived rats (Sömjen *et al.*, 1973b), show no significant increase, 24 hours after injection of estradiol-17β, in wet weight, RNA, protein, or DNA content (Fig. 4). Similarly, no weight increase in uteri of

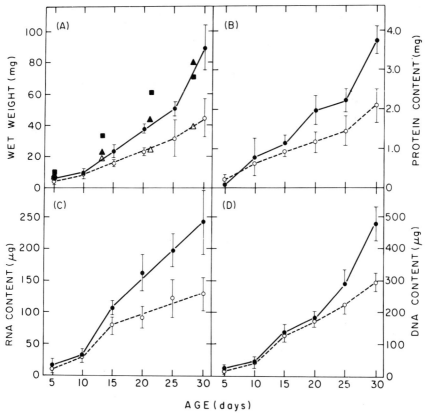

FIG. 4. Responsiveness to estradiol-17β during postnatal development of the uterus. Wistar-derived rats were given a single i.p. injection of either 1% ethanol (control) or estradiol-17β on the day indicated and killed 24 hours later. Rats 15 days or older received 0.5 μg estradiol, 10-day-old rats 0.4 μg, and 5-day-old rats 0.2 μg estradiol. O– – –O, control; ●———●, estradiol-17β. Vertical lines indicate 95% confidence intervals (from Sömjen *et al.*, 1973b). In (A), data are also presented from Raynaud (1973) obtained in Sprague–Dawley specific-pathogen-free rats after a single s.c. injection of estradiol-17β or R2858. Values are averages of responses at 24 and 40 hours for the dose (not necessarily the highest) which gave the greatest response within the ranges tested (0.5–5 μg for estradiol and 0.005–5 μg for R2858). △, 10% ethanol in physiological saline; ▲, estradiol-17β; ■, R2858.

5-day-old Sprague–Dawley specific-pathogen-free rats was found by Raynaud (1973) using estradiol doses up to 5 μg per rat.

However, stimulation of the synthesis of the estrogen-induced protein first described by Notides and Gorski (1966) was demonstrated by Walker *et al.* (1976) in uteri of 5-day-old Wistar-derived rats using autoradiography of sodium dodecyl sulfate polyacrylamide gels, and previously by Katzenellenbogen and Greger (1974) in 6-day-old Sprague–Dawley rats by use of a double-isotope-labeling technique (see the recent summary by Katzenellenbogen and Gorski, 1975b).

Thus, a situation exists in the 5- to 6-day-old rat uterus in which only certain responses among the repertoire of known reactions are manifested following a single injection of estrogen. The possible implication of this differential responsiveness which does not seem to result from changes in the proportions of cell types (Kaye *et al.*, 1974) will be explored below after the completion of this survey of changes in responsiveness during postnatal development.

Luck *et al.* (1973) compared the effects of estrogen injection on wet weight, and synthesis and content of total RNA, protein and DNA in 7-, 13-, and 20-day-old rats (strain unspecified). They reported increases in these parameters in 7-day-old rats, but no increase in DNA content at 20 days. Sömjen *et al.* (1973b) found no increase in total nucleic acid and in total protein synthesis in 10-day-old Wistar-derived rats (Fig. 4), contrasted with the stimulation of the synthesis of specific proteins such as ornithine decarboxylase or the estrogen-induced protein (IP).

In uteri of Sprague–Dawley rats, a significant stimulation of uterine wet weight after a single injection of estradiol-17β could not be obtained until the age of 13 days (Raynaud, 1973; Katzenellenbogen and Greger, 1974). The latter authors found that estradiol elicits only a minimal stimulation of 2-deoxyglucose phosphorylation at 9 days; this parameter showed a maximum stimulation at 19 days. In this series of experiments, a significant increase in the wet weight of uteri 24 hours after estradiol injection was observed by 12 days after birth (cf. Fig. 4). The magnitude of the wet-weight increase at 12 days is the same after a single injection on that day as after three successive daily injections beginning on day 12. When injections are begun on day 13, three daily injections lead to a greater response (230%) than the 80% increase obtained after a single injection (Katzenellenbogen and Greger, 1974). The highest response to three daily injections of estradiol was seen at 23 days, the oldest age tested. This difference in the ability of single or multiple injections of estradiol to stimulate sustained growth based on cell division fits well with the previously reported inability of estrogen to stimulate the incorporation of [³H]thymidine into DNA in 15-day-old rats, compared with the 2-fold increase in this measure of DNA synthetic rate found in 20-day-old rats (Kaye *et al.*, 1972).

These changes during postnatal ontogeny of the uterus have led to the suggestion of postnatal sequential acquisition of responsiveness (Kaye *et al.*, 1974) and the comparison of the early and late responses of the uterus (Katzenellenbogen and Greger, 1974) with the differences in the early and long-term uterotrophic responses of fully competent uteri (from 20-day-old rats) toward estradiol and estriol. The inability of single doses of estriol to stimulate long-term growth and cell division in the uterus can be overcome by administration of estriol at 4-hour intervals. Miller (1969), who reported this, discusses earlier work on the subject and suggestions of previous authors linking this phenomenon with the greater retention of estradiol than estriol by the uterine and vaginal receptor system. The distinction between the activities of these two estrogens has been sharpened by several laboratories which have shown, among other things, that estriol is approximately half as effective as estradiol as an inducer of IP, an early effect (Katzenellenbogen and Gorski, 1972); while a 2 nM concentration of estradiol will saturate 50% of nuclear estrogen-binding sites, almost double the concentration of estriol is required (Ruh *et al.*, 1973). A series of studies by the group of Clark, Peck, and Anderson has recently culminated in the formulation of the distinction shown in Fig. 5 (Clark and Peck, 1976) between short-term nuclear retention of estrogen (responsible for its early effect,

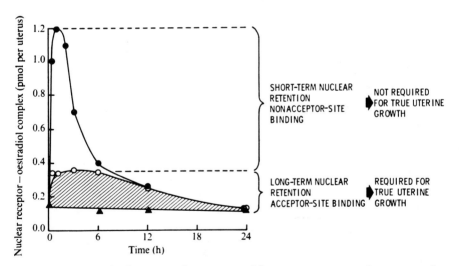

FIG. 5. Relationship between nuclear retention of the estrogen receptor and uterine growth. Immature rats, 21–23 days old, were injected with either 0.1 or 2.5 μg of estradiol, and the accumulation and retention of the estrogen receptor by the uterine nuclear fraction was examined by the [³H]estradiol exchange assay. Uterine growth responses (DNA, RNA, and protein content, wet and dry weight) were measured 24–48 hours after injection (data not shown) and were stimulated maximally by 0.1 μg of estradiol. ●, 2.5 μg of estradiol; ○, 0.1 μg of estradiol; ▲, saline (from Clark and Peck, 1976).

which is insufficient for true uterine growth) and long-term nuclear retention, which is required for the stimulation of true uterine growth. Ruh and Baudendistel (1977) have compared the nuclear accumulation and retention of estrogens and "short-acting estrogens" (synthetic antiestrogens), and suggest that the nuclear salt-resistant form of estrogen binding which is characteristic of the long-acting true estrogens is essential for uterine growth, while the nuclear salt-extractable form of binding may only be capable of initiating short-term responses. They have also presented evidence that the short- and long-acting estrogens may bind to different sites on chromatin (Baudendistel and Ruh, 1976).

At this point in the analysis of the ontogeny of responsiveness, it therefore seems that the most economical working hypothesis would be that there are multiple classes of acceptor sites in chromatin (cf. work of Spelsberg et al., 1971, 1973, 1976 on progesterone; Alberga et al., 1971; Eriksson et al., 1976); more classes of acceptor sites would become available, and at different rates, during development. By the age of 20 days in rats, all classes of sites would seem to be available, but the maximum number of sites in certain classes may continue to grow after 20 days. Once again, this hypothesis is based on the assumption that only a fraction of the several thousand acceptor sites per cell are "effector sites" (Rosen and O'Malley, 1975) that fulfill the requirement of the pharmacologist's definition of a receptor, as the direct mediator of the response studied. If such a development of different classes of acceptor sites does take place during the first month after birth, it would have to depend on changes in chromatin which could most easily be accounted for by nonhistone protein changes which are part of the inherited developmental program of the uterus. One particular change, that which permits rapid resynthesis of cytoplasmic estrogen receptors (Gorski et al., 1971), if it took place during the second week after birth, could explain the lack of difference in response to single and repeated doses of estrogen until the third week of life, as described above.

6. α-Fetoprotein and Responsiveness to Estrogens

Raynaud (1973) proposed that the high concentrations of α-fetoprotein in the circulation of infant rats prevented the action of estradiol. For example, in 5-day-old rats, α-fetoprotein bound estradiol sufficiently well that the availability of estradiol for cytoplasmic binding was reduced below the point where it could cause an increase in uterine wet weight. However, the synthetic estrogen R2858 (11β-methoxy-17-ethynyl-1,3,5(10)-estratriene-3,17β-diol, moxestrol), which does not bind to α-fetoprotein, caused a maximal 31% increase in the wet weight of 5-day-old uteri, compared to an increase of 160% on day 21. Therefore, because there is an increase in responsiveness to R2858 as well as to estradiol-17β during postnatal development, and because both ornithine decarboxylase and IP can be induced by estradiol-17β in 5-day-old rats (see Section II,A,5), the extent to which binding of estrogens to α-fetoprotein reduces the extent of estradiol's interaction with its uterine cytoplasmic receptor should be evaluated by a simultaneous comparison of the concentration dependence of several responses to estrogen in the 5-day-old as compared with the 3-week-old rat.

The influence of neonatal ovariectomy on the growth of the uterus might be considered a test for the efficacy of the naturally secreted ovarian estrogens, for inhibition of uterine growth would simultaneously demonstrate responsiveness of the uterus and a biologically significant concentration of estrogen–receptor complex in uterine cells. This parameter has been measured at 10 days of age with inconsistent results. The Holtzman rats, used by Clark and Gorski (1970) in their study of receptors (see Section II,A,1), after ovariectomy when 2 days old, had uteri averaging 9.9 ± 0.6 mg in weight, insignificantly less than uteri from intact rats, which weighed 10.2 ± 0.5 mg. In contrast, a reduction in the weight of the uterus at 10 days (from 6.3 ± 0.4 to 4.5 ± 0.3 mg) following ovariectomy of Sprague–Dawley rats at 1–2 days has been shown by Baker and Kragt (1969). The strain difference in uterine weights before as well as after ovariectomy suggests once again that there are sufficient strain differences in development of responsiveness to explain why all strains of rats do not show an effect of neonatal ovariectomy at 10 days. There is most likely an effect in all strains at some time between 10 and 15 days, similar to the decrease from 14.8 ± 0.6 to 9.7 ± 0.5 mg in uteri of Sprague–Dawley rats measured at 15 days after birth (Baker and Kragt, 1969). The treatment for 4-day periods beginning on days 2, 6, 10, 14, and 18, of Sprague–Dawley rats with rabbit antiserum against estradiol-17β-6-bovine serum albumin also led to a significant lowering of uterine weights at all ages (Reiter *et al.*, 1972, although not as effectively as ovariectomy. The presence of such an influence of circulating estrogens on uterine weight, even when serum estradiol levels are less than 1 nM and the circulating α-fetoprotein is present at a concentration of greater than 1 μM (cf. above, Figs. 2 and 3), shows that α-fetoprotein cannot completely block the action of endogenously secreted estradiol on the uterus. However, in 5-day-old rats, the concentrations of circulating estrogen in conjunction with the concentration of α-fetoprotein is insufficient to cause the translocation of estrogen receptors from cytoplasm to nucleus in the uterus (Sömjen *et al.*, 1974). Nevertheless, even the use of a higher dose of estradiol, which leads to a detectable concentration of estrogen receptors in the nucleus and to a subsequent response such as stimulation of IP synthesis, cannot elicit general growth responses which we postulate require a later development of competence in the rat uterus.

Thus, as the physiological concentrations of both estrogen and α-fetoprotein change during postnatal development, the definition of the concentration of estrogen which can be neutralized for each system remains to be determined in each case. This problem will be raised again in considering the problem of protection of the susceptible female rat hypothalamus against neonatal sterilization by the high concentrations of estrogens circulating in newborn rats (Section III,C).

A contrary viewpoint to that of Raynaud (1973) on the biological significance of α-fetoprotein interaction with estradiol is the recent claim of Uriel *et al.* (1976) that α-fetoprotein is itself the major high-affinity estrogen binder in rat uterine cytosols and "mediates the early intracellular events associated with estrogen entry." These authors presented immunological evidence that the characteristic 8 S cytoplasmic estrogen receptor, when dissociated in 0.4 M KCl to 4–5 S units, can be adsorbed by anti-α-fetoprotein bound to Bio-Gel γG beads. From a general biological viewpoint, it should be remembered that human α-fetoprotein is a much weaker binder of estradiol than rat α-fetoprotein (see Section II,A,4; Swartz and Soloff, 1974) and that plasma from 5-day-old rats, with an α-fetoprotein concentration of approximately 20 μM (Fig. 3), fails to substitute for uterine cytosol in the formation of 5 S estradiol receptor in isolated nuclei from 5-day-old rat uteri (Sömjen *et al.*, 1974), nor does the α-fetoprotein–estradiol complex bind to DNA (Fox, 1975a).

Recently, two groups have directly disproved the contention of Uriel *et al.* (1976). Ruoslahti and Attardi (1978) have repeated the experiment of Uriel *et al.* by treating the cytosol from uteri of 2-week-old mice with Sepharose-coupled anti-α-fetoprotein serum. The cytosol was then adjusted to 0.4 M KCl concentration and treated a second time with anti-α-fetoprotein serum or with a control adsorbent; both samples were labeled with [3H]estradiol and centrifuged on sucrose gradients containing 0.4 M KCl. Receptor binding in the 4.5 S region of the gradients was identical in the sample treated twice with anti-α-fetoprotein serum and in the control sample. Radanyi *et al.* (1977) have also found that the 8 S receptor does not contain α-fetoprotein, and in addition they have shown that α-fetoprotein (4.5 S) can be distinguished from the estrogen receptor which has a sedimentation coefficient of 5.5 S when rat uterine cytosol is centrifuged in a sucrose gradient containing 0.4 M KCl. This group also found that the half-time of dissociation of estradiol–α-fetoprotein complexes was 100–200 times shorter than that of estradiol–receptor complexes.

B. UTERI OF OTHER SPECIES AND OTHER ORGANS OF THE REPRODUCTIVE SYSTEM

1. Uterus

Recently, Pasqualini *et al.* (1976) extended the data available on estrogen receptors during uterine development by demonstrating a specific cytoplasmic and nuclear receptor for [³H]estradiol in fetal guinea pig uterus at 34–35 days of gestation. The cytoplasmic receptor showed the familiar sedimentation constant of 8.5–9 S and the expected K_d of 0.4 nM (cf. Section II,A,1). At this prenatal age, 90 fmoles of [³H]estradiol were bound per mg protein in cytosol; binding increased to a peak value of 572 fmoles/mg protein at 55–60 days of gestation, and then declined after birth. Nuclear receptors were sequentially extracted with 0.1 M Tris, 0.3 M NaCl, and 1 M NaCl. At the end of fetal life (55–60 days), there was a total of 2.5 nmoles/mg protein of [³H]estradiol binding in these three combined extracts, a value which fell to 1.5 nmoles at 5 days after birth, and to 0.04 nmoles at 4 weeks after birth. Although a 1 M NaCl solution extracts 90–95% of nuclear DNA (Pasqualini *et al.*, 1972), a significant number of "resistant" sites were found which could be extracted successively by 3 M NaCl and 0.2 M NaOH.

The mouse uterus has been used as a classic material for studying the mechanism of action of estrogens, particularly in regard to growth and cell division (cf. Martin and Finn, 1971). An 8 S cytoplasmic receptor is present in the uteri of 1- to 5-day-old mice (Eide *et al.*, 1975) in which an increase in a cervicovaginal antigen (Forsberg and Kvinnsland, 1972) has been reported following two injections of 5 μg of estradiol-17β (Kvinnsland, 1973).

High doses of estradiol-17β (5 μg) reduce the duration of all phases of the mitotic cycle in uteri of neonatal mice [consult Eide (1975a) for references to estrogen effects on the mitotic cycle in uteri of both mice and rats]. Eide invokes this shortening of the mitotic cycle by estrogen to explain why he finds an increased labeling index (but no significant increase in grain count) in uterus, 12 hours after injection of 5 μg of estradiol-17β into neonatal mice. This increase was found only in the epithelium of the uterus and not in stroma. In the uterine cervix, a contrary effect was found, i.e., a decrease in both labeling index and grain counts from 5 through 18 hours after estrogen injection. Eide points out that the experiments of Kaye *et al.* (1972) and Sömjen *et al.* (1973b) (see Section II,A,5), which were performed on immature rat uteri at 24 hours after estrogen treatment, could not have detected the results of the transitory rise in labeling index he reports at 12 hours after estrogen administration. In addition, we could not expect measurement of thymidine incorporation to show an increase in specific activity related to DNA when no increase in grain counts per cell were observed. This problem, like many others in the mechanism of estrogen action, will become much more amenable for resolution when estrogen-responsive cell cultures of uterine epithelium are successfully prepared, perhaps through the use of media containing D-valine (Gilbert and Migeon, 1975) which permits selective growth of epithelial cells by virtue of their content of D-amino acid oxidase.

The interactions between estrogens and uterine receptors in rats and mice are probably similar enough to permit the type of comparison made above;

for example, the IP found in rat uterus has recently been detected in mouse uterus (Sömjen and Kaye, 1976).

Immature rabbit uterus (cf. Borthwick and Smellie, 1975) and calf endometrium (see review by Jensen and De Sombre, 1972) have provided convenient material for the study of estrogen effects on RNA polymerases. The volume of material available from calf uterus has been utilized for studies on both cytoplasmic (Erdos *et al.*, 1971) and nuclear receptors (Maurer and Chalkley, 1967) and on "acceptors" (Puca *et al.*, 1974, 1975) for estradiol. Bovine endometrium has been utilized for studying the relationship between the concentration of plasma estrogen and the concentration of cytoplasmic estrogen receptors (Kimball and Hansel, 1974).

2. Vagina

Although the vagina has been a classical organ for testing the mitotic response to estrogens (Emmens *et al.*, 1962), it has received much less attention than the uterus in studies of estrogen receptors. However, the outbreak of vaginal and cervical adenocarcinoma, predominantly of the clear-cell variety, in young women whose mothers had been treated with high doses of diethylstilbestrol during the first trimester of pregnancy (see the review of Prins *et al.*, 1976) as well as the associated nonneoplastic genital tract anomalies (Herbst *et al.*, 1972), focus special attention on problems of the ontogeny of the vagina and on the study of vaginal steroid-hormone receptors. While the retention of estradiol in vagina has been measured (see Lisk *et al.*, 1976, for previous references), there appears to be no information available to date on the ontogeny of estrogen receptors in this organ. The effects of estradiol on the metabolism of the vagina have been reviewed by Katzman *et al.* (1971). The opposite effects of estradiol in causing a shortening of the cell cycle of uterine cells and a lengthening of the cycle in cervical and vaginal fornix cells have been discussed by Eide (1975b), who includes references to previous publications. Further estrogen effects on neonatal vagina will be cited in Section III,C,2 in the discussion of neonatal sterilization.

3. Ovary and Oviduct

The complex hormonal interactions among both steroid and protein hormones in the synergistic stimulation of follicular growth (Goldenberg *et al.*, 1972) and in the control of hormone receptors during ovarian development have recently been summarized by Richards and Midgley (1976). The role of estrogen in these processes focuses attention on the detection and measurement of estrogen receptors in the ovary, which is at the same time a site of estrogen synthesis.

Nuclear concentration of [^{3}H]estradiol in primitive germ cells of the ovary and in all cells of the fetal rat oviduct immediately before birth was demonstrated by Nakai *et al.* (1972), using dry-mount autoradiography. They found 80% of silver grains over nuclei which represented a 4-fold concentration of silver grains per unit area over nuclei as compared to cytoplasm. In ovaries of 2-day-old rats, Sheridan *et al.* (1974d), using dry-mount and thaw-mount autoradiography (see Stumpf and Sar, 1975a), observed that estradiol-17β was concentrated in the nuclei of stromal cells and to a lesser extent in granulosa cells surrounding the oocytes. At the age of 23–25 days, all the cells of the oviduct still showed nuclear concentration of silver grains (Stumpf, 1969), with heavier labeling of muscle and connective-tissue cell nuclei than epithelial nuclei; in the ovary, the granulosa cells showed the heaviest labeling, with some concentration of estradiol-17β in the nuclei of thecal cells. In whole immature rat ovary, Saiduddin and Zassenhaus (1975) measured dissociation constants of 5.2 and 3.2 nM, respectively, for nuclear and cytoplasmic binding of estradiol, with 35 fmoles/mg protein bound in nuclei and 40 fmoles/mg protein bound in cytoplasm. In regard to the function of these estrogen receptors in ovarian cells, Reiter *et al.* (1972) suggested that endogenous estrogen is necessary for the normal rate of postnatal ovarian maturation in rats, on the basis of experiments using antiestrogen serum (cf. Section II,A,6 for the effect of this serum on uterine growth). That estradiol release can indeed be stimulated from rat ovary during the second week of life has recently been shown by Lamprecht *et al.* (1976). In other species, for example, it has recently been reported (Shemesh *et al.*, 1977) that as early as the 45th day of gestation, bovine embryonic ovaries are capable of producing 1.2 ng of estrogens during culture in medium 199 for 24 hours and of responding to LH with an increase in estrogen production (for data on the chick ovary, see Section V,A).

Richards (1975b) has found that the concentration of estrogen-receptor sites in nuclei of granulosa cells from immature ovaries (approximately 2000 sites/cell) is more than double that found in the remaining ovarian cell types. Stimulants of follicular growth (pregnant mare serum gonadotropin and ovine follicle stimulating hormone), while enhancing endogenous estrogen production, caused a decrease in the nuclear estrogen-receptor concentration. Luteinizing hormone also causes reduced estrogen-receptor concentration in granulosa cells. Following hypophysectomy, which leads to a decrease in endogenous estrogen concentration, estradiol in very high (mg) doses more than restored the concentration of its own receptor and potentiated the action of human follicle stimulating hormone in causing follicular maturation (antrum formation) and maintenance of high concentration of estradiol receptor in granulosa cells. In combination with a high dose of ovine luteinizing hormone, however, estradiol treatment resulted in atresia (degeneration of the follicle). The combination of follicle stimulating hormone and luteinizing hormone, in addition to estradiol, stimulated luteinization in hypophysectomized rats. Thus, the loss of estradiol receptors in granulosa cells was associated with either atresia or luteinization. Richards (1975b) suggested that differentiation of granulosa cells into one of these two pathways may be determined by the nature of the prior exposure to follicle stimulating hormone as well as their stage of differentiation. From the point of view of the complex hormonal interactions in this system, it is interesting that doses of progesterone which were capable of altering uterine morphology, even in the presence of high estrogen concentrations, had no effect on ovarian weight gain or histology or on the concentration of estradiol nuclear-receptor sites in granulosa cells.

Among the hypotheses proposed to account for the progressive stages of follicular development and the final stage of increased responsiveness to gonadotropins, Richards and Midgley (1976) include the possibility of stepwise changes in the responsiveness of granulosa cells to estrogen and to follicle stimulating hormone or to combinations of the two hormones, similar to the sequential development of responsiveness to estradiol in the immature rat uterus (described in Section II,A,5).

In contrast to the corpora lutea of the rat and of all other species tested, which are maintained by progesterone, Rennie (1968a,b) found that the corpus luteum of the rabbit requires estrogen for its maintenance. Scott and Rennie (1971) reported a cytosol estrogen receptor in rabbit corpus luteum with a sedimentation coefficient of 6.3 S, a dissociation constant of 0.02 nM, and a concentration of 33 fmoles/mg protein. Lee *et al.* (1971) showed a decline in the concentration of rabbit luteal receptor in mid-pseudopregnancy, before the decline in luteal weight, and suggested that the reduced availability of estrogen receptor leads to decreased responsiveness and eventual regression of rabbit corpora lutea. Miller and Toft (1976) reported the rabbit luteal cytoplasmic receptor to be a molecule with a sedimentation coefficient of 6–8 S, a dissociation constant of $< 10^{-10} M$, and a concentration highest on day 12 of pregnancy and lowest near the end of pregnancy (day 30) or pseudopregnancy (day 18). Further work from the group of Jacobson *et al.* (1972) showed that prostaglandin $F_{2\alpha}$ (400 μg/kg) given on day 9 of pseudopregnancy reduced the weight of rabbit corpora lutea by only one-fifth at the same time that estradiol receptor concentration dropped by three-fourths.

Taking the above suggestion of Lee *et al.* (1971) into account, along with the observation by Hilliard *et al.* (1974) that the life of rabbit corpora lutea can be extended for 6 to 10 days by hysterectomy, Miller and Keyes (1976) showed that continuous treatment with estradiol-17β could extend the period of pseudopregnancy but only in hysterectomized rabbits, and therefore suggested that it is not a drop in estradiol concentration which is physiologically responsible for ending pseudopregnancy. Rather, they propose that the uterus produces a luteolytic factor which might be a prostaglandin [prostaglandins are known to be luteolytic (Scott and Rennie, 1970)]. This "prostaglandin-like" substance which could decrease the concentration of estrogen receptor would therefore be responsible for the decrease in estrogen responsiveness. Such a mechanism, if corroborated in detail, would provide an example of regulation of a steroid-hormone-dependent process by changes in the concentration of available receptor rather than in the concentration of circulating hormone.

In the corpus luteum of the pregnant rat, Richards (1974) found a cytoplasmic estrogen receptor with a K_d of 0.22 nM and a concentration of 14 pM. Nuclear exchange assays showed that the concentration of nuclear receptor sites per cell rose between days 3 and 12 of pregnancy to a peak value of approximately 2200 sites/nucleus, then declined on day 22 of pregnancy. Because estrogens are able to prevent the drop in progesterone production by corpora lutea of rats hysterectomized and hypophysectomized on day 12 of pregnancy, it was suggested (Takayama and Greenwald, 1973) that estrogens act as a luteotropin in the rat as well as in the rabbit (see above). Richards (1975a) found that there is a regulation of estradiol-receptor availability in corpus luteum involving an increase in the total amount of receptor, to a peak in the second half of pregnancy (Fig. 6), followed by a rapid decline at the end of pregnancy. This decline, Richards (1975a) points out, is not caused by a fall in endogenous estrogen concentration, because Shaikh (1971) has shown increased production of estrone and estradiol at the end of pregnancy.

To investigate the midgestation rise of luteal-cell estrogen receptors (Fig. 6) which parallels a rise in the concentration of rat placental luteotropin, Richards and Gibori (1976) hysterectomized (to remove the source of placental luteotropin) and hypophysectomized rats on day 10 of pregnancy and then treated them with 12-day-pregnant rat serum containing placental luteotropin, or with estrogen. Luteal-cell receptor content fell, within a day after ablation, by 90% for estradiol receptors and by 50% for luteinizing-hormone receptors. Rat pregnancy serum completely reversed this fall in the concentrations of both luteal receptors, but estradiol was capable only of increasing the concentration of its own receptor. As expected, hysterectomy on day 12 of pregnancy (by removing the source of placental luteotropin), but not hypophysectomy, caused a 75% reduction in nuclear estrogen receptor by day 15 which could be completely reversed by estradiol administration.

Cytosol receptors for estrogens in corpora lutea in cows 18–42 months old were characterized by Kimball and Hansel (1974) as a typical 8 S binding protein with a K_d of 2.7 mM; the receptor concentration increased from day 5

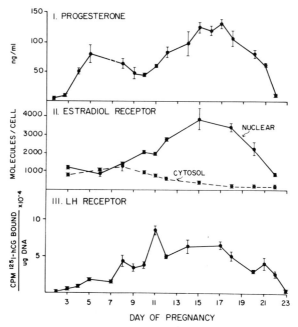

FIG. 6. Relationships between hormone receptors in corpora lutea and progesterone concentrations in peripheral serum. Progesterone concentrations and receptors for estradiol and lutenizing hormone were measured as described by Richards (1974, 1975a,b) (from Richards and Midgley, 1976).

to day 10 of the estrous cycle, then declined at days 17–18 when luteal regression began. At day 21, the concentration of luteal estrogen receptor rose to a higher concentration than found at any other time during the cycle. These authors interpret the pattern of variation in receptor concentration to mean that estrogen acts (at least in part) to produce luteolysis in the cow, a conclusion which had been reached previously by Knobil (1973) in the case of primates.

4. Testis and Epididymis

In the testis, as in several other organs of the immature rat, receptors for estrogens were first detected by Stumpf (1969) using dry-mount autoradiography to show nuclear concentration of [³H]estradiol in interstitial cells. Cytosol receptors for estradiol-17β were found (Brinkmann *et al.*, 1972) to have a K_d of 0.3 nM and a concentration of approximately 20 fmoles/mg protein in whole testis from 26-day-old rats. The characteristic 8 S form of the receptor was found to be concentrated in interstitial tissue as compared to tubular preparations. Kato *et al.* (1974x) reported a sedimentation coefficient for the cytoplasmic estrogen receptor of 9.9 S, higher than that found by Brinkmann *et al.* (1972) or van Beurden-Lamers *et al.* (1974). The values 0.4 nM for K_d and a concentration of 15 fmoles/mg protein (Kato *et al.*, 1974b) are in good agreement with the values cited above.

The 8 S cytoplasmic receptor was detected in testes of rats 14 days after birth but not in younger rats (de Boer *et al.*, 1976) by use of competition studies with 200-fold excess of diethylstilbestrol to distinguish specific 8 S receptor binding from binding to α-fetoprotein (cf. Section II,A,3). The specific nuclear estrogen receptor (Mulder *et al.*, 1973) could be detected in testes of rats (de Boer *et al.*, 1976) as young as 4 days old; its concentration, as estimated from centrifugation on sucrose gradients, appeared to decrease between day 4 and day 7, which is the reverse of the behavior of the estrogen receptors in immature rat uterus (cf. Section II,A,1). An 8 S cytoplasmic receptor for estradiol was also observed by Danzo *et al.* (1975a) in testes of 21-day-old rabbits in the course of a study of estradiol binding to rabbit epididymis (see below).

The earliest detection of estradiol receptors in the development of testis was reported by Pasqualini *et al.* (1976), along with their observation of estradiol receptors in uterus of fetal guinea pigs (Section II,B,1). The cytosol receptor in fetal guinea pig testis showed a K_d of 0.6 nM and a concentration rising from a value of 38 fmoles/mg protein in 34- to 35-day-old fetuses to 56 fmoles/mg protein in 49- to 50-day-old fetuses, one-tenth the value in fetal uteri of the same age.

The presence of such a high concentration of estradiol receptors in testes suggests that there are testicular responses to estrogen. Indeed, Samuels and his group have studied estrogen-stimulated enzymes in testes (1967), and they have also studied the induction by estrogen of Leydig cell tumors of mice, a particularly promising system. Recently, this group (Sato *et al.*, 1976) compared the properties of estrogen receptors in cryptorchid testes (to reduce the proportion of tubular components) in the tumor-susceptible BALB/c strain and in the nonsusceptible Z strain. The same K_d (6 nM) and the same sedimentation coefficient in 0.4 M KCl (3.8 S) for cytosol receptor was found in testes of both strains; however, the maximum number of binding sites in BALB/c mice was double that in Z mice. The maximum binding in the nuclear fraction in BALB/c was five times that in Z mice and was correlated with a lower percent extraction of nuclear estrogen receptors from chromatin in testes of BALB/c mice, at all concentrations of KCl tested.

It has also been suggested by Chowdhury *et al.* (1974) that high doses of estradiol benzoate (50 μg/adult rat) may act directly on the testes, utilizing the estrogen receptors present, to produce almost complete reduction in the plasma level of testosterone within a day after injection (the earliest time point tested), in the absence of any reduction in luteinizing-hormone levels.

As well as occurring in testes, estrogen receptors were also detected, by van Beurden-Lamers *et al.* (1974), in the epididymis (among several rat organs which bind estradiol). Danzo *et al.* (1975a,b) have studied the cytoplasmic and nuclear binding of estradiol in epididymis of immature (21- to 53-day-old) rabbits. The cytosol receptor was present as an 8 S species, and showed a K_d of 0.2–1 nM and a high concentration of 100–400 fmoles/mg of protein. However, in epididymal cytosol from mature rabbits (either intact or 4 days after castration), no estradiol binding protein could be detected. This is an interesting case of disappearance of a steroid receptor during development, perhaps after its role in promoting the growth of the organ has been accomplished.

Responses to estradiol in epididymis of castrated 38-day-old rats were shown by Peyre and La Porte (1966), who found that estradiol was approximately one-half as effective as testosterone in increasing the weight of the epididymis above the castrated control level, and was also effective in increasing the amount of total and free sialic acid in epididymis of castrated rats (cf. relative affinities of estrogens and androgens for androgen receptors in brain, Section III,C,1).

In male accessory glands of the calf, Jungblut *et al.* (1971) demonstrated estrogen receptors in both prostate glands and seminal vesicles. However, in the rat, van Beurden-Lamers *et al.* (1974) found an 8 S estradiol-17β receptor in prostate cytosol from adult rats at a concentration of approximately 10 fmoles/mg protein, but failed to find significant binding in seminal vesicles. No information on the ontogeny of these receptors seems to be available as yet.

In concluding their survey of estradiol-17β receptors in organs of male rats, van Beurden-Lamers *et al.* (1974) suggested that estradiol may not act independently in the male but may play a role in modulating the effects of other steroid hormones on the induction of protein synthesis.

III. THE MAMMALIAN NEUROENDOCRINE SYSTEM

Interest in the ontogeny of steroid receptors in the neuroendocrine sytem has been concentrated on the brain, and specifically on the hypothalamus, perhaps because of the elimination of the pituitary as the site of neonatal sterilization (see Pfaff *et al.*, 1974, and Section III,C,2, for references). Nevertheless, there are regulatory effects of estrogen in the pituitary gland (see below); thus, the ontogeny of pituitary estrogen receptors should provide an interesting comparison with the extensive information recently accumulated on the ontogeny of brain receptors for estrogen.

A. THE PITUITARY GLAND

The sensitivity of the pituitary response to gonadotropin-releasing hormone is partially controlled by estrogen (de Koning *et al.*, 1976; Drouin *et al.*, 1976). Moreover, an estrogen-dependent enzyme has been recently described (Baram *et al.*, 1977) in the pituitary which cleaves gonadotropin-releasing hormone between glycine and leucine (Koch *et al.*, 1974). There is an inductive action of estrogen in stimulation of prolactin synthesis in pituitary cells in culture (Lieberman *et al.*, 1978), and the synthesis of such liver enzymes as histidase (Feigelson, 1971) and of such liver hormone receptors as lactogen-specific binding sites (Posner, 1976) are mediated through effects of estrogen at the pituitary level.

The uptake and distribution studies which showed that the anterior pituitary gland was capable of binding estradiol almost as well as the uterus (which is one order of magnitude greater than in the hypothalamus, see below) have been summarized by Eisenfeld (1974, 1975). During rat development, the concentration of injected [^{3}H]estrogen in the pituitary is higher than in all the brain regions studied as early as 3–5 days after birth (Wooley *et al.*, 1969; Alvarez and Ramirez, 1970; Presl *et al.*, 1970; Kato *et al.*, 1971b). It is now clear that the apparent inability of neonatal pituitary to concentrate estradiol as compared to plasma is an artifact caused by the high levels of α-fetoprotein in neonatal plasma (Section II,A,3; Ginsburg *et al.*, 1972). These authors found that concomitant with the disappearance of a low-affinity binding component (by 20 days), a high-affinity ($K_d \sim 0.3$ nM) cytoplasmic estradiol receptor was demonstrable at 19 days. The number of sites in the whole pituitary increased from 2×10^9 at 19 days to 1×10^{10} at 31 days, and reached 3×10^{10} at 51 days, with no prominent difference between the sexes.

A recent comparison by van Beurden-Lamers *et al.* (1974) of high-affinity binding proteins in cytosol of several organs showed a characteristic 8 S form in adult male pituitary glands and an average receptor concentration of 75 fmoles/mg protein, compared to 2 fmoles/mg protein in the hypothalamus. Specific binding of estradiol-17β in nuclei of pituitary glands of 30- to 35-day-old male and female rats (Clark *et al.*, 1972) showed dissociation constants of 2.4 and 2.1 nM, respectively, and a concentration of 14.4 pmoles/g in the male, insignificantly different from the value of 16.6 in the female. In male and female calf pituitaries, Armstrong and Villee (1976) found the same concentration of a 9 S estrogen cytosol receptor.

McEwen *et al.* (1976) measured the binding of estrogen in nuclei of rat pituitary gland (Fig. 7) and found a peak concentration at the age of 10–11 days (2.8 fmoles/μg DNA) and a pattern of binding during development very

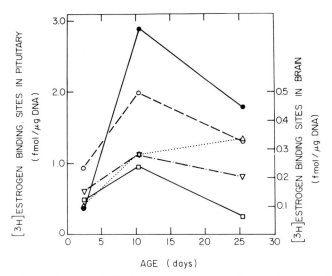

FIG. 7. Nuclear binding sites for [³H]estrogen in pituitary and brain of immature female rats. Measurements were made 2 hours after injection of a near-saturating dose of [³H]diethylstilbestrol or [³H]estradiol-17β (≥100 pmoles/g). ●————●, pituitary; ○- - -○, hypothalamus; △· · ·△, preoptic area; ▽-·-·-▽, amygdala; □- - -□, cortex (drawn from data of Table 2 of McEwen *et al.*, 1976). Note difference in ordinate for pituitary.

similar to that previously found for rat uterus (Sömjen *et al.*, 1973a; cf. Fig. 1, Section II,A,1). At all three ages tested, beginning at the age of 2–3 days, binding in the pituitary was higher than in the hypothalamus (Fig. 7), which follows from the fact that while a large proportion of cells in the pituitary can accumulate estrogen, only a very small number of hypothalamic neurons show nuclear estrogen concentration.

Despite the high concentration of estrogen receptors in the pituitary and the fact that there is reduced pituitary retention of estradiol after neonatal androgenization (see discussion by Zigmond, 1975, and Section III,C), the ontogeny of high-affinity specific receptors in this organ seems to have been neglected in comparison with the brain.

B. The Brain: The Demonstration of Neonatal Receptors

In the same year that Jensen and Jacobson (1962) published their germinal comparison of [³H]estradiol uptake in uterus and other visceral organs, Michael (1962) used an autoradiographic technique to measure the spread of [¹⁴C]diethylstilbestrol-*n*-butyrate from a local implant and found uptake of ¹⁴C into neurons of cat hypothalamus. Subsequent studies on localization of estrogen uptake are summarized by Eisenfeld (1974) and work on estrogen binding by Vertes *et al.* (1973). The recent book "Anatomical Neuroendocrinology," edited by Stumpf and Grant (1975), contains reviews (including atlases) on autoradiographic localization of estrogen in the brains of mouse (Stumpf and Sar, 1975b), rat (Stumpf *et al.*, 1975), primates (Keefer and Stumpf, 1975), and dove (Martinez-Vargas *et al.*, 1975), as well as an article comparing the distribution of estrogen and androgen in the brains of 2-day-old female rats (Sheridan *et al.*, 1975). Recently, Stumpf and Sar (1976) have compared the distribution in brain of sites for estrogen, progestin, androgen, and glucocorticosteroid hormones. A critical review of distribution studies is part of the article by Zigmond (1975) on steroid hormones in the central nervous system, while a comprehensive review by McEwen *et al.* (1974) considers the brain as a steroid responsive organ. The reviews cited above document the extensive data on the autoradiographic localization of estradiol-17β receptors in the hypothalamus and preoptic area of the brain, which was provided by many laboratories and included the demonstration of nuclear uptake of estradiol in the brains of newborn rats.

The elucidation of the concentration and localization of specific high-affinity estrogen receptors in brain during development has been beset by difficulties arising from the high concentration of α-fetoprotein in blood and cerebrospinal fluid and brain cytosol preparations (see Section II,A,3; Plapinger *et al.*, 1973; Attardi and Ruoslahti, 1976), as well as the localization of estrogen-sensitive areas to small portions of the hypothalamus, preoptic area, and amygdala.

Plapinger *et al.* (1973) characterized the neonatal "4 S" binding in brain extracts as indistinguishable from the fetoneonatal plasma-binding protein. A direct identification of the fetoneonatal estradiol-binding protein in rodent brain with α-fetoprotein was based on immunodiffusion and radioassay evidence and showed α-fetoprotein in brain cytosol preparations to decline from a value of 7 μg/mg protein in 1-day-old mice to 1.5 μg at 4–5 days, 0.24 μg at 9–10 days, and reach an undetectable level in 20- to 22-day-old mice (Attardi and Ruoslahti, 1976). These authors also found the sedimentation coefficient for the estradiol binding protein in brains of 1- to 5-day-old rats to be 4.6 S compared to 4.7 S for purified α-fetoprotein, and they found dissociation constants for [^{3}H]estradiol of 23 and 24 nM, respectively (cf. Section II,A,3) with 0.7–0.8 moles of estradiol bound per mole of mouse α-fetoprotein. Treatment of cytosol from brains of 1- to 5-day-old mice with antimouse α-fetoprotein antibodies removed the binding in the 4 S region almost completely while leaving intact the binding to the 8 S estradiol receptor (see below).

The earliest studies of age-dependent uptake of estrogen in the brain

(Eisenfeld and Axelrod, 1966) revealed no difference in the accumulation of [³H]estradiol in hypothalamus of 100-gm immature female rats compared with adult females, while Wooley *et al.* (1969), Presl *et al.* (1970), and Kato *et al.* (1971b) found a higher uptake of [³H]estradiol in brain regions of 3- to 12-day-old rats than in brains of older rats—consistent with the very high concentrations of α-fetoprotein in the circulation and in organ extracts in infant rats discussed above (Section II,A,e).

Uptake studies were clearly inadequate; in addition, a distinction must be made, as emphasized by Westley and Salaman (1976), between the measurement of cytoplasmic receptors representing only the potential for binding and the quantification and localization of nuclear binding which can show where estrogens may in fact be acting.

As the methods for overcoming the nonspecific binding of α-fetoprotein improved, the age at which unequivocal measurement of receptor concentrations became possible declined, as will be seen from the studies presented below in roughly chronological order.

Cytoplasmic and nuclear binding in rat hypothalamus were distinguished by Vertes and King (1971), who found both of these parameters higher (per mg protein) in 60- than in 28-day-old rats. Similarly, Kato *et al.* (1971a, 1974a) detected a rudimentary peak of [³H]estradiol binding in the 8.5 S region upon sucrose gradient analyses of cytosol from hypothalamus of 7-day-old rats, a peak which rapidly increased in size when cytosol from hypothalami was analyzed during growth of rats from 14 to 28 days old. This 8.5 S peak declined to two-thirds of its value before vaginal opening and then rose again after puberty (Kato, 1973). As the size of the 8.5 S peak increased during the postnatal period, a nonspecific 4 S binding component (most likely α-fetoprotein) decreased (cf. situation in uterus, Section II,A,3). Indeed, Ginsburg *et al.* (1972) reported that the relatively low-affinity binding component in all areas of both male and female rat brains disappeared by approximately 20 days, revealing a high-affinity ($K_d \sim 0.3$ nM) binding in female hypothalamus but not in other brain regions studied. The number of sites rose from 4×10^9 (within the adult range) at 19 days to 1×10^{10} at 28 days. Competition by 1 μM ethinyl estradiol against *in vitro* uptake of [³H]estradiol by basal hypothalamus was used by Kulin and Reiter (1972) to show that specific saturable estrogen receptors are present as early as 5 days after birth in the female rat.

Pasqualini and Palmada (1972) have reported estrogen receptors in the cytosol fraction of guinea pig brain as early as day 25 of gestation. These receptors showed sedimentation coefficients of 8.5–9 S and 4–5 S. In addition, an estrogen receptor was extracted from brain nuclei using 1 M NaCl.

Clark *et al.* (1972) used a 100-fold concentration of diethylstilbestrol as a competitor for [³H]estradiol during *in vitro* measurements of nuclear receptors in hypothalami of 30- to 35-day old male and female rats. In female hypothalami, a nuclear receptor ($K_d \sim 1$ nM) with a concentration between 0.1 and 0.5 pmoles/gm was found, which was 0.6–3% of the concentration found in the female anterior pituitary. However, in the nuclear fraction of male hypothalamus no specific component was found whose concentration could be reduced by diethylstilbestrol (Clark *et al.*, 1972), although nonspecific sites were found to be higher in the male than in the female. This finding of a lack of specific nuclear binding in the male hypothalamus will be examined again in the following section dealing with the effects of neonatal steroids on sexual differentiation of the brain in the light of its discrepancy with autoradiographic data (Attramadal, 1970; Stumpf *et al.*, 1971). The presence of cytoplasmic "8 S" receptors which are not transferred to the nucleus has also been reported by Shyamala (1972) in mouse mammary tumors. This phenomenon contrasts with the model of Williams and Gorski (1972) of equilibrium distribution of estradiol binding in rat uterus.

The measurement of estradiol receptors in cytosol by sucrose density-gradient techniques (Plapinger and McEwen, 1973) provided quantitative confirmation of the observation by Kato (1972) that the concentration of "8 S" cytoplasmic receptors in brain increases with age. The concentration of [³H]estradiol bound by the hypothalamus–preoptic area–amygdala–midbrain increased from 18 fmoles/gm wet weight at 6 days to a value of 58 fmoles/gm at 33 days, and to a value of 74 fmoles/gm in 77- to 80-day-old (adult) rats.

By using a method (Ginsburg *et al.*, 1974) which measured only slowly dissociating, high-affinity diethylstilbestrol-suppressible binding and did not detect α-fetoprotein, Barley *et al.* (1974) measured estradiol receptors in cytosol from combined hypothalamus and amygdala of male and female 5-day-old rats in comparison with estrogen receptors in the cortex. In all these areas from either sex, dissociation constants of 0.6 nM were determined, compared to 0.1-0.2 nM in adult female brain areas (see below). The hypothalamus plus amygdala of both male and female 5-day-old rats contained 1.1×10^9 estradiol binding sites/gm wet weight while cortical areas contained slightly higher concentrations, 1.6×10^9 and 1.3×10^9 sites/g, respectively. In comparison, in adult females there was a higher concentration in hypothalamus (2.0×10^9 sites/gm), approximately the same as in the newborn in amygdala (0.8×10^9 sites/gm), but only 0.2×10^9 sites/gm in cortex. In extracts of 5-day-old brain areas, the synthetic estrogen R2858 (see Section II,A,6) showed an affinity similar to estradiol for the cytoplasmic receptor; diethylstilbesterol showed an even higher affinity (Section II,A,3).

Autoradiographic studies on brains of 2-day-old rats to which 1 μg of [³H]estradiol was administered subcutaneously (Sheridan *et al.*, 1974a) detected neurons that concentrate estradiol in the preoptic region, the basal hypothalamus, and the amygdala. This article should be consulted for its summary of previous autoradiographic studies and for its atlases of estradiol distribution, which emphasize how focal the concentration of estradiol is, even within these limited areas. If the distribution in the cortex of newborn animals is more diffuse and therefore undetectable by present autoradiographic techniques, it would resolve the apparent contradiction mentioned above between biochemical and autoradiographic studies (but see further, below). The importance of choosing a high enough dose of labeled hormone to overcome binding by α-fetoprotein was elegantly demonstrated by McEwen *et al.* (1975). A comparison of the binding of low doses (3–4 pmoles/gm) of [^{3}H]estradiol-17β and [^{3}H]R2858 to nuclei from pooled hypothalamus, preoptic area, and amygdala (HPA) from brains of 3-day-old rats (McEwen *et al.*, 1975) showed 35 times greater binding of [^{3}H]R2858 (190 fmoles/mg DNA) than [^{3}H]estradiol (5.4 fmoles/mg DNA). At doses of 41–47 pmoles/gm, 2–3 times more [^{3}H]diethylstilbestrol was bound to nuclei from HPA than [^{3}H]estradiol (91 compared with 34 fmoles/mg DNA). The intermediate level of diethylstilbestrol binding to HPA nuclei is related to the affinity of the steroids for α-fetoprotein; estradiol > diethylstilbestrol > R2858 (cf. Section III,D). However, when α-fetoprotein has disappeared from the circulation by 26 days, the binding of diethylstilbestrol and estradiol to brain nuclei is equal. In cortex of 3-day-old female rats, high doses of [^{3}H]diethylstilbestrol (>100 pmoles/g) bind to nuclei at a concentration of approximately 100 fmoles/mg DNA. Again, note that these binding levels in brain are two orders of magnitude lower than in uterus (Section II,A,1) and pituitary (Section IV,A) when expressed as binding/DNA in the whole tissue block studied. Thus, even if in the limited regions of highest binding in the brain (e.g., the arcuate nucleus) not all cells are labeled, how low must be the proportion of labeled cells in the cortex, detected biochemically in newborn rats, which disappear between 10 and 21 days after birth (McEwen *et al.*, 1975)!

In cytosol from brain of both male and female (19-week-old) human fetuses, a specific high-affinity ($K_d \sim 10^{-8}\ M$) limited-capacity estrogen-binding component has been detected by Davies *et al.* (1975) in the hypothalamus, limbic system, and cortex. This component can be distinguished from sex-hormone-binding globulin, a β-globulin which is elevated during pregnancy. Recall that human α-fetoprotein in amniotic fluid is not an effective binder of estradiol (Section II,A,3).

During 1976, extensive work from the groups of Attardi (on cytosol receptors) and those of McEwen and Westly and Salaman, on both nuclear and cytoplasmic receptors, provided a picture of the ontogeny of estradiol receptors in brain that these authors used for their proposals concerning the brain's neonatal sexual differentiation (Section III,C,1).

While the overall number of high-affinity ($K_d = 0.3$–1 nM) specific binding sites for [³H]estradiol in cytosol from mouse brain was found by Attardi and Ohno (1976) to remain at the level of 7–9 fmoles/mg protein, in groups of mice spanning the ages 3–23 days after birth, this gross measurement masked a redistribution of receptors during growth, as shown in Fig. 8. There was an order-of-magnitude increase in the ratio of receptors in the hypothalamus–preoptic area (HPOA) to receptors in the cortex during growth from the neonatal to the adult stage. This change is due to the combination of an increase in the concentration of receptors in HPOA (to 17.4 fmoles/mg protein) coupled with a decrease in cortical receptors to 1.6 fmoles/mg protein. Cortical receptor concentration was found to decline steadily with age, while cytosol receptors in HPOA showed a peak concentration at 9–12 days (Fig. 8) followed by a decline at 19–22 days, before reaching adult levels. The cytosol receptor peak at 9–12 days is similar to the peak in uterine estrogen receptors found at 10 days (cf. Fig. 1). Attardi and Ohno (1976) also measured specific binding of the androgen [³H]5α-dihydro-testosterone in developing mouse brain, and found a situation which contrasts with [³H]estradiol binding (Fig. 9). The binding of androgen increases roughly in parallel in all three brain regions measured, from neonatal to adult stages. These authors found similar dissociation constants and concentrations of binding sites for estradiol and dihydrotestosterone in brain cytosol from male and female mice.

Maclusky *et al.* (1976) used [³H]R2858 to detect the small quantities of 8 S cytosol receptor present in the hypothalamus, preoptic area, septum,

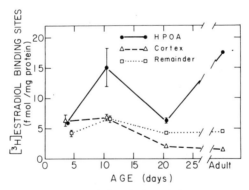

FIG. 8. Cytosol binding sites for estradiol in the hypothalamus–preoptic area (HPOA), cerebral cortex, and the remainder of the brain of female mice. Cytosol was incubated with 0.92 nM [³H]estradiol, with or without 1 μM unlabeled estradiol-17β, and centrifuged on glycerol gradients. Specific binding was determined by integration of the 8 S peaks and subtraction of nonspecific radioactivity in this region. Two to four groups of mice (12–27 mice per group) were used for each point. Curves were drawn from data of Table 2 in Attardi and Ohno (1976). Compare Fig. 9; note difference in ordinate.

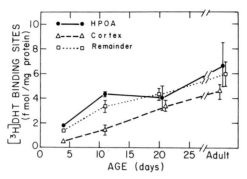

FIG. 9. Cytosol binding sites for 5α-dihydrotestosterone (DHT) in the hypothalmus–preoptic area (HPOA), cerebral cortex, and the remainder of the brain of female mice. Cytosol was incubated with 2.1 nM DHT, with or without 1 μM unlabeled DHT, and centrifuged on glycerol gradients. Specific binding was determined by integration of the 8 S peaks and subtraction of nonspecific radioactivity in this region. Two to four groups of mice (generally the same groups represented in Fig. 8 on estradiol binding) containing 12–27 mice per group were used for each point. Curves were drawn from data of Table 2 in Attardi and Ohno (1976). Compare Fig. 8; note difference in ordinate.

amygdala, and cortex of 3- to 5-day-old female rats and were thus able to demonstrate a 40–60% reduction of available receptor capacity in the cytosol following estrogen treatment. This group (McEwen *et al.*, 1976) also measured nuclear estrogen binding in brain areas of developing female rats (Fig. 7) and found the highest binding in the hypothalamus as well as a rise in nuclear binding in this region between days 2–3 and days 10–11, followed by a decline at days 25–26. The pattern is consistent with the data presented above (Fig. 8) for cytoplasmic receptors, including a lower value for cortical binding in 25- to 26-day-old rats as compared with 2- to 3-day-old rats.

The group of Westley and Salaman investigated both cytoplasmic and nuclear estrogen receptors in the brain of 5-day-old rats, using passage through an LH 20 column (Ginsburg *et al.*, 1974) to remove free and low-affinity bound estradiol. This technique revealed a small peak of estradiol receptor sedimenting at 7–8 S which was completely suppressed by a 200-fold excess of diethylstilbestrol (Westley *et al.*, 1976). This 8 S receptor was further purified severalfold by ammonium sulfate precipitation, and showed a K_d for estradiol of 0.26 nM, close to that of the receptor in adult hypothalamus (0.15 nM) and significantly different from the value of 0.61 nM shown by the receptor in crude cytosol from brain of 5-day-old rats. These observations confirm a previous suggestion of this group (Barley *et al.*, 1974) that the apparent lower affinity of the neonatal receptor for estradiol (see above) is due to the presence of α-fetoprotein in the incubation, and leave no reason to reject the simplest assumption that the cytoplasmic estrogen receptors of neonatal and adult brain are identical.

Intracerebral injection of [^{3}H]estradiol, with or without the addition of a 20-fold excess of diethylstilbestrol (Salaman *et al.*, 1976), showed a maximal accumulation of diethylstilbestrol-suppressible radioactivity in the nuclear fraction of neonatal brain 0.5–1 hour after injection, localized mainly in the hypothalamic-amygdaloid regions, which was extractable by 0.4 *M* KCl and showed a greater concentration in the female than in the male (see the discussion of aromatization in Section III,C,1). The subcutaneous injection of 20 μCi of [^{3}H]estradiol led to a higher concentration of radioactivity in the initial homogenates than after intracerebral injection of 2.5 μCi [^{3}H]estradiol but led to a lower total and diethylstilbestrol-suppressed nuclear binding (Westley and Salaman, 1977). Using subcutaneous administration, the sex difference in favor of the female was only marginal. These authors point out that while intracerebral injections of steroids are useful for providing high concentrations of nuclear binding in several brain regions, the subcutaneous route probably results in a closer approximation of *in vivo* nuclear estradiol binding.

With this reminder of our primarry concern with conditions *in vivo*, we proceed from the description of the changes in estradiol receptors during the postnatal development of the brain to consider the observations that stimulated most of the work on neonatal brain receptors for steroids, the phenomenon most widely called neonatal androgenization.

C. Sexual Differentiation of the Brain

In contrast to the temporary action of steroid hormones on adult responsive cells, neonatal exposure of specific brain cells to androgens or estrogens causes permanent differentiation of the brain in the direction of maleness (*androgenization*), with subsequent loss in the adult of the characteristic female response to estrogen stimulation—the release of luteinizing-hormone-releasing factor from the hypothalamus.

The discovery by Pfeiffer (1936) that the transplantation of testes to the neck of newborn female rats caused sexual differentiation of the brain to proceed in a male direction preceded by two generations the development of techniques for the study of the interaction of steroid hormones with specific molecules in the brain. The reviews of Harris and Levine (1965) and Goy (1970) provide a broad view of the physiological and psychological approaches to the study of sexual differentiation of the brain, while the popular review of McEwen (1976) presents a current view of this problem in addition to studies of corticosterone in the brain and the changes in mood and sensitivity to sensory stimuli brought about by adrenal steroids.

1. The Model of Action via Estrogen Receptors

When a single injection of 10 μg of testosterone propionate was given to 5-day-old female rats, 96 out of 136 animals (71%) were sterilized (Gorski and Barraclough, 1963); a dose of 5 μg resulted in 44% sterility. The injection of 5 μg of estradiol benzoate caused sterility in 41 out of 48 rats (85%), while injection of 1 μg resulted in 42% sterility (Gorski, 1963). Thus, it has been known for many years that both androgen and estrogen in microgram amounts are capable of causing a syndrome termed *neonatal androgenization*, or masculinization, and that paradoxically, estrogen is more potent than androgen in accomplishing this effect.

While the characteristics of the anovulatory syndrome can vary with the steroid used (McEwen *et al.*, 1974, includes references to "masculinization" by progesterone and deoxycorticosterone) and with the dose of androgen administered (Barraclough and Gorski, 1961; Gorski and Barraclough, 1963), the complete syndrome of neonatal sterilization is characterized postpuberally by a male (tonic) pattern of release of luteinizing hormone, a state of constant vaginal estrus, accompanied by permanent infertility, enlargement of the endometrial glands, polyfollicular ovaries with no corpora lutea, a tendency toward a male behavior pattern, and a male pattern of hepatic steroid metabolism. In addition to the studies cited dealing with the rat, Sheridan *et al.* (1975) list reports of permanent changes in the central nervous system of mouse, hamster, guinea pig, rabbit, monkey, and human after exposure to steroids during perinatal development.

The most probable current model for neontal sexual differentiation of the rodent brain is based on the following group of observations which, when assembled, produce a consistent explanation.

(a) The undifferentiated state of mammals during development is female (Jost, 1970; Jost *et al.*, 1973). The female is characterized in the adult by a cyclic pattern of luteinizing-hormone release.

(b) Both nuclear and cytoplasmic receptors for estrogens (Section III,D,2) and androgens (Section III,D,2; Sheridan *et al.*, 1975) are present in the brain during the critical first week of life.

(c) Testosterone, and other Δ^4,3-keto androgens in which the A ring is not reduced, can be aromatized in the brain to estradiol (Naftolin *et al.*, 1975), which is the steroid responsible for neonatal sterilization.

(d) Testosterone, which is normally secreted by the testes of the newborn male rodent (Resco *et al.*, 1968; Döhler and Wuttke, 1975) is converted to estradiol in the hypothalamic region in which steroids regulate gonadotropin release in the adult.

(e) Estradiol circulating in the female (Section II,A,2) is prevented from reaching the brain region controlling gonadotropin release by the high concentration of α-fetoprotein in the blood and cerebrospinal fluid (Section II,A,3; Weisz and Gibbs, 1974).

(f) Testosterone, which is not bound by α-fetoprotein, can cause masculinization after injection into the female and conversion to estradiol in the brain. High doses of estradiol or low doses of estrogens which are poorly bound to α-fetoprotein can also cause masculinization.

Statements (c)–(f) are supported by the following experimental data and considerations. Small amounts of estradiol (not unequivocally identified) were found by Knapstein et al. (1968) after perfusion of rhesus monkey brains with [^{14}C]dehydroepiandrosterone, but the implications of this work were not immediately pursued. Later work confirmed this observation in showing, among other things, that human hypothalamus and median eminence (but not cortex) from 10- and 22-week-old male fetuses, could convert [^{14}C]androstenedione to estrone and estradiol *in vitro* (Naftolin et al., 1971) and that [^{3}H]androstenedione was converted to [^{3}H]estrone and [^{3}H]estradiol by the isolated perfused rhesus monkey brain (Flores et al., 1973). In the hypothalamus and combined septal and amygdaloid regions from brains of 5-day-old female rats, Weisz and Gibbs (1974) identified [^{3}H]estradiol after an injection of [^{3}H]testosterone. Aromatization was also demonstrated in the rabbit brain (Reddy et al., 1973) and, most pertinent in this context, by hypothalami from 21-day-old male and female rat fetuses, and by the limbic systems of male fetuses, as well as by both hypothalami and limbic systems of 1-, 5-, and 10-day-old adult rats (Reddy et al., 1974). No significant conversion was shown by any of the cortex samples. Fetal hypothalamic cells in culture efficiently aromatize androstenedione and 19-OH androstenedione (Canick et al., 1977).

Naftolin et al. (1975), in their review of estrogen formation in the brain, trace the considerations which led to the idea that "central androgen actions" might require estrogen as a key metabolite. Although androgens require conversion to ring-A-reduced metabolites such as dihydrotestosterone prior to action in secondary sex organs (Fang et al., 1969), such androgen metabolites did not affect rat brain differentiation (Lüttge and Whalen, 1970; Brown-Grant et al., 1971; McDonald and Doughty, 1972a). The higher potency of estrogens than androgens in causing "male" differentiation of the brain in rats was discussed above. In fact, 0.1 μg of mestranol (17α-ethinyl-3-methoxyestra-1,3,5(10)-triene-17β-ol) was found to be a minimum effective dose in 5-day-old female rats for inhibition of sexual development (Kincl et al., 1965). Prior treatment with the antiestrogen MER-25 was reported to prevent the sterilizing effect of testosterone on newborn female rats (McDonald and Doughty, 1972b, but see below).

In their study of estrogen receptors in the hypothalamic and cortical regions from brains of 5-day-old male and female rats, Westley and Salaman (1976) presented data that show that the circulating estrogen is effectively prevented from reaching brain nuclei by the concentration of α-fetoprotein which is also in circulation at that age. Measurement of nuclear receptor sites for estradiol by exchange binding, in the absence of prior administration of estrogen, is dependent on the amount of estrogen which has been transferred from the cytosol and retained in the nucleus, and therefore is a measure of the amount of estrogen which was actually available for binding to cytosol receptors rather than the estrogen in the circulation. In the hypothalamus of 5-day-old female rats, no such nuclear binding was detected (Westley and Salaman, 1976). (Previously, Sömjen et al. [1974] had shown that this type of endogenous binding of estradiol in uteri from rats of this age was below the detection limits of sucrose-gradient centrifugation). When 50 μg of testosterone was injected subcutaneously 3 hours before killing 5-day-old female rats, Westley and Salaman (1976) found 7.2×10^6 nuclear estradiol exchangeable sites/μg DNA in hypothalamus. One hour after a much smaller dose (0.27 μg) of diethylstilbestrol, which is poorly bound by α-fetoprotein, 8.8×10^6 nuclear estradiol binding sites/μg DNA were detected. The intact 5-day-old male showed 2.4×10^6 sites/μg DNA, which was reduced to undetectable levels by removing the source of testosterone by castration the day before measurement. Injection of 0.27 μg diethylstilbestrol 1 hour previously revealed 12.1×10^6 estradiol binding sites/μg DNA in nuclei from the hypothalamus of 5-day-old male rats. Nuclear binding was undetectable in the cortical region of the brain in all the groups of 5-day-old rats investigated, with the exception of male and female rats previously injected with diethylstilbestrol, both of which showed a number of sites in the cortex equal to that found in the hypothalamic region.

Very recently, Booth (1977) reported that the aromatization inhibitor, androst-4-ene-3,6,17-trione (Schwartzel et al., 1973) protected against the defeminizing action of neonatal testosterone in male rats castrated at birth and subsequently tested for (a) the ability to cause luteinization of implanted ovaries and (b) female sexual behavior. The organization of normal male behavior (ejaculation) was also suppressed in rats which had received the aromatization inhibitor, supporting the view that testosterone acts after aromatization not only to impose male-type abnormal brain differentiation in females but also to evoke the normal male neuroendocrine state.

While the general scheme outlined above involving aromatization is therefore supported by several converging lines of evidence, a less unitary view is taken by Attardi and Ohno (1976) and by Sheridan et al. (1974b), who discuss several inconsistent observations. For example, testosterone propionate implants in the cortex of neonatal female rats also cause androgen sterilization

(Lobl and Gorski, 1974), and in the hamster, silastic implants of dihydrotes-tosterone or androsterone (also nonaromatizable) reduce the duration of lordosis (female position for acceptance of the male), albeit much less effectively than testosterone (Gerall *et al.*, 1975). While the antiandrogen cyproterone acetate could be pictured as preventing neonatal androgenization by its ability to inhibit binding to the androgen receptor in mouse brain cytosol, Vreeburg *et al.* (1975) found that cyproterone acetate does not compete with estradiol for binding in hypothalamic or pituitary cytosols of adult rats. The compound MER-25, which has been used as an antiestrogen and was reported to prevent masculinization by testosterone (see above) and by the synthetic estrogen R2858 (Doughty *et al.*, 1975a,b), has a low affinity for estrogen cytosol receptor, in the micromolar range (Barley *et al.*, 1974; Ruh and Ruh, 1974), and was the poorest antagonist for estrogen among four antiestrogens tested (Ruh and Ruh, 1974). In fact, other groups have not obtained a blocking effect on testosterone masculinization by MER-25 (Gottlieb *et al.*, 1974; Brown Grant, 1974; Hayashi, 1974); tests with more effective antiestrogens should settle this point. Attardi *et al.* (1976) have also shown that the cytosol androgen receptor in mouse brain has an affinity for estradiol (K_d = 8–9 nM), which is only one order of magnitude lower than its affinity for androgens.

On the other hand, the demonstration by Westley and Salamon (1977) that all the radioactivity found in nuclei of brain cells from 5-day-old rats after testosterone treatment can be accounted for by conversion to estrogen maintains the situation that as yet no radiochemically measurable nuclear androgen binding has been found in neonatal brain (Barnea *et al.*, 1972; Sheratt *et al.*, 1969; Vertes *et al.*, 1973). But this negative evidence does not stand unopposed. Autoradiographic evaluation of nuclear binding of [³H]testosterone or of a testosterone metabolite (Sheridan *et al.*, 1974a,b, 1975) compared with binding of [³H]estradiol (Sheridan *et al.*, 1974c) showed that while [³H]testosterone-labeled neurons from both the medial preoptic nucleus and the nucleus interstitialis striae terminalis showed the same number of grains, after labeling with [³H]estradiol, the medial preoptic nucleus showed twice the number of grains seen in the labeled neurons of the nucleus interstitialis striae terminalis.

In evaluating this apparent discrepancy between the autoradiographic and biochemical data, it should be remembered that the autoradiographic data for the presence of specific estradiol receptors in neonatal cat hypothalamus were obtained when biochemical techniques had not yet been successfully used to demonstrate measurable amounts of specific estrogen receptors in the hypothalamus. Thus, specific areas of the neonatal brain as well as adult brain may have both androgen and estrogen receptors, as has been elegantly proved for uterus, prostate, and seminal vesicle (Jungblut *et al.*, 1971). It should also be recalled that in developing chick oviduct, following estrogen-induced differentiation of tubular gland cells, both estrogen and progesterone can induce ovalbumin synthesis [see reviews by Rosen and O'Malley (1975) and Schimke *et al.* (1975) in a previous volume of this treatise].

At the present time, while the theory of aromatization is supported by an impressive set of observations, direct androgenization by testosterone by interaction with its specific receptor system cannot be ruled out as an additional or alternative mechanism.

In addition to these considerations concerning a function for estrogen receptors in the hypothalamus of neonatal rodents, it is not yet clear whether or not the neonatal estrogen receptors found in the cortex mediate the varied neonatal effects of estrogen which have been reported. These include accelerating brain development and increasing brain excitability (Heim and Timiras, 1963; Heim, 1966); causing increased myelination (Curry and Heim, 1966) which could also involve an effect on cholesterol metabolism; changing the concentrations of amino acids (Hudson *et al.*, 1970) and 5-hydroxytryptamine (Giulian *et al.*, 1973) in the brain and inhibiting the incorporation of [^{3}H]lysine into neuroproteins (Litteria and Thorner, 1976, see previous work cited in this paper).

2. Estrogen Receptors in Neonatally Sterilized Rodents

One result of neonatal androgenization is a reduction in the sensitivity to estrogen of the uterus (Harris and Levine, 1965) and the brain, e.g., in responding to estradiol by lordosis behavior (Gerall and Kenney, 1970). Other reports of reduced sensitivity to estrogen in masculinized rats are cited by Flerko *et al.* (1969) and McEwen *et al.* (1974). Several groups sought to explain this lowering of sensitivity on the basis of reduced estrogen uptake in rat hypothalamus in animals aged 4 weeks or older which have been treated neonatally with testosterone.

Decreased hypothalamic binding was found in whole tissue (Flerko *et al.*, 1969; Green *et al.*, 1969; McGuire and Lisk, 1969; McEwen and Pfaff, 1970; Tuohimaa and Johansonn, 1971), in nuclear fractions (Vertes and King, 1969), by autoradiography (Anderson and Greenwald, 1969), and by the use of the antiestrogen clomiphene to detect estrogen-specific binding (Maurer and Wooley, 1971). Vertes *et al.* (1973) studied both the cytoplasmic and nuclear binding of estradiol-17β in 14-, 21-, and 28-day-old rats and 60-day-old ovariectomized rats, after injection of 1 mg of testosterone propionate two days after birth. There was no effect of androgenization on estradiol binding at 14 days, but at 21 and 28 days, while the cytoplasmic binding determined by the protamine precipitation method (Steggles and King, 1970) was even higher than in oil-injected control rats, the KCl-extractable nuclear binding was lower than in nonandrogenized rats. The authors suggested that these data resulted from "a defect in the development of nuclear acceptor property in the androgenized hypothalamus" which alters, among other responses to estrogen, the resynthesis of estrogen receptor.

However, this picture of a selective effect of neonatal androgen treatment on nuclear estrogen receptors in prepuberal rats does not seem to apply to the uterus, for which Vertes *et al.* (1973) reported an increased uptake of [^{3}H]estradiol in 28-day-old rats compared with a decrease in both nuclear and cytoplasmic uptake in 60-day-old animals. Very recently, Gellert *et al.* (1977) measured the 8 S cytosol receptor and nuclear receptors by exchange binding in uteri of 23- and 31-day-old rats which had been given injections of 100 μg of estradiol benzoate at the age of 3 days. These authors found a reduction in the 8 S estrogen receptors at both ages studied, but no change in nuclear binding. Interestingly, the weight of the uterus did not change after treatment with estradiol (2 μg/kg body weight) at 22 days, but it did show a significant increase when tested at 30 days. These observations on the lack of a direct correlation between the concentration of nuclear and cyto-plasmic receptors and response to estrogen are consistent with the presence of a higher concentration of cytoplasmic estrogen receptors than is required for a maximal response (Anderson *et al.*, 1973), and underscore the continued pertinence of these authors' observation that "any consideration of the effect of nuclear RE (receptor–estrogen complex) on the rates of response must await the methodology to differentiate between total nuclear RE and RE bound to nuclear acceptor sites." The considerations schematized in Fig. 5 may be the basis of such methodology.

Vertes *et al.* (1973) emphasize, as did Maurer and Wooley (1971) pre-viously, that androgenization does not lead to complete loss of estrogen receptors, and they discuss the decreased cytoplasmic and nuclear uptake of [^{3}H]estradiol in uteri and anterior pituitary of adult androgenized rats; they also raise the problems involved in a molecular explanation of the role of estrogen binding in hypothalamic feedback control.

The interesting situation in vaginal epithelium following neonatal an-drogenization by estrogen, testosterone, or dihydrotestosterone appears to be a combination of direct and indirect (hypothalamic) effects which differ with the dose of the steroid [Iguchi and Takasugi (1976), Iguchi *et al.* (1976), and Ohta and Iguchi (1976) all contain further references]. This sytem should provide an interesting animal model for receptor studies in the light of human vaginal neoplasia associated with diethylstilbestrol (Section II,B,2).

A proposal that a hypothalamic mechanism exists which detects the rela-tive concentration of androgens and estrogen has been made by Fox (1975b), but aside from invoking interactions with receptors or acceptor sites, no mechanism for such a "detection" system has been suggested. However, an effect on binding of one steroid by another in the same cell has several precedents (see discussion by Sheridan *et al.*, 1974c). Estradiol is capable of stimulating the synthesis of receptors for other gonadal steroid hormones, in addition to regulating the replenishment of its own receptor (Gorski *et al.*, 1971).

IV. MAMMALIAN VISCERAL ORGANS

A. LIVER

Both avian and amphibian liver have long been known as estrogen-responsive organs, and avian liver estrogen receptors have been described (Section V,B). Although Rao and Talwar (1969) showed retention of estradiol-17β in liver of female rats, and Smirnova *et al.* (1974) claimed binding of negligibly small amounts of estradiol-17β in rat liver, it is only very recently that Eisenfeld *et al.* (1976) have demonstrated an 8 S cytoplasmic estrogen-binding component as well as nuclear receptors for estradiol in the liver of female rats. The concentration of cytoplasmic receptor reaches a value of 58 fmoles/mg protein in liver of adult rats, but it is less than one-sixth of this value in 27-day-old rats. This increase in concentration with maturity is consistent with the low concentration of estrogen receptors previously reported for liver of immature rats (Clark and Gorski, 1969; Jensen *et al.*, 1969; Smirnova *et al.*, 1974), and the lack of autoradiographic evidence for nuclear localization (Stumpf, 1969). The cytosol receptor in adult liver showed a K_d of 0.07 nM; high-affinity binding for estradiol was also found in the cytosol from livers of mouse, rabbit, and green monkey.

The increased concentration of estrogen receptors in adult liver is correlated (Fig. 10) with estrogen induction of plasma renin substrate (precursor of angiotensin). Eisenfeld *et al.* (1976) suggest that the elevation of several plasma proteins by estrogen results from their increased synthesis in the liver and that these proteins could contribute to the potentially lethal side effects of estrogen-containing contraceptives.

The induction by estrogen of hepatic histidase during postnatal development (Feigelson, 1968) was shown to require an intact pituitary (Feigelson, 1971). Histidase induction by estrogen should be compared with the induction of histidase by glucocorticoids (Feigelson, 1973) and the ability of glucocorticoids to prematurely evoke hepatic synthesis of glucokinase (Jamdar and Greengard, 1970) and tryptophan oxygenase (Greengard and Dewey, 1971).

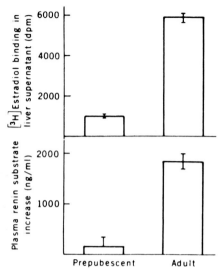

FIG. 10. Developmental correlation of estrogen binding in liver and estrogen induction of plasma renin substrate. Macromolecular binding of 2 nM [³H]estradiol was measured by gel filtration after incubation in ice for 1 hour in 0.2 ml of liver supernatant from 27-day-old prepubescent rats and 200 g adult female rats of the control groups (top). Groups of five animals each of prepubescent and adult rats received subcutaneous injections of 100 μg of 17α-ethinyl estradiol or the vehicle alone (propylene glycol as control) at 0 and 24 hours. At 48 hours plasma renin substrate was measured by radioimmunoassay. The control levels of plasma renin substrate were 1040 ± 80 ng/ml for the prepubescent group and 1100 ± 80 ng/ml for the adult group. The graph indicates the increase above control in the estrogen-treated groups (bottom). The bars represent the standard error of the mean (from Eisenfeld *et al.*, 1976).

B. KIDNEY

Pasqualini *et al.* (1974) found that kidney from fetal guinea pigs contained specific cytosol and nuclear receptors for estradiol and aldosterone but not for progesterone. Their cytosol binding studies showed material with two equilibrium dissociation constants of 0.25 and 7.7 nM. Salt extracts of the nucleus contained a 3.7 S receptor. The cytosol receptor, which was undetectable at 34–35 days of gestation, increased to 35 fmoles/mg protein at 59 days and then decreased to one-half this value at 1 day after birth (Pasqualini *et al.*, 1976). Nuclear receptors, by contrast, were measurable at 34–35 days (11 fmoles/mg protein), reached 147 fmoles/mg protein at 59 days, and also decreased to about one-half this value at 24 hours after birth.

C. LUNG

In the same study on fetal guinea pig organs previously referred to (Sections II,B,1 and III,B), Pasqualini *et al.* (1976) studied the ontogeny of estradiol receptors in fetal lung, finding the same general pattern as in the other organs, namely, a rise in concentration until the end of gestation followed by a decrease immediately after birth. In fetal lung cytosol the values found were 24 fmoles/mg protein at 34–35 days, 434 fmoles/mg protein at 59 days, and 232 fmoles/mg protein 1 day after birth. The values for nuclear binding at these three time periods (in fmoles/mg protein) were 27, 329, and 63, respectively. One should compare these values for fetal organs with the highest value found for fetal uterus (Section II,B), which was 500 fmoles/mg protein at the end of gestation (55–60 days).

V. THE CHICK EMBRYO

The chick oviduct has provided material for highly advanced molecular-biological studies on estrogen control of gene expression; an example is the recent finding by Tsai *et al.* (1976) of nonhistone protein(s) in chromatin from estrogen-stimulated chicks which acts as a positive regulator for *in vitro* expression of the ovalbumin gene. However, it is only recently, in the autoradiographic studies of Martinez-Vargas *et al.* (1975b) and in the series of papers by Teng and Teng (1975a,b, 1976a,b), that any information on the ontogeny of estrogen receptors in developing chicks has become available.

A. BRAIN

After injection of [³H]estradiol into chicks on day 6 of incubation, radioactivity was found throughout the brain but with no nuclear concentration; by day 10, both male and female embryos at stages 33–35 (Hamburger and Hamilton, 1951) showed nuclear concentration of radioactivity in the medial preoptic and ventral hypothalamic regions (Martinez-Vargas *et al.*, 1975b).

In birds, the undifferentiated sex is male, and femaleness seems to be imposed by estrogens. Thus, in contrast with the neonatal androgenization of rodents discussed in Section III,C, when Japanese quail males were injected with estradiol benzoate or testosterone propionate on the 10th day of incubation, they did not show male copulatory behavior upon maturation (Adkins, 1975). The paper of Martinez-Vargas *et al.* (1975b) should be consulted for a discussion of this early imprinting of sex behavior by gonadal steroids in avian systems.

B. Müllerian Duct

In the chick embryo, the Müllerian ducts remain undifferentiated through the 6th day of incubation, after which they begin to involute in the male by day 8 and disappear by day 13. The left Müllerian duct of the female, on the contrary, develops after estrogen stimulation into the functional oviduct of the mature hen, and only the right Müllerian duct regresses in the female. Teng and Teng (1975a) demonstrated a cytosol receptor in the left Müllerian duct of 15-day-old embryos which showed 8 S and 4 S forms and had a K_d of 3.2 nM and a maximal number of sites of 2.2 fmoles/ng DNA. This level is attained by a linear increase in the concentration of cytosol receptors (Teng and Teng, 1975b) from day 8, the earliest age tested, through day 12 (Fig. 11). The maximal level reached was maintained through 4 days after hatching (normal hatching time is 21 days). There was no significant difference in the K_d and no indication of more than a single estrogen binding site at any of the times tested. Endogenous nuclear estrogen binding sites (Teng and Teng, 1976a) rose from a value of 0.09 fmoles/μg DNA at 10 days of incubation to 0.59 fmoles/μg DNA at 18 days, while the total number of binding sites in the nucleus rose during this same period from 1.7 fmoles/μg DNA to a peak value of 2.6 fmoles/μg DNA at 15 days (compared to 2.35 fmoles/μg DNA for cytoplasmic sites at 15 days). These values reflect the observation that 87–

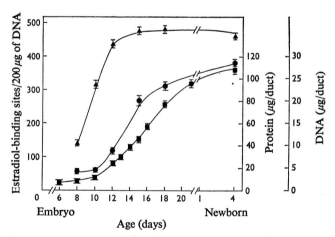

FIG. 11. Relationship between the number of cytoplasmic estradiol-binding sites and the development of Müllerian ducts in female chick embryos. Points representing the cytosol protein (●) or DNA (■) content per Müllerian duct were the average of three to four measurements. The measurement of estradiol-binding sites (▲) was expressed as fmoles of estradiol bound/200 μg of DNA. Procedures used were described by Teng and Teng (1975a). (From Teng and Teng, 1975b.)

95% of the cytoplasmic receptor was transferred into nuclei of developing chick Müllerian duct. The significant amount of endogenous nuclear receptor found at 10 days is consistent with the observation of ovarian estrogen production by 6 days in the chick embryo (Weniger, 1958). However, even before 6 days, responsiveness of Müllerian duct cells to estrogen has been demonstrated. Teng and Teng (1976b) administered diethylstilbestrol to female embryos on the 5th day of incubation. The regression of the right Müllerian duct was inhibited; moreover, both Müllerian ducts showed increased growth and precocious differentiation of epithelial gland cells accompanied by a decrease in the concentration of cytoplasmic estrogen receptors, but no change in nuclear estrogen binding sites.

C. Liver

Chick liver, in which estrogen induces vitellogenin synthesis (reviewed by Tata, 1976), has also been shown to contain estrogen receptors, although the cytosol receptors reported have been of low affinity, $K_d = 5 \times 10^{-6}\ M$ (Gschwendt, 1975), and did not enhance the transfer of [^{3}H]estradiol to nuclei (Arias and Warren, 1971) or to chromatin (Gschwendt, 1975). Recently, the group of E. E. Baulieu (personal communication) has found a low-affinity cytosol binding protein in avian liver dissimilar to that found in other organs.

Nuclear receptors have been reported to be soluble in saline–Tris buffers (Mester and Baulieu, 1972), or were solubilized in $2\ M$ KCl/$5\ M$ urea (Gschwendt, 1976). Binding of [^{3}H]estradiol to chromatin (Gschwendt and Kittstein, 1974) or insoluble receptors in the residual nuclear protein fraction (Lebeau *et al.*, 1973), have also been reported. The latter insoluble nuclear binding sites showed a K_d of ~1 nM, and were more concentrated in estradiol-treated chicks or laying hens (2000–3000 sites/cell) than in immature (3- to 4-week-old) chicks or male chickens (Lebeau et al., 1973).

C. Lazier (personal communication) has studied the ontogeny of a specific high-affinity ($K_d \sim 2$ nM), 4.5 S receptor in salt extracts of liver nuclei from the developing chick embryo. The receptor has a concentration of 150–200 sites/cell in 10-day-old embryos; injection of estradiol into the yolk sac on day 10 leads to an increase in nuclear receptor sites measured on day 12 (to 900–1000 sites/cell). This ability to respond to estrogen, by an increase in estrogen receptors, precedes the development of induction of vitellogenin synthesis by estradiol, traces of which can be induced on day 13. The sequential development of responsiveness to estrogen in chick liver is reminiscent of that found in rat uterus (Section II,A,5).

VI. CONCLUDING REMARKS

Studies on the ontogeny of estrogen receptors stemmed from the interest in steroid involvement in differentiation. In the case of the sexual determination of the rodent hypothalamus by gonadal steroids (which takes place during the first few postnatal days), the demonstration of specific high-affinity receptors for estrogens in the hypothalamic and preoptic areas of the brain, combined with the aromatization of androgens in these same cells and the protective action of circulating α-fetoprotein, has provided a consistent explanation for normal differentiation of sexual function and for neonatal androgenization by high doses of gonadal steroids. Concerning differentiation of the uterus, it appears that while the complete cytoplasmic and nuclear receptor mechanisms are present at birth, there is a postnatal development of competence for a complete response to estrogen, culminating in growth and cell division. Techniques now seem available to investigate the role of estrogens in differentiation of the Müllerian duct, particularly in the chick embryo. The presence of estrogen receptors in several organs of the rodent embryo, and the wide variation in the pattern of estrogen receptor changes (e.g., increase during early life in uterus and hypothalamus; reduction with age or disappearance in cortex; a complex pattern in the ovary related to the development of follicles and the corpus luteum) make the investigation of each system a separate challenge.

However, while the survey presented in this chapter thus reveals a variety of mechanisms for the control by estrogen of endocrine and neuroendocrine functions in mammals and birds, it reasserts the central role of the cytoplasmic and nuclear receptors for estrogen and at the same time emphasizes the essential steps which must precede and follow the formation of the estrogen–receptor complex in the cell. An adequate analysis of the ontogeny of a steroid responsive system must therefore take into account variations in all of the following.

a. The Provision of Estrogen. Generally, this will be by endocrine secretion which varies as a function of age, or it may result from synthesis in the estrogen-responsive cells by aromatization from suitable androgens. The rate of estrogen removal from the system must also be taken into account.

b. Interaction of Circulating Estrogen with Plasma-Binding Proteins. For example, in the case of the rodent, the concentration of α-fetoprotein in embryonic and perinatal stages is critical.

c. The Concentration of Cytoplasmic Receptor. Receptor availability depends on the concentration and timing of the previous exposure to estrogen and the rate of receptor replenishment, which in turn can be controlled by the action of other steroid hormones and by protein hormones.

d. The Concentration of Nuclear Receptor. The transport of the cytoplasmic estrogen–receptor complex into the nucleus is dependent on the integrity of the receptor complex and its concentration, while its retention in the nucleus depends on its binding to chromatin.

e. Interaction with Chromatin. This is the least understood of any of the facets of estrogen action mentioned up to this point. The number of chromosomal binding sites ("acceptors") which actually function as loci of stimulation of mRNA synthesis ("effector sites") is unknown. The state of chromatin in a cell can be affected simultaneously by estrogens and other steroid hormones (such as progesterone or cortisone) to change the cell's response to estrogen, either temporarily, or permanently in the course of differentiation.

f. Posttranscriptional Effects on Induced Syntheses. Controls in this area, and the utilization of the proteins induced by estrogen, which may include, e.g., catabolic enzymes capable of splitting other products induced by estrogen, have hardly been explored.

The above very partial list may serve as a signpost showing both from where and how far we have come in the past few years as well as how far we must still proceed in order to understand the ontogeny of estrogen–receptor interactions.

ACKNOWLEDGMENTS

I am grateful to my colleagues of the Department of Hormone Research for their helpful comments and to my colleagues abroad who graciously provided me with unpublished material for inclusion in this review. The work in our department was supported in part by grants (to H. R. Lindner) from the Ford Foundation and Population Council, New York.

REFERENCES

Adkins, E. K. (1975). *J. Comp. Physiol. Psychol.* **89**, 61.
Alberga, A., Massol, N., Raynaud, J.-P., and Baulieu, E.-E. (1971). *Biochemistry* **10**, 3835.
Alvarez, E. O., and Ramirez, V. D. (1970). *Neuroendocrinology* **6**, 349.
Anderson, C. H., and Greenwald, G. S. (1969). *Endocrinology* **85**, 1160.
Anderson, J. N., Clark, J. H., and Peck, E. J. (1972). *Biochem. J.* **126**, 561.
Anderson, J. N., Peck, E. J., and Clark, J. H. (1973). *Endocrinology* **92**, 1488.
Arias, F., and Warren, J. C. (1971). *Biochim. Biophys. Acta* **230**, 550.
Armstrong, E. G., Jr., and Villee, C. A. (1976). *Abstr., 58th Annu. Meet. Am. Endocr. Soc.*, p. 344.
Attardi, B., and Ohno, S. (1976). *Endocrinology* **99**, 1279.
Attardi, B., and Ruoslahti, E. (1976). *Nature (London)* **263**, 685.
Attardi, B., Geller, L. N., and Ohno, S. (1976). *Endocrinology* **98**, 864.

Attramadal, A. (1970). Z. *Zellforsch Mikrosk. Anat.* **104**, 572.

Aussel, C., Uriel, J., and Mercier-Bodard, C. (1973). *Biochimie* **55**, 1431.

Baker, F. D., and Kragt, C. L. (1969). *Endocrinology* **85**, 522.

Baram, T., Hazum, E., Fridkin, M., and Koch, Y. (1977). *Proc. Int. Congr. Hum. Reprod.,* *2nd, 1977* p. 164.

Barley, J., Ginsburg, M., Greenstein, B. D., Maclusky, N. J., and Thomas, P. J. (1974). *Nature (London)* **252**, 259.

Barnea, A., Weinstein, A., and Lindner, H. R. (1972). *Brain Res.* **46**, 391.

Barraclough, C. A., and Gorski, R. A. (1961). *Endocrinology* **68**, 68.

Baudendistel, L. J., and Ruh, T. S. (1976). *Steroids* **28**, 223.

Baulieu, E. E., Atger, M., Best-Belpomme, M., Corvol, P., Courvalin, J. C., Mester, J., Milgrom, E., Robel, P., Rochefort, H., and De Catalogne, D. (1975). *Vitam. Horm. (N.Y.)* **33**, 649.

Booth, J. E. (1977). *J. Endocrinol.* **72**, 53.

Borthwick, N. M., and Smellie, R. M. S. (1975). *Biochem. J.* **147**, 91.

Brinkmann, A. O., Mulder, E., Lamers-Stahlhofen, G. J. M., Mechielson, M. J., and van der Molen, H. J. (1972). *FEBS Lett.* **26**, 301.

Brown-Grant, K. (1974). *J. Endocrinol.* **62**, 683.

Brown-Grant, K., Munck, A., Naftolin, F., and Sherwood, M. R. (1971). *Horm. Behav.* **2**, 173.

Canick, J. A., Vaccaro, D. E., Ryan, K. J., and Leeman, S. E. (1977). *Endocrinology* **1**, 250.

Chan, L., and O'Malley, B. W. (1976). *N. Eng. J. Med.* **294**, 1332, 1372, and 1430.

Cheng, H. C., and Johnson, D. C. (1973–1974). *Neuroendocrinology* **13**, 357.

Cheng, H. C., and Johnson, D. C. (1974). *Endocrinology* **95**, 1462.

Chowdhury, M., Tcholakian, R., and Steinberger, E. (1974). *J. Endocrinol.* **60**, 375.

Cittanova, N., Gricorova, A. M., Benassayag, C., Nunez, E., and Jayle, M. F. (1974). *FEBS Lett.* **41**, 21.

Clark, J. H., and Gorski, J. (1969). *Biochim. Biophys. Acta* **192**, 508.

Clark, J. H., and Gorski, J. (1970). *Science* **169**, 76.

Clark, J. H., and Peck, E. J. (1976). *Nature (London)* **260**, 635.

Clark, J. H., Campbell, P. S., and Peck, E. J., Jr. (1972). *Neuroendocrinology* **77**, 218.

Curry, J. J., and Heim, L. M. (1966). *Nature (London)* **209**, 915.

Danzo, B. J., Eller, B. C., Judy, L. A., Trautman, J. R., and Orgebin-Crist, M. C. (1975a). *Mol. Cell Endocrinol.* **2**, 91.

Danzo, B. J., Sutton, W., and Orgebin-Crist, M. C. (1975b). *Abstr., 57th Annu. Meet., Am. Endocr. Soc.* p. 218.

Davies, I. J., Naftolin, F., Ryan, J. K., and Siu, J. (1975). *J. Clin. Endocrinol. Metab.* **40**, 909.

de Boer, W., Mulder, E., van der Molen, H. J. (1976). *J. Endocrinol.* **70**, 397.

De Konig, J., van Dieten, J. A. M. J., and van Rees, G. P. (1976). *Mol. Cell. Endocrinol.* **5**, 321.

Döhler, K. O., and Wuttke, W. (1975). *Endocrinology* **97**, 898.

Doughty, C., Booth, J. E., McDonald, P. G., and Parrott, R. F. (1975a). *J. Endocrinol.* **67**, 419.

Doughty, C., Booth, J. E., McDonald, P. G., and Parrott, R. F. (1975b). *J. Endocrinol.* **67**, 459.

Drouin, J., Lagace, L., and Labrie, F. (1976). *Endocrinology* **99**, 1477.

Edelman, I. S. (1975). *J. Steroid Biochem.* **6**, 147.

Eide, A. (1975a). *Cell Tissue Res.* **156**, 551.

Eide, A. (1975b). *Cell Tissue Kinet.* **8**, 249.

Eide, A., Hoisaeter, P. A., and Kvinnsland, S. (1975). *J. Steroid Biochem.* **6**, 1121.

Eisenfeld, A. J. (1974). *In* "Control of the Onset of Puberty" (M. M. Grumbach, G. D. Grave, and F. E. Mayer, eds.), pp. 271–312. Wiley, New York.

Eisenfeld, A. J. (1975). *In* "Anatomical Neuroendocrinology" (W. E. Stumpf and L. D. Grant, eds.), pp. 52–61. Karger, Basel.

Eisenfeld, A. J., and Axelrod, J. (1966). *Endocrinology* **79**, 38.

Eisenfeld, A. J., Aten, P., Weinberger, M., Haselbacher, G., and Halpern, K. (1976). *Science* **191**, 862.

Emmens, C. W., Cox, R. I., and Martin, L. (1962). *Recent Prog. Horm. Res.* **18**, 415.

Erdos, T., Bessada, R., Best-Belpomme, M., Fries, J., Gospodarowicz, D., Menahem, M., Reti, E., and Veron, A. (1971). *Adv. Biosci.* **7**, 119.

Eriksson, H., Hardin, J., Peck, E. Jr., and Clark, J. (1976). *Abstr., 58th Annu. Meet., Am. Endocr. Soc.* p. 97.

Fang, S., Anderson, K. M., and Liao, S. (1969). *J. Biol. Chem.* **244**, 6584.

Feherty, P., Robertson, D. M., Waynforth, H. B., and Kellie, A. E. (1970). *Biochem. J.* **120**, 837.

Feigelson, M. (1968). *J. Biol. Chem.* **243**, 5088.

Feigelson, M. (1971). *Biochim. Biophys. Acta* **230**, 309.

Feigelson, M. (1973). *Biochim. Biophys. Acta* **304**, 669.

Flerkó, B., Mess, B., and Illei-Donhoffer, A. (1969). *Neuroendocrinology* **4**, 164.

Flores, F., Naftolin, F., Ryan, J. K., and White, R. J. (1973). *Science* **180**, 1074.

Forsberg, J. G., and Kvinnsland, S. (1972). *J. Exp. Zool.* **180**, 403.

Fox, T. O. (1975a). *Nature (London)* **258**, 441.

Fox, T. O. (1975b). *Proc. Natl. Acad. Sci. U.S.A.* **72**, 4303.

Gellert, R. J., Lewis, J., and Petra, P. (1977). *Endocrinology* **100**, 520.

Gerall, A. A., and Kenney, A. McM. (1970). *Endocrinology* **87**, 560.

Gerall, A. A., McMurray, M. M., and Farrell, J. (1975). *J. Endocrinol.* **67**, 439.

Gilbert, S. F., and Migeon, B. R. (1975). *Cell* **5**, 11.

Ginsburg, M., Morris, I. D., Maclusky, N. J., and Thomas, P. J. (1972). *J. Endocrinol.* **55**, xx.

Ginsburg, M., Greenstein, B. D., McClusky, N. J., Morris, I. D., and Thomas, P. J. (1974). *Steroids* **23**, 773.

Giulian, D., Pohorecky, L. A., and McEwen, B. S. (1973). *Endocrinology* **93**, 1329.

Glascock, R. F., and Hoekstra, G. W. (1959). *Biochem. J.* **72**, 673.

Goldenberg, R. L., Vaitukaitis, J. L., and Ross, G. T. (1972). *Endocrinology* **90**, 1492.

Gorski, J., Sarff, M., and Clark, J. (1971). *Adv. Biosci.* **7**, 5.

Gorski, R. A. (1963). *Am. J. Physiol.* **205**, 842.

Gorski, R. A., and Barraclough, C. A. (1963). *Endocrinology* **73**, 210.

Gottlieb, H., Gerall, A. A., and Thiel, A. (1974). *Physiol. Behav.* **12**, 61.

Goy, R. W. (1970). *In* "The Neurosciences: Second Study Program" (F. O. Schmitt, ed.), pp. 196–207. Rockefeller Univ. Press, New York.

Green, R., Luttge, M. G., and Whalen, R. E. (1969). *Endocrinology* **85**, 373.

Greengard, O., and Dewey, H. K. (1971). *Proc. Natl. Acad. Sci. U.S.A.* **68**, 1698.

Gschwendt, M. (1975). *Hoppe-Seyler's Z. Physiol. Chem.*, **356**, 157.

Gschwendt, M. (1976). *Eur. J. Biochem.* **67**, 411.

Gschwendt, M., and Kittstein, W. (1974). *Biochim. Biophys. Acta* **361**, 84.

Hamburger, V., and Hamilton, H. L. (1951). *J. Morphol.* **88**, 49.

Hamburgh, M., and Barrington, E. J. W. (1971). "Hormones in Development." Appleton, New York.

Harris, G. W., and Levine, S. (1965). *Physiology* **181**, 379.

Hayashi, S. (1974). *Endocrinol. Jpn.* **21**, 453.

Heim, L. M. (1966). *Endocrinology* **78**, 1130.

Heim, L. M., and Timiras, P. S. (1963). *Endocrinology* **72**, 598.

Herbst, A. L., Kurman, R. J., Scully, R. E., and Poskanzen, D. E. (1972). *N. Engl. J. Med.* **287**, 1259.

Hilliard, J., Scaramuzzi, R. J., Penardi, R., and Sawyer, C. H. (1974). *Proc. Soc. Exp. Biol. Med.* **145,** 151.

Hudson, D. B., Vernadakis, A., and Timiras, P. S. (1970). *Brain Res.* **23,** 196.

Iguchi, T., and Takasugi, N. (1976). *Endocrinol. Jpn.* **23,** 327.

Iguchi, T., Ohta, Y., and Takasugi, N. (1976). *Dev. Growth Differ.* **18,** 69.

Jacobson, H. I., Bullock, D. W., and Keyes, P. L. (1972), *Proc. Int. Cong. Endocrinol., 4th, 1972* p. 188.

Jamdar, S. C., and Greengard, O. (1970). *J. Biol. Chem.* **245,** 2779.

Jensen, E. V., and De Sombre, E. R. (1972). *In* "Biochemical Action of Hormones" (G. Litwack, ed.), Vol. 2, p. 215. Academic Press, New York.

Jensen, E. V., and Jacobson, H. I. (1960). *In* "Biological Activities of Steroids in Relation to Cancer" (G. Pincus and E. P. Vollmer, eds.), p. 161. Academic Press, New York.

Jensen, E. V., and Jacobson, H. I. (1962). *Recent Prog. Horm. Res.* **18,** 387.

Jensen, E. V., Numata, M., Smith, S., Suzuki, T., Brecher, P. I., and De Sombre, E. R. (1969). *Dev. Biol., Suppl.* **3,** 151.

Jost, A. (1970). *Philos. Trans. Ry. Soc. London, Ser. B* **259,** 119.

Jost, A., Vigier, B., and Perchellet, J. B. (1973). *Recent Prog. Horm. Res.* **29,** 1.

Jungblut, P. W., Hughes, S. F., Göhrlich, L., Gowers, U., and Wagner, R. K. (1971). *Hoppe-Seyler's Z. Physiol. Chem.* **352,** 1603.

Kato, J. (1972). *Proc. Intl. Congr Endocrinol., 4th, 1972* p. 119.

Kato, J., Atsumi, Y., and Inaba, M. (1971a). *J. Biochem. (Tokyo)* **70,** 1051.

Kato, J., Sugimura, N., and Kobayashi, T. (1971b). *In* "Hormones in Development" (M. Hamburgh and E. J. W. Barrington, eds.), pp. 689–703. Appleton, New York.

Kato, J., Atsumi, Y., and Inaba, M. (1974a). *Endocrinology* **94,** 309.

Kato, J., Onouchi, T., Akinaga, S., and Ita, N. (1974b). *Endocrinology* **94,** 902.

Katzenellenbogen, B. S., and Gorski, J. (1972). *J. Biol. Chem.* **247,** 1299.

Katzenellenbogen, B. S., and Gorski, J. (1975a). *In* "Biochemical Actions of Hormones (G. Litwack, ed.), Vol. 3 pp. 187–243. Academic Press, New York.

Katzenellenbogen, B. S., and Gorski, J. (1975b). *In* "Methods in Enzymology" (B. W. O'Malley and J. G. Hardman, eds.), Vol. 36, p. 444. Academic Press, New York.

Katzenellenbogen, B. S., and Greger, N. G. (1974). *Mol. Cell. Endocrinol.* **2,** 31.

Katzman, P. A., Larson, D. L., and Podratz, K. C. (1971). *In* "The Sex Steroids: Molecular Mechanisms" (K. W. McKerns, ed.), pp. 107–147. Appleton, New York.

Kaye, A. M., Sheratzky, D., and Lindner, H. R. (1972). *Biochim. Biophys. Acta* **261,** 475.

Kaye, A. M., Icekson, I., Lamprecht, S. A., Gruss, R., Tsafriri, A., and Lindner, H. R. (1973). *Biochemistry* **12,** 3072.

Kaye, A. M., Sömjen, D., King, R. J. B., Sömjen, G. J., Ickeson, I., and Lindner, H. R. (1974). *Adv. Exp. Med. Biol.* **44,** 383.

Keefer, D. A., and Stumpf, W. E. (1975). *In* "Anatomical Neuroendocrinology" (W. E. Stumpf and L. D. Grant, eds.), p. 153. Karger, Basel.

Kimball, F. A., and Hansel, W. (1974). *Biol. Reprod.* **11,** 566.

Kincl, F. A., Folch, P. A., Maquero, M., Herrara Lasso, L., Oriol, A., and Dorfman, R. I. (1965). *Acta Endocrinol. (Copenhagen)* **49,** 193.

King, R. J. B. (1972). *Bibliogr. Reprod.* **20,** 1.

King, R. J. B. (1976). *In* "Essays in Biochemistry" (P. N. Campbell and W. N. Aldridge, eds.), Vol. 12, pp. 71–76. Academic Press, New York.

King, R. J. B., and Mainwaring, I. W. (1974). "Steroid-Cell Interactions." Butterworth, London.

Knapstein, P., David, A., Wu, C. H., Archer, D. F., Flickinger, G. L., and Touchstone, J. C. (1968). *Steroids* **11,** 885.

Knobil, E. (1973). *Biol. Reprod.* **8**, 246.

Koch, Y., Baram, T., Chobsieng, P., and Fridkin, M. (1974). *Biochem. Biophys. Res. Commun.* **61**, 95.

Kulin, H. E., and Reiter, E. O. (1972). *Endocrinology* **90**, 1371.

Kvinnsland, S. (1973). *Life Sci.* **12**, 373.

Lamprecht, S. A., Kohen, F., Ausher, J., Zor, U., and Lindner, H. R. (1976). *J. Endocrinol.* **68**, 343.

Lebeau, M.-C., Massol, N., and Baulieu, E. E. (1973). *Eur. J. Biochem.* **36**, 294.

Lee, C., and Jacobson, H. I. (1971). *Endocrinology* **88**, 596.

Lee, C., Keyes, P. L., and Jacobson, H. I. (1971). *Science* **173**, 1032.

Liao, S. (1975). *Int. Rev. Cytol.* **41**, 87.

Lieberman, M., Maurer, R., and Gorski, J. (1978). Submitted for publication.

Lisk, R. D., Reuter, L. A., and Grogan, T. J. (1976). *Biol. Reprod.* **15**, 485.

Litteria, M., and Thorner, M. W. (1976). *Brain Res.* **103**, 584.

Lobl, R. T., and Gorski, R. A. (1974). *Endocrinology* **94**, 1325.

Luck, D. N., Gschwendt, M., and Hamilton, T. H. (1974). *Nature (London), New Biol.* **245**, 24.

Lüttge, W. G., and Whalen, R. E. (1970). *Horm. Behav.* **1**, 265.

McCormack, S. A., and Glasser, S. R. (1976). *Endocrinology* **99**, 701.

McDonald, P. G., and Doughty, C. (1972a). *J. Reprod. Fertil.* **30**, 55.

McDonald, P. G., and Doughty, C. (1972b). *J. Endocrinol.* **55**, 455.

McEwen, B. S. (1976). *Sci. Am.* **235**, 48.

McEwen, B. S., and Pfaff, D. W. (1970). *Brain Res.* **21**, 1.

McEwen, B. S., Denef, C. J., Gerlach, J. L., and Plapinger, L. (1974). *In* "The Neurosciences, Third Study Program" (F. O. Schmitt and F. G. Worden, eds.), p. 599. MIT Press, Cambridge, Massachusetts.

McEwen, B. S., Plapinger, L., Chaptal, C., Gerlach, J., and Wallach, G. (1975). *Brain Res.* **96**, 400.

McEwen, B. S., Lieberburg, I., McClusky, N., and Plapinger, L. (1976). *Ann. Biol. Anim., Biochim., Biophys.* **16**, 471.

McGuire, J. L., and Lisk, R. D. (1969). *Nature (London)* **221**, 1068.

Maclusky, N. J., Chaptal, C., Lieberburg, I., and McEwen, B. S. (1976). *Brain Res.* **114**, 158

Martin, L., and Finn, C. A. (1971). *In* "Basic Actions of Sex Steroids on Target Organs" (P. O. Hubimont, F. Leroy, and P. Galand, eds.), p. 172. Karger, Basel.

Martinez-Vargas, M. C., Stumpf, W. E., and Sar, M. (1975a). *In* "Anatomical Neuroendocrinology" (W. E. Stumpf and L. D. Grant, eds.), pp. 166–175. Karger, Basel.

Martinez-Vargas, M. C., Gibson, D. B., Sar, M., and Stumpf, W. E. (1975b). *Science* **190**, 1307.

Maurer, H. R., and Chalkley, G. R. (1967). *J. Mol. Biol.* **27**, 431.

Maurer, H. R., and Wooley, D. E. (1971). *Endocrinology* **88**, 1281.

Meijs-Roelofs, H. M. A., Uilenbroek, J. Th. J., DeJong, F. H., and Welschen, R. (1973). *J. Endocrinol.* **59**, 295.

Mester, J., and Baulieu, E. E. (1972). *Biochim. Biophys. Acta* **261**, 236.

Michael, R. P. (1962). *Science* **136**, 322.

Michel, G., Jung, I., Baulieu, E.-E., Aussel, C., and Uriel, J. (1974). *Steroids* **24**, 437.

Miller, B. G. (1969). *J. Endocrinol.* **43**, 563.

Miller, J. B., and Keyes, P. L. (1976). *Biol. Reprod.* **15**, 511.

Miller, J. B., and Toft, D. O. (1976). *Abstr. 58th Annu. Meet., Am. Endocr. Soc.,* p. 196.

Mueller, G. G., Herranen, A. M., and Jervell, K. F. (1958). *Recent Prog. Horm. Res.* **14**, 95.

Mulder, E., Brinkman, A. O., Lamers-Stahlhofen, G. J. M., and van der Molen, H. J. (1973). *FEBS Lett.* **31**, 131.

Naftolin, F., Ryan, K. J., and Petro, Z. (1971). *J. Clin. Endocrinol. Metab.* **33**, 368.

Naftolin, F., Ryan, K. J., Davies, I. J., Reddy, V. V., Flores, F., Petro, Z., Kuhn, M., White, R. J., Takaoka, Y., and Wolin, L. (1975). *Recent Prog. Horm. Res.* **31**, 295.

Nakai, T., Sakamoto, S., Kigawa, T., and Shigematsu, A. (1972). *Endocrinol. Jpn.* **19**, 47.

Notides, A., and Gorski, J. (1966). *Proc. Natl. Acad. Sci. U.S.A.* **56**, 230.

Nunez, E., Engelman, F., Benassayag, C., Savu, L., Crépy, O., and Jayle, M.-F. (1971a). *C. R. Hebd. Seances Acad. Sci.* **272**, 2396.

Nunez, E., Savu, L., Engelman, F., Benassayag, C., Crépy, O., and Jayle, M.-F. (1971b) *C. R. Hebd. Seances Acad. Sci.* **273**, 242.

Nunez, E., Engelman, F., Benassayag, C., and Jayle, M.-F. (1971c). *C. R. Hebd. Seances Acad. Sci.* **273**, 831.

Nunez, E., Vallette, G., Benassayag, C., and Jayle, M.-F. (1974). *Biochem. Biophys. Res. Commun.* **57**, 126.

Ohta, Y., and Iguchi, T. (1976). *Endocrinol. Jpn.* **23**, 333.

O'Malley, B. W., and Hardman, J. G., eds. (1975). "Methods in Enzymology," Vol. 36, Part A. Academic Press, New York.

Pasqualini, J. R., and Palmada, M. (1972). *C. R. Hebd. Seances Acad. Sci.* **274**, 1218.

Pasqualini, J. R., Sumida, C., and Gelly, C. (1972). *J. Steroid Biochem.* **3**, 543.

Pasqualini, J. R., Sumida, C., and Gelly, C. (1974). *J. Steroid Biochem.* **5**, 977.

Pasqualini, J. R., Sumida, C., Gelly, C., and Nguyen, B. L. (1976). *J. Steroid Biochem.* **7**, 1031.

Peyre, A., and La Porte, P. (1966). *C. R. Seances Soc. Biol. Ses Fil.* **160**, 2178.

Pfaff, D. A., Diakow, C., Zigmond, R. E., and Kow, L. M. (1974). *In* "The Neurosciences, Third Study Program" (F. O. Schmitt and F. G. Worden, eds.), pp. 621–646. MIT Press, Cambridge, Massachusetts.

Pfeiffer, C. A. (1936). *Am. J. Anat.* **58**, 195.

Plapinger, L., and McEwen, B. S. (1973). *Endocrinology* **93**, 1119.

Plapinger, L., McEwen, B. S., and Clemens, L. E. (1973). *Endocrinology* **93**, 1129.

Posner, B. I. (1976). *Endocrinology* **99**, 1168.

Presl, J., Röhling, S., Horsky, J., and Herzmann, J. (1970). *Endocrinology* **86**, 899.

Prins, R. P., Morrow, C. P., Townsend, D. E., and Disaia, P. J. (1976). *Obstet. Gynecol.* **48**, 246.

Puca, G. A., and Bresciani, F. (1969). *Nature (London)* **223**, 745.

Puca, G. A., Sica, V., and Nola, E. (1974). *Proc. Natl. Acad. Sci. U.S.A.* **71**, 979.

Puca, G. A., Nola, E., Hibner, U., Cicala, G., and Sica, V. (1975). *J. Biol. Chem.* **260**, 6452.

Radanyi, C., Mercier-Bodard, C., Secco-Millet, C., Baulieu, E. E., and Richard-Foy, H. (1977). *Proc. Natl. Acad. Sci. U.S.A.* **74**, 2269.

Rao, K. N., and Talwar, G. P. (1969). *Indian J. Biochem.* **6**, 71.

Raynaud, J.-P. (1973). *Steroids* **21**, 249.

Raynaud, J.-P., Mercier-Bodard, C., and Baulieu, E. E. (1971). *Steroids* **18**, 767.

Reddy, V. V. R., Naftolin, F., and Ryan, K. J. (1973). *Endocrinology* **92**, 589.

Reddy, V. V. R., Naftolin, F., and Ryan, K. J. (1974). *Endocrinology* **94**, 117.

Reiter, E. O., Goldenberg, R. L., Vaitukaitis, J. L., and Ross, G. T. (1972). *Endocrinology* **91**, 1537.

Rennie, P. (1968a). *Endocrinology* **83**, 314.

Rennie, P. (1968b). *Endocrinology* **83**, 323.

Resco, J. A., Feder, H. H., and Goy, R. W. (1968). *J. Endocrinol.* **40**, 485.

Richards, J. S. (1974). *Endocrinology* **95**, 1046.

Richards, J. S. (1975a). *Endocrinology* **96**, 227.

Richards, J. S. (1975b). *Endocrinology* **97**, 1174.

Richards, J. S., and Gibori, G. (1976). *Abstr., 58th Annu. Meet., Am. Endocr. Soc.* p. 200.

Richards, J. S., and Midgley, A. R., Jr. (1976). *Biol. Reprod.* **14**, 82.

Rosen, J. M., and O'Malley, B. W. (1975). In "Biochemical Actions of Hormones" (G. Litwack, ed.), Vol. 3, p. 271. Academic Press, New York.

Ruh, T. S., and Baudendistel, L. J. (1977). *Endocrinology* 100, 720.

Ruh, T. S., and Ruh, M. F. (1974). *Endocrinology* 97, 1114.

Ruh, T. S., Katzenellenbogen, B. S., Katzenellenbogen, J. A., and Gorski, J. (1973). *Endocrinology* 92, 125.

Ruoslahti, E., and Attardi, B. (1978). *Steroids* (in press).

Ruoslahti, E., and Terry, W. D. (1976). *Nature (London)* 260, 804.

Saiduddin, S., and Zassenhaus, P. H. (1975). *Abstr. 57th Annu. Meet., Am. Endocr. Soc.* p. 327.

Salaman, D. F., Thomas, P. J., and Westley, B. R. (1976). *Ann. Biol. Anim., Biochim., Biophys.* 16, 479.

Samuels, L. T., Uchikawa, T., and Huseby, R. A. (1967). *Ciba Found. Colloq. Endocrinol.* [*Proc.*] 16, 211.

Sandberg, A. A., Slaunwhite, W. R., Jr., and Antoniades, H. N. (1957). *Recent Prog. Horm. Res.* 13, 209.

Sato, B., Huseby, R. A., and Samuels, L. T. (1976). *Abstr., 58th Annu. Meet., Am. Endocr. Soc.* p. 206.

Schimke, R. T., McKnight, G. S., and Shapiro, D. J. (1975). In "Biochemical Actions of Hormones" (G. Litwack, ed.), Vol. 3, pp. 246–269. Academic Press, New York.

Schwartzel, W. C., Kruggel, W. G., and Brodie, H. J. (1973). *Endocrinology* 92, 866.

Scott, R. S., and Rennie, P. I. C. (1970). *J. Reprod. Fertil.* 23, 415.

Scott, R. S., and Rennie, P. I. C. (1971). *Endocrinology* 89, 297.

Sell, S., Becker, F. F., Leffert, H. L., and Watabe, H. (1976). *Cancer Res.* 36, 4.

Shaikh, A. A. (1971). *Biol. Reprod.* 5, 297.

Shemesh, M., Ailenberg, M., Mileguir, F., and Ayalon, N. (1977). *Abstr. 10th Annu. Meet. Soc. Study Reprod.* p. 77.

Sheratt, M., Exley, D., and Rogers, A. W. (1969). *Neuroendocrinology* 4, 374.

Sheridan, P. J., Sar, M., and Stumpf, W. E. (1974a). *Endocrinology* 94, 1386.

Sheridan, P. J., Sar, M., and Stumpf, W. E. (1974b). *Endocrinology* 95, 1749.

Sheridan, P. J., Sar, M., and Stumpf, W. E. (1974c). *Am. J. Anat.* 140, 589.

Sheridan, P. J., Sar, M., and Stumpf, W. E. (1974d). *Acta Endocrinol. (Copenhagen)* 76, 570.

Sheridan, P. J., Sar, M., and Stumpf, W. E. (1975). In "Anatomical Neuroendocrinology" (W. E. Stumpf and L. D. Grant, eds.), p. 134. Karger, Basel.

Shyamala, G. (1972). *Biochem. Biophys. Res. Commun.* 46, 1623.

Smeaton, T. C., Arcondoulis, D. E., and Steele, P. A. (1975). *Steroids,* 26, 181.

Smirnova, O. V., Smirnov, A. N., and Rozen, V. B. (1974). *Biokhimiya* 39, 648.

Soloff, M. S., Creange, J. E., and Potts, G. O. (1971). *Endocrinology* 88, 427.

Sömjen, D., and Kaye, A. M. (1976). *Mol. Cell. Endocrinol.* 4, 353.

Sömjen, D., Sömjen, G. J., King, R. J. B., Kaye, A. M., and Lindner, H. R. (1973a). *Biochem. J.* 136, 25.

Sömjen, D., Kaye, A. M., and Lindner, H. R. (1973b). *Dev. Biol.* 31, 409.

Sömjen, G. J., Kaye, A. M., and Lindner, H. R. (1974). *Mol. Cell. Endocrinol.* 1, 341.

Sömjen, G. J., Kaye, A. M., and Lindner, H. R. (1976). *Biochim. Biophys. Acta* 428, 787.

Spelsberg, T. C., Steggles, A. W., and O'Malley, B. W. (1971). *Biochim. Biophys. Acta* 254, 129.

Spelsberg, T. C., Mitchell, W. M., Chytil, F., Wilson, E. M., and O'Malley, B. W. (1973). *Biochim. Biophys. Acta* 312, 765.

Spelsberg, T. C., Pikler, G. M., and Webster, R. A. (1976). *Science* 194, 197.

Steggles, A. W., and King, R. J. B. (1970). *Biochem. J.* 118, 695.

Stumpf, W. E. (1968). *Endocrinology* 83, 777.

Stumpf, W. E. (1969). *Endocrinology* **85**, 31.

Stumpf, W. E. (1971). *Am. Zool.* **11**, 725.

Stumpf, W. E., and Grant, L. D., eds. (1975). "Anatomical Neuroendocrinology." Karger, Basel.

Stumpf, W. E., and Sar, M. (1975a). *In* "Methods in Enzymology" (B. W. O'Malley and J. G. Hardman, eds.), Vol. 36, p. 135. Academic Press, New York.

Stumpf, W. E., and Sar, M. (1975b). *In* "Anatomical Neuroendocrinology" (W. E. Stumpf and L. D. Grant, eds.), p. 82. Karger, Basel.

Stumpf, W. E., and Sar, M. (1976). *J. Steroid Biochem.* **7**, 1163.

Stumpf, W. E., Baerwaldt, C., and Sar, M. (1971). *In* "Basic Actions of Sex Steroids on Target Tissues" (P. O. Hubinont, F. LeRoy, and P. Galand, eds.), p. 3. Karger, Basel.

Stumpf, W. E., Sar. M., and Keefer, D. A. (1975). *In* "Anatomical Neuroendocrinology (W. E. Stumpf and L. D. Grant, eds.), p. 104. Karger, Basel.

Swartz, S. K., and Soloff, M. S. (1974). *J. Clin. Endocrinol. Metab.* **39**, 589.

Takayama, M., and Greenwald, G. S. (1973). *Endocrinology* **92**, 1405.

Tata, J. R. (1976). *Cell* **9**, 1.

Teng, C. S., and Teng, C. T. (1975a). *Biochem. J.* **150**, 183.

Teng, C. S., and Teng, C. T. (1975b). *Biochem. J.* **150**, 191.

Teng, C. S., and Teng, C. T. (1976a). *Biochem. J.* **154**, 1.

Teng, C. S., and Teng, C. T. (1976b). *J. Cell Biol.* **70**, 144a.

Toft, D., and Gorski, J. (1966). *Proc. Natl. Acad. Sci. U.S.A.* **55**, 1574.

Tsai, S. Y., Harris, S. E., Tsai, M. J., and O'Malley, B. W. (1976). *J. Biol. Chem.* **251**, 4713.

Tuohimaa, P., and Johansonn, R. (1971). *Endocrinology* **88**, 1159.

Uriel, J., de Nechaud, B., and Dupiers, M. (1972). *Biochem. Biophys. Res. Commun.* **46**, 1175.

Uriel, J., Bouillon, D., Aussel, C., and Dupiers, M. (1976). *Proc. Natl. Acad. Sci. U.S.A.* **73**, 1452.

van Beurden-Lamers, W. O., Brinkmann, A. O., Mulder, E., and van der Molen, H. (1974). *Biochem. J.* **140**, 495.

Vertes, M., and King, R. J. B. (1969). *J. Endocrinol.* **45**, xxii.

Vertes, M., and King, R. J. B. (1971). *J. Endocrinol.* **51**, 271.

Vertes, M., Barnea, A., Lindner, H. R., and King, R. J. B. (1973). *In* "Receptors for Reproductive Hormones" (B. W. O'Malley and A. R. Means, eds.), pp. 137–173. Plenum, New York.

Vreeburg, J. T. M., Schretlen, P. J. M., and Baum, M. J. (1975). *Endocrinology* **97**, 969.

Walker, M. D., Gozes, I., Kaye, A. M., Reiss, N., and Littauer, U. Z. (1976). *J. Steroid Biochem.* **7**, 1083.

Weisz, J., and Gibbs, C. (1974). *Neuroendocrinology* **14**, 72.

Weisz, J., and Gunsalus, P. (1973). *Endocrinology* **93**, 1057.

Weniger, J. P. (1958). *C. R. Hebd. Seances Sci.* **246**, 1094.

Westley, B. R., and Salaman, D. F. (1976). *Nature (London)* **262**, 407.

Westley, B. R., and Salaman, D. F. (1977). *Brain Res.* **119**, 375.

Westley, B. R., Thomas, P. J., Salaman, D. F., Knight, A., and Barley, J. (1976). *Brain Res.* **113**, 441.

Williams, D., and Gorski, J. (1972). *Proc. Natl. Acad. Sci. U.S.A.* **69**, 3464.

Wooley, D. E., Holinka, C. F., and Timiras, P. S. (1969). *Endocrinology* **84**, 157.

Yamamoto, K. R., and Alberts, B. (1975). *Cell* **4**, 301.

Yamamoto, K. R., and Alberts, B. M. (1976). *Annu. Rev. Biochem.* **45**, 721.

Yamamoto, K. R., Gehring, U., Stampfer, M. R., and Sibley, C. H. (1975). *Recent Prog. Horm. Res.* **32**, 3.

Zigmond, R. E. (1975). *In* "Handbook of Psychopharmacology" (L. L. Iverson, S. D. Iverson, and S. H. Snyder, eds.), p. 239. Plenum, New York.

CHAPTER 5

Epidermal Growth Factors

Graham Carpenter and Stanley Cohen

I. INTRODUCTION

Among the basic challenges confronting modern biological research is the understanding of the biochemical processes which regulate or otherwise influence the proliferation of mammalian cells. Endocrinological studies have established the importance of circulating hormones, such as growth hormone and thyroxine, in the processes of growth, development, and differentiation. The identification of the role of specific hormones in animal systems generally has been carried out by classical extirpation procedures that, by nature, are limited to those instances in which the hormone is made exclusively in a particular organ that can be successfully removed by surgical procedures. A further limitation of animal studies is the difficulty in delineating the direct and indirect effects of hormone withdrawal or administration; for example, many of the effects of growth hormone appear to be mediated by somatomedin (Van Wyk and Underwood, 1975).

Another experimental approach to the control of cell proliferation has been the development of culture techniques and media for the propagation of eukaryotic cells *in vitro*. The results have demonstrated the dependence of cell proliferation on the presence of macromolecular growth factors in serum (Holley and Kiernan, 1968; Temin *et al.*, 1972). Because the isolation of specific growth factors is a prerequisite for a meaningful biochemical investigation and understanding of cell proliferation, many attempts have been made to purify the active components of serum (Temin *et al.*, 1972; Gospodarowicz and Moran, 1976). However, because of the complexity of serum, the extremely low concentration of growth factors in serum, the presence of growth-inhibitory molecules, and the lack of rapid and specific assays, relatively slow progress has been made in this area. Recently, mitogenic polypeptides, referred to as somatomedins and nonsuppressible insulin-like activity, have been isolated from serum (Fryklund *et al.*, 1974; Van Wyk *et al.*, 1975; Rinderknecht and Humble, 1976). Reflecting the low concentrations of growth factors in serum, the isolation of these polypeptides has required industrial cooperation for the processing of thousands of liters of serum.

Although many growth factors are present in serum, it is reasonable to assume that they are not synthesized within the circulatory system but rather are produced and stored at other distinct sites. Also, it is known that body fluids such as lymph and urine contain growth factors (Sato, 1975; Holley and Kiernan, 1968). A number of mitogenic polypeptides have been successfully isolated from sources other than serum: nerve growth factor from the mouse submaxillary gland (Cohen, 1960), epidermal growth factor from mouse submaxillary gland (Cohen, 1962) and from human urine (Cohen and Carpenter, 1975), fibroblast growth factor from bovine pituitary and brain (Gospodarowicz, 1975), and ovarian growth factor from bovine pituitary (Gospodarowicz *et al.*, 1974). Growth factors have also been isolated from media "conditioned" by the growth of cultured cells: multiplication-stimulating activity from media "conditioned" by rat liver cells (Smith and

Temin, 1974) and macrophage growth factor and colony-stimulating factor from L-cell "conditioned" media (Stanley *et al.*, 1976).

Of the growth factors which have been purified to date, epidermal growth factor (EGF) is one of the most biologically potent and best characterized as to its physical, chemical, and biological properties. The scope of this review will attempt to be comprehensive; however, the main focus will be on those advances in the study of epidermal growth factor which have occurred in the last three years. The reader is referred to previous reviews for supplementary information on earlier studies (Cohen, 1972; Cohen and Taylor, 1974; Cohen and Savage, 1974).

II. ISOLATION OF EPIDERMAL GROWTH FACTORS

A. MOUSE-DERIVED EGF (mEGF)

During the course of studies on the nerve growth factor of the submaxillary gland of the mouse (Cohen, 1960), it was noticed that daily injections of extracts of this gland into newborn mice resulted in gross anatomical changes which were different from those produced by purified nerve growth factor. These changes were precocious opening of eyelids and eruption of the incisors. The factor responsible for these effects was isolated (Cohen, 1962) by a series of ion-exchange and gel-filtration columns and found to be a low molecular weight, heat-stable, nondialyzable polypeptide which was designated mEGF. It was estimated that mEGF accounted for approximately 0.5% of the dry weight of the submaxillary gland protein.

An improved procedure for the isolation of EGF from mouse submaxillary glands has been reported (Savage and Cohen, 1972). This is a rapid two-step purification procedure, based on the observation that, at low pH, columns of polyacrylamide (Bio-Gel) are capable of selectively and reversibly adsorbing EGF from crude homogenates of the submaxillary gland of adult male mice. Subsequent chromatography on DEAE–cellulose resulted in a pure preparation of mEGF identical to that obtained by the more time-consuming procedures and with a 3- to 4-fold increase in yield. Typical purifications of mEGF from the salivary glands of 150 mice resulted in 4–6 mg of growth factor by the older procedure compared to 16–21 mg by the improved methodology. The yield of EGF from submaxillary glands was further increased 50–100% by the administration of testosterone to male mice one week prior to isolation (Cohen and Savage, 1975).

Rapid isolation procedures which yield milligram quantities of purified growth factor are an important technical consideration in the study of mitogens. In addition to time saved from arduous purification procedures and the difficulties in assessing the physiological significance of a mitogen isolated in low yield, the availability of milligram quantities of growth factor allows for physical and chemical studies which require large amounts of material.

B. Human EGF (hEGF)

The isolation of growth factors from biological material is often complicated by the lack of a specific and rapid assay. The development of a radioreceptor competitive binding assay, utilizing monolayers of human fibroblasts and ^{125}I-labeled mEGF, permitted the detection and isolation of epidermal growth factor from protein concentrates of human urine (Cohen and Carpenter, 1975). The purification of hEGF required five chromatographic steps and yielded approximately 100 μg of growth factor from 10 gm of starting material, an acetone powder obtained from benzoic acid preparation of 15 liters of urine from pregnant women. The partial purification of hEGF directly from human urine by affinity chromatography has been reported (Starkey et al., 1975). This procedure did not, however, lend itself to a large-scale processing of starting material.

III. CHEMICAL AND PHYSICAL PROPERTIES OF EGF

A. Mouse-Derived EGF

Because purified mEGF can be obtained rapidly and in relatively large quantities, it has been possible to determine many of the chemical and physical characteristics of this polypeptide. The long-range objectives of these investigations are to identify residues in the molecule which are essential for its mitogenic activity and to determine how the conformation of EGF is related to its biological effects. Many studies of structure–function relationships of a variety of polypeptide hormones have indicated that the biological activity of these molecules is stringently dependent on a precise chemical and physical structure.

Studies by Taylor et al. (1972) reported many of the basic chemical and physical characteristics of mEGF. The growth factor is a heat-stable, nondialyzable, single polypeptide chain of 53 amino acid residues, and is devoid of alanine, phenylalanine, and lysine residues. No free sulfhydryl groups, hexosamine, or neutral sugar groups were detected. The molecular weight, as determined by amino acid composition, was reported as 6045, in agreement with molecular weight estimates of 6400 and 7000, determined by sedimentation equilibrium and gel filtration, respectively. The isoelectric point for mEGF was reported at pH 4.60. The extinction coefficient ($E_{1\,cm}^{1\%}$ at 280 nm) was determined to be 30.9, and a sedimentation constant of 1.25 S was reported (Cohen, 1962).

Studies by Savage *et al.* (1972, 1973) have reported the primary amino acid sequence of mEGF and the location of the three intramolecular disulfide bonds (Fig. 1). The disulfide bonds in mEGF were required for biological activity (Taylor *et al.* 1972). Reduction of the disulfides in the presence of mercaptoethanol and urea yielded an inactive polypeptide. The biological activity, however, was restored by removal of the mercaptoethanol and urea by dialysis and subsequent reoxidation by air.

The isolation of intact mEGF from crude extracts of the submaxillary gland was dependent on the pH. If the pH of the extract was lowered from 4.5 to 3.5, a derivative of mEGF (mEGF$_{1-51}$) was produced, presumably by an acidic protease, that lacked the carboxy-terminal Leu-Arg residues (Savage and Cohen, 1972). Exposure of intact mEGF to mild tryptic digestion resulted in cleavage of the peptide bond between residues 48 and 49, producing a pentapeptide containing residues 49–53 and a derivative of mEGF composed of residues 1–48 (Savage *et al.*, 1972). As mentioned previously (Section II,A), intact mEGF was adsorbed to Bio-Gel at a low pH; however, mEGF$_{1-48}$ did not exhibit this chromatographic property, but mEGF$_{1-51}$ and the pentapeptide containing residues 49–53 were adsorbed. The unusual doublet of tryptophan at residues 49 and 50 may confer this abnormal chromatographic property on the mEGF polypeptide. The relationship of these derivatives of mEGF to the biological activity of the intact growth factor will be presented in Sections V, VII,E, and VIII.

Circular dichroic (CD) examination of the far-ultraviolet spectrum of

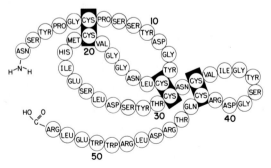

FIG. 1. Amino acid sequence and location of disulfide linkages of mouse-derived EGF. (From Savage *et al.*, 1973.)

mEGF indicated the absence of significant α-helical structure, the presence of approximately 25% β-helix, and a random coil content of 75% (Taylor *et al.*, 1972). These results have been confirmed by Holladay *et al.* (1976), who extended CD studies of mEGF to include the near-ultraviolet spectra. These workers reported that while intact mEGF has 22% β-structure, derivates of the native molecule, namely $mEGF_{1-48}$ and cyanogen-bromide-treated mEGF (CNBr-EGF), have approximately 10% and 12% β-structure, respectively. Thus the carboxy-terminal residues 49–53 and the peptide bond between residues 21 and 22 which is cleaved by cyanogen bromide appear to contribute to the ordered structure in the intact molecule.

Holladay and colleagues (1976) have extended these results by applying a set of rules (Chou and Fasman, 1974) to predict secondary structure and bends to the known amino acid sequence of mEGF. This analysis of the secondary structure of mEGF predicted sections of β-structure at residues 19–23 and 29–37. Chain reversals (β-turns) beginning at residues 3, 6, 10, 15, 27, 37, and 40 were predicted. Although one section of α-helix at residues 46–53 was predicted, it had a high $<P\beta>$ value and may exist as β-structure. Because the CD spectra of $mEGF_{1-48}$ and CNBr-EGF, modified at residue 21, indicated a loss of β-structure compared to the intact molecule, this predicted structure is in accord with that indicated by the CD spectra if, in fact, the carboxy-terminal residues contribute to the β-structure.

The sedimentation constant of 1.25 S (Cohen, 1962) and frictional ratio (f/f_0) of 1.12 (L. Holladay, personal communication) for mEGF suggests that the polypeptide is relatively compact and globular. Based on the predicted secondary structure and the CD spectra, a space-filling model of mEGF has been constructed (L. A. Holladay, personal communication). The model also indicates that mEGF exists as a very compact structure, due mainly to the many β bends and three disulfide bonds. Interestingly, one face of the model is composed of a three-tiered β-sheet region. At present, it is not possible to describe with certainty the relationship of this area of β-structure to the biological activity of mEGF.

Examination of the CD spectra of mEGF under different conditions indicated that the molecule has a stable tertiary structure (Holladay *et al.*, 1976). Equilibrium studies on the reversible unfolding of mEGF in the presence of a denaturant showed that the transition midpoint is quite high (i.e., 6.89 *M* guanidinium hydrochloride at 25°C) as compared to other proteins. By extrapolation, an estimate of 16 kcal/mole was made for the free energy of unfolding (ΔG^0) in the absence of denaturant. The thermal stability of mEGF has also been examined and various thermodynamic properties estimated for mEGF at 40°C in the absence of denaturant. The data indicated that the apparent free energy of unfolding (ΔG^0_{app}) is 18 kcal/mole; the apparent enthalpy of unfolding (ΔH_{app}) is 24.4 kcal/mole; and the apparent entropy of unfolding (ΔS_{app}) is 20.4 cal/(mole deg). The absolute magnitude of the apparent heat capacity (ΔC_p) was estimated at less than 0.5 kcal/(mole deg), substantially less than that reported for other proteins. It was suggested that the small ΔC_p value for mEGF is due in part to the relatively high degree of exposure of the hydrophobic side chains in native EGF to the solvent as suggested by CD spectra analysis and the space-filling model. In the absence of completely buried aromatic residues, it is not clear what forces beyond the three disulfide bonds produce such a highly stable native conformation of mEGF, although the β-structure may play a large role. These data indicate that mEGF is one of the most energetically stable proteins that has been described. The physiological significance of this unusual stability may be understood when the physicochemical properties of other growth factors are reported.

B. HIGH MOLECULAR WEIGHT FORM OF mEGF

In crude homogenates of the mouse submaxillary gland, EGF was found to be a component of a high molecular weight complex (Taylor *et al.*, 1970, 1974). On the basis of purification yields, the high molecular weight form of EGF was estimated to comprise 2–3% of the dry weight of the submaxillary glands of male mice. The complex has a molecular weight of approximately 74,000, as judged by sedimentation equilibrium, and is composed of 2 molecules of mEGF (6045 molecular weight) and 2 molecules of binding protein (29,300 molecular weight). The high molecular weight complex is stable over the pH range 5–8. Isoelectric focusing within this pH range indicated an isoelectric point of 5.4 for the complex. Other properties of the high molecular weight complex include a sedimentation value of 4.81 S, an extinction coefficient ($E_1^{1\%}{}_{cm}$ at 280 nm) of 19.1, and a diffusion constant ($D_{20,w}^0$) of 6.7 $\times$ 10^{-7} cm^2/second.

The high molecular weight complex can be dissociated into subunits by ion-exchange chromatography at pH 7.5 or gel filtration at pH values below 5 or above 8. Low molecular weight mEGF released by dissociation of the complex is identical to the mEGF described in the preceding sections. The dissociated mEGF and binding protein reassociate at a neutral pH to form a high molecular complex of approximately the same molecular weight as the native complex. The capacity of mEGF to reassociate with its binding protein is dependent on the presence of the carboxy-terminal arginine residue (Server *et al.*, 1976). mEGF$_{1-51}$, lacking the carboxy-terminal Arg-Leu residues, does not recombine with the binding protein. The importance of the carboxy-terminal arginine residue was demonstrated by treating native mEGF with carboxypeptidase B to produce a derivative lacking the carboxy-terminal arginine residue. This derivative shows no capacity to re-combine with the binding protein.

The biological significance of the carboxy-terminal arginine residue of mEGF had been indicated by the identification of the binding protein's enzymatic activity toward arginine esters (Taylor *et al.*, 1970, 1974). The male mouse submaxillary gland has been reported to contain a number of enzymes capable of hydrolyzing arginine esters (Angelletti *et al.*, 1967; Calissano and Angelletti, 1968). The γ subunit proteins associated with nerve growth factor (NGF) isolated from the mouse submaxillary gland also possess arginine esterase activity (Greene *et al.*, 1968). Although the arginine es-teropeptidases associated with NGF and mEGF have similar molecular weights, amino acid compositions, and substrate specificities, they differ in their electrophoretic properties. Also, while they cross-react immunologi-cally, they are not identical antigenically, and the mEGF-binding protein does not substitute for the γ subunits in the formation of 7 S NGF (Server and Shooter, 1976). The results indicate specific associations between each of these growth factors and particular arginine esteropeptidases. Since both mEGF and NGF have carboxy-terminal arginine residues and are associated with arginine esteropeptidases, it is possible that these low molecular weight polypeptides are produced from precursor proteins by the action of the peptidases (Taylor *et al.*, 1970; Angelletti and Bradshaw, 1971; Server and Shooter, 1976). Evidence for the generation of the other polypeptide hormones from larger precursors by the action of arginine esteropeptidases has been reported (Schachter, 1969; Habner *et al.*, 1973; Steiner *et al.*, 1974). Precursor molecules for mEGF have not been identified. Interest-ingly, the arginine esterase protein associated with mEGF does exhibit biological activity, enhancing the mitogenic properties of mEGF in cell culture systems (discussed in Section VII,D).

C. Human EGF

Although human EGF has not been as well characterized as the mouse-derived polypeptide, the available data indicate that the two polypeptides are very similar but not identical with respect to their chemical and physical properties (Cohen and Carpenter, 1975).

Polyacrylamide disc gel electrophoresis at pH 9.5 (Fig. 2) shows that hEGF migrates slightly faster than mEGF, indicating a greater net negative charge for the human polypeptide at this pH. At a low pH (Fig. 2), both growth factors migrate at approximately the same rate. The different elec-

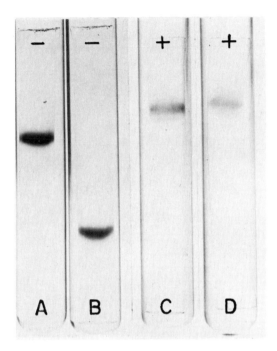

FIG. 2. Disc gel electrophoresis of hEGF and mEGF. Tubes A and C contain mEGF; tubes B and D contain hEGF. The pH of the gels in tubes A and B was 9.5 and in tubes C and D, 2.3. Samples of 10–20 μg of protein were applied. (From Cohen and Carpenter, 1975.)

trophoretic properties of human and mouse EGF are reflected in their respective amino acid compositions as shown in Table I. As small quantities, less than 50 ug, of hEGF were available for analysis, the data are considered as the probable amino acid composition of hEGF. Nevertheless, it is clear that the two molecules exhibit considerable similarities and definite differences with respect to their amino acid compositions. The amino acid sequence of human EGF has not been determined owing to the limited amount of material available. However, as discussed in the following section, the similarity of mouse and human EGF to human urogastrone, a polypeptide of known amino acid sequence, suggests a primary structure for hEGF. Studies of hEGF by gel-filtration chromatography and sedimentation equilibrium indicate molecular weight values of approximately 5700 and 5291, respectively. Because mEGF and hEGF exhibit identical biological activities and have some common antigenic sites, the results support the idea that the human growth factor is an evolved form of the mouse polypeptide.

TABLE I
AMINO ACID COMPOSITIONS OF mEGF, hEGF, AND β-UROGASTRONE

Amino acid	Mouse EGF[a]	Human EGF[b] (probable)	β-Urogastrone[c]
		Residues per mole	
Lys	0	3	2
His	1	2	2
Trp	2	1	2
Arg	4	2	3
Asp	7	7	7
Thr	2	0	0
Ser	6	3	3
Glu	3	5	5
Pro	2	2	1
Gly	6	5	4
Ala	0	2	2
Half-Cys	6	6	6
Val	2	2	3
Met	1	1	1
Ile	2	2	2
Leu	4	4	5
Tyr	5	2	5
Phe	0	0	0
Total	53	49	53

[a] From Taylor *et al.*, 1972.
[b] From Cohen and Carpenter, 1975.
[c] From Gregory, 1975.

D. RELATIONSHIP OF EGF AND UROGASTRONE

A new aspect of the biology of EGF recently has emerged with the publication of the amino acid sequence and disulfide linkages of urogastrone, a gastric antisecretory hormone isolated from human urine (Gregory, 1975). A comparison of the amino acid sequences of human urogastrone and mEGF is shown in Fig. 3. Of the 53 amino acid residues comprising each of the two polypeptides, 37 are common to both molecules, and the 3 disulfide bonds are formed in the same relative positions. Sixteen variable residues occur at intervals along the polypeptide chain; of these, 14 could result from single base changes in the triplet code. The structural similarity of urogastrone and mEGF is further supported by their capacities to elicit nearly identical

```
                                                      10
Asn  Ser │Tyr  Pro  Gly│ Cys  Pro │Ser│ Ser │Tyr│ Asp  Gly

Asn  Ser │Asp  Ser  Glu│ Cys  Pro │Leu│ Ser │His│ Asp  Gly
                                            20
Tyr  Cys  Leu │Asn  Gly│ Gly  Val  Cys  Met │His│ Ile  Glu

Tyr  Cys  Leu │His  Asp│ Gly  Val  Cys  Met │Tyr│ Ile  Glu
                                  30
│Ser│ Leu  Asp │Ser│ Tyr │Thr│ Cys  Asn  Cys  Val │Ile│ Gly

│Ala│ Leu  Asp │Lys│ Tyr │Ala│ Cys  Asn  Cys  Val │Val│ Gly
                      40
Tyr │Ser│ Gly │Asp│ Arg  Cys  Gln │Thr│ Arg  Asp  Leu │Arg│

Tyr │Ile│ Gly │Glu│ Arg  Cys  Gln │Tyr│ Arg  Asp  Leu │Lys│
     50
Trp  Trp  Glu  Leu  Arg  ———   EGF  (mouse)

Trp  Trp  Glu  Leu  Arg  ———   UROGASTRONE
```

FIG. 3. Amino acid sequences of mouse EGF and human urogastrone (Gregory, 1975).

biological responses. mEGF was shown to possess gastric antisecretory activity, and urogastrone to possess the biological activity of EGF, as judged by its ability to induce precocious eyelid opening in the newborn mouse.

The available data concerning the amino acid compositions of human EGF and human urogastrone are presented in Table I. Although the amino acid composition of human EGF must be considered preliminary, the data indicate a very close similarity in the chemical compositions of hEGF and human urogastrone. The results suggest that urogastrone may be identical, or very closely related, to human EGF in both structure and function.

IV. CONTROL OF EGF LEVELS AND SECRETION IN THE SUBMAXILLARY GLAND OF THE MOUSE

A. CONTROL OF SUBMAXILLARY GLAND CONTENT OF mEGF

The amount of EGF in the submaxillary gland of the adult male mouse is approximately 1 μg/mg wet tissue, as judged by radioimmunoassay (Byyny *et al.*, 1972). No other organ or tissue examined to date contained more than 1 ng/mg wet tissue. These results have been confirmed by a membrane radioreceptor assay (Frati *et al.*, 1976). Interestingly, the mouse submaxillary gland is also a rich source of other growth factors: nerve growth factor (Cohen, 1960) and colony stimulating factor (Sheridan and Stanley, 1971). Human EGF has not been detected in the human salivary glands.

EGF was found in the tubular duct cells of the mouse submaxillary gland (Turkington *et al.*, 1971; Cohen and Savage, 1974) and in granules isolated from this gland (Pasquini *et al.*, 1974). The tubular cells of the mouse submaxillary gland exhibit sexual dimorphism. The morphology and granule content of these cells are dependent on the hormonal status of the animal. The cells are developed fully in the male only after puberty; castration results in the atrophy of the tubular portion of the gland. The injection of testosterone into female mice results in a hypertrophy and hyperplasia of these cells (Lacassagne, 1940). The quantity of EGF present in the submaxillary gland closely parallels the development of the tubular system (Cohen, 1965a). In the immature 15-day-old male mouse, the amount of submaxillary gland EGF is very low, about 0.02 ng/mg wet tissue. The concentration increases rapidly with age until maximum levels of about 1000 ng/mg wet tissue are reached in adult male mice aged 50 days or more (Byyny *et al.*, 1972). In contrast to the adult male mouse, the concentration of EGF in the submaxillary gland of the adult female is only 70 ng/mg wet tissue. The androgen dependence of EGF concentrations in the mouse submaxillary gland was shown by the reduction of EGF levels in the castrated male (113 ng/mg wet tissue) and the increased levels of EGF in the testosterone-treated female (2900 ng/mg wet tissue) (Byyny *et al.*, 1972).

The response of submaxillary gland EGF levels to androgens has been characterized (Barthe *et al.*, 1974). Administration of testosterone to adult female mice increases the levels of submaxillary gland EGF several hundredfold within 7 days. Of the androgens tested, dihydrotestosterone and 3α-androstanediol are 13.4- and 5-fold, respectively, more potent than testosterone. 3β-Androstanediol is slightly less than 0.1-fold as effective as testosterone. The relative potencies of these four steroids as they affect submaxillary gland EGF agree well with their relative effects in other androgen-sensitive systems. The sensitivity of submaxillary EGF concentration to androgens has been proposed as an index of biological androgen activity.

The tfm/y mouse has a genetic defect which results in target organ insensitivity to androgens. The morphological and histochemical development of submaxillary glands of the tfm/y mouse is similar to that of normal females (Andrews and Bullock, 1972). The hormonal unresponsiveness is thought to be due to an inability to concentrate androgens in the nucleus of the target cell (Goldstein and Wilson, 1972; Dunn *et al.*, 1973). The concentration of EGF in the submaxillary glands of tfm/y mice is low, approximately 2 ng/mg wet tissue, and is not increased by the administration of androgens (Barthe *et al.*, 1974).

The effect of progestins, alone and in combination with testosterone, on the concentrations of EGF in the submaxillary glands of normal female mice has been reported (Bullock *et al.*, 1975). Medroxyprogesterone acetate produces a 40-fold increase in submaxillary EGF levels. Cyproterone acetate has no androgenic activity when administered alone and acts as a potent antiandrogen when used in combination with testosterone. The only synandrogenic response is elicited with high doses of progesterone caproate. Neither progesterone nor medroxyprogesterone has any effect on EGF levels in tfm/y mice, suggesting that the action of progestins may be mediated by the androgen receptor in the submaxillary gland.

The androgen-dependent levels of EGF in the submaxillary gland do not reflect levels in plasma and other body fluids (Byyny *et al.*, 1974). While there are 1000 ng of EGF/mg wet submaxillary gland tissue in the mouse, the concentration in plasma is 1 ng/ml; in milk, approximately 300 ng/ml; and in saliva or urine, about 1000 ng/ml. The plasma levels of immunoactive EGF are not significantly different in adult male and female mice. Testosterone treatment of females or castrated males does not alter EGF plasma levels. Also, EGF concentrations in the plasma of immature male mice are not detectably different from adult levels.

B. Synthesis and Secretion of mEGF

The release of submaxillary EGF into the circulatory system is controlled, either directly or indirectly, by α-adrenergic agents (Byyny *et al.*, 1974). α-Adrenergic agents are known to bring about the degranulation of the peritubular cells in the submaxillary gland (Junquiera *et al.*, 1964). The intravenous administration of an α-adrenergic agent, such as phenylephrine, into adult male mice, results in a 65% decrease in submaxillary gland EGF within 60 minutes and a concomitant increase in plasma EGF levels from 1.2 to 152 ng/ml.

The administration of isoprenaline (isoproterenol), a stimulant of exocrine secretion by the submaxillary glands of mice, reduces the content of amylase in the gland by 90% but does not significantly decrease the amount of glandular EGF (Roberts and Reade, 1975) or increase plasma EGF levels (Byyny *et al.*, 1974). Also, the rise in plasma EGF after administration of an α-adrenergic agent was blocked by the prior injection of α-adrenergic blocking agents.

Although mEGF is synthesized in the submaxillary gland (Turkington *et al.*, 1971) and perhaps stored in granules (Pasquini *et al.*, 1974), plasma levels of the growth factor are not decreased by excision of the submaxillary glands (Byyny et al., 1974). Thus it appears that there is a secondary site(s) of EGF synthesis in the mouse.

V. BIOLOGICAL ACTIVITY OF EGF IN VIVO

The initial observation which led to the recognition of epidermal growth factor and to its biological assay was that daily subcutaneous injections of extracts of the mouse submaxillary gland into newborn mice resulted in the precocious opening of the eyelids (6–7 days instead of the normal 12–14 days) and precocious eruption of the incisors (Cohen, 1962). Similar effects were demonstrable in newborn rats, rabbits, and dogs. These gross biological changes, as shown in Fig. 4, were ascribed mainly to an enhancement of epidermal growth and keratinization, as ascertained from histological studies (Cohen and Elliot, 1963). A thickening of the epithelial layer also was noted in the oral cavity and esophagus. It is not known whether mEGF directly stimulated keratinization or whether accelerated keratin formation was a consequence of the stimulation of basal cell proliferation. Increased epidermal mitotic activity has been found in the skin of newborn mice treated with mEGF (Birnbaum et al., 1976). Curiously, in somewhat older mice (12–20 days), the daily injection of mEGF had little visible effect on dorsal skin but produced a marked thickening of tail and foot-pad epidermis.

The eyelid-opening effect of mEGF in newborn rats was demonstrable at a dosage level of 0.1 μg per gram per day. The complete sequence of 53 amino acid residues of native mEGF was not essential to elicit this in vivo response (Savage et al., 1972). The following biologically active derivatives were obtained: $mEGF_{1-51}$, $mEGF_{1-48}$, and $mEGF_{1-47}$. Thus removal of up to 6 amino acid residues from the carboxy-terminal region of native mEGF did not alter the eyelid-opening activity. However, in view of the finding (discussed in Section VIII) that $mEGF_{1-48}$ had a distinctly lower binding affinity than mEGF to cultured fibroblasts, it was possible that native mEGF, when injected subcutaneously, was rapidly cleaved to $mEGF_{1-48}$ by a trypsin-like activity. Therefore, both molecules evoked an equal biological response. Performic acid oxidized mEGF and S-aminoethylated mEGF were inactive.

The histological appearance of epidermal hypertrophy and hyperplasia following the injection of mEGF into newborn rats was confirmed by a number of chemical measurements, including dry weight, DNA and RNA content, and the levels of a number of epidermal enzymes (Angeletti et al., 1964). The hyperkeratosis caused by mEGF was accompanied by an increase in the disulfide group content of the epidermal cells and a decrease in free sulfhydryl groups (C. Frati et al., 1972).

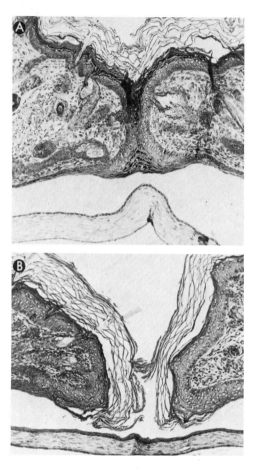

FIG. 4. Cross sections of the eyelid area from control (A) and experimental (B) 8-day-old rats. The experimental animal received daily injections (1 μg per gram body weight) of mEGF. (From Cohen and Elliot, 1963.)

Relatively early (4-hour) but transient increases in the levels of both ornithine decarboxylase (Stastny and Cohen, 1970) and histidine decarboxylase (Blosse *et al.*, 1974) in the skin of young mice following the administration of mEGF have been reported. Unexpectedly, the activity of ornithine decarboxylase in the testes and to some extent in other organs of neonatal mice was elevated by the subcutaneous injection of mEGF. In addition, the accumulation of putrescine in the testes was noted (Stastny and Cohen, 1972). Further evidence that the *in vivo* effects of the administration of mEGF were not limited to epidermal tissue has been reported by Sundell *et al.* (1975). The constant infusion of mEGF into fetal lambs for 3–5 days stimulated the growth of epithelia in a number of sites, including the lung, where clear histological effects were noted in both the upper and lower airways. The authors suggested that mEGF may be capable of protecting the lamb from the development of hyaline membrane disease.

A possible therapeutic use for this polypeptide in nonhealing corneal epithelial defects and erosions was suggested by the finding that the topical application of mEGF to the eyes of rabbits with corneal wounds induced a marked hyperplasia of the epithelium and accelerated the repair process (Frati *et al.*, 1972; Savage and Cohen, 1973; Ho *et al.*, 1974).

Additional *in vivo* effects of mEGF have been reported. Reynolds *et al.* (1965) and Rose *et al.* (1976) reported an enhancement of methylcholanthrene-induced epidermal carcinogenesis in mice treated with mEGF. Heimberg *et al.* (1965) have noted that at high dosage levels of mEGF (2 μg per gram per day), a distinct growth inhibition of the neonatal rat occurred. This effect was accompanied by the accumulation of lipids, mainly triglycerides, in the liver.

The completely unforeseen finding that the amino acid sequence of mouse EGF shows considerable homology with that of human urogastrone led to the observation that, in addition to its effects on tissue growth, mEGF has a direct effect upon gastric acid secretion in both rats and dogs (Bower *et al.*, 1975). Doses of 10 μg/kg in rats and 0.5 μg/kg in dogs rapidly and markedly inhibited the gastric acid secretion evoked by histamine or pentagastrin infusion. Both human urogastrone and human EGF exhibit the *in vivo* eyelid-opening properties of mouse EGF (Gregory, 1975; Cohen and Carpenter, 1975).

Despite these many and diverse *in vivo* biological effects of EGF, the exact physiological role of this biologically active polypeptide remains to be established.

VI. BIOLOGICAL ACTIVITY OF EGF IN ORGAN CULTURE

Mouse-derived EGF has been shown to stimulate epithelial cell proliferation in a number of organ culture systems, including chick embryo skin (Cohen, 1965b), chick and human embryo cornea (Savage and Cohen, 1973), and mouse mammary glands and mammary carcinomas (Turkington, 1969a,b). The influence of mEGF on chick corneal epithelium is shown in Fig. 5. In organ cultures of rat palatal shelves, mEGF drastically altered the developmental sequence of events which occur during normal palatal fusion, inhibiting the normal degenerative changes and increasing the number of epidermal desmosomes and associated tonofilaments (Hassell, 1975).

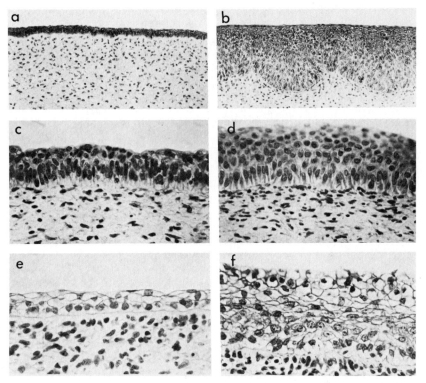

FIG. 5. Cross sections of control (a) and mEGF-treated (b) corneas from 13-day chick embryos after 6 days of culture (×100); cross sections of control (c) and mEGF-treated (d) corneas from 16-cm fetus after 4 days of culture (×250); cross sections of control (e) and mEGF-treated (f) head skin from 6-cm fetus after 4 days of culture (×250). (From Cohen and Savage, 1974.)

The stimulation of epidermal proliferation in organ cultures of chick embryo skin was influenced by a number of conditions, such as the age of the embryo from which the skin was explanted and the presence of dermis. Despite these difficulties, mEGF was found to cause both metabolic and morphological alterations in sheets of pure epidermis derived from the back skin of 9-day chick embryos cultured on Millipore filters. These results are summarized in the following paragraphs.

mEGF rapidly stimulated the transport of certain metabolites. Within 15 minutes following the addition of mEGF, there were stimulations of approximately 2-fold of the uptakes of radioactive α-aminoisobutyric acid and uridine into the trichloroacetic-acid-soluble fraction of the cells. These increases in transport were not prevented by inhibitors of protein synthesis, such as cycloheximide, indicating that the synthesis of new proteins was not required for these permeability changes (S. Cohen, unpublished experiments).

Within 90 minutes following the addition of mEGF to epidermal cultures, there was a conversion of preexisting ribosomal monomers into functional polysomes. Accompanying this alteration was an increase in protein synthesis and an increase in the synthesis of all classes of cytoplasmic RNA detectable on sucrose gradients. The ribosomal monomer-to-polysome conversion did not appear to require the synthesis of new protein (Cohen and Stastny, 1968). The total ribosomal population, isolated from cells treated with mEGF for 4 hours, was more active in a cell-free protein synthesizing system than ribosomes isolated from control cells (Hoober and Cohen, 1967b). It was suggested that ribosomes prepared from EGF-treated cells had a greater ability to bind messenger RNA in a functional manner.

The similarities between the response of epidermal cells to mEGF and the response of many other cell types to a growth-stimulating condition or mitogen prompted an investigation of the effects of mEGF on the induction of ornithine decarboxylase. The activity of this enzyme is enhanced under a variety of conditions, the central element of which appears to be growth stimulation. The addition of mEGF to chick epidermal cells induced within 4 hours a marked (40-fold) but transient increase of ornithine decarboxylase activity, and led to the intracellular accumulation of putrescine (Stastny and Cohen, 1970).

In the presence of mEGF a 2-fold increase in total protein and RNA content was detected during the first 48 hours of incubation (Hoober and Cohen, 1967a), as was stimulation of thymidine incorporation into DNA (Bertsch and Marks, 1974).

Thus, a series of metabolic alterations which accompany the growth-stimulatory effects of mEGF on epidermal cells have been described. Because many of these changes take place in a variety of cells when a growth stimulus is applied, these biochemical events seem to reflect the inherent program and capabilities of the cells rather than the specific nature of the growth stimulus. Human EGF, when tested in organ culture systems, appeared to act in a manner identical to that of mouse EGF (Starkey *et al.*, 1975).

VII. BIOLOGICAL ACTIVITY OF EGF IN CELL CULTURE

As a result of the advantages of cell culture systems for controlled biochemical investigation, the capacity of EGF to stimulate the growth of cultured mammalian cells has received considerable attention in the last three or four years. To date, no significant differences have been detected between the biological activities of mouse EGF and human EGF in cell culture experiments. Therefore, the two polypeptides will not be treated separately in this section.

A. MITOGENIC PROPERTIES OF EGF

Most studies of the action of EGF in cell culture have described the increased incorporation of labeled thymidine into DNA following the addition of the growth factor to quiescent cells. Although it is often assumed that (a) increased incorporation of labeled thymidine represents stimulation of DNA synthesis in a significant fraction of the cell population and (b) that stimulation of DNA synthesis is followed by an increase in cell division, these assumptions are not always true. For example, hEGF produced a 10-fold increase in thymidine incorporation in human fetal lung fibroblasts (WI-38), but did not increase cell numbers by more than 10% (Carpenter and Cohen, 1976a). Autoradiography of these cells showed that the increased incorporation of labeled thymidine in the presence of hEGF resulted from only a small percentage, approximately 6%, of labeled nuclei. This accounted for the negligible effect of hEGF on cell numbers. In another study (Richman *et al.*, 1976), the addition of mEGF in combination with insulin and glucagon to rat hepatocytes stimulated 71% of the cells to synthesize DNA, but no increase in cell numbers occurred. Investigations of the mitogen properties of "conditioned" media (Shodell, 1972), serum (Leffert, 1974; Wolf *et al.*, 1975), and hormones such as insulin and hydrocortisone (Baseman and Hayes, 1975) indicate that in many instances it is possible to dissociate activities which promote DNA synthesis and cell division. Unfortunately, many studies of the mitogenic activity of agents such as EGF measure only DNA synthesis, as judged by the incorporation of labeled thymidine. Autoradiographic data often are not presented to indicate the percent of the cell population that responded to the mitogen, nor are experiments described which indicate whether or not the mitogen stimulated cell division. These problems pose difficulties for the interpretation of some experimental results. In this review, therefore, the effects of EGF on cell proliferation will be treated separately from the influences of the mitogen on DNA synthesis.

1. Effect of EGF on the Proliferation of Human Fibroblasts

The interaction of human EGF with diploid human fibroblasts (HF cells) provides a unique opportunity to examine the effect of a naturally occurring human mitogenic polypeptide on the growth of human cells (Cohen and Carpenter, 1975; Carpenter and Cohen, 1976a). The mitogenic effect of mouse EGF toward HF cells has been described (Cohen *et al.*, 1975; Lembach, 1976a).

The effect of picomolar concentrations of hEGF on the growth of human fibroblasts plated at a low density in media containing 10% calf serum is shown in Fig. 6 (Carpenter and Cohen, 1976a). Although the presence of exogenous hEGF decreased slightly the average population-doubling times of HF cells, the most significant effect was a 4-fold increase in the saturation density of the cultures. The morphological appearance of HF cells grown to

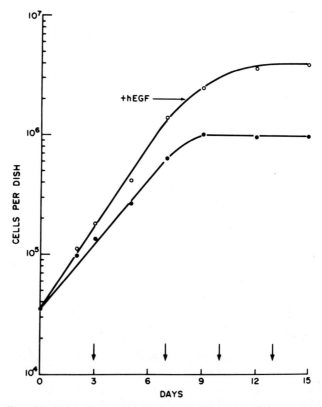

FIG. 6. Effect of hEGF on the growth of human fibroblasts in medium containing 10% calf serum. Cells were plated at approximately 3×10^4 cells per dish into 60 mm Falcon culture dishes containing growth medium plus 10% calf serum. The cells were incubated overnight, and hEGF (4 ng/ml) was added to one-half the dishes (day 0). At indicated times thereafter, duplicate dishes from cultures growing in the presence (O) or absence (●) of hEGF were removed and the cell numbers determined. At the times indicated by the arrows, the medium in each set of cultures was removed, and fresh growth medium plus 10% calf serum was added. Human EGF was also added to the appropriate dishes at these times. (From Carpenter and Cohen, 1976a.)

their saturation densities in the presence or absence of hEGF is shown in Fig. 7. The cells cultured in the absence of hEGF formed a tightly packed monolayer with typical fibroblastic morphology and orientation. Neither the saturation density nor morphological appearance of these cultures was due to depletion of nutrients from the medium. The appearance of a tightly packed, confluent monolayer of cells and the absence of an increase in net cell number typify a growth-limiting mechanism, referred to as density-dependent inhibition of growth (DDIG), contact inhibition of growth, or topoinhibition, that is characteristic of the behavior of normal cells *in vitro*. Density-dependent control of the growth of mammalian cells in culture has been reviewed (Holley, 1975). In contrast, cells grown in the presence of hEGF, as shown in Figs. 6 and 7, not only grew to high saturation densities but did so with the formation of multiple cell layers. Under these conditions, the proliferation of HF cells in the presence of hEGF was not limited at a confluent monolayer by DDIG mechanisms.

It was not possible to obtain single-cell suspensions of HF cells grown to high densities in the presence of hEGF by standard trypsinization procedures. Interestingly, single-cell suspensions could be obtained by incubation

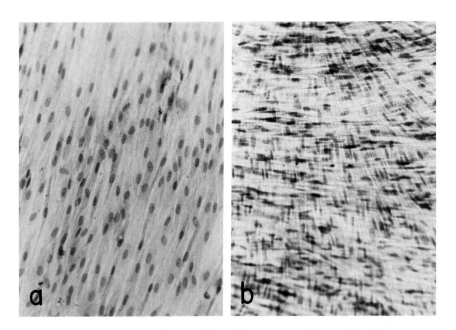

FIG. 7. Effect of hEGF on the morphological appearance of human fibroblasts grown to saturation density in medium containing 10% calf serum. Cells were grown to maximal saturation densities with (b) or without (a) hEGF. (From Carpenter and Cohen, 1976a.)

with trypsin, collagenase, and either hyaluronidase or chondroitinase (G. Carpenter and S. Cohen, unpublished results). This suggested that the growth of cells to high densities with the formation of multiple cell layers in the presence of hEGF was accompanied by the synthesis and excretion of extracellular matrix materials. Lembach (1976b) has reported that the addition of mEGF to confluent cultures of HF cells, preincubated in the absence of serum, increased the incorporation of [³H]glycosamine into the glycosaminoglycans and glycoproteins of both cellular and extracellular fractions. A direct effect of EGF on collagen synthesis, however, has not been reported. Although fibroblasts obtained from adults or newborns, such as HF cells from foreskin of the newborn, exhibit DDIG, human lung fibroblasts obtained from fetal tissue grow to high cell densities with the formation of an extracellular collagenous matrix and multiple cell layers (Elsdale and Foley, 1969). The relationship between the production of extracellular matrix material and the capacity of EGF-treated cells to grow to high densities with the formation of multiple cell layers cannot be ascertained in the absence of further experimental evidence.

In addition to DDIG, other growth-regulating mechanisms are defined by the serum requirements of fibroblasts. The influence of hEGF on the serum requirement of HF cells is shown by the data in Table II. The results

TABLE II

EFFECT OF hEGF ON PROLIFERATION OF HF CELLS IN SERUM-LIMITED MEDIA[a]

Additions to growth medium	Cell density (cells $\times$ 10^{-2} per cm^2)			
	Day 0	Day 3	Day 6	Day 9
10% calf serum		290	624	681
10% calf serum + hEGF	64	410	1486	1866
1% calf serum		119	230	245
1% calf serum + hEGF	63	247	571	848
10% γ-globulin-free calf serum		162	335	389
10% γ-globulin-free calf serum + hEGF	95	263	1028	1437
10% bovine plasma		108	152	161
10% bovine plasma + hEGF	96	217	780	1242

[a] HF cells were plated in 60 mm Falcon culture dishes containing Dulbecco's Modified Eagle Medium plus indicated serum components. The cells were incubated overnight, the cell density was determined (day 0), and hEGF (4 ng/ml) was added to the indicated dishes. At indicated times thereafter duplicate cultures of cells growing in the presence or absence of hEGF were removed and cell numbers determined. On days 3 and 6 the medium in each group of cultures were removed and fresh media with appropriate serum additions were added. Human EGF was also added to the indicated dishes at these times.

demonstrate that while HF cells grew poorly in media containing 1% serum, γ-globulin-free serum, or plasma, the cells were able to proliferate in these serum-deficient media when hEGF was added. Growth in serum-deficient media containing hEGF was equivalent to or better than that achieved in the presence of complete calf serum (10%). These data indicate that hEGF was able to substitute for the growth factors present in the γ-globulin fraction of serum (Jainchill and Todaro, 1970) and the factors in platelets (Kohler and Lipton, 1974). It is not known, however, what natural role EGF might play in the growth-promoting activity of serum. The addition of rabbit anti-hEGF globulin to human serum did not reduce the capacity of this serum to support the proliferation of HF cells (G. Carpenter and S. Cohen, unpublished results), indicating that hEGF, in an immunoreactive form, was not an essential growth-promoting component of this serum. The addition of anti-hEGF did block the mitogenic effects of exogenous hEGF, described in Fig. 6.

The data described above show that treatment of human fibroblasts *in vitro* with hEGF results in cell proliferation which is not responsive to mechanisms, such as DDIG or the presence of low or incomplete serum, which would otherwise limit cell growth. Interestingly, transformation of fibroblasts by oncogenic agents also renders cells insensitive to these growth-regulating mechanisms.

An improved medium (MCDB 104) for the clonal growth of human diploid fibroblasts has been developed which supports cell proliferation at low serum concentrations—less than 1% (McKeehan *et al.*, 1977). In this medium, mEGF stimulated the clonal growth of human skin fibroblasts in the presence of either total serum proteins (10 μg/ml) or crystalized Cohn fraction V from bovine plasma (less than 75 μg/ml) (W. L. McKeehan, personal communication).

2. *Effect of EGF on the Proliferation of Other Cell Types*

The effect of EGF on the proliferation of various cell types indicates that its mitogenic capacity does not depend on species specificity nor on embryological origin—a determinant which has been suggested to account for the mitogenic properties of fibroblast growth factor (Gospodarowicz and Moran, 1976). mEGF has been reported to stimulate the growth of human tumor cells, HeLa and KB (Covelli *et al.*, 1972a), human epidermal cells (Rheinwald and Green, 1977), human glia cells (Westermark, 1976), and the mouse cell lines 3T3 (Armelin, 1973; Rose *et al.*, 1975) and 3T6 (P. S. Rudland *et al.*, personal communication). In serum-limited cultures, mEGF stimulated the growth of SV40-transformed 3T3 cells (G. Carpenter and S. Cohen, unpublished results). hEGF stimulated the proliferation of rabbit epidermal cells (CCL 68) and normal rat and rabbit kidney cells (S. Cohen

and G. Carpenter, unpublished experiments). Also, mEGF is a potent mitogen for bovine granulosa cells (Gospodarowicz and Ill, 1977). Addition of the
growth factor to granulosa cells maintained in 1% or 10% calf serum significantly increased the final cell densities; however, the cells did not form
multiple layers as described for human fibroblasts. The concentration of
mEGF required to stimulate the proliferation of granulosa cells was excep-
tionally low. A half-maximal response was observed at $6 \times 10^{-13} M$, approximately 300-fold lower than that required for the stimulation of fibroblast
growth.

The effect of EGF on cultured cells was limited in that cell division was
not enhanced in some cell types. Only marginal effects on cell proliferation
were observed in cultures of vascular smooth muscle cells (D. Gospodarowicz et al., 1977b) and human lung fibroblasts (WI-38) (Carpenter and
Cohen, 1976a). EGF had no detectable effect on the growth of chick embryo
fibroblasts, although it did stimulate embryonic chick epidermis. Also, EGF
did not affect the growth of adrenal cortex cells (Gospodarowicz et al., 1977)
or vascular endothelial cells (D. Gospodarowicz et al., 1977b).

As indicated below (Section VIII), many other cell types have been
analyzed in terms of their capacity to bind [^{125}I]EGF or to increase DNA
synthesis in the presence of EGF. In many instances, however, the capacity
of EGF to promote cell division has not been demonstrated. Undoubtedly,
the lists of cells for which EGF does or does not promote cell proliferation
will be expanded in the near future.

B. Stimulation of DNA Synthesis by EGF

Because the stimulation of DNA synthesis in cultured cells by EGF has
been most fully characterized in studies utilizing human fibroblasts, this
system will be described (Cohen et al., 1975; Carpenter and Cohen, 1976a;
Hollenberg and Cuatrecasas, 1973, 1975). Results obtained with these cells
are consistent with experimental data obtained with other cell types: human
glia cells (Westermark, 1976; Lindgren and Westermark, 1976), rabbit lens
epithelium (Hollenberg, 1975), 3T3 (Rose et al., 1975), and 3T6 (P. S. Rudland, personal communication) cells.

The time course of DNA synthesis following the addition of hEGF or fresh
serum to confluent quiescent HF cells, preincubated in medium containing
1% calf serum for 48 hours, is shown in Fig. 8. Under these conditions, an
increased rate of DNA synthesis was detectable after 12 hours, and maximal
stimulation occurred at approximately 24 hours. The incorporation of labeled
thymidine during a 4-hour pulse at 20–24 hours was maximal in the presence
of 2 ng/ml ($3.7 \times 10^{-10} M$) hEGF; the response was half-maximal at a concen-

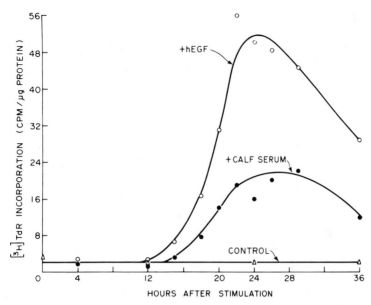

FIG. 8. Time course of [³H]thymidine incorporation following stimulation of human fibroblasts by hEGF. Confluent, quiescent cultures were stimulated by the addition of hEGF, 4 ng/ml (○) or fresh calf serum, 10% (●). Control cultures received no additions (△). At indicated times duplicate cultures were selected and labeled for 1 hour with [³H]thymidine. (From Carpenter and Cohen, 1976a.)

tration of 0.25 ng/ml ($4.6 \times 10^{-11} M$) hEGF. Comparable results have been obtained with other cell types and slightly different experimental conditions. The initiation of DNA synthesis in granulosa cells, however, was stimulated by much lower concentrations of EGF; the half-maximal response was obtained at 1 pg/ml ($2 \times 10^{-13} M$) and the maximal stimulation at 0.1 ng/ml ($2 \times 10^{-11} M$) (Gospodarowicz and Ill, 1977).

It has been noted in both cell culture (Cohen *et al.*, 1975) and organ culture systems (Bertsch and Marks, 1974) that high concentrations of mEGF had inhibitory effects on thymidine incorporation into DNA. This can be an important and not always considered factor when survey-type studies of a number of growth factors are being conducted.

The presence of low concentrations of serum was required for the stimulation of DNA synthesis by EGF (Fig. 9). Under these conditions, serum had a permissive effect for hormone action; however, the basis of this action is not understood. With human fibroblasts serum did not appear to be required for cell survival (Lembach, 1976a; Carpenter and Cohen, 1976a) as in other cell systems, such as 3T3 (Gospodarowicz and Moran, 1974) and glia cells (Westermark, 1976). Serum proteins per se may be responsible for this permis-

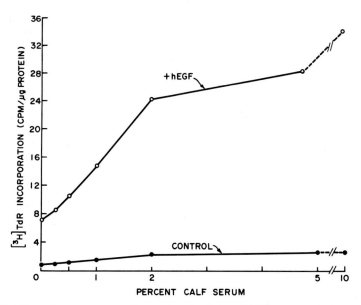

FIG. 9. Effect of serum concentration on the stimulation of DNA synthesis in human fibroblasts by hEGF. In order to deplete cells of serum proteins, confluent cultures of HF cells were shifted into medium containing 0.5% calf serum and incubated for 48 hours. The cells were washed twice with Hanks' balanced salt solution. Media containing 0.1% bovine serum albumin plus varying amounts of calf serum were added, and the cells were incubated for 48 hours prior to the addition of hEGF, 4 ng/ml. Cells were labeled with [³H]thymidine for a 4-hour period 20 hours after the addition of hEGF (○). Control cultures (●) did not receive hEGF. (From Carpenter and Cohen, 1976a.)

sive effect, or the serum proteins may serve an indirect function as carriers of bound factors, such as trace elements, that are required for the stimulation of DNA synthesis. The latter possibility is suggested by experiments in which transferrin and iron (P. S. Rudland, personal communication) or selenium (McKeehan *et al.*, 1976) have reduced the concentration of serum required for cell proliferation. Also, it has been shown that the addition of a mixture of defined hormones to growth medium could entirely replace the serum requirement of cell lines, such as GH_3, BHK, and HeLa (Hayashi and Sato, 1976). It is possible that a combination of defined hormones might obviate the serum requirement for the mitogenic activity of EGF.

The stimulation of DNA synthesis in human fibroblasts by EGF was increased 2-fold by the addition of ascorbic acid (3 ug/ml) to the growth medium (Carpenter and Cohen, 1976a; Lembach, 1976a). The presence of ascorbic acid also partially replaced the serum requirement for EGF-induced stimulation of DNA synthesis. Ascorbic acid is known to function as a cofactor and modulator of proline hydroxylase, which is necessary for the synthesis of collagen and related proteins. Lembach (1976a) has demonstrated that ascorbic acid enhanced the incorporation of [³H]proline into proteins secreted into the extracellular medium. The relationship of extracellular collagen-like proteins to the control of DNA synthesis and cell growth, although intriguing, remains speculative.

The stimulation of [³H]thymidine incorporation in human fibroblasts by hEGF and the effects of serum and ascorbic acid are reflected in increased percentages of labeled nuclei in the cultures (Table III). In this experiment labeled thymidine was added 12 hours after the administration of hEGF, and the cells were incubated for an additional 18 hours. No more than 56% of the cells, however, were stimulated to synthesize DNA. Failure to stimulate a higher percentage of the population may be due to (a) the wide range of interdivision times in human fibroblasts (Absher *et al.*, 1975) or (b) the presence of nondividing cells within the population (Yanishevsky *et al.*, 1974). The former alternative would predict the presence of a fraction of the cell population that would respond to hEGF but would traverse from the G_1 to the S phase of cell cycle at a slow rate and not be detected within the labeling interval employed. The latter explanation would suggest the presence of nondividing cells that do not enter the S phase. It is not possible, at present, to discriminate between these two possibilities. As described below (Section VIII), all cells in these cultures of human fibroblasts were capable of binding EGF. Therefore, the presence of a nonresponsive fraction of cells does not appear to be due to the loss of surface receptors in these cells.

TABLE III

AUTORADIOGRAPHIC EXAMINATION OF HF CELLS STIMULATED BY hEGF[a]

	Percent labeled nuclei	
Additions	Cells maintained in 1% serum	Cells maintained in 5% serum
None	0.9	3.0
hEGF	21.2	40.8
hEGF + ascorbic acid	33.5	55.9
Ascorbic acid	1.3	3.7
Calf serum	14.6	11.2

[a] The medium in confluent cultures of HF cells, grown in the presence of 10% calf serum, was replaced by fresh medium containing either 1% or 5% calf serum. After incubation for 48 hours in these media, the following additions were made: hEGF (4 ng/ml), ascorbic acid (25 µg/ml), fresh calf serum (10%). The cells were labeled with [³H]thymidine between 12 and 30 hours after additions were made to the media, and autoradiography was performed (Carpenter and Cohen, 1976a).

To analyze the stimulation of cells by a polypeptide mitogen, it is important to determine whether the initial interaction (binding) of the mitogen with the cell surface is sufficient to ensure a sequence of intracellular events which will commit the cell to DNA synthesis and mitosis. Such a scheme has been referred to as a "trigger" mechanism and has been proposed to explain the metabolic effects of some polypeptide hormones. However, the stimulation of DNA synthesis in quiescent cells by serum (Ellem and Mironescu, 1972; Rubin and Steiner, 1975; Lindgren *et al.*, 1975), multiplication stimulating factors (Smith and Temin, 1974), or concanavalin A (Kaplowitz and Moscona, 1976; Gunther *et al.*, 1974) has been reported to require the presence of the mitogen for several hours. Similar results have been reported for the stimulation of HF cells by hEGF. The data in Fig. 10 indicate that the addition of antibody prepared against hEGF, at any time during the first 3 hours of exposure of fibroblasts to hEGF, blocked the stimulation of DNA synthesis. Addition of antibody at 7.5 hours after incubation of the cells with hEGF resulted in a stimulation of thymidine incorporation that was 50% of that observed in the absence of antibody. It is not known whether equivalent periods of time would be required for the stimuation of cell division by EGF. Because the binding of hEGF to human fibroblasts is a

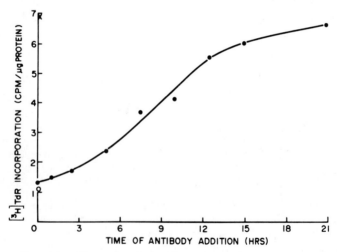

FIG. 10. Effect of the addition of antibody to hEGF on the stimulation of DNA synthesis in human fibroblasts by hEGF. Human EGF (4 ng/ml) was added to quiescent, confluent cultures and at various times thereafter 150 µg of DEAE-purified antibody to hEGF were added to duplicate cultures. Twenty-one hours after the addition of hEGF to the cultures, [³H]thymidine was added and the cells labeled for 4 hours. Control cultures received hEGF but no antibody (X) or no additions (O). (From Carpenter and Cohen, 1976a.)

comparatively rapid event [maximal binding is achieved within 40 minutes (Section VIII,A)], the initial binding of the mitogen to the cell surface is not sufficient to induce DNA synthesis. Similar results have been reported for the stimulation of human glia cells by mEGF (Lindgren and Westermark, 1976). It does not appear, therefore, that the stimulation of DNA synthesis by EGF occurs by a "trigger"-type mechanism which starts a defined and irreversible sequence of biochemical reactions. Rather, it appears that the program of biochemical reactions induced by the interaction of mitogens with cells is, at various points, reversible. The commitment of the cell to DNA synthesis is dependent in an unknown way on the continuous presence of the mitogenic agent. Biochemical events which occur prior to the point of cellular commitment to DNA synthesis, e.g., changes in cyclic nucleotide concentrations and increased transport of nutrients, may constitute positive but reversible controls over the initiation of DNA synthesis.

C. Pleiotropic Effects of EGF

The biochemical responses to the initiation of cell growth have been termed a positive pleiotropic response and are independent of the particular mitogen employed and for the most part common to all cell types (Hershko et al., 1971). For example, the biochemical changes which occur during a nutritional shift-up in *Escherichia coli* parallel many of the events taking place in mammalian cells following the administration of a growth-stimulating agent.

Some of the initial metabolic alterations which occur following the interaction of EGF with mammalian cells have been studied. Within 20 minutes after the addition of mEGF to 3T3 cells, the influx of $^{86}Rb^+$, taken as a measure of K^+ transport (Rozengurt and Heppel, 1975), and the uptake of deoxyglucose (Barnes and Colowick, 1976) were increased. After approximately 50 minutes of incubation of human fibroblasts with mEGF, the uptake of α-aminoisobutyrate was increased slightly (Hollenberg and Cuatrecasas, 1975). Data showing an increase in RNA synthesis, as judged by [^{3}H]uridine incorporation, after approximately 5 hours have been reported (Hollenberg and Cuatrecasas, 1973). Increased macropinocytosis and membrane ruffling have been observed at 12 hours after the addition of mEGF to human glia cells (Brunk et al., 1976). Interaction of mEGF with human fibroblasts resulted in enhanced incorporation of [^{3}H]glucosamine into the glycosaminoglycans and glycoproteins of both cellular and extracellular fractions (Lembach, 1976b). These effects were detectable at 4 hours following growth factor addition and increased rapidly thereafter.

These metabolic changes represent only a partial list of the pleiotropic response. Undoubtedly many additional effects of EGF will be reported in the near future. At present, it is not possible to ascertain which effects are due directly and specifically to EGF and which occur indirectly as part of a complex series of biochemical reactions required for DNA synthesis and cell division.

D. Effects of EGF Binding Protein on Cellular Metabolism

As described previously (Section III,B), mEGF is associated in a specific manner with a binding protein, identified as an arginine esteropeptidase, in extracts of the mouse submaxillary gland. In view of the mitogenic activity of proteases toward mammalian cells, the mEGF-binding esterase has been tested for its effect on cell proliferation.

Addition of purified mEGF-binding esterase to quiescent cultures of human fibroblasts did not result in the initiation of DNA synthesis (Lembach, 1976a). However, addition of the arginine esterase and mEGF resulted in a marked potentiation, approximately 3-fold, of the stimulation of DNA synthesis achieved by the growth factor alone. Thrombin, which has arginine esterase activity, also potentiated the mitogenic effect of mEGF toward 3T3 cells (Zetter *et al.*, 1976). Furthermore, inhibitors of arginine esterase activity blocked cell multiplication in a reversible manner (Taylor and Lembach, 1973). Although proteases are known to modify the outer surface of cells, the relationship between this action and their mitogenic activity is unknown.

E. Structure of mEGF and Mitogenic Activity *in Vitro*

Derivatives of mouse-derived EGF lacking the carboxy-terminal two amino acids, $mEGF_{1-51}$, or lacking the carboxy-terminal five amino acids, $mEGF_{1-48}$, have been tested for their ability to stimulate DNA synthesis in quiescent cultures of human fibroblasts (Cohen *et al.*, 1975). The results showed that $mEGF_{1-51}$ was as effective as native mEGF, while EGF_{1-48} exhibited approximately 1–5% of the growth-stimulating activity of the intact growth factor. The carboxy-terminal pentapeptide, residues 49–53, was totally inactive, and no synergism was observed in combination with $mEGF_{1-48}$.

Thus the Trp-Trp-Glu sequence (residues 49–51) is necessary for full activity of mEGF *in vitro*. As shown in Section VIII, this sequence has been found to significantly influence the binding of mEGF to human fibroblasts.

VIII. INTERACTION OF ^{125}I-LABELED EGF WITH BIOLOGICAL MATERIAL

A. INTERACTION OF [125I]EGF WITH CULTURED CELLS

Although the ability of polypeptide mitogens, such as EGF, to stimulate the transport of nutrients, the synthesis of macromolecules, and cell division as part of the pleiotropic response has been documented in a variety of experimental systems, less is known about the biochemical steps involved in the initial interaction(s) of these agents with the cell surface. Because the binding of macromolecular mitogens to the cell surface membrane is reasoned to be the first step necessary for the expression of their biological activity, it is important to define the biochemical events involved in the binding of the hormone to the cell surface and to determine the metabolic fate of the bound hormone. Events which occur subsequent to binding may be important because, as mentioned previously (Section VII,B), it does not appear that EGF exerts its mitogenic activity by a "trigger"-type mechanism. Recent reviews have discussed, at length, many aspects of membrane receptors for polypeptide hormones (Pardee, 1975; Kahn, 1976; Cuatrecasas and Hollenberg, 1976; Nicholson, 1976; Edelman, 1976).

The interaction of [125I]EGF with cultured cells has been most extensively studied with monolayers of diploid human fibroblasts (Hollenberg and Cuatrecasas, 1973, 1975; Carpenter *et al.*, 1975; Cohen *et al.*, 1975; Carpenter and Cohen, 1976b) and will be described in this section. Because the binding characteristics of [125I]mEGF and [125I]hEGF are very similar, the interaction of these labeled polypeptides with cultured fibroblasts will not be discussed separately. The binding of [125I]EGF to rabbit lens epithelial cells (Hollenberg, 1975) and [125I]hEGF to human glia cells (B. Westermark and S. Cohen, unpublished experiments) have also been studied and will be commented on only in those instances in which the results differ significantly from those obtained with human fibroblasts.

[125]I-labeled EGF has been prepared by the lactoperoxidase procedure (Carpenter *et al.*, 1975) and by the Chloramine T method (Hollenberg and Cuatrecasas, 1973; Carpenter and Cohen, 1976b). Although both procedures are effective, the Chloramine T technique is more easily carried out. [131I]mEGF has also been prepared (Covelli *et al.*, 1972b).

Mouse EGF reacted with radioactive NaI has been separated by ion-exchange chromatography or preparative gel electrophoresis into fractions containing monoiodo-mEGF, diiodo-mEGF, and unlabeled mEGF (Carpenter *et al.*, 1975; Covelli *et al.*, 1972b). Both iodinated derivates are as biologically active *in vivo* and *in vitro* as the unlabeled molecule.

1. Characteristics of the Binding of [125I]EGF to Cultured Cells

An autoradiogram of [125I]hEGF incubated with human fibroblasts in the presence and absence of an excess of unlabeled mEGF is shown in Fig. 11 (Carpenter and Cohen, 1976b). The lack of nonspecific binding is evidenced by the small number of radioactive grains in the cells incubated with un-labeled hormone. Quantitatively, the level of nonspecific binding obtained with [125I]hEGF or [125I]mEGF is less than 2%, and all binding data dis-cussed below represent specific binding. As shown in Fig. 11, the cell-bound radioactive hormone appears to be uniformly distributed at this time inter-val, although it is not possible to distinguish radioactive grains bound to the surface from those that may be internalized. Significantly, greater than 95% of the cells in the culture dishes were heavily labeled. Because approxi-mately 50–60% of the HF cells incubated with hEGF are stimulated to synthesize DNA (Section VII,B), cells which are not responsive to the hor-mone do not lack receptors for the growth factor.

The time course of binding of [125I]hEGF to confluent monolayers of HF

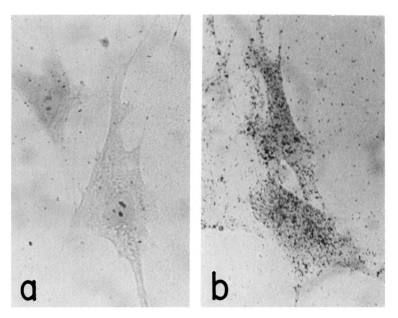

Fig. 11. Autoradiography of cell-bound [125I]hEGF. Labeled hEGF (3.5 ng/ml, 145,000 cpm/ng) was added to sparse cultures of human fibroblasts in the standard binding medium (a) in the presence and (b) in the absence of unlabeled mEGF (10 μg/ml). After a 40-minute binding period at 37°C, the cells were washed, fixed with glutaraldehyde, covered with a layer of NTB-2 emulsion, and exposed for approximately 6 weeks (Carpenter and Cohen, 1976b).

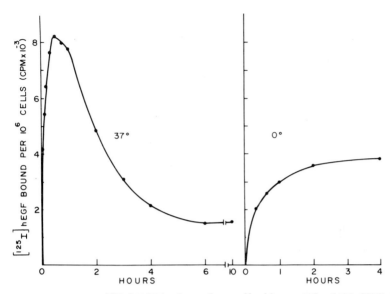

FIG. 12. Time course of [^{125}I]hEGF binding to human fibroblasts at 37° and 0°C. [^{125}I]hEGF (final concentration 4 ng/ml, 24,400 cpm/ng) was added to each culture dish containing the standard binding medium. At the indicated time intervals, duplicate dishes were selected and the cell-bound radioactivity was determined (Carpenter and Cohen, 1976b).

cells at 37°C and 0°C is shown in Fig. 12 (Carpenter and Cohen, 1976b). Maximal binding was reached after incubations of 30–40 minutes at 37° or approximately 2.5 hours at 0°. On continued incubation at 37°, the amount of cell-bound radioactivity decreased until a constant level of 15–20% of the initial maximal amount of cell-bound isotope remained associated with the cells. Continued incubation at 0°, however, did not result in a net decrease of cell-bound radioactivity, suggesting the involvement of a temperature-dependent mechanism for the loss of cell-bound radioactivity observed at 37°.

Experiments were conducted to determine the basis for the decrease in binding at 37°. The hormone remaining in the medium after 6 hours at 37° (see Fig. 12) was fully active in binding to a monolayer of "fresh" cells. This indicated that the loss of binding observed at 37° was not due to extensive degradation or inactivation of free hormone in the medium. That the loss of binding which occured at 37° was due to a cellular function was indicated by the demonstration that cells which had been incubated with the hormone for 6 hours at 37° and washed to remove unbound radioactivity were unable to bind "fresh" hormone. Control experiments showed only a slight decrease (10%) in hEGF binding capacity following a 6-hour incubation in binding medium in the absence of hEGF. The loss of cell-associated radioactivity at

37°, therefore, is due to a hormone-dependent cell function. The most plausible explanation for this phenomenon is the loss or inactivation of hEGF-specific cell surface receptors subsequent to hormone binding (see Section VIII,A,3).

Similar results have been obtained for the kinetics of binding of [^{125}I]hEGF at 37°C to human glia cells (S. Cohen and B. Westermark, unpublished results), and 3T3 and SV40 3T3 cells (G. Carpenter and S. Cohen, unpublished results). Other workers have not observed a loss of cell-bound radioactivity following maximal binding of [^{125}I]mEGF to human fibroblasts (Hollenberg and Cuatrecasas, 1975) and rat lens epithelial cells (Hollenberg, 1975). These results were due, most likely, to the fact that the incubations were carried out at 24° for not longer than 60 minutes.

The binding of [^{125}I]EGF to human fibroblasts is a saturable process (Hollenberg and Cuatrecasas, 1973, 1975; Carpenter et al., 1975; Carpenter and Cohen, 1976b). Maximal binding is achieved at a concentration of 1–2 × 10^{-9} M EGF; half-maximal binding is reached at 3–4 × 10^{-10} M EGF. The average number of mEGF binding sites per cell has been calculated to be approximately 90,000 (Carpenter et al., 1975) and 40,000 (Hollenberg and Cuatrecasas, 1975) for two independent strains of human foreskin fibroblasts. It is not known whether these differences in calculated numbers of EGF binding sites represent inherent differences in the two strains of fibroblasts or the different conditions employed in the binding assayed. Ladda (1975) has reported that the number of mEGF receptors in cultures of human fibroblasts is decreased as much as 10-fold during the in vitro "aging" of the cells. Other factors which may influence the binding of the growth factor, such as the stage of the cell cycle, have not been reported. The average number of mEGF binding sites in cultures of rat lens epithelial cells was calculated to be about 40,000 sites per cell (Hollenberg, 1975).

The nature of cell-bound [^{125}I]hEGF was examined by extracting the cells with 0.1 N HCl which solubilized 80% of the cell-bound radioactivity. When labeled hEGF was incubated with HF cells for 40 minutes at 37°C, washed, and extracted with acid, 98% of the extracted material was of the same molecular weight as native hEGF, as determined by gel-filtration chromatography. The ability of extracted radioactive material to rebind to "fresh" cells was examined after labeled hEGF had been incubated with HF cells for 15 minutes prior to extraction with acid. The results demonstrated that the extracted material was able to rebind to fibroblasts with an affinity nearly identical to that of the native growth factor. These experiments indicate that the structure of hEGF is not grossly altered during the initial binding reaction.

The capacity of a wide variety of cell types to bind [^{125}I]EGF has been recorded (L. Frati et al., 1972; O'Keefe et al., 1974; Carpenter et al., 1975).

Cells which were able to bind the growth factor in a specific manner included human fibroblasts (skin and lung), human conjunctiva, HeLa, mouse fibroblasts (3T3 and SV40 3T3), normal rat kidney fibroblasts, mouse chondrocytes, Chang liver cells, human melanoma, human glia and glioma, rabbit lens epithelial cells, and rat corneal epithelial cells. Significant levels of specific binding were not detected in the following cells: human lymphocytes, mouse thymocytes, mouse spleen cells, mouse sarcoma (XC), mouse adrenal (Y-1), Chinese hamster ovary (CHO), and chick embryo fibroblasts. The binding of labeled EGF to crude membrane fractions from different tissue is described below (Section VIII,B).

A correlation has been observed between the capacity of cells to bind [^{125}I]EGF and transformation of those cells by the murine and feline RNA sarcoma viruses. For example, normal rat kidney cells bound [^{125}I]mEGF, but these cells transformed by the Kirsten virus did not bind the labeled polypeptide (Carpenter *et al.*, 1975). This observation has been extended to include rat and mouse fibroblasts, mink kidney cells, and cat embryo cells (Todaro *et al.*, 1977). Transformation of these cells by the Maloney, Kirsten, or Gardner sarcoma viruses resulted in loss of [^{125}I]hEGF binding capacity. Transformation by DNA viruses, SV40 and polyoma, or the Schmidt–Ruppin avian sarcoma virus, however, did not affect binding of the labeled growth factor. Also, infection by nontransforming murine, feline, or primate leukemia viruses did not block binding. It was suggested that a product of the sarcoma virus genome specifically changes cell EGF receptors or induces the synthesis of an EGF-like molecule.

A commonly observed phenomenon in the study of hormone action is that a maximum biological response is obtained when only a fraction of the available receptors are occupied. This is also observed by comparison of the EGF binding isotherm and biological dose–response curves. Maximal stimulation of DNA synthesis in human fibroblasts by EGF is achieved at concentrations that are considerably less than concentrations required for maximal binding of the polypeptide. The data indicated that maximal stimulation of DNA synthesis is achieved when approximately 25% of the total number of available receptors are occupied by EGF (Hollenberg and Cuatrecasas, 1975; Carpenter and Cohen, 1976b). Hollenberg (1975) has reported that in rat lens epithelial cells, approximately 75% of the receptors are occupied when the maximal stimulation of DNA synthesis is achieved. Although unoccupied receptors in these systems are frequently termed "spare" receptors, they cannot be considered inactive and may, in fact, be involved in eliciting the biological response of the hormone. Possible functions of unoccupied receptors have been discussed at length elsewhere (Levitzki *et al.*, 1975; Cuatrecasas and Hollenberg, 1976; Kahn, 1976).

In addition to being a rapid and saturable process, the binding of

[^{125}I]EGF to HF cells is highly specific. A large number of hormones and polypeptide growth factors have been tested for their ability to compete with [^{125}I]EGF in the binding to HF cells. None was found to compete with labeled EGF in the radioreceptor assay. Two derivatives of mEGF, mEGF$_{1-48}$ and mEGF$_{1-51}$ (see Section III,A), were examined for their abilities to compete with native [^{125}I]mEGF for receptors on HF cells (Carpenter et al., 1975). The data indicate that mEGF$_{1-51}$, which is as biologically active as the native polypeptide, also was as effective as the intact growth factor in the competitive radio-receptor assay. mEGF$_{1-48}$, however, was only 5–10% as effective as native mEGF in competing with [^{125}I]mEGF in the binding assay. As discussed previously (Section VII,E), this derivative has only 1–5% of the activity of intact mEGF as judged by their relative abilities to stimulate DNA synthesis in quiescent HF cells. These results suggest that the altered binding affinity of mEGF$_{1-48}$ is due to the absence of the Try-Trp-Glu sequence at residues 49–51. However, the isolated carboxy-terminal pentapeptide containing residues 49–53 did not compete in the binding assay. It would appear, therefore, that optimal binding of EGF to receptors on HF cells not only requires residues 49–51 but is dependent on other sequences in the polypeptide as well. Also, because both the binding affinity and biological activity of mEGF$_{1-48}$, relative to the intact molecule, are reduced by nearly equal amounts, it would appear that the EGF binding sites detected on human fibroblasts are physiologically relevant to the mitogenic activity of this growth factor.

2. Metabolism of Cell-Bound [^{125}I]EGF

As noted in Section VIII,A,1, upon extended incubation of human fibroblasts with [^{125}I]hEGF at 37°C, the quantity of cell-bound radioactivity decreased following initial attainment of the maximal level of hormone binding. The parameters which influence the release of the cell-bound labeled hormone and the chemical nature of the released radioactive material were examined.

The temperature dependence of the release of cell-bound radioactivity is shown in Fig. 13. The data show that, following incubation of [^{125}I]hEGF with HF cells for 40 minutes at 37° and removal of the unbound hormone in the media, cell-bound radioactivity decreased with a half-life of approximately 20 minutes at 37° (curve A). If the cells were incubated with [^{125}I]hEGF at 0° for 2 hours, washed to remove unbound hormone, and reincubated at 0°, the amount of cell-bound radioactivity slowly decreased until approximately 55% of the radioactivity was released from the cells after 4–6 hours (curve B). Interestingly, when the hormone was initially incubated with the cells at 37° and the reincubation after removal of unbound hormone carried out at 0°, very little cell-bound radioactivity dissociated from the cell (curve C).

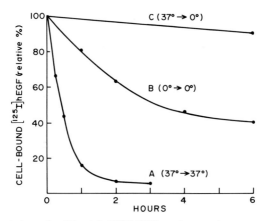

FIG. 13. Dissociation of cell-bound [^{125}I]hEGF under varying temperature conditions, Curve A: [^{125}I]hEGF (6 ng/ml, 21,200 cpm/ng) was preincubated with fibroblasts for 40 minutes at 37°C. The cells were then washed and standard binding medium was re-added. The cultures were incubated at 37°C, and at the indicated intervals the cell-bound radioactivity was determined. Curve B: Identical to curve A, except that the initial binding period was 2 hours at 0°C, and the dissociation temperature was 0°C. Curve C: Identical to curve A, except the dissociation temperature was 0°C. The results are expressed as the relative percentage of cell-bound radioactivity remaining at the indicated times, taking as 100% the amount of radioactivity present after the initial binding period. (From Carpenter and Cohen, 1976b.)

The nature of the material released into the medium at 37° and 0° was analyzed by gel filtration. Essentially all the radioactive material released at 0° cochromatographed with intact hEGF; however, most of the radioactivity released at 37° was low molecular weight material. This low molecular weight material was identified as iodotyrosine. These data indicate that at 0°, cell-bound [^{125}I]hEGF dissociates from the cell surface as an intact polypeptide, whereas at 37° most of the hormone is rapidly degraded. It is not possible, however, to determine whether the entire polypeptide chain is degraded or whether only that portion of the molecule containing the iodinated tyrosine residues is subject to proteolysis. It is important to bear in mind that it is not known if the iodine label on EGF is distributed among all the tyrosine residues in the polypeptide chain or is preferentially localized on one or two residues.

Various chemical agents block the degradation of cell-bound [^{125}I]EGF. These materials include: (a) certain protease inhibitors (tosyl-L-lysine chloromethyl ketone and the benzyl ester of guanidobenzoic acid); (b) inhibitors of metabolic energy (dinitrophenol, azide, and cyanide); (c) local anesthetics (lidocaine, procaine, and cocaine); (d) the lysosomotrophic agent chloroquine; and (e) ammonium chloride, an inhibitor of overall protein degradation. Of these, ammonium chloride is the most potent—degradation of cell-bound [^{125}I]hEGF is inhibited by 98% in the presence of 10 mM ammonium chloride.

In addition to the dependence of the degradation of cell-bound [^{125}I]hEGF on temperature and metabolic energy, and its inhibition by chloroquine and membrane-active agents such as the local anesthetics and the ammonium ion, other experiments indicate, although indirectly, that cell-bound [^{125}I]hEGF is internalized prior to degradation. For example, when the labeled hormone is bound to cells at 0°C, the cell-bound radioactivity is much more sensitive (compared to [^{125}I]hEGF bound to cells at 37°) to high molecular weight reagents, such as trypsin or antibody to hEGF. Because endocytosis of cell-bound material is minimized at the lower temperature, these results are consistent with the notion that cell-bound [^{125}I]hEGF is internalized before it is degraded. However, the relevance of this internalization and degradation process to the mitogenic activity of EGF is not known.

3. EGF-Mediated Loss and Recovery of Receptor Activity

The regulation of the activity of membrane receptors by homologous ligands has been described for insulin (Gavin *et al.*, 1974), growth hormone (Lesniak and Roth, 1976), thyrotropin-releasing hormone (Hinkle and Tashjian, 1975), isoproterenol (Mukherjee *et al.*, 1975), α-bungarotoxin (Devreotes and Fambrough, 1975), concanavalin A (Oliver *et al.*, 1974), and Ricinus communis agglutinin (Oliver *et al.*, 1974). This phenomenon, often referred to as "desensitization" or "down-regulation," is also observed with cultured cells incubated with EGF. If cells are incubated with a saturating level of EGF, washed to remove unbound hormone, and the cell-bound material allowed to degrade, the capacity of the cells to bind "fresh" hormone is reduced to approximately 20% of maximal observed during the initial incubation. We suggest that the EGF:receptor complex is internalized. Binding capacity for [^{125}I]hEGF is recovered rapidly when serum is added to the culture medium (Fig. 14). The recovery of receptor activity in the presence of serum is inhibited by the addition of cycloheximide or actinomycin D, suggesting that macromolecular synthesis is required (a) to resynthesize receptor molecules, (b) to recycle "old" receptors, or (c) to insert into the membrane receptors from an intracellular pool.

B. BINDING OF [^{125}I]EGF TO TISSUES

Specific binding of [^{125}I]mEGF to animal tissues *in vivo* and *in vitro* has been demonstrated. Radioactive mEGF was injected intraperitoneally into male rats, and the level of growth factor in various organs, relative to the

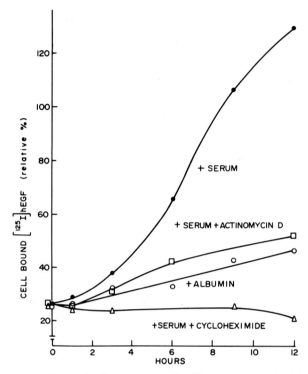

FIG. 14. Recovery of hEGF binding capacity in fibroblasts. An excess of unlabeled mEGF (1 μg/ml) was added to replicate culture dishes containing standard binding medium at 37°C. After a 1-hour period, the cells were washed to remove unbound mEGF, binding medium was re-added, and the cultures were incubated for 4 hours at 37°C to permit degradation of the bound hormone. Then the medium was replaced with medium containing (a) 0.1% albumin (○), (b) 10% calf serum (●), (c) 10% calf serum plus cycloheximide (20 μg/ml) (Δ), or (d) 10% calf serum plus actinomycin D (1 μg/ml) (□). At the indicated times duplicate dishes from each group were selected, washed, and assayed for their binding capacity for [^{125}I]hEGF (6 ng/ml) in the standard binding medium (40 minutes at 37°C). The extent of [^{125}I]hEGF binding in replicate cultures, not exposed to mEGF, was taken as 100% and the results are expressed as the relative percentage of cell-bound radioactivity (Carpenter and Cohen, 1976b).

concentration in blood, was determined (Covelli *et al.*, 1972b; L. Frati *et al.*, 1972). The results showed that mEGF was concentrated into the cornea and the epidermis. High levels of specific binding *in vitro* were obtained with crude membrane preparations from cornea and epidermal tissue (O'Keefe *et al.*, 1974). These results support the *in vivo* biological activity of EGF in these two tissues (Section V) and indicate that the *in vivo* effects are a direct effect of EGF and are not mediated by other factors.

Crude membrane preparations obtained from human placenta and rat liver have been shown to possess high levels of $[^{125}I]$mEGF binding activity (O'Keefe *et al.*, 1974). Liver and placenta membranes bind approximately 0.4 and 8.0 pmoles of $[^{125}I]$mEGF per mg of protein, respectively. The binding is rapid, reversible, and saturable, and no degradation of bound $[^{125}I]$mEGF was detected. The physiological significance of large amounts of specific $[^{125}I]$mEGF binding activity in these tissues, particularly placenta, is not understood at present.

IX. EPILOGUE

The existence in both mouse and man of epidermal growth factors having similar chemical characteristics and identical biological activities indicates that this polypeptide has been retained throughout a long evolutionary process and probably has a function of general significance in Nature. The conservation of specific receptors for EGF in a wide variety of cells in a number of species supports this idea. Although many of the chemical and biological properties of EGF have been described, it is evident that much remains to be done before this polypeptide is "understood" as to the nature of its biological significance and its molecular mechanism of action. In these regards, imaginative, incisive experimentation is clearly of the highest priority.

The capacity of EGF to elicit biological actions *in vivo*, especially the stimulation of epidermal cell proliferation, was established more than a decade ago. However, it is not known what role, if any, EGF fulfills during normal growth and development. More recently it has been demonstrated that the topical application of EGF to wounds of the corneal epithelium has a significant and beneficial effect on the wound-healing process. Whether or not this growth factor is part of the natural mechanism for tissue repair has not been determined. Such a function would not be unexpected, as wound healing does involve both cell proliferation and the secretion of extracellular materials. Cell culture experiments have shown that EGF promotes the growth of epithelial cells and the growth of fibroblasts which is accompanied by the accumulation of extracellular macromolecules.

The inhibition of gastric acid secretion by EGF and its chemical homology with urogastrone, although exciting, are difficult to reconcile with a mitogenic function of this growth factor. One interpretation of this observation is that EGF has multiple physiological functions that may be quite independent of one another. In this respect it should be noted that EGF induces ornithine decarboxylase in the testes and that the placenta has a high level of EGF receptors.

Although the primary site of EGF synthesis and storage in the mouse has been identified, the significance of the androgen dependence of EGF levels in the submaxillary gland and the control of secretion of this polypeptide by α-adrenergic agents are not understood. Of special importance will be information relating to the site(s) of synthesis/storage of EGF in humans. At present there are no pertinent data on this subject. As the *in vivo* actions of EGF are described more clearly, it is possible that clinical applications for EGF will be found.

Important to the understanding of the biology of EGF will be investigations of the mechanism by which this polypeptide exerts specific biochemical effects. One mechanism that has been proposed to explain the activity of certain polypeptide hormones entails the interaction in the plasma membrane of a hormone–receptor complex with another protein, e.g., adenyl cyclase, in a manner so as to alter the conformation/activity of this protein. In this manner, interaction of the hormone with the cell exterior is capable of generating a chemical signal on the interior side of the plasma membrane. Presumably it is this induced chemical signal which effects, directly or indirectly, a biological response characteristic of the particular hormone. There is, however, no reason to assume that all polypeptides communicate with the cell interior in this manner. For example, the diphtheria toxin is able to penetrate the cell membrane and directly effect a biochemical response in the cytoplasm.

Studies of the biochemical mechanism of action of EGF have received a considerable impetus from recent demonstrations of (a) the mitogenic activity of EGF on cells cultured *in vitro* and (b) the labeling of EGF with ^{125}I. Binding studies have shown that [^{125}I]EGF interacts in a specific manner with the surface of cultured cells that are responsive to the hormone. However, there is no direct evidence to suggest a mechanism by which EGF bound to the cell surface is able to elicit a biochemical response, such as increased DNA synthesis. Of interest is the observation that cell-bound EGF is rapidly internalized and degraded. It will be important to determine whether or not metabolism of the cell-bound growth factor is related to its mechanism of action. The process by which EGF and serum regulate the expression of EGF receptors in intact cells also may be critical to the determination of the growth factor's capacity to elicit mitogenic effects.

ACKNOWLEDGMENTS

This work was supported by U.S.P.H.S. Grants HD00700 and AM01176. S. C. is an American Cancer Society Research Professor.

REFERENCES

Absher, P. M., Absher, R. G., and Barnes, W. D. (1975). *Adv. Exp. Med. Biol.* **53**, 191.

Andrews, E. J., and Bullock, L. P. (1972). *Anat. Rec.* **174**, 361.

Angeletti, R. H., and Bradshaw, R. A. (1971). *Proc. Natl. Acad. Sci. U.S.A.* **68**, 2417.

Angeletti, P. U., Salvi, M. L., Chesanow, R. L., and Cohen, S. (1964). *Experientia* **20**, 1.

Angeletti, R. A., Angeletti, P. U., and Calissano, P. (1967). *Biochim. Biophys. Acta* **139**, 372.

Armelin, H. A. (1973). *Proc. Natl. Acad. Sci. U.S.A.* **70**, 2702.

Barnes, D. W., and Colowick, S. P. (1976). *J. Cell. Physiol.* **89**, 633.

Barthe, P. L., Bullock, L. P., Mowszowicz, I., Bardin, C. W., and Orth, D. N. (1974). *Endocrinology* **95**, 1019.

Baseman, J. B., and Hayes, N. S. (1975). *J. Cell Biol.* **67**, 492.

Bertsch, S., and Marks, F. (1974). *Nature (London)* **251**, 517.

Birnbaum, J. E., Sapp, T. M., and Moore, J. B. (1976). *J. Invest. Dermatol.* **66**, 313.

Blosse, P. T., Fenton, E. L., Henningsson, S., Kahlson, G., and Rosengren, E. (1974). *Experientia* **30**, 22.

Bower, J. M., Camble, R., Gregory, H., Gerring, E. L., and Willshire, I. R. (1975). *Experientia* **31**, 826.

Brunk, U., Schellens, J., and Westermark, B. (1976). *Exp. Cell Res.,* **103**, 295.

Bullock, L. P., Barthe, P. L., Mowszowiez, I., Orth, D. N., and Barthe, C. W. (1975). *Endocrinology* **97**, 189.

Byyny, R. L., Orth, D. N., and Cohen, S. (1972). *Endocrinology* **90**, 1261.

Byyny, R. L., Orth, D. N., Cohen, S., and Doyne, E. S. (1974). *Endocrinology* **95**, 776.

Calissano, P., and Angeletti, P. U. (1968). *Biochim. Biophys. Acta* **156**, 51.

Carpenter, G., and Cohen, S. (1976a). *J. Cell. Physiol.* **88**, 227.

Carpenter, G., and Cohen, S. (1976b). *J. Cell. Biol.* **71**, 159.

Carpenter, G., Lembach, K. J., Morrison, M., and Cohen, S. (1975). *J. Biol. Chem.* **250**, 4297.

Chou, P. Y., and Fasman, G. D. (1974). *Biochemistry* **13**, 222.

Cohen, S. (1960). *Proc. Natl. Acad. Sci. U.S.A.* **46**, 302.

Cohen, S. (1962). *J. Biol. Chem.* **237**, 1555.

Cohen, S. (1965a). *Collect. Pap. Annu. Symp. Fundam. Cancer Res.* **19**, 251.

Cohen, S. (1965b). *Devel. Biol.* **12**, 394.

Cohen, S. (1972). *J. Invest. Dermatol.* **59**, 13.

Cohen, S., and Carpenter, G. (1975). *Proc. Natl. Acad. Sci. U.S.A.* **72**, 1317.

Cohen, S., and Elliot, G. A. (1963). *J. Invest. Dermatol.* **40**, 1.

Cohen, S., and Savage, C. R., Jr. (1974). *Recent Prog. Horm. Res.* **30**, 551.

Cohen, S., and Savage, C. R., Jr. (1975). *In* "Methods in Enzymology" (B. W. O'Malley and J. G. Hardman, eds.), Vol. 37, Part B, p. 424. Academic Press, New York.

Cohen, S., and Stastny, M. (1968). *Biochim. Biophys. Acta* **166**, 427.

Cohen, S., and Taylor, J. M. (1974). *Recent Prog. Horm. Res.* **30**, 533.

Cohen, S., Carpenter, G., and Lembach, K. J. (1975). *Adv. Metab. Disord.* **8**, 265.

Covelli, I., Mozzi, R., Rossi, R., and Frati, L. (1972a). *Hormones* **3**, 183.

Covelli, I., Rossi, R., Mozzi, R., and Frati, L. (1972b). *Eur. J. Biochem.* **27**, 225.

Cuatrecasas, P., and Hollenberg, M. D. (1976). *Adv. Protein Chem.* **30**, 251.

Devreotes, P. N., and Fambrough, D. M. (1975). *J. Cell Biol.* **65**, 335.

Dunn, J. F., Goldstein, J. L., and Wilson, J. D. (1973). *J. Biol. Chem.* **248**, 7819.

Edelman, G. M. (1976). *Science* **192**, 218.

Ellem, J. A. O., and Mironescu, S. (1972). *J. Cell. Physiol.* **79**, 389.

Elsdale, T., and Foley, R. (1969). *J. Cell Biol.* **41**, 298.

Frati, C., Covelli, I., Mozzi, R., and Frati, L. (1972). *Cell Differ.* **1**, 239.

Frati, L., Daniels, S., Delogu, A., and Covelli, I. (1972). *Exp. Eye Res.* **14**, 135.
Frati, L., Cenci, G., Sbaraglia, G., Teti, D. V., and Covelli, I. (1976). *Life Sci.* **18**, 905.
Fryklund, L., Uthne, K., Sievertsson, H., and Westermark, B. (1974). *Biochem. Biophys. Res. Commun.* **61**, 950.
Gavin, J. R., III, Roth, J., Neville, D. M., Jr., DeMeyts, P., and Buell, D. N. (1974). *Proc. Natl. Acad. Sci. U.S.A.* **71**, 84.
Goldstein, J. L., and Wilson, J. D. (1972). *J. Clin. Invest.* **51**, 1647.
Gospodarowicz, D. (1975). *J. Biol. Chem.* **250**, 2515.
Gospodarowicz, D., and Ill, C. R. (1977). In press.
Gospodarowicz, D., and Moran, J. S. (1974). *Proc. Natl. Acad. Sci. U.S.A.* **71**, 4584.
Gospodarowicz, D., and Moran, J. S. (1976). *Annu. Rev. Biochem.* **45**, 531.
Gospodarowicz, D., Jones, K. L., and Sato, G. (1974). *Proc. Natl. Acad. Sci. U.S.A.* **71**, 2295.
Gospodarowicz, D., Ill, C. R., Hornsby, P., and Gill, G. (1977a). *Endocrinology* **100**, 1080.
Gospodarowicz, D., Moran, J. S., and Braun, D. L. (1977b). *J. Cell. Physiol.*, **91**, 377.
Greene, L. A., Shooter, E. M., and Varon, S. (1968). *Proc. Natl. Acad. Sci. U.S.A.* **60**, 1383.
Gregory, H. (1975). *Nature (London)* **257**, 325.
Gunther, G. R., Wang, J. L., and Edelman, G. M. (1974). *J. Cell Biol.* **62**, 366.
Habner, J. F., Kemper, B., Potts, J. T., Jr., and Rich, A. (1973). *Endocrinology* **92**, 219.
Hassell, J. R. (1975). *Dev. Biol.* **45**, 90.
Hayashi, I., and Sato, G. (1976). *Nature (London)* **259**, 132.
Heimberg, M., Weinstein, I., LeQuire, V. S., and Cohen, S. (1965). *Life Sci.* **4**, 1625.
Hershko, A., Mamont, P., Shields, R., and Tomkins, G. M. (1971). *Nature (London), New Biol.* **232**, 206.
Hinkle, P. M. and Tashjian, A. H., Jr. (1975). *Biochemistry* **14**, 3845.
Ho, P. C., Davis, W. H., Elliot, J. H., and Cohen, S. (1974). *Invest. Ophthalmol.* **13**, 804.
Holladay, L. A., Savage, C. R., Jr., Cohen, S., and Puett, D. (1976). *Biochemistry* **15**, 2624.
Hollenberg, M. D. (1975). *Arch. Biochem. Biophys.* **171**, 371.
Hollenberg, M. D., and Cuatrecasas, P. (1973). *Proc. Natl. Acad. Sci. U.S.A.* **70**, 2964.
Hollenberg, M. D., and Cuatrecasas, P. (1975). *J. Biol. Chem.* **250**, 3845.
Holley, R. W. (1975). *Nature (London)* **258**, 487.
Holley, R. W., and Kiernan, J. A. (1968). *Proc. Natl. Acad. Sci. U.S.A.* **60**, 300.
Hoober, J. K., and Cohen, S. (1967a). *Biochim. Biophys. Acta* **138**, 347.
Hoober, J. K., and Cohen, S. (1967b). *Biochim. Biophys. Acta* **138**, 357.
Jainchill, J. L., and Todaro, G. J. (1970). *Exp. Cell Res.* **59**, 137.
Junquiera, L. C., Toledo, A. M., and Saad, A. (1964). *In* "The Salivary Glands and Their Secretions" (L. M. Sreeby and J. Meyer, eds.), p. 105. Macmillan, New York.
Kahn, C. R. (1976). *J. Cell Biol.* **70**, 261.
Kaplowitz, P. B., and Moscona, A. A. (1976). *Exp. Cell Res.* **100**, 177.
Kohler, N., and Lipton, A. (1974). *Exp. Cell Res.* **87**, 297.
Lacassagne, A. (1940). *C. R. Seances Soc. Biol. Ses Fil.* **133**, 180.
Ladda, R. (1975). *Fed. Proc., Fed. Am. Soc. Exp. Biol.* **34**, 276.
Leffert, H. L. (1974). *J. Cell Biol.* **62**, 767.
Lembach, K. J. (1976a). *Proc. Natl. Acad. Sci. U.S.A.* **73**, 183.
Lembach, K. J. (1976b). *J. Cell. Physiol.* **89**, 277.
Lesniak, M. A., and Roth, J. (1976). *J. Biol. Chem.* **251**, 3730.
Levitzki, A., Segel, L. A., and Steer, M. L. (1975). *J. Mol. Biol.* **91**, 125.
Lindgren, A., and Westermark, B. (1976). *Exp. Cell Res.* **99**, 357.
Lindgren, A., Westermark, B., and Ponten, J. (1975). *Exp. Cell Res.* **95**, 311.
McKeehan, W. L., Hamilton, W. G., and Ham, R. G. (1976). *Proc. Natl. Acad. Sci. U.S.A.* **73**, 2023.

McKeehan, W. L., Hamilton, W. G., and Ham, R. G. (1977). *In Vitro* **13,** 399.

Mukherjee, C., Caron, M. G., and Lefkowitz, R. J. (1975). *Endocrinology* **99,** 347.

Nicholson, G. L. (1976). *Biochim. Biophys. Acta* **457,** 57.

O'Keefe, E., Hollenberg, M. D., and Cuatrecasas, P. (1974). *Arch. Biochem. Biophys.* **164,** 518.

Oliver, J. M., Ukena, T. E., and Berlin, R. D. (1974). *Proc. Natl. Acad. Sci. U.S.A.* **71,** 394.

Pardee, A. B. (1975). *Biochim. Biophys. Acta* **417,** 153.

Pasquini, F., Petris, A., Sbaraglia, G., Scopelliti, R., Cenci, G., and Frati, L. (1974). *Exp. Cell Res.* **86,** 233.

Reynolds, V. H., Boehm. F. H., and Cohen, S. (1965). *Surg. Forum* **16,** 108.

Rheinwald, J. G., and Green, H. (1977). *Nature* **265,** 421.

Richman, R. A., Claus, T. H., Pilkus, S. J., and Friedman, D. L. (1976). *Proc. Natl. Acad. Sci. U.S.A.* **73,** 3589.

Rinderknecht, E., and Humble, R. E. (1976). *Proc. Natl. Acad. Sci. U.S.A.* **73,** 2365.

Roberts, M. L., and Reade, P. C. (1975). *Arch. Oral Biol.* **20,** 693.

Rose, S. P., Pruss, R. M., and Herschman, H. R. (1975). *J. Cell. Physiol.* **86,** 593.

Rose, S. P., Stan, R., Passovoy, D. S., and Herschman, H. R. (1976). *Experientia* **32,** 913.

Rozengurt, E., and Heppel, L. A. (1975). *Proc. Natl. Acad. Sci. U.S.A.* **72,** 4492.

Rubin, H., and Steiner, R. (1975). *J. Cell. Physiol.* **85,** 261.

Sato, G. (1975). *In* "Biochemical Actions of Hormones" (G. Litwack, ed.), Vol. 3, p. 391. Academic Press, New York.

Savage, C. R., Jr., and Cohen, S. (1972). *J. Biol. Chem.* **247,** 7609.

Savage, C. R., Jr., and Cohen, S. (1973). *Exp. Eye Res.* **15,** 361.

Savage, C. R., Jr., Inagami, T., and Cohen, S. (1972). *J. Biol. Chem.* **247,** 7612.

Savage, C. R., Jr., Hash, J. H., and Cohen, S. (1973). *J. Biol. Chem.* **248,** 7669.

Schachter, M. (1969). *Physiol. Rev.* **49,** 509.

Server, A. C., and Shooter, E. M. (1976). *J. Biol. Chem.* **251,** 165.

Server, A. C., Sutter, A., and Shooter, E. M. (1976). *J. Biol. Chem.* **251,** 1188.

Sheridan, J. W., and Stanley, E. R. (1971). *J. Cell. Physiol.* **78,** 451.

Shodell, M. (1972). *Proc. Natl. Acad. Sci. U.S.A.* **69,** 1455.

Smith, G. L., and Temin, H. M. (1974). *J. Cell. Physiol.* **84,** 181.

Stanley, E. R., Cifone, M., Heard, P. M., and Defendi, V. (1976). *J. Exp. Med.* **143,** 631.

Starkey, R. H., Cohen, S., and Orth, D. N. (1975). *Science* **189,** 800.

Stastny, M., and Cohen, S. (1970). *Biochim. Biophys. Acta* **204,** 578.

Stastny, M., and Cohen, S. (1972). *Biochim. Biophys. Acta* **261,** 177.

Steiner, D. F., Kemmler, W., Tager, H. S., and Peterson, J. D. (1974). *Fed. Proc., Fed. Am. Soc. Exp. Biol.* **33,** 2105.

Sundell, H., Serenius, F. S., Barthe, P., Friedman, Z., Kanarek, K. S., Escobedo, M. B., Orth, D. N., and Stahlman, M. T. (1975). *Pediatr. Res.* **9,** 371.

Taylor, J. M., and Lembach, K. J. (1973). *Biochim. Biophys. Acta* **329,** 58.

Taylor, J. M., Cohen, S., and Mitchell, W. M. (1970). *Proc. Natl. Acad. Sci. U.S.A.* **67,** 164.

Taylor, J. M., Mitchell, W. M., and Cohen, S. (1972). *J. Biol. Chem.* **247,** 5928.

Taylor, J. M., Mitchell, W. M., and Cohen, S. (1974). *J. Biol. Chem.* **249,** 2188.

Temin, H. M., Pierson, R. W., Jr., and Dulak, N. C. (1972). *In* "Growth, Nutrition and Metabolism of Cells in Culture" (G. H. Rothblat and V. J. Cristofalo, eds.), Vol. 1, p. 50. Academic Press, New York.

Todaro, G. J., DeLarco, J. E., and Cohen, S. (1976). *Nature (London)* **264,** 26.

Turkington, R. W. (1969a). *Cancer Res.* **29,** 1459.

Turkington, R. W. (1969b). *Exp. Cell Res.* **57,** 79.

Turkington, R. W., Males, J. L., and Cohen, S. (1971). *Cancer Res.* **31,** 252.

Van Wyk, J. J., and Underwood, L. E. (1975). *Annu. Rev. Med.* **26,** 427.

Van Wyk, J. J., Underwood, L. E., Baseman, J. B., Hintz, R. L., Clemmons, D. R., and Marshall, R. N. (1975). *Adv. Metab. Disord.* **8**, 127.

Westermark, B. (1976). *Biochem. Biophys. Res. Commun.* **69**, 304.

Wolf, L., Kohler, N., Roehm, C., and Lipton, A. (1975). *Exp. Cell Res.* **92**, 63.

Yanishevsky, R., Mendelsohn, M. L., Mayall, B. H., and Cristofalo, V. J. (1974). *J. Cell. Physiol.* **84**, 165.

Zetter, B. R., Chen, L. B., Sun, T. T., and Buchanan, J. M. (1976). *J. Cell Biol.* **70**, 282a.

CHAPTER 6

Sites of Action of Androgens and Follicle Stimulating Hormone on Cells of the Seminiferous Tubule

Irving B. Fritz

I. INTRODUCTION AND PERSPECTIVES

If pituitary hormones are removed, the formation of spermatozoa ceases (Smith and Engle, 1927; Smith, 1930). Half a century and thousands of commentaries later, sufficient publications have appeared on different aspects of the testis and on hormonal influences on spermatogenesis in mammals to fill a fair-sized library. Unfortunately, however, our understanding of the modes of hormonal actions is not directly proportional to this huge number of articles, reviews, symposia, and books (for a recent review, see Fawcett, 1976). When one attempts to relate what is known about the effects of hormones in isolated systems to a broader understanding of the hormonal control of spermatogenesis, the difficulties are compounded. Knowledge of the molecular mechanisms of action of hormones on spermatogenesis remains rudimentary.

Before there can be progress in gaining insight into the mechanisms by which hormones regulate testicular functions, it is obviously crucial to determine which of the many types of cells in the testis respond directly to the hormone. The most important hormones required for the maintenance of spermatogenesis in adult hypophysectomized rats are androgens. Provided testosterone administration is begun immediately after removal of the pituitary of adult rats, neither luteinizing hormone (LH) nor follicle-stimulating hormone (FSH) is necessary to maintain spermatozoa production at levels required for fertility (see review by Steinberger, 1971). We can interpret these observations only partially. The absence of an LH requirement when testosterone is administered is not surprising, because the primary target for LH is the testicular Leydig (interstitial) cell, which increases production of testosterone in response to LH. The ability of LH, at low doses, to replace the requirement for relatively high concentrations of testosterone is consistent with the high local concentrations of androgens in the vicinity of the seminiferous tubule, resulting from release of testosterone from stimulated interstitial cells. Levels of androgens in testis fluid are known to be much higher than in peripheral blood (Harris and Bartke, 1974; Bartke and Voglmayr, 1977).

On the other hand, the absence of an apparent requirement for FSH to maintain spermatogenesis under these conditions is puzzling. It is well appreciated that FSH is needed to initiate the first wave of spermatogenesis. Along with testosterone or LH, FSH is also required to restore spermatogenesis in regressed testes following long-term hypophysectomy (Steinberger, 1971). These observations can be rationalized by assuming that various effects elicited by FSH on immature testicular cells are not essential in mature cells, or that androgens can duplicate these actions under conditions in which spermatogenesis is already proceeding to completion. Because long-term treatment of hypophysectomized rats with androgens alone results in partial restoration of testicular function, the conclusion emerges that testosterone must be able to elicit some of the effects which FSH induces.

In support of this conjecture, it is now known that FSH and androgens can independently elicit at least one identical metabolic response in adult rats *in vivo*, and in cultures of Sertoli cells prepared from immature rats: namely, the stimulation of production and secretion of androgen-binding protein (ABP) (see Section III,C). The combined effect of both hormones on ABP formation is greater than that elicited by either hormone alone, but less than additive in Sertoli cell cultures (Louis and Fritz, 1977). In contrast, only FSH increases the production of cyclic 3',5'-adenosine monophosphate (cAMP) in isolated Sertoli cells from testes of immature rats (Dorrington *et al.*, 1974, 1975; Steinberger *et al.*, 1975; Steinberger and Steinberger, 1976a), and testosterone is without effect.

During maturation of the testis, Sertoli cells form tight junctional complexes with each other and in the process create a barrier separating the basal compartment of the seminiferous tubule from the adluminal compartment (for review, see Fawcett, 1975a). Recent information indicates that formation of this barrier is under hormonal regulation (Bressler, 1976). It is conceivable that once the barrier within the seminiferous tubule becomes functional, FSH is no longer absolutely required, and testosterone is sufficient to maintain both it and the composition of tubular fluid in the adluminal compartment in which meiosis proceeds to completion. If this reasoning is correct, one would expect that the action of FSH on its primary cellular target, namely, Sertoli cells, would be most evident in immature or regressed testes. This is the case for the stimulation by FSH of cAMP production (Dorrington and Fritz, 1974b; Means and Huckins, 1974), 17β-estradiol production (Dorrington *et al.*, 1976a), and DNA synthesis (Griswold *et al.*, 1975, 1976, 1977) by isolated Sertoli cells and testicular preparations. In all three examples cited, the effects of FSH greatly diminish or cannot be detected in preparations of testes from normal rats older than 30–40 days of age. Similarly, FSH stimulation of the incorporation of labeled amino acids into proteins by testis slices is observed in preparations from immature but not from mature normal rats (Means and Hall, 1968; Means, 1975).

These observations are consistent with the interpretation that FSH acts primarily on immature testicular somatic cells but that the influence of FSH diminishes during gonadal maturation. Thus, FSH would be required to initiate spermatogenesis, perhaps by stimulating Sertoli cells to form the barrier separating basal from adluminal compartments in the seminiferous tubule (Fawcett, 1975a), and by stimulating formation of the unique tubular fluid (Setchell and Waites, 1975). These requirements would be most clearly evident during the first wave of spermatogenesis, but would also be apparent during restoration after testicular regression, and probably also during reinitiation of spermatogenesis in seasonal breeders. At other times, testosterone alone may be sufficient to maintain testicular functions in structures which have already been formed during normal maturation and development. However, androgens alone are postulated to be insufficient to permit normal Sertoli-cell development during initiation of spermatogenesis.

Within this framework, a simplified view of the probable primary sites of hormonal action on spermatogenesis is provided (Fig. 1). The actions of FSH are assumed to be of greater importance during the initiation processes than during the maintenance of steady-state production of spermatozoa. However, it is quite conceivable that all sites of hormone actions shown are required for maximal efficiency of spermatogenesis. A guide to the literature which supports this overall scheme is provided in the following sections.

II. EVIDENCE THAT ANDROGEN INFLUENCES ON SPERMATOGENESIS ARE MEDIATED VIA DIRECT EFFECTS ON TESTICULAR SOMATIC CELLS AND NOT ON GERMINAL CELLS

A. GENERAL BACKGROUND

In this section, the argument will be developed that the androgen requirement for germinal cell differentiation and development results from the dependence of germinal cells on interactions with neighboring testicular somatic cells, and that only the somatic cells respond directly to androgens.

It has long been postulated that Sertoli cells serve an essential nutritive function for germinal cells. Cytological observations suggested that these epithelial cells in the seminiferous tubule played the role of "nurse" cells as well as providing mechanical support for the developing germinal epithelial cells (von Ebner, 1888; Elftman, 1963; Vilar *et al.*, 1962; Nicander, 1967; Sapsford and Rae, 1968; Flickinger, 1967; Flickinger and Fawcett, 1967; Fawcett, 1974, 1975a). Demonstration of the existence of a "blood–testis barrier"* (for review, see Setchell and Waites, 1975), and the identification of the importance of Sertoli cells in forming and maintaining this barrier (Fawcett *et al.*, 1970; Ross, 1970, 1976) provided a key to understanding the possible mechanisms by which Sertoli cells could influence germinal-cell development. From available data, it may be concluded that Sertoli cells are responsible for restricting the passage of molecules from the basal compart-

---

*The term "blood–testis" barrier is used in compliance with terminology employed by Setchell and Waites (1975). The barrier is actually a "lymph–testis" barrier. Blood vessels to the seminiferous tubule do not have permeability characteristics different from those in other organs (Fawcett *et al.*, 1970). The testis barrier exists between the compartment basal to tight junctions among Sertoli cells and that luminal to these junctions (Fawcett, 1975a). This barrier is therefore not formally analogous to the blood–brain barrier, in which blood vessels have unique permeability properties. In both organs, however, the cells are surrounded by a unique chemical environment. In this sense, fluid in the adluminal compartment of the seminiferous tubule may be compared with the cerebrospinal fluid of the CNS.

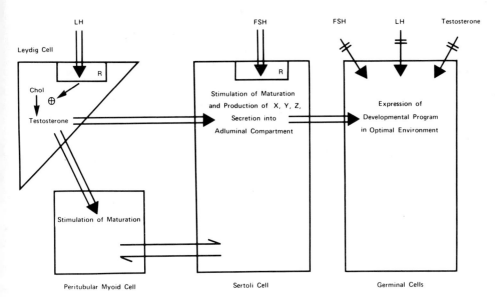

FIG. 1. Summary of probable primary cellular sites of hormonal action on spermatogenesis. Symbols used: Chol denotes cholesterol; R denotes specific receptor complexes to the polypeptide hormones LH in Leydig cells, or FSH in Sertoli cells. In both cases, activation of adenylate cyclase occurs with increased production of cAMP, and in both cases cAMP derivatives can elicit the late responses. However, it is unknown whether cAMP is an obligatory intermediate (see Section III,D). For details concerning the actions of FSH and androgens on Sertoli cells, see Sections III,C,1 and III,C,2, and for discussion of the nature of interactions between myoid and Sertoli cells, see Section III,C,3. Evidence for the absence of direct androgen effects on germinal cells is presented in Section II. Production and secretion of "X, Y, and Z" by Sertoli cells refers to the special products found in tubular fluid of the seminiferous tubule, such as androgen binding protein and other compounds formed by Sertoli cells (see Section IV).

ment to the adluminal compartment, and that they secrete components into tubular fluid. The components in tubular fluid, at concentrations often much higher than in plasma or lymph (i.e., ABP, K^+, myoinositol, etc.), provide a unique physical and chemical microenvironment in the vicinity of germinal cells which are completing meiosis, and which are undergoing the remarkable events associated with cytodifferentiation during spermiogenesis. I assume that this particular microenvironment is required to allow implementation of preexisting programs in various germinal cells. If so, the actions of androgens on Sertoli cell functions will indirectly exert considerable influence on the development of germinal cells. Data to be presented in the subsequent sections demonstrate that germinal cells can develop in the absence of a direct androgen response. The combined data support the view that the primary targets for androgens in the adult mammalian seminiferous tubule are somatic cells.

B. Consideration of *Tfm* Locus in Relation to Spermatogenesis

1. Indirect Demonstration of the Absence of a Direct Androgen Requirement for Spermiogenesis

A locus exists on the X chromosome which is required for androgen responsiveness. In testicular feminized mice, a point mutation in the *Tfm* locus on the X chromosome results in total androgen resistance and a characteristic syndrome of feminization, in which the prostate, seminal vesicles, and epididymides are absent, and spermatogenesis is impaired (Lyon and Hawkes, 1970; Ohno, 1971). This is associated with the absence of specific intracellular androgen receptors (Bardin *et al.*, 1973). It follows that the loss of the X chromosome, or inactivation of the X chromosome, in cells from XY wild-type animals will simultaneously result in a loss of the *Tfm* locus and therefore in an inability of affected cells to respond to androgens.

During spermatogenesis, diploid primary spermatocytes divide during meiosis to form haploid secondary spermatocytes, which then undergo a second meiotic division to generate haploid spermatids. It is apparent that half the haploid cells will carry the X chromosome and half will carry the Y chromosome. In this latter population which lacks the X chromosome, there will be no new synthesis of androgen receptors because of the absence of the X-linked *Tfm* locus.

It therefore would appear that Y-chromosome-bearing secondary spermatocytes and spermatids can complete their development in the absence of a direct androgen response. Because there is no reason to believe that X-chromosome-bearing spermatids and Y-chromosome-bearing spermatids have different hormonal requirements, it may be concluded that all of spermiogenesis (i.e., maturation of spermatids to form spermatozoa) can proceed in the absence of a direct androgen influence on germinal cells. As only slight RNA synthesis occurs in early spermiogenesis and none in late spermiogenesis (Monesi, 1965, 1971; Kierszenbaum and Tres, 1975; Söderström and Parvinen, 1976), indicating the absence of transcription in these haploid cells, the lack of an androgen action at these stages is not unexpected.

It should be noted, however, that this reasoning ignores the presence of intercellular bridges between similar germinal cells at all stages of development (Fawcett, 1961, 1974). The possible flow of components among cells in the germinal cell syncytium casts doubt on all indirect arguments concerning the effects of the absence of the X chromosome in half of the haploid cells, because it is possible that the products of X-chromosome expression could be transported to Y-chromosome-bearing cells. In addition, it is possible that preexisting androgen receptors in progenitor cells (spermatocytes) will be retained by spermatids.

2. *Indirect Demonstration of the Absence of a Direct Androgen*
   Requirement for the Development of Secondary
   Spermatocytes from Leptotene or Zygotene Primary
   Spermatocytes

Inactivation of the X chromosome occurs during spermatogenesis in mammals and in all other male heterogametic organisms (Monesi, 1974). Evidence compatible with genetic inactivation of the single X chromosome during meiosis includes histological criteria of heteropycnosis in the XY chromosome pair of primary spermatocytes, and the failure to detect RNA synthesis from labeled uridine in the vicinity of the sex vesicle (i.e., the condensed XY chromosome pair) in autoradiographs of prophase spermatocytes pulse-labeled with [³H]uridine. This has been observed in spermatocytes of mice (Monesi, 1965), hamsters (Utakoji, 1967), and grasshoppers (Henderson, 1964).

In the testis of the vole, all spermatocytes (and even spermatogonia) are deficient in the X chromosome and possess only the O/Y sex pair (Ohno *et al.*, 1963). In this species, "... predirected nondisjunction of the X occurs in primordial germ cells in fetal testes... Only the OY differentiate into definitive spermatogonia" (Ohno, 1969). Consequently, the X chromosome is transmitted to offspring only from the maternal gamete, because testes from postnatal voles contain spermatogonia having an OY sex chromosomal composition.

From arguments presented above, it follows that spermatocytes from mice, hamsters, and voles lack the capacity to respond to androgens. It may therefore be concluded that meiosis, as well as subsequent stages of spermiogenesis, can proceed in the absence of a direct androgen influence on germinal cells. This presupposes that preexisting androgen receptors from progenitor cells are not retained by daughter cells in sufficient concentrations to be effective.

3. *Indirect Demonstration of the Absence of a Direct Androgen*
   Requirement for the Development of Primary Spermatocytes
   from Spermatogonia

As indicated above, the X chromosome is not present in spermatogonia or in more differentiated germinal cells of the adult vole (Ohno *et al.*, 1963). Because the locus for androgen responsiveness is linked to the X chromosome, it follows that all of spermatogenesis can proceed in the vole in the absence of a direct androgen influence on germinal cells.

It is well known that in regressed testes of hypophysectomized rats, primary spermatocytes are present, albeit in reduced quantities (Clermont and Harvey, 1967; Steinberger, 1971). The progress of [³H]thymidine pulse-labeled preleptotene spermatocytes to pachytene spermatocytes proceeds nearly normally in testes of hypophysectomized rats treated with FSH alone (Vernon *et al.*, 1975). In cryptorchid testes of *Tfm* mutants, pachytene spermatocytes are present (Lyon and Hawkes, 1970; Lyon, 1973). From these data, it may be concluded that normal preleptotene and pachytene spermatocytes can be formed in the absence of androgens or androgen-responsive cells. As indicated earlier, pachytene spermatocytes, in which the X chromosome is normally inactivated, can differentiate to form spermatozoa. It may therefore be deduced, on the basis of arguments advanced, that all of germinal-cell development, from spermatogonium to spermatozoa, can proceed in the absence of X chromosomal expression, implying that a direct androgenic action on germinal cells is not necessary for spermatogenesis.

C. Direct Demonstration That Androgen-Resistant Spermatozoa May Be Produced

Lyon and colleagues (1975) have succeeded in producing male chimeric (allophenic) mice of a genotype mosaic ^{Tfm}X/Y $\leftrightarrow$ X/Y by the technique of embryo aggregation (Tarkowski, 1970). Two fertile chimeric mice of this genetic composition were able to sire numerous offspring bearing the *Tfm* mutation, thereby proving unequivocally that ^{Tfm}X-bearing viable spermatozoa were being produced. These data indicate, in the words of the authors, "that the requirement for testosterone in spermiogenesis does not involve the cell-autonomous action of the *Tfm* locus in the germ cells" (Lyon *et al.*, 1975). The most likely interpretation of these data invokes the interaction of normal X/Y testicular somatic cells with the ^{Tfm}X/Y germinal cells, allowing androgen-responsive somatic cells to support the development of *Tfm* germinal cells in the mosaic. It should be noted that *Tfm*-bearing spermatozoa must have originated from a single *Tfm*-bearing stem cell. The presence of intercellular bridges among cohorts of developing germinal cells derived from ^{Tfm}X/Y stem cells would not permit possible exchange of material with adjacent nests of germinal cells derived from normal X/Y stem cells in the testicular mosaic. In addition, all progenitor cells of the ^{Tfm}X-bearing sperm are deficient in the capacity to synthesize the effective androgen receptor, thereby making it impossible for daughter germinal cells to have inherited the androgen receptor required for responsiveness. It may therefore be concluded that androgens do not act directly on germinal cells, at least via the specific androgen receptor controlled by the *Tfm* locus. Androgen actions by mechanisms independent of this special receptor have not been reported, but the possibility has not been unequivocally ruled out.

Ohno (1977) has discussed the possibility that male germ cells may utilize an autosomally inherited, isozymic form of the nuclear-cytosol androgen receptor protein, but feels that this is unlikely.

III. RESPONSES OF TESTICULAR SOMATIC CELLS IN THE SEMINIFEROUS TUBULE TO ANDROGENS AND FSH

A. CELL TYPES INVOLVED

From evidence and viewpoints presented above, it appears likely that the hormonal control of spermatogenesis is mediated indirectly on germinal cells via direct influences on testicular somatic cells. It is therefore important to review the responses of peritubular myoid cells and Sertoli cells to hormones, because these comprise the primary nongerminal populations of cells in the seminiferous tubule. Fibroblasts and endothelial cells in the outer layers of boundary tissue, separating the seminiferous epithelium from the interstitial tissue, will not be discussed because of lack of information concerning possible hormonal effects. Similarly, it is not possible to evaluate the potential hormonal control of changes in the microvascular architecture around seminiferous tubules. Kormano (1967) has described dramatic changes in the peritubular capillaries which take place as the seminiferous tubules mature during puberty (Kormano, 1967; Setchell, 1970). These changes may be correlated with the equally dramatic developmental events occurring during the postnatal maturation of Sertoli cells and peritubular myoid cells, to be discussed below, but it is not currently possible to do more than suggest a temporal correlation among these events, all of which may be under the regulation of changing hormonal levels occuring during this time.

B. PERITUBULAR MYOID CELLS AND ANDROGENS

The postnatal development of peritubular cells has been investigated by several authors (Leeson and Leeson, 1963; Mancini *et al.*, 1964; Ross, 1967). The hormonal control of the state of differentiation of peritubular myoid cells *in vivo* has been explored by Bressler and Ross (1972). In transplants of testes from newborn mice, placed intratesticularly into normal adult mice, the peritubular myoid cells differentiated normally. However, if neonatal testes were transplanted into hypophysectomized mice, the peritubular cells remained immature in ultrastructural appearance. Administration of testosterone to hypophysectomized hosts permitted normal myoid cell development in the testis transplants from neonatal mice (Bressler and Ross, 1972).

From these results, it may be concluded that testosterone (or its products) can influence peritubular myoid cell differentiation. Similar conclusions can be drawn from the experiments of Hovatta (1972), who examined the influence of hormones on organ cultures of testis from immature rats. Contractility *in vitro* was dependent on testosterone. The antiandrogen cyproterone acetate inhibited the development of contractility in cultures prepared from testes of young rats, and also inhibited the structural development of peritubular myoid cells (Hovatta, 1972). Other data consistent with an action of androgens on peritubular myoid cells include the demonstration by autoradiography of receptors for labeled testosterone and 5α-dihydrotestosterone in myoid cells from testes of hypophysectomized rats (Sar *et al.*, 1975).

The functions of peritubular myoid cells in the seminiferous tubule are not clear. It is unlikely that junctional complexes between myoid cells constitute an essential part of the "blood–testis" barrier. For example, markers such as lanthanum acetate penetrate past the myoid cell layer but cannot pass the tight junctions between Sertoli cells (Dym and Fawcett, 1970; Fawcett *et al.*, 1970). In addition, the arrangement of peritubular myoid cells varies greatly among species, with a single continuous cell layer in rodents, and a loose multilayer of myoid cells in the tubules of testes from primates and larger animals (Fawcett, 1973). The intercellular spaces between myoid cells vary between 20 nm in rat testis to very much wider spaces in human testis (Bressler and Ross, 1972), again making it unlikely that myoid cells are directly involved in the "blood–testis" barrier.

The peritubular myoid cell, which has many structural characteristics of smooth muscle cells, is thought to be associated with local tubule contractions, perhaps facilitating the flow of tubular fluid and spermatozoa to the rete testis (Clermont, 1958; Leeson and Leeson, 1963; Ross, 1967; Fawcett *et al.*, 1970; Bressler and Ross, 1972). The peritubular myoid cells may have other general functions, such as a role in maintaining the structural integrity of the tubule wall, and specific functions yet to be defined. A unique biochemical marker for peritubular myoid cells has not thus far been reported. Possible relationships of peritubular myoid cells to Sertoli cells are discussed briefly below (Section III,C,3). Actions of hormones other than androgens on peritubular myoid cells have not been reported.

C. SERTOLI CELLS

1. Biochemical Responses to FSH

a. General Considerations. This topic has been extensively reviewed (Hansson *et al.*, 1975a, 1976; Means, 1975; Means *et al.*, 1976; A. Stein-

berger *et al.*, 1975; E. Steinberger, 1971, 1975; A. Steinberger and Steinberger, 1976a). I shall refer frequently to work from these laboratories in
summarizing the present state of the art in this fast-moving area, but I shall
concentrate upon recent work from our group. I do this because I know it
best, and because perspectives to be presented are somewhat different from
those cited in the above reviews.

In experiments designed to define the minimal number of hormones required to restore spermatogenesis during specific cycles of the seminiferous
epithelium in regressed testes of hypophysectomized rats, we observed that
each of the cycles was partially or completely dependent on testosterone or
LH (Vernon *et al.*, 1975). The requirements for FSH were difficult to define,
but the data indicated that the progress of pulse-labeled preleptotene spermatocytes to pachytene spermatocytes could occur in the presence of FSH
alone (Go *et al.*, 1971; Vernon *et al.*, 1975). In addition, FSH treatment
increased the efficiency with which labeled pachytene spermatocytes progressed to stage 7 spermatids in testes of testosterone or LH-treated rats
(Vernon *et al.*, 1975). The progression of labeled round spermatids to spermatozoa proceeded well in the absence of FSH, provided testosterone or LH
was administered. From these observations we were led to consider the
hypothesis that has been developed in this review, namely, that hormones
may act directly and primarily on Sertoli cells to create an environment in
the tubule required by germinal cells for their development (Fritz *et al.*,
1971; Fritz, 1973; Vernon *et al.*, 1975). This viewpoint provided the stimulus
to isolate Sertoli cells for the determination of their biochemical responses.

b. Production of cAMP. From observations on the stimulation by FSH
of increased production of cAMP by Sertoli-cell-enriched tubule preparations from testes of immature, irradiated, or hypophysectomized rats (Dorrington *et al.*, 1972; Dorrington and Fritz, 1974a), we were able to correlate
the magnitude of the response with the relative number of Sertoli cells in the
testis preparation. We further showed that the following testicular cell types
did not respond to FSH with an increased rate of cAMP production: Leydig
cells, spermatocytes, spermatids, and spermatozoa (Dorrington and Fritz,
1974a,b; Dorrington *et al.*, 1974, 1975).

To extend this correlation, it was necessary to examine the effects of FSH
on isolated Sertoli cells. Efforts had been made by others to prepare Sertoli
cells in culture (Kodani and Kodani, 1966). Unfortunately, these preparations were heavily contaminated by fibroblasts and peritubular myoid
cells, as shown by Steinberger *et al.* (1970). Subsequently, Welsh and Wiebe
(1975) improved the procedure for preparing Sertoli-cell-enriched preparations. By using a sequential enzymatic treatment of testes from immature
rats, and by subsequent culture in a chemically defined medium, our group
independently developed a procedure to prepare relatively homogeneous
preparations of Sertoli-cell aggregates (~90% Sertoli cells, with the remain-

der being primarily germinal cells) (Dorrington *et al.*, 1974, 1975). The structural and ultrastructural characterization of these cell preparations unequivocally proved their identity as Sertoli cells (Tung *et al.*, 1975, 1976; Tung and Fritz, 1975). Addition of FSH to isolated Sertoli cells prepared in this manner from testes of immature rats was shown to increase cAMP production (Dorrington *et al.*, 1974, 1975), alter their structure (Tung *et al.*, 1975), and increase the rates of various biochemical responses to be described below.

Previous morphological investigations by others (Murphy, 1965; Castro *et al.*, 1970) had indicated that Sertoli cells were a likely target for FSH. The experiments described above with isolated cells provided proof that Murphy's postulate was correct. Our observations that FSH increased cAMP production by isolated Sertoli cells (Dorrington *et al.*, 1974) were rapidly confirmed (Heindel *et al.*, 1975; Steinberger and Steinberger, 1976a). Experimental results obtained with germinal-cell-depleted testes were consistent with an FSH action on adenylate cyclase of Sertoli cells (Means *et al.*, 1976).

c. Production of Androgen Binding Protein. Once the Sertoli-cell preparations were available, it was possible to examine other biochemical changes in response to FSH. The first product explored was androgen binding protein (ABP). Preliminary reports from our group (Vernon *et al.*, 1973a) and by Ritzén *et al.* (1973) simultaneously demonstrated the presence of ABP in testis extracts. ABP was shown to have a high affinity for testosterone and 5α-dihydrotestosterone (K_d of approximately 1 nM), but a much lower affinity for other steroids (Hansson *et al.*, 1974; Vernon *et al.*, 1974). In our initial report, we presented data showing that testicular levels declined during regression after hypophysectomy (Vernon *et al.*, 1973a), and we subsequently observed that administration of FSH *in vivo* increased ABP levels in testes of adult rats (Vernon *et al.*, 1973b, 1974). Hansson *et al.* (1973) observed the same phenomenon in testes of immature hypophysectomized rats. At the 1974 NICHD Testis Workshop, three laboratories summarized data confirming and extending observations on the fall in testicular ABP levels after hypophysectomy and the rise after FSH administration (French *et al.*, 1974; Sanborn *et al.*, 1974; Fritz *et al.*, 1974).

These data were interpreted to indicate that ABP was probably produced by Sertoli cells, based on the following pieces of evidence:

(1) FSH was known to act on Sertoli cells to increase cAMP production, and not on other testicular cells (see Section III,C,1,b above). Therefore, an increased testicular ABP production following FSH probably reflected an increased production by Sertoli cells.

(2) FSH stimulation of ABP production was obtained in testes depleted of

germ cells after hypophysectomy, and high levels of testicular ABP were observed in cryptorchid rats and in mice rendered germinal-cell-depleted by genetic impairments (Vernon *et al.*, 1973b, 1974; Fritz *et al.*, 1974). Similarly, FSH increased ABP production *in vivo* by testes rendered germ-cell-depleted by irradiation (Tindall *et al.*, 1974; French *et al.*, 1974), or by drugs toxic to rapidly dividing cells (French *et al.*, 1974). These data, coupled with the absence of detectable ABP levels in Leydig cells (Vernon *et al.*, 1974), supported the possibility that testicular ABP originated from Sertoli cells.

In isolated preparations of primary cultures of Sertoli cells prepared from testes of immature rats, FSH (or $N^6,O^{2'}$-dibutyryl cAMP) increased ABP production and secretion (Fritz *et al.*, 1974, 1975, 1976c). These observations were also rapidly confirmed (Steinberger *et al.*, 1975; Steinberger and Steinberger, 1976a). Similar conclusions were drawn from observations on FSH effects *in vivo* in Sertoli cell enriched irradiated testes (Fakunding *et al.*, 1976; Tindall *et al.*, 1974).

The conclusion emerges that Sertoli cells respond to FSH with increased rates of production of cAMP and ABP, and that cAMP derivatives can duplicate the actions of FSH. Although the function of ABP remains obscure, levels of ABP provide an excellent indicator of Sertoli-cell function. The physical and chemical properties of ABP, which have been elucidated through the efforts of French, Ritzen, Hansson, and their colleagues (for review, see Hansson *et al.*, 1975a, 1976) should provide important keys with which to explore these interrelations more closely. In conclusion, there is general agreement that the *in vivo* stimulation by FSH of the production of cAMP and ABP by testis is a consequence of the stimulation of Sertoli cells. Recently, Means *et al.* (1976) raised the possibility that the early effects of FSH on ABP production *in vivo* may be dependent on testosterone production (Fakunding *et al.*, 1976). In isolated Sertoli-cell preparations, however, stimulation of ABP production by FSH appears to be independent of testosterone (Fritz *et al.*, 1976c; Louis and Fritz, 1977). In androgen-resistant *Tfm* rats, ABP levels in the testis are high (Hansson *et al.*, 1976), suggesting that nonandrogenic hormones alone have sustained ABP production.

d. Other Biochemical Responses: Possible Interactions with Interstitial Cells. Sertoli cells have an exceedingly complex life cycle. During fetal development, they have been implicated as the source of Müllerian inhibiting factor (Josso, 1973; Blanchard and Josso, 1974; Donahoe *et al.*, 1977). It is not known whether this function is under hormonal regulation. The morphological changes which occur postnatally have been well characterized (Flickinger, 1967), but definition of the corresponding biochemical events during maturation is in its infancy.

FSH receptors appear relatively early during postnatal development of the rat, and the total number of receptors per testis is apparently constant from approximately the third week of life onwards (Means and Huckins, 1974; Steinberger *et al.*, 1974). It appears likely that Sertoli cells are the only cells in the testis that bind FSH (Means and Vaitukitis, 1972; Steinberger and Steinberger, 1976a).

It is therefore of considerable interest that FSH is implicated in the maturation of Leydig cells, and in the responsiveness of Leydig cells to LH (Odell *et al.*, 1973, 1974; Chen *et al.*, 1976; Van Beurden *et al.*, 1976). Administration of FSH to immature rats *in vivo* increases the number of LH receptors per Leydig cell, and increases the rate of testosterone production (Chen *et al.*, 1976). While it is possible that FSH could act directly on Leydig cells, this has not been demonstrated. In fact, the apparent absence of FSH receptors on Leydig cells, and the inability to detect increased cAMP production by isolated Leydig cells incubated with FSH, would suggest that the FSH influence on Leydig cells is indirectly mediated. Perhaps FSH acts on immature Sertoli cells to release factor X which is required for maturation of Leydig cells.

During this same time of development, rates of metabolic pathways in Sertoli cells are changing. For example, the mitotic index is decreasing (Steinberger *et al.*, 1970), and the ability to convert testosterone to 17β-estradiol is diminishing (Dorrington *et al.*, 1976a). While the capacity for cell division exists, FSH increases the rates of DNA synthesis and mitosis by Sertoli cells in culture. This can be demonstrated in preparations from testes of rats up to 30 days of age, but not in cells from testes of rats 40 days of age or older (Griswold *et al.*, 1975, 1976, 1977). The effects of FSH can be duplicated by dibutyryl cAMP or by cholera toxin (Fritz *et al.*, 1976a).

Addition of FSH to immature Sertoli cells in culture greatly stimulates the conversion of testosterone and 19-hydroxy derivatives to 17β-estradiol (Dorrington and Armstrong, 1975; Armstrong *et al.*, 1975; Dorrington *et al.*, 1976b). These effects can be duplicated by dibutyryl cAMP or by cholera toxin (Fritz *et al.*, 1976a). The possible functions of estradiol produced by immature but not by mature Sertoli cells are not clear. It is known that estradiol receptors exist in Leydig cells, but not in other testicular cells (see Section III,C,2,a below). Recently it has been observed that *in vivo* administration of estradiol to immature or hypophysectomized rats inhibits the FSH-induced increase in responsiveness of Leydig cells to LH (Van Beurden *et al.*, 1976; Chen *et al.*, 1977). This inhibition by estradiol is not associated with the number of Leydig-cell receptors, but appears to act at the level of inhibiting one or more steps of the reaction sequence between cholesterol and testosterone (Chen *et al.*, 1977).

Speculatively, the FSH action on Sertoli cells to increase estradiol production only during immaturity (Dorrington *et al.*, 1976a) may be related to the presence of testicular estradiol receptors only in Leydig cells (Brinkmann *et al.*, 1972). During Leydig-cell maturation, additional LH receptors are being synthesised in response to FSH (Chen *et al.*, 1976), stimulated perhaps by maturation factors released from Sertoli cells. During Sertoli-cell maturation, tight junctional complexes associated with blood–testis barrier formation are completed, Sertoli-cell division slows down, and then ceases as the tubule reaches its full length. During this period of sexual maturation, testosterone production by Leydig cells in response to LH is being inhibited by estradiol released from the Sertoli cell. As Sertoli cells mature, associated with the terminal differentiation characterized by lack of cell division, FSH no longer stimulates estradiol formation. Leydig cells, which at this stage of maturation contain their adult complement of LH receptors, have increased androgen production in response to LH because the process is no longer inhibited by the low estrogen levels. With increased testosterone levels puberty commences, along with an increase in spermatogenesis. This speculative scheme attempts to relate the apparently coordinate actions of FSH on Sertoli-cell maturation, Leydig-cell maturation, estradiol production, and influences of estrogens on Leydig cells. It will be of interest to determine if these humorally mediated interactions between Sertoli cells and Leydig cells in response to FSH and LH are indeed crucial in determining the onset of testosterone production and puberty. One other factor to be considered relates to the apparent androgen requirement for Leydig-cell maturation (Hansson *et al.*, 1976; Purvis *et al.*, 1977). Perhaps Sertoli cells require stimulation by both FSH and androgens to elaborate Leydig-cell maturation factors. These postulated interactions between Sertoli cells and Leydig cells during early sexual development are summarized in Fig. 2. The scheme shown is an elaboration of that proposed by Odell *et al.* (1974).

This scheme relates only to the situation prevailing in *immature* rats, in which estrogens produced by Sertoli cells directly inhibit testosterone production by neighboring Leydig cells. In contrast, the inhibition by estrogens of testosterone production in *mature* animals is mediated by inhibition of LH secretion by the pituitary (Van Beurden *et al.*, 1977). The scheme does not consider the possible role of androgen other than testosterone secreted by the testis in relatively large amounts during the prepubertal period.

The generalized increase in protein synthesis by testis slice preparations from immature rats in response to FSH (Means and Hall, 1968) is also observed in isolated Sertoli-cell preparations (Dorrington *et al.*, 1975), and *in vivo* in Sertoli-cell-enriched preparations (Fakunding *et al.*, 1976). No reports have appeared proving the cellular site of increased RNA synthesis in testes of rats following FSH administration (Means, 1975; Reddy and Villee,

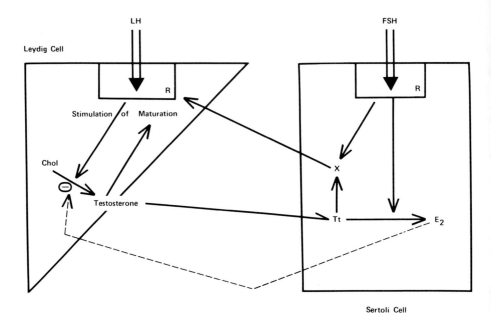

FIG. 2. Postulated interactions between Sertoli cells and Leydig cells during prepubertal sexual maturation. Symbols used are the same as those described in Fig. 1. In addition, Tt represents testosterone and E_2 denotes 17β-estradiol. The solid arrows represent stimulation, whereas the dotted arrow designates inhibition by estradiol of one or more reactions of the pathway between cholesterol and testosterone, perhaps by blocking enzyme formation, or by preventing required structural arrangements for operation of the multienzyme pathway. In this scheme, the diminution of estrogen production by mature Sertoli cells permits testosterone formation to increase in response to LH. The basis for the postulated set of interactions is duscussed in Section III,C,1,d.

1975), but Sertoli cells are thought to be implicated, because FSH elicits this effect in germinal-cell-depleted testes (Means *et al.*, 1976).

2. Responses to Androgens

a. Specific Androgen Receptors. Sertoli cells produce and secrete ABP, which has primarily an extracellular function, presumably associated with the transport of androgens to the rete testis and the epididymis. In addition, the testis contains intracellular androgen receptors, present both in cytoplasmic and nuclear fractions, having chemical and physical properties similar to those described for receptors purified from other steroid-responsive organs. The properties of androgen receptors in testis are very similar to those of androgen receptors in epididymis and in prostate, but are easily distinguished from ABP. These properties have been recently reviewed by Hansson *et al.* (1975a, 1976).

The localization of steroid receptors in various cells of the testis has been investigated with autoradiographic techniques, following the injection of various steroids under defined conditions (Sar *et al.*, 1975; Frederik *et al.*, 1976). Results indicate that labeled estradiol is located primarily in interstitial cells. These data are consistent with the demonstration by alternate techniques that testicular estradiol receptors are not in the seminiferous tubule but only in Leydig cells (Mulder *et al.*, 1973; Brinkmann *et al.*, 1972). Labeled testosterone distribution is more disperse, according to Sar *et al.* (1975). However, Frederik *et al.* (1976) report that labeled testosterone appears to be located in Leydig cells initially, and subsequently in Sertoli cells and other cells near the limiting membrane of seminiferous tubules. In contrast, Hansson *et al.* (1976) interpret the data of Sar *et al.* (1975) to suggest that germinal cells also retain label, suggesting the presence of specific androgen receptors in germinal cells as well as in Leydig cells, peritubular myoid cells, and Sertoli cells. In more recent experiments employing electron microscopic autoradiography, Frederik *et al.* (1977) demonstrated that testosterone was localized in highest concentrations within the basal parts of Sertoli-cell cytoplasm, and in lipid inclusions of Sertoli cells. The levels of androgen receptors in rat testis have been determined at varying periods after hypophysectomy. It is of interest that the amount per testis did not decrease in fully regressed testes, suggesting that the androgen receptor was not present in advanced germinal cells (Mulder *et al.*, 1975). The presence of the specific androgen receptor in isolated Sertoli cells has recently been demonstrated (Mulder *et al.*, 1976).

If particular cells lack an androgen receptor, they cannot respond to androgens. However, the converse does not necessarily hold. Thus, the presence of a "specific" steroid receptor does not demonstrate that the cell necessarily responds to steroids under physiological conditions. Many cell types are likely to contain androgen receptors, and yet be nonresponsive to testosterone (Ohno, 1976). By this reasoning, the implied or proved presence of androgen receptors in Leydig cells, Sertoli cells, peritubular myoid cells, spermatogonia, or spermatocytes (Sar *et al.*, 1975; Hansson *et al.*, 1976; Mulder *et al.*, 1974, 1975, 1976), and the possible presence of androgen receptors in spermatids (Sanborn *et al.*, 1975), can be interpreted to indicate only that these cells can potentially respond to androgens. To prove that the receptors are functionally important, it is necessary to demonstrate a response of the cells to androgen. The demonstration of the absence of a steroid receptor is more easily interpretable than the demonstration of the presence of a steroid receptor in particular cells. For example, the absence of an estradiol receptor in the cells of the seminiferous tubule (Mulder *et al.*,

1973) suggests the futility of searching for an estrogen action on germ cells, Sertoli cells, or peritubular myoid cells. Similarly, the absence or diminution of androgen receptors in cells of *Tfm* mice or rats is compatible with the androgen nonresponsiveness in *Tfm* animals (Ohno, 1971; Bardin *et al.*, 1973; Hansson *et al.*, 1976). From arguments presented in Section II, it apperas that even if androgen receptors are shown to be in germinal cells, the germinal cells are unlikely to be androgen responsive.

   b. Androgen Binding Protein Production.   The synthesis and secretion of ABP by testis *in vivo* is not only under FSH control (as described above in Section III,C,1,c), but it is regulated by androgens and LH (for review, see Hansson *et al.*, 1976). Following hypophysectomy of adult rats, after testes have regressed and testicular ABP levels are low, testosterone must be administered over a long duration (30 days) to restore ABP concentrations toward normal (Elkington *et al.*, 1975). In adult rats, or in rats hypophysectomized prior to maturation, administration of testosterone immediately after removal of the pituitary can maintain ABP production (Elkington *et al.*, 1975; Weddington *et al.*, 1975). In contrast, testosterone alone is reported unable to restore testicular ABP levels in immature hypophysectomized rats after testes have been allowed to regress (Weddington *et al.*, 1975). Testosterone treatment to hypophysectomized immature rats does, however, increase the sensitivity to FSH, and lower amounts are required to stimulate ABP production (Hansson *et al.*, 1974, 1975b). Administration of LH to long-term hypophysectomized adult rats for 3 days increased testicular ABP levels to 50% of control levels (Vernon *et al.*, 1974). The more rapid effects with LH treatment than with testosterone could be a reflection of higher testosterone concentrations in the vicinity of the seminiferous tubule when LH was administered than when testosterone was given, or the FSH contamination in the LH preparation employed (NIH ovine LH) was sufficient to permit a synergistic stimulation. From available data, it appears that testosterone does influence the testis to increase ABP production, but that it is more effective in *maintaining* function than in *initiating* activities in a regressed or immature testis.

   As suggested in the introduction (Section I), this information is compatible with initiation events being under the primary control of FSH, while maintenance events in the testis may be under the primary control of testosterone. It is consistent with the ability of testosterone to maintain spermatogenesis in rats if administered immediately after hypophysectomy (Clermont and Harvey, 1967). In contrast, testosterone alone reinitiates spermatogenesis with the greatest of difficulty, if at all, in regressed testes (Steinberger, 1971). For greatest efficiency FSH is needed, especially in the initial cycles of the seminiferous epithelium. Once spermatogenesis has proceeded to the formation of stage 7 spermatids, FSH can be withdrawn with no loss of efficiency in the production of spermatozoa by hypophysectomized rats maintained with testosterone or LH (Vernon *et al.*, 1975). It would be of interest to determine if similar phenomenology prevailed with respect to testosterone control of ABP production *in vivo*. However, preliminary experiments summarized by Hansson *et al.* (1976) do not support this possibility. They treated long-term hypophysectomized rats for only 5 days with FSH before stopping FSH and beginning testosterone administration. In experiments of a similar design on the control of spermatogenesis, it was necessary to provide FSH for 12 to 24 days before reaching a state that allowed labeled round spermatids to progress to spermatozoa in hypophysectomized rats given testosterone or LH alone (Vernon *et al.*, 1975).

The *in vivo* stimulation of testicular ABP production by androgens (Hansson *et al.*, 1976; Means *et al.*, 1976; Elkington *et al.*, 1975) implies that androgens act directly on Sertoli cells, because testicular ABP is thought to be produced only by Sertoli cells. This ignores the possibility that androgens could influence Sertoli cells indirectly via direct actions on other testicular cells, such as peritubular myoid cells, or even on other organs.

Ritzén *et al.* (1975) reported preliminary observations on the effects of hormones on ABP production by organ cultures of whole testis prepared from immature rats and incubated in various media for 24 hours. The increase in ABP secretion which occurred in the presence of testosterone during the later stages of culture is consistent with direct actions of androgen on one or more types of testicular cells.

The production and secretion of ABP by isolated Sertoli cells in culture have recently been shown to be increased by androgens (Louis and Fritz, 1977). The extent of stimulation observed was dependent on the time of addition of testosterone, 5α-dihydrotestosterone, or 5α-androstane,3α,17β-diol to the medium, with greatest effects obtained when androgens were added at the time of plating. Sertoli cells maintained in culture in a chemically defined medium became progressively less sensitive to subsequent addition of testosterone. Steroid-specificity investigations showed that only androgens increased ABP production, whereas 17β-estradiol, progesterone, and corticosterone were without effect. Androgens and FSH appear to act by different mechanisms to stimulate ABP production by isolated Sertoli cells. The combined stimulation was greater than that elicited by either hormone above, but less than additive (Louis and Fritz, 1977). When both hormones were added at the time of plating, initial rates of production of ABP were sustained for 9 days in primary culture. These results seem to parallel some of the *in vivo* effects reported above, in that isolated Sertoli cells deprived of androgens act like whole testis *in vivo* deprived of LH or androgens. In both cases, sustained function (i.e., production of ABP) is best maintained when androgens are present at all times. Restoration of function in regressed testes *in vivo*, or in isolated Sertoli cells deprived of androgens *in vitro*, is difficult to achieve with androgens alone. This seems to be more pronounced in testes from sexually immature rats than in testes from adult rats. Knowledge of the underlying mechanisms remains obscure. How does testosterone maintain preexisting function without having the apparent capacity to restore deteriorated function completely? Interactions among androgens, FSH, and other agents on Sertoli cells, and on cell–cell relations in the testis, are clearly complex.

However, in spite of confusion in this area, it appears justified to conclude that the *in vivo* influences of androgens on ABP production by testis are mediated via direct stimulation of Sertoli cells.

3. Possible Interactions of Sertoli Cells with Peritubular Myoid Cells

Bressler and Ross (1972) have suggested that these two cell types influence each other during maturation, and that they may respond as a unit to changing levels of hormones during development. This argument is based primarily on morphological and ultrastructural considerations of the interrelations between Sertoli cells and peritubular myoid cells. The more recent demonstration that Sertoli-cell maturation during development (Flickinger, 1967; Flickinger and Fawcett, 1967) is dependent on testosterone (Bressler, 1976) casts additional light on these problems. By transplanting testes from immature mice into testes of adult hypophysectomized or normal mice, Bressler (1976) was able to demonstrate that normal development of Sertoli cells did not occur in hypophysectomized hosts unless testosterone was administered. These results are similar to those reported earlier for the development of peritubular myoid cells (Bressler and Ross, 1972), and discussed above (see Section III,B). It is possible that testosterone acts directly and independently on each of these cell types during development, but it is also possible that the two cell types, which are in intimate proximity, influence each other during maturation.

In this connection, recent unpublished observations by Pierre Tung in my laboratory are pertinent. Tung observed that primary cultures of Sertoli cells, which ordinarily deteriorate within 2–3 weeks when grown in a chemically defined medium, can be sustained for months if they are plated on top of a layer of peritubular myoid cells. The Sertoli cells remain functional, as evidenced by their structural integrity and the continuing secretion of ABP. It therefore appears that peritubular myoid cells supply something to Sertoli cells, either by diffusion or by cell–cell contact, which allows them to continue functioning in a culture medium devoid of serum proteins. Fibroblasts from various sources, including the tunica albuginea, are unable to substitute for peritubular myoid cells in permitting sustained Sertoli-cell survival and function in coculture. The nature of the specific interactions between peritubular myoid cells and Sertoli cells in a cocultured system remain to be defined (P. S. Tung and I. B. Fritz, unpublished observations).

4. Dependence of Initiation of Spermatogenesis on the Maturation of Sertoli Cells

Antisera specific to rat FSH have been administered to 20-day-old imma-ture rats for 14 days. This resulted in a diminution of testis weight to 50% of the control value without influencing the weights of epididymides, seminal vesicles, or the ventral prostate (Raj and Dym, 1976). The serum testos-terone level was not lowered significantly, and Leydig-cell morphology was normal. The diameter of the seminiferous tubules was decreased by 20%, the number of pachytene spermatocytes was reduced by 35%, and the number of spermatids decreased by 67% (Raj and Dym, 1976). It is therefore evident that FSH is required for normal development of spermatogenesis and testicular maturation. The only structural change thus far reported in Sertoli cells in immature rats deprived of FSH by passive immunization is a diminution in the smooth endoplasmic reticulum (Chemes *et al.*, 1976; Raj and Dym, 1976).

The formation of tight junctions between Sertoli cells which occurs during sexual development of mice (Flickinger, 1967; Nagano and Suzuki, 1976b), rats (Gilula *et al.*, 1976), and dogs (Connell, 1976) is associated with the formation of the barrier which separates the basal from the adluminal com-partments of the seminiferous tubule (Fawcett, 1975a). In testis organ cul-tures from immature rats, the formation of tight junctions is reported to be enhanced by testosterone (Hovatta, 1972). Similarly, the maturation of Ser-toli cells from testes of immature mice does not occur when transplanted into hypophysectomized hosts unless testosterone is administered (Bressler, 1976). Yet, Sertoli cells from *Tfm* mice form tight junctional complexes, and paranucleolar bodies, characteristic of mature Sertoli cells (Chung, 1974). Similar results have been reported on tight junctions between Sertoli cells of testes from *Tfm* men (Nagano and Suzuki, 1976a). These data indicate that in the absence of androgen responsiveness, Sertoli-cell maturation can occur to a considerable extent. The implication is that FSH, or other factors, can permit nearly normal Sertoli-cell development in the absence of androgens. Yet, testes of rats passively immunized with specific anti-LH sera regress to an extent approaching that obtained after hypophysectomy, and Sertoli-cell ultrastructure is altered considerably (Raj and Dym, 1976; Chemes *et al.*, 1976).

Primary cultures of Sertoli cells prepared from testes of immature rats can form and maintain tight junctional complexes characteristic of those described *in vivo*. Addition of FSH or serum is required to permit development and maintenance of these junctional complexes (Lea *et al.*, 1975; Solari and Fritz, 1978). The role of testosterone in the isolated cells has not yet been evaluated.

Combined information is insufficient to allow understanding of the hormonal requirements for Sertoli-cell maturation associated with "blood–testis" barrier formation and subsequent completion of germinal-cell development. It is clear that FSH is required for initiation of these processes, but a definitive role for FSH in spermatogenesis in the adult has not otherwise been defined. It is nevertheless noteworthy that FSH treatment alone is sufficient to allow pulse-labeled preleptotene spermatocytes to progress to pachytene spermatocytes in regressed testes of hypophysectomized rats (Go *et al.*, 1971; Vernon *et al.*, 1975). Perhaps this effect, as well as the decreased degeneration of type A spermatogonia after administration of FSH to immature rats (Means, 1974), is a reflection of the influence of FSH on Sertoli cells, inducing altered interactions of Sertoli cells with germinal cells in their vicinity.

D. Mechanism of Action of FSH on Sertoli Cells

Labeled FSH binds to the plasma membranes of Sertoli cells, activates adenylate cyclase, increases cAMP production, and increases protein kinase activity (Means, 1974, 1975; Means *et al.*, 1976). Subsequently, a host of responses occurs in isolated cells prepared from testes of immature rats. These responses include structural changes, increased conversion of testosterone to 17β-estradiol, and increased rates of protein synthesis, ABP production, and DNA synthesis (for documentation see Section III,C,1 above; Fritz *et al.*, 1975). Thus far, all the effects elicited by FSH on cultured Sertoli cells have been duplicated by addition of cAMP derivatives, or of cholera toxin, to the medium (Fritz *et al.*, 1976b). From these data it appears reasonable to postulate that responses of Sertoli cells to FSH may be mediated via cAMP. This postulate would be consistent with that generally suggested for a variety of polypeptides (ACTH, LH, TSH, glucagon) on their respective target cells, in which the polypeptide first binds to a specific receptor (discrimination); then initiates some sort of conformational change in the receptor complex which activates adenylate cyclase to increase cAMP production (transduction); and cAMP (the second messenger) then activates a specific protein kinase, resulting eventually in a cascade of phosphorylations leading to activation or inhibition of enzymes and a measurable late metabolic or physiological response. This "conventionally" accepted pathway would accurately describe the increase in hepatic conversion of glycogen to glucose after stimulation by epinephrine or glucagon, or the increase in adipocyte conversion of triglyceride to fatty acid after epinephrine or ACTH (for reviews, see Robison *et al.*, 1971; Krebs *et al.*, 1973; Steinberg, 1973). Support for this general scheme has also previously been derived from the stimulation by cholera toxin of a variety of responses characteristic of each cell type following addition of the hormone specific for that cell type. Until recently, it was thought that cholera toxin acted in all these cases exclusively by stimulating adenylate cyclase activity, and that the increased cAMP levels then initiated a cascade of events leading to characteristic responses identical to those elicited by the polypeptide. In this view, cholera toxin simply by-passed the specific physiological receptor, and instead elicited increased formation of the second messenger in responsive cells (for review, see Moss *et al.*, 1976b, 1977).

However, a paradox exists which is difficult to rationalize within the context of cAMP as obligatory intermediary. This consists of the discrepancies in relative concentrations of polypeptide required to achieve stimulation of cAMP production and stimulation of the later metabolic responses. In a variety of systems (TSH and thyroid cells, LH and granulosa or Leydig cells, and ACTH and adrenal cells), higher concentrations of polypeptide are required to increase cAMP levels than to increase the formation of the cell's product. For example, in Leydig-cell preparations, doses of LH which are sufficient for half-maximal stimulation of testosterone production are insufficient to elevate cAMP levels detectably (Catt and Dufau, 1976).

The same sort of phenomenon is evident in responses of Sertoli cells to FSH (Table I) (Fritz *et al.*, 1976b). The FSH concentration for half-maximal stimulation of ABP production is several orders of magnitude lower than that needed for half-maximal stimulation of cAMP, with concentrations required

TABLE I

DOSE–RESPONSE RELATIONS OF BIOCHEMICAL EFFECTS OF FSH AND CHOLERA
TOXIN ON CULTURED SERTOLI CELLS PREPARED FROM TESTES OF 20-DAY-OLD RATS

Response measured	Concentration required for 50% of maximal stimulation of response	
	FSH (NIH S-11) ng/ml	Cholera toxin (pg/ml)
cAMP production	709	44,800
Conversion of testosterone to 17β-estradiol	250	234
DNA synthesis	190	14.8
ABP production	4.02	2.43

for stimulation of estradiol formation and DNA synthesis in between these two extremes. Interestingly, the same hierarchy has been observed with cholera toxin concentration–response curves (Table I). Again, Sertoli cells require greatest concentrations for increased cAMP production and least for ABP synthesis. These data suggest that an increase in cAMP following FSH or cholera toxin could still be an obligatory step in the overall set of responses, but that the increase may be nondetectable because of compartition, or for other reasons not yet experimentally approachable. In this rationalization, it must be assumed that the maximum observable increase in cAMP levels, in response to FSH or to cholera toxin, is not as physiologically important as a slight increase above background in a specific intracellular compartment, and that the cumulative effect of this early but slight rise in cAMP is amplified considerably before the late response becomes manifest.

In spite of this rationalization, the discrepancy still remains (Table I). In addition, it has recently been discovered that cholera toxin may act by mechanisms other than simply increasing adenylate cyclase activity. Moss *et al.* (1976a) and Aloj *et al.* (1977) have presented data suggesting that cholera toxin acts directly on cell membranes, dependent on interaction with a membrane ganglioside-(G_{M1}) to alter permeability properties. New information has recently been discovered concerning the enzymatic activity of the A protomer of cholera toxin which can catalyze the hydrolysis of NAD, or the transfer of the ADP–ribose moiety to arginine (Moss *et al.*, 1976b, 1977). These exceedingly interesting properties of cholera toxin may well provide additional insight into the mechanisms by which polypeptide hormones act, because the toxin can mimic the actions of TSH, LH, ACTH, hCG, and FSH. The hormone specificity for a particular tissue may be a consequence of the specificity of particular gangliosides and proteins on the surface of the target cell in relation to the complementary structure of the unique β subunit of the polypeptide hormone. This interaction could trigger a membrane event, as suggested by Kohn *et al.* (1977) for the case of TSH actions on thyroid cells. The common α subunit (in LH, hCG, FSH, and TSH) would then activate cAMP production, which in turn either modulates the previously elicited membrane event or initiates the cascade of metabolic reactions associated with protein kinase activation. In this scheme, reviewed by Kohn *et al.* (1977), cAMP could duplicate all the actions of the hormone, but it need not be an obligatory intermediate.

Further studies of FSH actions on Sertoli cells should contribute to elucidation and evaluation of the above pathways. Equally important, investigations of these processes should simultaneously lead to increased insight into the molecular mechanisms by which alteration of the properties of the cell membrane following FSH addition can lead to changes in rates of multiple metabolic processes in Sertoli cells. The coordinate nature of these changes during maturation of Sertoli cells has been emphasized above (Section III,C,1).

IV. SPECULATIONS ON MECHANISMS BY WHICH TESTICULAR SOMATIC CELLS MAY INFLUENCE GERMINAL CELL DEVELOPMENT

The most obvious manner in which Sertoli cells could influence germinal cells is by secretion of regulatory substances. A unique tubular fluid exists in the adluminal compartment, consisting of a high-potassium, low-sodium, hyperosmotic environment, and containing concentrations of inositol, aspartate, and glutamate well in excess of those in plasma (for review, see Setchell and Waites, 1975). In addition, the barrier restricts passage of macromolecules in both directions, so that the concentration of γ-globulins in rete testis fluid is only a fraction of that in plasma whereas ABP, which is high in tubular fluid, is nondetectable in plasma by methods usually employed.

The composition of tubular fluid is thought to be controlled by Sertoli cells, which not only constitute the structural barrier by formation of tight junctional complexes with adjacent Sertoli cells (for review, see Fawcett, 1975a), but also secrete at least some of the materials found in tubular fluid. The best-studied example is ABP (see Section III,C,1,c and III,C,2,b). A protein with inhibin-like properties has recently been found in the medium of Sertoli-cell cultures (Steinberger and Steinberger, 1976b). We have shown that *myo*-inositol is synthesized from glucose by isolated Sertoli cells in culture, and is secreted into the medium (R. Robinson and I. B. Fritz, unpublished observations). Similarly, plasminogen activator is secreted into the medium by isolated Sertoli cells in culture, and FSH increases this activity (Lacroix *et al.*, 1977). From these examples, it seems justified to assume that other components of tubular fluid may be shown to originate from Sertoli cells.

The role of any of the components in tubular fluid in the development and differentiation of germinal cells has yet to be discovered. In organ or cell cultures, germinal cells do not progress beyond the formation of pachytene spermatocytes (Steinberger *et al.*, 1970). It is probable that the failure of germ cells to complete meiosis and to undergo spermiogenesis in culture is a consequence of many factors: inadequate chemical composition of culture medium, a tendency for the loss of intercellular bridges between cohorts of germinal cells, and improper conditions for sustained function of Sertoli cells. Yet, it is remarkable that the seminiferous epithelial cells from tubules which have been maintained in organ culture for weeks, and then transplanted to testis of a suitable host, have been shown to be capable of completing spermatogenesis *in vivo* (Steinberger *et al.*, 1970). This experiment demonstrates that nothing required for development of the germinal cells has been lost from the seminiferous tubule during culture, but that the culture medium thus far employed provides an inappropriate environment for permitting germinal-cell development. A recent report, however, suggests successful completion of meiosis of human spermatocytes, provided coconut milk is added to the medium (Ghatnekar *et al.*, 1974). Until conditions are defined which will permit completion of meiosis *in vitro*, it will remain difficult, if not impossible, to determine how the unique composition of components in primary tubular fluid in the adluminal compartment influences specific stages of germinal-cell development in vertebrates. It is apparent that *in vitro* conditions have not thus far been found which adequately simulate *in vivo* conditions.

It is of interest that during the first wave of spermatogenesis in immature rats, pachytene spermatocytes are present prior to the formation of an intact "blood–testis" barrier (Vitale *et al.*, 1973). This conclusion is evident from the penetration of a marker (horseradish peroxidase) to areas around pachytene spermatocytes in testes of 15-day-old rats. Horseradish peroxidase did not penetrate to the adluminal compartment in testes of 18-day-old or older rats (Vitale *et al.*, 1973). These data are consistent with the ability of organ cultures of testes from immature rats to permit the formation of pachytene spermatocytes (Steinberger *et al.*, 1970), suggesting that in the first wave, the composition of tubular fluid surrounding the germinal cells is not crucial for the initiation of meiosis up to the pachytene stage.

Presumably, the spermagonia and stem cells in the basal compartment are bathed in a fluid having the same composition as that of lymph and interstitial tissue fluid. This assumes that cells in the boundary tissue, including the peritubular myoid cells, permit diffusion but do not add components to the intercellular space of the basal compartment. No measurements have thus far been possible to test these assumptions. In some manner yet to be determined, maturing spermatocytes move into the adluminal compartment and thereby enter a different chemical environment. As Fawcett (1975b) has stated, "the Sertoli cells that form the walls of the adluminal compartment are strategically situated to create, by their metabolic and secretory activities, a special environment that may favor germ cell differentiation." However, mechanisms involved in facilitating the meiotic and postmeiotic stages of development in the adluminal compartment remain totally obscure.

The biochemistry of meiosis in male gametogenesis has thus far been most intensively investigated in liliaceous plants (Stern and Hotta, 1968, 1969,

1970, 1973, 1977). Although it is obviously dangerous to try to extrapolate from information gained on *Trillium* to possible mechanisms involved in the seminiferous tubule of mammals, it is nevertheless of importance to be aware of possible similarities. An intact, isolated anther, consisting of germinal cells and somatic cells, can be cultured in a defined medium, permitting the completion of meiosis and the division of microspores in organ culture *in vitro*. If, however, isolated microsporocytes teased from the anther are cultured *in vitro*, the formation of microspores and germinating pollen does not take place. It appears that somatic cells, or their products, are required in *Trillium* for postmeiotic events, and possibly for commitment of germinal cells to meiosis. The level of description of the biochemical events in meiosis in *Trillium* is considerably more advanced than that available in mammals. Nevertheless, the complexity of the process unfortunately remains resistant to biochemical understanding of the underlying mechanisms of regulation. It is optimistic to hope that understanding of the mechanisms of chromosomal pairing and genetic recombination in mammals will soon reach that already achieved in *Trillium*. It is therefore not encouraging to realize that even in *Trillium*, the questions about meiosis exceed the answers by orders of magnitude, and the nature of the interactions between germ cells and somatic cells remains obscure.

If this rather pessimistic view is correct, we are likely to remain ignorant, for many years, concerning the biochemistry of meiosis and postmeiotic events. However, we still can gain some solace from increasing opportunities to obtain information about triggers which control the commitment to meiosis, and the nature of cell–cell interactions in the gonads. For example, consider the recent observations on factors present in fetal ovarian cells which can induce germinal cells from fetal testes to initiate meiosis (Byskov and Saxén, 1976). In addition, an exciting set of developments has recently indicated that the HY antigen on the surface of germinal cells of the male bovine fetus appears to be responsible for inducing masculinization of the gonad of the female freemartin twin (Ohno, 1976). The nature of the HY antigen and its possible role in directing organogenesis have recently been well reviewed (Ohno, 1977; Wachtel, 1977; Silvers and Wachtel, 1977). It appears highly relevant to an understanding of cell–cell interactions between somatic and germinal cells. The HY antigen can conceivably function as a specific humoral mediator, or by direct cell–cell contact. The possibility of direct cell–cell mediated interactions during differentiation is only beginning to be explored. Thus far, demonstration of the existence of specific antigenic determinants on spermatocytes (O'Rand and Romrell, 1976; Millette and Bellvé, 1977; Tung and Fritz, 1978) and on mature Sertoli cells (Tung and Fritz, 1977) at least leaves open the possibility that unique recognition sites exist on the surfaces of cells of the testis. These recognition sites could conceivably facilitate interactions between Sertoli cells and germinal cells during different stages of the cycle of the seminiferous epithelium. In rats, this seems to be of special importance in stages VII–VIII of the cycle, when maturing spermatocytes are entering the adluminal compartment, and mature spermatids are being released into the lumen. Integration of Sertoli-cell functions during this and other critical stages of development is obviously crucial to permit coordination of events essential for germinal-cell development during spermatogenesis. From information reviewed I conclude that the hormonal control of testicular somatic-cell functions probably acts at these levels, and thereby regulates spermatogenesis.

ADDENDUM

Since this review was submitted, advances in various aspects of testicular function discussed have been considered at three major symposia. To the reader interested in updating information on spermatogenesis, a summary of the *4th Testis Workshop,* held at Toronto in May, 1977, is available (Fritz, I. B., and Dorrington, J. H., *Mol. Cell Endocrinol.,* **9:**121, 1977). Papers presented on "somatic cell-germinal cell relations" at "Round Table Discussions" at the XXVIIth International Congress of Physiological Sciences, held in Paris in July, 1977, are scheduled for publication in a forthcoming issue of "Annales de Biologie Animale, Biochimie, Biophysique" (C. Thibault, ed.). In addition, the proceedings of a symposium on the testis, sponsored by the Society for the Study of Reproduction, and held in Austin, Texas in August, 1977, are scheduled for publication in a forthcoming issue of "Biology of Reproduction."

ACKNOWLEDGMENTS

Work reviewed which emanated from this laboratory was supported by grants from the Canadian Medical Research Council and the Banting Foundation. It is a pleasure to express my gratitude and indebtedness to my colleague, Jennifer Dorrington, for stimulating discussion and for a critical reading of the review. The excellent secretarial assistance of Ms. Erene Stanley in typing this manuscript is thankfully acknowledged, as is the very useful library assistance by Ms. Linda Gee.

REFERENCES

Aloj, S. M., Kohn, L. D., Lee, G., and Meldolesi, M. F. (1977). *Biochem. Biophys. Res. Commun.* **74**, 1053.
Armstrong, D. T., Moon, Y. S., Fritz, I. B., and Dorrington, J. H. (1975). *Curr. Top. Mol. Endocrinol.* **2**, 85.

Bardin, C., Bullock, L. P., Sherins, R. J., Mowszowicz, I., and Blackburn, W. R. (1973). *Recent Prog. Horm. Res.* **29**, 105.

Bartke, A., and Voglmayr, J. K. (1977). *Biol. Reprod.* **16**, 274.

Blanchard, M., and Josso, N. (1974). *Pediatr. Res.* **8**, 968.

Bressler, R. S. (1976). *Am. J. Anat.* **147**, 447.

Bressler, R. S., and Ross, M. H. (1972). *Biol. Reprod.* **6**, 148.

Brinkmann, A. O., Mulder, E., Lamers-Stahlhofen, G. J. M., Mechielsen, M. J., and van der Molen, H. J. (1972). *FEBS Lett.* **26**, 301.

Byskov, A. G., and Saxén, L. (1976). *Dev. Biol.* **52**, 193.

Castro, R. E., Seigver, A. C., and Mancini, R. E. (1970). *Proc. Soc. Exp. Biol. Med.* **133**, 582.

Catt, K. H., and Dufau, M. L. (1976). *Biol. Reprod.* **14**, 1.

Chemes, H., Dym, M., and Raj, H. G. M. (1976). *Program Soc. Study Reprod., 9th Annu. Meet.* p. 23.

Chen, Y. D. I., Payne, A. H., and Kelch, R. P. (1976). *Proc. Soc. Exp. Biol. Med.* **153**, 473.

Chen, Y. D. I., Shaw, M., and Payne, A. H. (1977). *Mol. Cell. Endocrinol.* **8**, 291.

Chung, K. W. (1974). *Fertil. Steril.* **25**, 325.

Clermont, Y. (1958). *Exp. Cell Res.* **15**, 438.

Clermont, Y., and Harvey, S. C. (1967). *Ciba Found. Colloq. Endocrinol.* [*Proc.*] **16**, 173.

Connell, C. J. (1976). *J. Cell Biol.* **70**, 80a, (Abstr. 238).

Donahoe, P. K., Ito, Y., Price, J. M., and Hendren, W. H., III. (1977). *Biol. Reprod.* **16**, 238.

Dorrington, J. H., and Armstrong, D. T. (1975). *Proc. Natl. Acad. Sci. U.S.A.* **72**, 2677.

Dorrington, J. H., and Fritz, I. B. (1974a). *Endocrinology* **94**, 395.

Dorrington, J. H., and Fritz, I. B. (1974b). *In* "Gonadotropins and Gonadal Function" (N. R. Moudgal, ed.), p. 500. Academic Press, New York.

Dorrington, J. H., Vernon, R. G., and Fritz, I. B. (1972). *Biochem. Biophys. Res. Commun.* **46**, 1523.

Dorrington, J. H., Roller, N. F., and Fritz, I. B. (1974). *Curr. Top. Mol. Endocrinol.* **1**, 237.

Dorrington, J. H., Roller, N. F., and Fritz, I. B. (1975). *Mol. Cell. Endocrinol.* **3**, 57.

Dorrington, J. H., Fritz, I. B., and Armstrong, D. T. (1976a). *Program Int. Congr. Endocrinol., 5th, 1976* Abstract No. 768, p. 316.

Dorrington, J. H., Fritz, I. B., and Armstrong, D. T. (1976b). *Mol. Cell. Endocrinol.* **6**, 117.

Dym, M., and Fawcett, D. W. (1970). *Biol. Reprod.* **3**, 308.

Elftman, H. (1963). *Am. J. Anat.* **113**, 25.

Elkington, J. S. H., Sanborn, B. M., and Steinberger, E. (1975). *Mol. Cell. Endocrinol.* **2**, 157.

Fakunding, J. L., Tindall, D. J., Dedman, J. R., Mena, C. R., and Means, A. R. (1976). *Endocrinology* **98**, 392.

Fawcett, D. W. (1961). *Exp. Cell. Res., Suppl.* **8**, 174.

Fawcett, D. W. (1973). *Adv. Biosci.* **10**, 83.

Fawcett, D. W. (1974). *In* "Male Fertility and Sterility" (R. E. Mancini and L. Martinin, eds.), p. 13. Academic Press, New York.

Fawcett, D. W. (1975a). *Handb. Physiol. Sect. 7: Endocrinol.* **5**, 21.

Fawcett, D. W. (1975b). *In* "The Developmental Biology of Reproduction" (C. L. Markert and J. Papaconstantinou, eds.), p. 25. Academic Press, New York.

Fawcett, D. W. (1976). *In* "Reproduction and Human Welfare" (R. O. Greep, M. A. Koblinsky, and F. S. Jaffee, eds.), p. 165. MIT Press, Cambridge, Massachusetts.

Fawcett, D. W., Leak, L. V., and Heidger, P. M., Jr. (1970). *J. Reprod. Fertil., Suppl.* **10**, 105.

Flickinger, C. J. (1967). *Z. Zellforsch. Mikrosk. Anat.* **78**, 92.

Flickinger, C. J., and Fawcett, D. W. (1967). *Anat. Rec.* **158**, 207.

Frederik, P. M., Klepper, D., van der Vusse, G. J., and van der Molen, H. J. (1976). *Mol. Cell. Endocrinol.* **5**, 123.

Frederik, P. M., van der Molen, H. J., Klepper, D., and Galjaard, H. (1977). *J. Cell Sci.* (in press).

French, F. S., McLean, W. S., Smith, A. A., Tindall, D. J., Weddington, S. C., Petrusz, P. Sar, M., Stumpf, W. E., Nayfeh, S. N., Hansson, V., Trygstad, O., and Ritzén, E. M. (1974). *Curr. Top. Mol. Endocrinol.* 1, 265.

Fritz, I. B. (1973). *Curr. Top. Cell. Regul.* 7, 129.

Fritz, I. B., Vernon, R. G., Dorrington, J., and Go, V. L. W. (1971). *Program Am. Cell Biol.* Abstract No. 181, p. 95.

Fritz, I. B., Kopec, B., Lam, K., and Vernon, R. G. (1974). *Curr. Top. Mol. Endocrinol.* 1, 311.

Fritz, I. B., Louis, B. G., Tung, P. S., Griswold, M., Rommerts, F. G., and Dorrington, J. H. (1975). In "Hormonal Regulation of Spermatogenesis" (F. S. French *et al.*, eds.), p. 367. Plenum, New York.

Fritz, I. B., Griswold, M. D., Louis, B. G., and Dorrington, J. H. (1976a). *Mol. Cell. Endocrinol.* 5, 289.

Fritz, I. B., Griswold, M. D., Louis, B. G., and Dorrington, J. H. (1976b). *J. Cell Biol.* 70, No. 2, Part 2, 21a (Abstr. 63).

Fritz, I. B., Rommerts, F. G., Louis, B. G., and Dorrington, J. H. (1976c). *J. Reprod. Fertil.* 46, 17.

Ghatnekar, R., Lima-de-Faria, A., Rubin, S., and Menander, K. (1974). *Hereditas* 78, 265.

Gilula, N. B., Fawcett, D. W., and Aoiki, A. (1976). *Dev. Biol.* 50, 142.

Go, V. L. W., Vernon, R. G., and Fritz, I. B. (1971). *Can. J. Biochem.* 49, 768.

Griswold, M. D., Mably, E., and Fritz, I. B. (1975). *Curr. Top. Mol. Endocrinol.* 2, 413.

Griswold, M. D., Mably, E. R., and Fritz, I. B. (1976). *Mol. Cell. Endocrinol.* 4, 139.

Griswold, M. D., Solari, A., Tung, P. S., and Fritz, I. B. (1977). *Mol. Cell. Endocrinol.* 7, 151.

Hansson, V., Reusch, E., Trygstad, O., Torgersen, O., Ritzén, E. M., and French, F. S. (1973). *Nature (London), New Biol.* 246, 56.

Hansson, V., Trygstad, O., French, F. S., McLean, W. S., Smith, A. A., Tindall, D. J., Weddington, S. C., Petrusz, P., Nayfeh, S. N., and Ritzén, E. M. (1974). *Nature (London)* 250, 387.

Hansson, V., Ritzén, E. M., French, F. S., and Nayfeh, S. N. (1975a). *Handb. Physiol. Sect. 7: Endocrinol.* 5, 173.

Hansson, V., Weddington, S. C., McLean, W. S., Smith, A. A., Nayfeh, S. N., French, F. S., and Ritzén, E. M. (1975b). *J. Reprod. Fertil.* 44, 363.

Hansson, V., Calandra, R., Purvis, K., Ritzén, M., and French, F. S. (1976). *Vitam. Horm.* (N.Y.) 34, 187.

Harris, M. E., and Bartke, A. (1974). *Endocrinology* 95, 701.

Heindel, J. J., Rothenberg, R., Robison, G. A., and Steinberger, A. (1975). *J. Cyclic Nucleotide Res.* 1, 69.

Henderson, S. A. (1964). *Chromosoma* 15, 345.

Hovatta, O. (1972). *Z. Zellforsch. Mikrosk. Anat.* 131, 299.

Josso, N. (1973). *Endocrinology* 93, 829.

Kierszenbaum, A. L., and Tres, L. L. (1975). *J. Cell Biol.* 65, 258.

Kodani, M., and Kodani, K. (1966). *Proc. Natl. Acad. Sci. U.S.A.* 56, 1200.

Kohn, L. D., Aloj, S. M., Friedman, R. M., Grollman, E. G., Ledley, F. D., Lee, G., Meldolesi, M. F., and Mullin, B. R. (1977). In "Cell Surface Carbohydrate Chemistry" (R. E. Harmon, ed.). Academic Press, New York (in press).

Kormano, M. (1967). *Z. Anat. Entwicklungsgesch.* 126, 138.

Krebs, E. G., Stull, J. T., England, P. J., Huang, T. S., Brostrom, C. O., and Vandenheede, J. R. (1973). In "Protein Phosphorylation in Control Mechanisms" (F. Huijing and E. Y. C. Lee, eds.), p. 31. Academic Press, New York.

Lacroix, M., Smith, F., and Fritz, I. B. (1977). *Mol. Cell. Endocrinol.* **9**, 227.

Lea, P., Burdzy, K., and Fritz, I. B. (1975). *Proc. Micros. Soc. Canada* **3**, 100.

Leeson, C. R., and Leeson, T. S. (1963). *Anat. Rec.* **147**, 243.

Louis, B. G., and Fritz, I. B. (1977). *Mol. Cell. Endocrinol.* **7**, 9.

Lyon, M. F. (1973). *In* "Physiology and Genetics of Reproduction" (E. M. Coutinho and F. Fuchs, eds.), Part A, p. 63. Plenum, New York.

Lyon, M. F., and Hawkes, S. G. (1970). *Nature (London)* **227**, 1217.

Lyon, N. F., Glenister, P. H., and Lamoreux, M. L. (1975). *Nature (London)* **258**, 620.

Mancini, R. E., Vilar, O., Perez del Cerro, M., and Lavieri, J. C. (1964). *Acta Physiol. Lat. Am.* **14**, 382.

Means, A. R. (1974). *In* "Male Fertility and Sterility" (R. E. Mancini and L. Martini, eds.), p. 405. Academic Press, New York.

Means, A. R. (1975). *Handb. Physiol. Sect. 7: Endocrinol.* **5**, 203.

Means, A. R., and Hall, P. F. (1968). *Endocrinology* **82**, 597.

Means, A. R., and Huckins, C. (1974). *Curr. Top. Mol. Endocrinol.* **1**, 145.

Means, A. R., and Vaitukaitis, J. (1972). *Endocrinology* **90**, 39.

Means, A. R., Fakunding, J. L., Huckins, C., Tindall, D. J., and Vitale, R. (1976). *Recent Prog. Horm. Res.* **32**, 477.

Millette, C. F., and Bellvé, A. R. (1977). *J. Cell Biol.* **74**, 86.

Monesi, V. (1965). *Exp. Cell Res.* **39**, 197.

Monesi, V. (1971). *J. Reprod. Fertil., Suppl.* **13**, 1.

Monesi, V. (1974). *In* "Male Fertility and Sterility" (R. E. Mancini and L. Martini, eds.), p. 59. Academic Press, New York.

Moss, J., Fishman, P. H., Richards, R. L., Alving, C. R., Vaughan, M., and Brady, R. O. (1976a). *Proc. Natl. Acad. Sci. U.S.A.* **73**, 3480.

Moss, J., Manganiello, V. C., and Vaughan, M. (1976b). *Proc. Natl. Acad. Sci. U.S.A.* **73**, 4424.

Moss, J., Osborne, J. C., Jr., Fishman, P. H., Brewer, H. B., Jr., Vaughan, M., and Brady, R. O. (1977). *Proc. Natl. Acad. Sci. U.S.A.* **74**, 74.

Mulder, E., Brinkmann, A. O., Lamers-Stahlhofen, G. J. M., and van der Molen, H. J. (1973). *FEBS Lett.* **31**, 131.

Mulder, E., Van Beurden-Lamers, W. M. O., de Boer, W., Brinkman, A. O., and van der Molen, H. J. (1974). *Curr. Top. Mol. Endocrinol.* **1**, 343.

Mulder, E., Peters, M. J., de Vries, J., and van der Molen, H. J. (1975). *Mol. Cell. Endocrinol.* **2**, 171.

Mulder, E., Peters, M. J., Van Beurden, W. M. O., Goldieri, M., Rommerts, F. F. G., Janszen, F. H. A., and van der Molen, H. J. (1976). *J. Endocrinol.* **70**, 331.

Murphy, H. D. (1965). *Proc. Soc. Exp. Biol. Med.* **118**, 1202.

Nagano, T., and Suzuki, F. (1976a). *Cell Tissue Res.* **166**, 37.

Nagano, T., and Suzuki, F. (1976b). *Anat. Rec.* **185**, 403–412.

Nicander, L. (1967). *Z. Zellforsch. Mikrosk. Anat.* **83**, 375.

Odell, W. D., Swerdloff, R. S., Jacobs, H. S., and Hescox, M. A. (1973). *Endocrinology* **92**, 160.

Odell, W. D., Swerdloff, R. S., Bain, J., Wollesen, F., and Grover, P. K. (1974). *Endocrinology* **95**, 1380.

Ohno, S. (1969). *Annu. Rev. Genet.* **3**, 495.

Ohno, S. (1971). *Nature (London)* **234**, 134.

Ohno, S. (1976). *Cell* **7**, 315.

Ohno, S. (1977). *In* "The Testis in Normal and Infertile Men" (P. Troen and H. R. Nankin, eds.), p. 1. Raven, New York.

Ohno, S., Jainchill, J., and Stenius, C. (1963). *Cytogenetics* **2**, 232.

O'Rand, M. G. and Romrell, L. J. (1977) *Dev. Biol.* **55**, 347.

Purvis, K., Calandra, R., Naess, O., Attramadal, A., Torjesen, P. A., and Hansson, V. (1977) *Nature (London)* **265**, 169.

Raj, H. G. M., and Dym, M. (1976). *Biol. Reprod.* **14**, 489.

Reddy, P. R. K., and Villee, C. A. (1975). *Biochem. Biophys. Res. Commun.* **63**, 1063.

Ritzén, E. M., Dobbins, M. C., French, F. S., and Nayfeh, S. N. (1973). *Endocrinol., Proc. Int. Congr. 4th, 1972* Excerpta Med. Int. Congr. Ser. No. 256, Abstr. 199, p. 79.

Ritzén, E. M., Hagenas, L., French, F. S., and Hansson, V. (1975). *Curr. Top. Mol. Endocrinol.* **2**, 353.

Robison, G. A., Butcher, R. W., and Sutherland, E. W. (1971). "Cyclic AMP." Academic Press, New York.

Ross, M. H. (1967). *Am. J. Anat.* **121**, 523.

Ross, M. H. (1970). *In* "Morphological Aspects of Andrology" (A. F. Holstein and E. Florstmann, eds.), p. 83. Grosse Verlag, Berlin.

Ross, M. H. (1976). *Anat. Rec.* **186**, 79.

Sanborn, B. M., Elkington, J. S. H., and Steinberger, E. (1974). *Curr. Top. Mol. Endocrinol.* **1**, 291.

Sanborn, B. M., Steinberger, A., Meistrich, M. L., and Steinberger, E. (1975). *J. Steroid Biochem.* **6**, 1459.

Sapsford, C. S., and Rae, C. A. (1968). *J. Anat.* **103**, 214.

Sar, M., Stumpf, W. E., McLean, W. S., Smith, A. A., Hansson, V., Nayfeh, S. N., and French, F. S. (1975). *Curr. Top. Mol. Endocrinol.* **2**, 311.

Setchell, B. P. (1970). *In* "The Testis" (A. D. Johnson, W. R. Gomes, and N. L. Van Demark, eds.), Vol. 1, p. 101. Academic Press, New York.

Setchell, B. P., and Waites, G. M. H. (1975). *Handb. Physiol., Sect. 7: Endocrinol.* **5**, 143.

Silvers, W. K., and Wachtel, S. S. (1977). *Science* **195**, 956.

Smith, P. E. (1930). *Am. J. Anat.* **45**, 205.

Smith, P. E., and Engle, E. T. (1927). *Am. J. Anat.* **40**, 159.

Söderström, K. O., and Parvinen, M. (1976). *Mol. Cell. Endocrinol.* **5**, 181.

Solari, A., and Fritz, I. B. (1978). *Biol. Reprod.* (in press).

Steinberg, D. (1973). *In* "Protein Phosphorylation in Control Mechanisms" (F. Huijing and E. Y. C. Lee, eds.), p. 47. Academic Press, New York.

Steinberger, A., and Steinberger, E. (1976a). *Prog. Reprod. Biol.* **1**, 42.

Steinberger, A., and Steinberger, E. (1976b). *Endocrinology* **99**, 918.

Steinberger, A., Elkington, J. S. H., Sanborn, B. M., Steinberger, E., Heindel, J. J., and Lindsey, J. N. (1975). *Curr. Top. Mol. Endocrinol.* **2**, 399.

Steinberger, A., Thanki, K. J., and Siegal, B. (1974). *Curr. Top. Mol. Endocrinol.* **1**, 177.

Steinberger, E. (1971). *Physiol. Rev.* **51**, 1.

Steinberger, E. (1975). *Curr. Top. Mol. Endocrinol.* **2**, 337.

Steinberger, E., Steinberger, A., and Ficher, M. (1970). *Recent Prog. Horm. Res.* **26**, 547.

Stern, H., and Hotta, Y. (1968). *Curr. Top. Dev. Biol.* **3**, 37.

Stern, H. and Hotta, Y. (1969). *In* "Handbook of Molecular Cytology" (A. Lima-de-Faria, ed.), p. 520. North-Holland Publ., Amsterdam.

Stern, H., and Hotta, Y. (1970). *Methods Cell Physiol.* **4**, 497.

Stern, H., and Hotta, Y. (1973). *Annu. Rev. Genet.* **7**, 37.

Stern, H., and Hotta, Y. (1977). *Proc. R. Soc. London, B Ser.* **277**, 277.

Tarkowski, A. K. (1970). *Philos. Trans. R. Soc. London, B Ser.* **259**, 107.

Tindall, D. J., Schrader, W. T., and Means, A. R. (1974). *Curr. Top. Mol. Endocrinol.* **1**, 167.

Tung, P. S., and Fritz, I. B. (1975). *In* "Hormonal Regulation of Spermatogenesis" (F. S. French *et al.*, eds.), p. 495. Plenum, New York.

Tung, P. S., and Fritz, I. B. (1977). *J. Cell Biol.* **75**, No. 2, Part 2, 165a (Abstr. G162).

Tung, P. S. and Fritz, I. B. (1978). *Dev. Biol.* (in press).

Tung, P. S., Dorrington, J. H., and Fritz, I. B. (1975). *Proc. Natl. Acad. Sci. U.S.A.* **72**, 1838.

Tung, P. S., Lin, E. Y. C., and Fritz, I. B. (1976). *Scanning Electron Microsc.* **6**, 417.

Utakoji, T. (1967). *Exp. Cell Res.* **42**, 585.

Van Beurden, W. M. O., Roodnat, B., de Jong, F. H., Mulder, E., and van der Molen, H. J. (1976). *Steroids* **28**, 847.

Van Beurden, W. M. O., Mulder, E., de Jong, F. H., and van der Molen, H. J. (1977). *Endocrinology* **101**, 342.

Vernon, R. G., Dorrington, J. H., and Fritz, I. B. (1973a). *Endocrinol., Proc. Int. Congr. 4th, 1972* Excerpta Med. Found. Int. Congr. Ser. No. 256, Abstr. No. 200, p. 79.

Vernon, R. G., Kopec. B., and Fritz, I. B. (1973b). *J. Endocrinol.* **57**, ii, proc.

Vernon, R. G., Kopec, B., and Fritz, I. B. (1974). *Mol. Cell. Endocrinol.* **1**, 167.

Vernon, R. G., Go, V. L. W., and Fritz, I. B. (1975). *J. Reprod. Fertil.* **42**, 77.

Vilar, O., Perez del Cerro, M. I., and Mancini, R. E. (1962). *Exp. Cell Res.* **27**, 158.

Vitale, R., Fawcett, D. W., and Dym, M. (1973). *Anat. Rec.* **176**, 333.

von Ebner, V. (1888). *Arch. Mikrosk. Anat.* **31**, 236.

Wachtel, S. S. (1977). *Immunol. Rev.* **33**, 33.

Weddington, S. C., Hansson, V., Ritzén, E. M., Hagenas, L., French, F. S., and Nayfeh, S. N. (1975). *Nature (London)* **254**, 145.

Welsh, M. J., and Wiebe, J. P. (1975). *Endocrinology* **96**, 618.

CHAPTER 7

Biochemical Properties of the Intestinal Receptor System for the Steroid Hormone 1,25-Dihydroxyvitamin D

Anthony W. Norman

I. INTRODUCTION

Vitamin D, along with the peptide hormones calcitonin (CT) and parathyroid hormone (PTH), are the three most important regulators of calcium and phosphorus metabolism. Together these substances work to

ISBN 452805-8

effect an efficient homeostasis of these important minerals. The major pathways of calcium and phosphorus metabolism are intake and absorption by the intestinal mucosal tissue; transport systemically within the body to various sites, particularly the bone, where it is deposited and/or resorbed; and excretion in the urine and feces. The concentration of calcium in the blood is maintained at a remarkably constant 2.5 mM, considering the fluxes that occur among these various bodily compartments. It is also important to recognize that the constant plasma level of calcium is maintained in spite of wide fluctuations in the dietary availability of calcium. Thus a challenging problem to the organism is to adapt its intestinal absorption mechanism for calcium to reflect both the needs dictated by his physiological system and the availability of calcium in his diet.

It has long been known that both animals and man have a capacity to alter their efficiency of intestinal calcium absorption (Nicolaysen, 1943; Malm, 1953; Adams and Norman, 1970). The primary homeostatic regulator involved in mediation of calcium resorption is vitamin D (Norman, 1968; Omdahl and DeLuca, 1973; Norman and Henry, 1974a,b). The last decade has seen a major increase in our understanding of the biochemical mechanism of vitamin D, particularly with regard to its actions on stimulating intestinal calcium absorption. While ten years ago little was known about either the absorption, tissue localization, or proposed mode of action of this nutritionally important steroid, there has emerged in the intervening period of time a new model for the mechanism of action of vitamin D. The model is based on the concept that in terms of its structure and mode of action vitamin D is similar to the classical steroid hormones, e.g., estradiol, testosterone, hydrocortisone, aldosterone, or ecdysone. It now seems virtually certain that there is in reality an endocrine system for processing parent vitamin D into its hormonally active form 1,25-dihydroxyvitamin D [1,25(OH)$_2$D$_3$]. This substance then carries out its biological functions in a manner similar to that proposed for other steroid hormones. The purpose of this review article is to present recent data describing the intestinal receptor system for the steroid 1,25-dihydroxyvitamin D in the intestinal mucosa.

A. VITAMIN D AS A STEROID

Shown in Fig. 1 is a summary of the development of our understanding of the chemical structure of vitamin D. Structure 1 in Fig. 1 depicts the initial formulation of the steroidal nature of vitamin D as put forth by Askew and Windaus in the early 1930's (Askew *et al.*, 1932; Windaus *et al.*, 1932). It is apparent when the structure of vitamin D is drawn in this manner that there are many similarities to other classical steroid hormones; the only significant

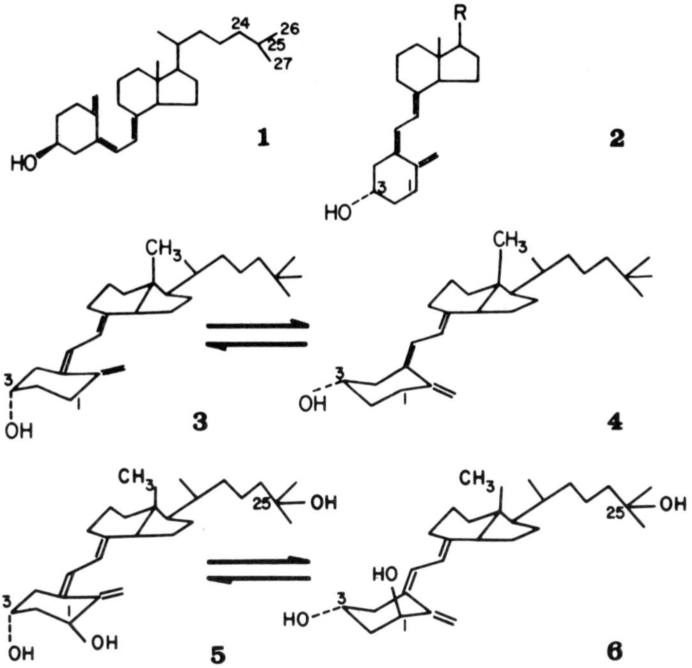

FIG. 1. Evolution of the conformational representations of vitamin D. Representation **1** resulted from the original chemical structural determination carried out in the 1930's. The first X-ray crystallographic analysis indicated the presence of a single A-ring chair conformation as in **3**, but this was normally simplified to that shown in **2**. Our recent reports (Wing *et al.*, 1974; Okamura *et al.*, 1974) emphasize that in solution there is a rapid equilibration between the two A-ring chair conformations as shown in **3** and **4** for vitamin D. In structures **3** and **4**, the 3-hydroxyl in both instances is geometrical. Structures **5** and **6** are a similar pair of rapidly equilibrating conformers of 1,25(OH)D$_3$.

difference, really, is the absence of the 9,10 carbon–carbon bond. This bond is broken or cleaved by the photochemical reaction which converts the provitamin either 7-dehydrocholesterol or ergosterol into vitamin D$_3$ or D$_2$, respectively. Vitamin D is then of necessity described as being a secosteroid. The prefix "seco" indicates that one of the rings has undergone fission by breakage of a carbon–carbon bond. In the case of vitamin D this is ring B, as indicated by the inclusion of "9,10 seco" in the official nomenclature. Cholecalciferol is technically termed 9,10-secocholesta-5,7,10(19)-trien-3β-ol.

Thus, while it should be apparent that vitamin D is structurally a legitimate steroid, it is also only fair to appreciate that its seco nature makes it a structurally unique steroid. Unlike the classical steroid hormones, which possess a fused array of A, B, C, and D rings, the secosteroid vitamin D and its metabolite $1,25(OH)_2 D_3$, lack the intact B ring. This novel structural characteristic of the calciferols imparts conformational mobility to the A and seco-B rings. Whereas all four of the rings of other steroid hormones are held relatively rigidly together, only the C and D rings of the calciferols are as conformationally restricted. This point was first evident but not well appreciated in the reports of Crowfoot and Dunitz (1948) and Hodgkin *et al.* (1963). These results established that the diene system extending from carbon 5 to carbon 8 is coplanar and transoid as opposed to the cisoid configuration given in the representation in Structure 2 of Fig. 1. The primary characteristic of Structure 2 is the emphasis on the "opened-up" B ring and the concomitant extension of the molecule in the A-ring region. While such a representation tends to some extent to deemphasize the structural similarity between vitamin D and other steroids, this is only a superficial effect and cannot really dictate changes in the biological mode of action for this substance. The X-ray crystallographic data of Crowfoot–Hodgkin also indicated that the A ring existed in a single chair conformation. This feature, however, is rarely incorporated into the planar structure, either in that given as Structure 1 or 2. More recently Knobler *et al.* (1972) reported X-ray crystallographic determination of another vitamin D analog that indicated the presence of an opposite chair conformation to that reported by the Crowfoot–Hodgkin group. This difference resulted from the fact that the A ring could be frozen via crystallization in either of the two possible chair conformations. The existence of these two different A-ring conformations is a direct consequence of the open-ring structure of vitamin D.

More recently, dramatic advances have been made in our understanding of the shape of vitamin D secosteroids. It is now apparent from the work carried out in our laboratory (Wing *et al.*, 1974, 1975) as well as that of Lamar and Budd (1974) that in solution, vitamin D secosteroids have a high degree of conformational mobility. The consequences of this mobility are shown in Structures 3 and 4 of Fig. 1 for vitamin D and Structures 5 and 6 of Fig. 1 for 1,25-dihydroxyvitamin D. *These secosteroids exist in solution as a pair of dynamically equilibrating chair–chair conformers.* Through the use of high-resolution pmr spectroscopy it was possible to demonstrate the rapid (many times per second) interconversion of these two A-ring chair–chair conformers. It has long been known that cyclohexane (the A ring of vitamin D is an analog of cyclohexane) itself exists in solution as a pair of rapidly equilibrating chair conformers. Thus it is not completely unexpected that the conformationally mobile A ring of vitamin D should be capable of exhibiting physical properties similar to cyclohexane. It is quite apparent that the molecular shape or conformation of vitamin D and all its metabolites has certain unique properties not shared by other classical steroid hormones.

One of the important consequences of the rapid chair–chair conformational inversion equilibrium is that for each conformational inversion every equatorially oriented functional group becomes axial and every axial position becomes equatorial. The actual equilibrium constant between the two chair forms depends upon the nature and location of the substituent groups on the A ring (Eliel *et al.*, 1965). For example, as shown in Structures 3 and 4 of Fig. 1, the three β-hydroxyl group can be either equatorial or axial. In fact, experimental analysis of the conformational ratio of the two forms present in solution indicates an equatorial-to-axial ratio (e/a ratio) of 55/45 (Wing *et al.*, 1974, 1975). The same considerations pertain to the pair of $1,25(OH)_2D_3$ molecules shown as Structures 5 and 6 in Fig. 1. At any given instant 45% of these molecules will have their 1α-hydroxyl oriented in the axial direction, while the other 55% of the molecules will have their 1α-hydroxyl oriented equatorially. Distribution or partition is governed by dynamic equilibrium between the two chair forms, so the A ring of any one molecule may flip from one chair conformation to the other some 10^6 times per second.

The essential conclusions of our evaluation of the conformation of vitamin D secosteroids in solution are as follows: (a) The A ring of vitamin D secosteroids exists in solution as a pair of rapidly equilibrating chair conformers; (b) the A-ring conformations are essentially independent of the nature of the side chain; and (c) the type and location of substituents on the A ring perturb the equilibrium ratio of the two conformers.

Thus a challenging problem to the biochemist is to relate the consequences of this unique chemical "fact of life" concerning the dynamic structure of vitamin D and its metabolites and derivatives to their detailed interactions with receptors, membranes, etc., in biological systems. A particularly interesting aspect of this problem is the opportunity offered to the synthetic organic chemist. As indicated above, the equilibrium ratio between the two A-ring conformers is determined by the nature and distribution of the chemical substituents on the A ring. Accordingly, it is possible to perturb or alter the equilibrium between the two conformers in solution by introduction of varying structural functionalities, e.g., as in the analog lacking the 3β-hydroxyl, 3-deoxy-1,25-dihydroxyvitamin D_3 (Norman *et al.*, 1975). Also in view of the stereospecificities of enzymes, receptors, or other binding proteins in their respective biological actions, it seems reasonable to postulate that only one of the two chair conformations represents the optimally active molecular topology. Are there any unique aspects of vitamin D receptors which permit them to "contend with" the unusual conformational mobility of these molecules? Alternatively, there may be unique features of vitamin D receptors which may introduce new properties not previously encountered in other steroid hormone receptor systems.

B. Endocrine System for Vitamin D Action

The most notable advance in our understanding of the mechanism of action of vitamin D has been the elucidation of the complex metabolic pathway for production of the biologically active form $1,25(OH)_2D_3$. These relationships are summarized in Fig. 2. To date four and possibly five naturally occurring biologically active metabolites of vitamin D_3 have been isolated and chemically characterized. Vitamin D may be either produced by a photochemical reaction occurring in the skin which converts 7-dehydrocholesterol to cholecalciferol (vitamin D_3) or ingested dietarily. It is in this latter sense that calciferol truly earns the designation as a vitamin. However, it should be emphasized that under normal circumstances with adequate ultraviolet exposure, there is no nutritional requirement for vitamin D. The vitamin D_3 then undergoes a two-step metabolic conversion: First, it is transported to the liver where it is hydroxylated at the 25 position by a vitamin D_3-25-hydroxylase enzyme system localized in the liver microsomal fraction (Horsting and DeLuca, 1969); next, 25-hydroxyvitamin $D_3(25\text{-}OH\text{-}D_3)$ is transported to the kidney where it further undergoes metabolism to produce $1,25(OH)_21,25(OH)_2D_3$ (Fraser and Kodicek, 1970). The renal 25-OH-vitamin D_3-1-hydroxylase is located in the mitochondrial fraction of the cortical region of the kidney (Midgett *et al.*, 1973). This 1-hydroxylase, as shown by Henry and Norman (1974), is a classical mixed-function oxidase and involves cytochrome *P*-450. In this respect there are many similarities between this enzyme concerned with the metabolism of 25-OH-D_3 and other classical sterol hydroxylases.

The kidney also has the potential in some species and under some physiological circumstances to produce 24,25-dihydroxyvitamin $D_3[24,25(OH)_2D_3]$. The physiological role of this steroid is not yet known, although it does have some biological activity with regard to stimulation of intestinal calcium absorption (Henry *et al.*, 1976). A third vitamin D metabolite is also capable of being produced by the kidney: this is 1,24,25-trihydroxyvitamin D_3 $[1,24,25(OH)_3D_3]$. To date, this steroid has only been detected under *in vitro* conditions, and on the basis of the results of Friedlander and Norman (1975) it is not yet certain whether this metabolite actually circulates in the animal *in vivo*. The biological activity of $1,24,25(OH)_3D_3$ is somewhat less than that of $24,25(OH)_2D_3$ (Procsal *et al.*, 1976).

It should be apparent from evaluation of Fig. 2 that the kidney makes an unusually important contribution to the metabolism and functioning of vitamin D. It is now generally accepted that the kidney, in addition to carrying out its normal renal functions, also acts as an endocrine organ for the metabolism of $25(OH)D_3$ into principally $1,25(OH)_2D_3$ and also possibly $24,25(OH)_2D_3$. A hormone is classically defined as being a systemic acting

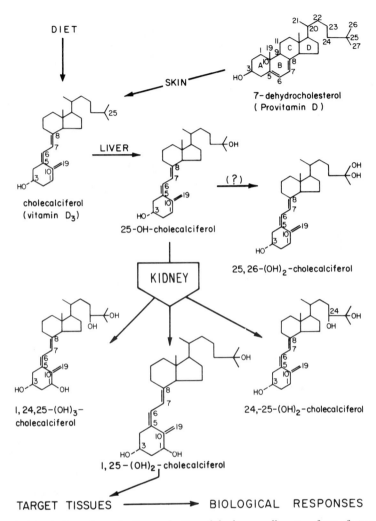

FIG. 2. Metabolic pathway for the production of the hormonally active form of vitamin D, 1,25-dihydroxycholecalciferol. The vitamin (calciferol) may either be produced by a photochemical reaction occurring in the skin to convert 7-dehydrocholesterol to calciferol or ingested dietarily. The calciferol then undergoes a two-step metabolic conversion: first, the liver produces 25-OH-cholecalciferol; second, the kidney produces 1,25-(OH)$_2$-cholecalciferol. 1,25-(OH)$_2$D$_3$ then proceeds through the circulation system to its various target organs, primarily the intestine and bone, where it interacts and produces its characteristic physiological response. The kidney also has the potential in some species and under some physiological circumstances to produce 24,25-(OH)$_2$-cholecalciferol. The physiological roles of 24,25-(OH)$_2$-D$_3$ and 1,24,25-(OH)$_3$-D$_3$ are not yet known.

substance produced by a specialized cell in response to a certain specified set of physiological stimuli or signals; very small amounts of the hormone then are released into the circulation and transported to distal target organs, where it interacts to elicit a set of specific physiological responses. It is usually the lack of these responses that indirectly generates the physiological signal that results in the secretion of the hormone. The classical method of demonstrating that an organ has an endocrine role in the economy of the organism is to create a deficit of its hormone either by surgical removal or by chemical inactivation of the organ in question. With reference to vitamin D and its renal product, $1,25(OH)_2D_3$, this criterion was first satisfied by the observations of Fraser and Kodicek (1970), who found that a nephrectomized rat could not produce $1,25(OH)_2D_3$. Furthermore, Wong et al. (1972a) clearly demonstrated that a vitamin D-deficient nephrectomized rat was unable to generate a biological response to moderate doses of either vitamin D_3 or 25-OH-D_3. In marked contrast, the same vitamin-deficient, nephrectomized animals gave a completely normal spectrum of biological responses when administered $1,25(OH)_2D_3$. These observations demonstrate that a deficit of the biologically active (hormonal form) of vitamin D could be created by surgical removal of the kidney and that this deficit could be overcome by administration of the renal product, the hormone $1,25(OH)_2D_3$. Thus these results collectively support the concept that the kidney is indeed an endocrine organ for the production of the biologically/hormonally active form of vitamin D, $1,25(OH)_2D_3$.

In other biochemical studies by Henry and Norman (1974a,b, 1975), Henry et al. (1974), Boyle et al. (1971), and Larkins et al. (1974), it has been clearly shown that the production of $1,25(OH)_2D_3$ by the kidney is subject to physiological regulation. The current view is that the production of $1,25(OH)_2D_3$ is stimulated by hypocalcemic conditions, and current data support the view that parathyroid hormone functions as a tropic factor to stimulate the rate of biosynthesis of the 1-hydroxylase. More recently, Henry and Norman (1975) and Brumbaugh et al. (1975) have presented evidence that $1,25(OH)_2D_3$ may localize in the parathyroid gland; presumably this is some kind of "feedback" designed to perhaps regulate the secretion of the tropic factor, parathyroid hormone. Shown in Fig. 3 is a summary of the proposed endocrine system of vitamin D with regard to calcium homeostasis.

C. BIOLOGICAL ACTIONS OF $1,25(OH)_2D_3$ IN THE INTESTINE

The primary focus of interest with regard to $1,25(OH)_2D_3$ has been an evaluation of its interaction with the target intestinal mucosal. Figure 4

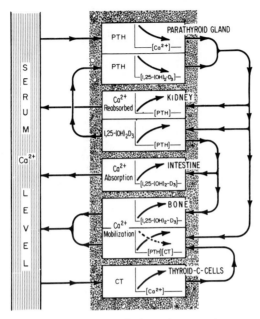

FIG. 3. Summary of calcium homeostasis.

summarizes our current understanding of the various steps of the action of $1,25(OH)_2D_3$ in initiating intestinal calcium transport. The basic effect of the steroid is to promote the intestinal movement of calcium from the lumen to the blood; however, a lag period of 9–12 hours is required for maximum effect [see Fig. 4(D).] The existence of this lag was first commented on by Irving (1944). Wasserman and Taylor (1968) were the first to describe the production of a specific protein response to the administration of vitamin D; this was identified as being a calcium-binding protein (CaBP). The precise subcellular localization of this protein is not known with certainty. What is known is that it is produced specifically in response to the presence of $1,25(OH)_2D_3$, and that it binds specifically calcium, strontium, or barium in preference to other divalent or monovalent cations. We have shown in collaboration with Wasserman and Taylor that the kinetics of the appearance of the CaBP after administration of $1,25(OH)_2D_3$ is virtually coincident with the hormone mediate stimulation of intestinal calcium transport [see Fig. 4(C)].

Figure 4(A) shows a time course of localization of radioactive $1,25(OH)_2D_3$ in the intestinal mucosa and more particularly its nuclear or chromatin fraction. The original approach pioneered in this laboratory toward developing a biochemical description of the action of calciferol was to administer small

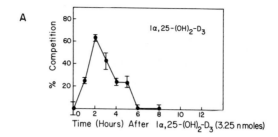

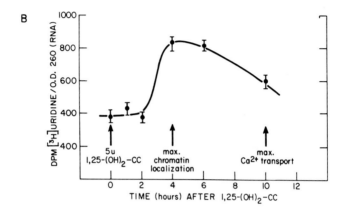

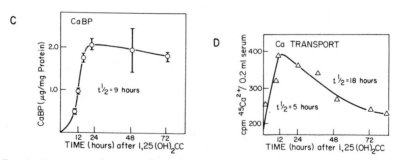

FIG. 4. Time course of several intestinal responses after treatment with 1,25-dihydroxychole-calciferol. All chicks were treated orally with 325 pmoles (5 U) of 1,25-$(OH)_2$-cholecalciferol dissolved in 1,2-propanediol. (A) Time course of appearance of 1,25$(OH)_2D_3$ in chick intestinal chromatin fraction as measured by steroid-competition analysis (Procsal *et al.*, 1975). (B) Increase in alkaline phosphatase activity of the intestinal brush border, $t_{1/2} = 22$ hours (Norman *et al.*, 1970). (C) Appearance of calcium-binding protein (CaBP), $t_{1/2} = 9$ hours. CaBP was determined by immunoassay in the laboratory of Professor R. A. Wasserman, Cornell University. (D) Increase in intestinal Ca^{2+} transport measured *in vivo* (Myrtle and Norman, 1971).

physiological doses of radioactive vitamin D and to trace the appearance of the radioactive label in the target tissue and ascertain its subcellular localization. In the course of these studies (Haussler and Norman, 1967, 1969; Haussler *et al.*, 1968; Myrtle *et al.*, 1970) it became apparent that not only was there a specialized localization of radioactivity within the target intestinal nuclear and chromatin fractions, but that this radioactivity was not chemically identical to the parent vitamin D. With the concomitant demonstration that this polar metabolite was highly biologically active in terms of stimulating intestinal transport of calcium (Haussler *et al.*, 1968; Myrtle and Norman, 1971), the extensive effort necessary to chemically characterize this substance was undertaken. This resulted in the simultaneous yet independent reports from three laboratories that the chemical structure of this vitamin D metabolite was $1,25(OH)_2D_3$ (Norman *et al.*, 1971; Lawson *et al.*, 1971; Holick *et al.*, 1971). As shown in Fig. 4(A), when a physiological dose of 325 pmoles of $1,25(OH)_2D_3$ are given, maximum localization occurs in the chromatin fraction within 4 hours. The logical extension of the results described in Figs. 4(A), 4(C), and 4(D) is that a significant contribution to the time lag and action of $1,25(OH)_2D_3$ may arise from the "activation" of information in the genome which is necessary for the expression of the biological response. As shown in Fig. 4(B), this was tested directly by measuring the effects of administration of small amounts of $1,25(OH)_2D_3$ on the subsequent synthesis of RNA. The intracardial administration of vitamin D-deficient chicks of as little as 325 pmoles of $1,25(OH)_2D_3$ resulted in a 100–150% stimulation of the incorporation of [^{3}H]uridine into the RNA isolated from the whole intestinal mucosa [Fig. 4(B)]. As can be noted by comparison with the time course in the other parts of Fig. 4, the kinetics of the stimulatory effects on RNA synthesis correlated well with the time course for maximum localization of this steroid in the intestine (3–4 hours) and the maximal appearance of the intestinal CaBP which occurs 9–12 hours after the administration of the steroid, as well as with the maximal stimulation of intestinal calcium absorption (which occurs at 9–12 hours). In separate studies Emtage *et al.* (1973) and Christakos and Norman (1978) have isolated a messenger RNA present in the intestinal mucosa which is capable of synthesizing a protein which cross-reacts immunologically with the antibody for calcium-binding protein.

Also in results not shown here, it has been demonstrated (Norman, 1965; Zull *et al.*, 1966; Tsai *et al.*, 1973) that actinomycin D, an inhibitor of DNA-directed RNA synthesis, is capable of blocking the biological responses of intestinal calcium absorption which was produced by both vitamin D and $1,25(OH)_2D_3$. As reported in detail by Tsai *et al.* (1973), this inhibition was not due to a blockage by actinomycin D of the localization of $1,25(OH)_2D_3$ in the intestine. It was unequivocally demonstrated that there were normal quantities of this steroid present in the intestine after dosing the animals with this antibiotic.

It appears that there is almost a complete confirmation of the genome-activation theory for the mechanism of action of vitamin D, at least with regard to the synthesis of calcium-binding protein. In the remainder of this article, a detailed discussion will be given of the interaction of $1,25(OH)_2D_3$ with the receptor system present in the intestinal mucosa which is employed to generate the biological responses characteristic of vitamin D.

II. BIOCHEMICAL PROPERTIES OF INTESTINAL RECEPTOR SYSTEM

A. SUBCELLULAR LOCALIZATION OF $1,25(OH)_2D_3$ GIVEN *IN VIVO*

Shown in Fig. 5 is a summary of results obtained concerning the subcellular localization of $1,25(OH)_2D_3$ in the intestinal mucosa when, in separate experiments, either tritiated vitamin D_3, $25(OH)D_3$, or tritiated $1,25(OH)_2D_3$ was administered to vitamin D-deficient chicks. In the course of these studies it became apparent that not only was there a specialized localization of radioactivity within the target intestinal nuclear and chromatin fraction, but that this radioactivity was not chemically identical to the parent vitamin D. Irrespective of whether radioactive vitamin D, $25(OH)D_3$, or $1,25(OH)_2D_3$ is given (see Fig. 5), there results 20, 8, or 4 hours later a maximum localization of radioactivity in the intestinal nuclear fraction. In each instance the nuclear fraction has associated with it approximately 70–80% of the total radioactivity present within the target tissue. Extraction and chromatographic evaluation (columns composed of either Sephadex LH-20, silicic acid, or celite) of the radioactivity resulting from the separate administration of the three steroids indicate that it was exclusively in the chemical form of 1,25-dihydroxyvitamin D_3. Further evaluation of the localization of the radioactivity present in the crude nuclear fraction of the intestine indicated that it was also present when purified nuclei were prepared (Haussler *et al.*, 1969) or when the subnuclear chromatin fraction was prepared (Haussler *et al.*, 1968). Subsequently it was possible to carry out dose–response type studies where increasing quantities of the three calciferol steroids were separately administered to groups of rachitic chicks (see middle panels of Fig. 5). This was followed by subsequent preparation according to our standard procedures (Haussler and Norman, 1969) of an intestinal chromatin fraction which had been briefly washed with a 1% solution of

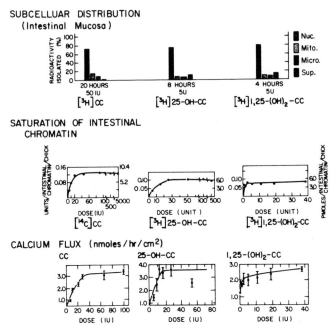

FIG. 5. Correlation of the subcellular distribution of radioactivity after doses of radioactive [³H]D₃, [³H]25-Oh-D₃, or [³H]1,25-(OH)₂-D₃ in the intestinal mucosa (top), with saturation of intestinal chromatin-binding sites (middle), and with stimulation of intestinal calcium transport (bottom). The subcellular distribution of radioactivity in the intestinal mucosa after separate doses of the three radioactive steroids was carried out as described by Haussler and Norman (1967) or Tsai *et al.* (1973). In each instance, the nuclear fraction accumulated the largest proportion of radioactivity. When this radioactivity was extracted and chromatographed according to the procedures of Haussler *et al.* (1969), irrespective of which calciferol steroid had been given initially, the radioactivity in the nuclear fraction was found to be exclusively 1,25(OH)₂D₃. Middle panel: Haussler and Norman (1967) described the existence of a "receptor" fraction in the intestinal nucleus or chromatin which has only a finite number of binding sites for 1,25-(OH)₂-D₃. Shown in the middle and bottom panels is the correlation between magnitude of dose of calciferol, 25-OH-D₃, or 1,25-(OH)₂D₃ required to saturate the intestinal chromatin-binding sites and to produce a maximum stimulation of intestinal calcium transport.

Triton X-100. When such a procedure was employed, evidence for a finite number of binding sites for 1,25(OH)₂D₃ in the intestinal chromatin fraction became apparent. It was then possible to correlate the dose of vitamin D steroid necessary to saturate intestinal chromatin fraction with a dose of vitamin D steroid required to give a maximum stimulation of intestinal calcium transport (see bottom panels of Fig. 5).

Of major concern in the course of these experiments was an effort to demonstrate specificity of the association of 1,25(OH)₂D₃ with the intestinal chromatin fraction. One approach to this problem was to effect the simultaneous administration of a tritiated vitamin D compound with an equivalent amount of ^{14}C-labeled cholesterol. A receptor molecule or binding site for vitamin D or its metabolites should have little affinity for cholesterol or its metabolites. In addition, ^{14}C-labeled cholesterol would be capable of serving as a marker for nonspecific lipid–lipid interaction, particularly as might occur with membrane components of the intestinal cell. Thus the ^{14}C-labeled cholesterol present in a given fraction provides a means of estimating the amount of steroid which is nonspecifically associated with that particular subcellular component. The ratio of tritium-bound steroid to ^{14}C-bound steroid will increase when the nuclear fraction is further purified. An infinite ratio might be anticipated when a pure receptor molecule specific for vitamin D or its metabolites had been isolated.

Results from separate experiments for each of the tritium-labeled vitamin D, 25(OH)D, or 1,25(OH)$_2$D$_3$ are shown in Table I. With each steroid there was a dramatic increase in the ^{3}H:^{14}C ratio of the purified chromatin fraction as compared with the starting homogenate. Further, it can be seen that treatment of the rachitic chicks with nonradioactive vitamin D several hours prior to dosing with the ^{3}H-labeled vitamin D$_3$ prevents a subsequent localization of any tritium-labeled steroids in the intestinal mucosa. Apparently any receptor sites specific for vitamin D$_3$ or its metabolites, i.e., particularly 1,25(OH)$_2$D$_3$, were previously saturated by the prior administration of the nonradioactive vitamin D$_3$. Collectively these results strongly support the suggestion that there are indeed specific binding sites present for 1,25(OH)$_2$D$_3$ in the chromatin fraction of the intestinal cell nucleus.

B. Nuclear and Chromatin Localization of 1,25(OH)$_2$D$_3$ under Conditions *In Vitro*

In view of the results reported above which were obtained after administration of vitamin D and its metabolites *in vivo*, and in consideration of the current status of investigations under way in many laboratories with other classical steroid hormones, attempts were made under conditions *in vitro* to duplicate the subcellular localization of 1,25(OH)$_2$D$_3$ in the intestinal chromatin fraction. Summaries of our more pertinent results obtained in this respect are given in Table II and Fig. 6. We have attempted to identify the properties, specificity, and the requirements of an intestinal homogenate system which is capable of affecting the localization of 1,25(OH)$_2$D$_3$ in the intestinal chromatin fraction. As shown in Table II, incubation of intestinal homogenates with 32–325 pmoles of [^{3}H]1,25(OH)$_2$D$_3$ at room temperature

TABLE I

RELATIVE AMOUNTS OF ^{3}H-LABELED CHOLECALCIFEROL AND ITS METABOLITES, 25-(OH)-[3H]CHOLECALCIFEROL AND ITS METABOLITES, OR 1,25-(OH)$_2$-[3H]CHOLECALCIFEROL AND ITS METABOLITES TO [4-^{14}C]CHOLESTEROL AND ITS METABOLITES IN SUBCELLULAR FRACTIONS OBTAINED FROM RACHITIC CHICK INTESTINAL MUCOSA[a]

Cell fraction	Isotope ratio[b]		% Competition of ^{3}H-binding	Isotope ratio[c]	Isotope ratio[d]
	Rachitic (−D) chicks	Normal (+D) chicks			
Homogenate	0.62	0.40	34	0.91	8.53
Crude nuclear fraction	0.71	0.39	41	1.43	9.58
Mitochondria	0.30	0.39	0	0.48	5.36
Microsomes	0.20	0.32	0	0.49	5.66
Supernatant fraction	1.67	0.51	65	4.50	11.7
Purified nuclei	0.95	0.38	70	—	—
Chromatin fraction	2.0	0.40	76	2.00	12.5
Membrane fraction	0.38	0.53	0	—	—
(from nuclei)	0.38	0.53	0	—	—
Purified chromatin[e]	10.0	0.10	99	17.7	36.4
Receptor fraction	25.0	0.93	99	—	—

[a] Vitamin D-deficient chicks received 10 IU of ^{3}H-labeled cholecalciferol (D$_3$), 5 U (0.325 nmole) of 25-OH-[3H]cholecalciferol or 1,25-(OH)$_2$[3H]cholecalciferol, and an equivalent amount of [4-^{14}C]cholesterol in 0.2 ml of 1,2-propanediol via intracardinal injection 16, 16, or 8 hours, respectively, prior to death. Normal chicks were pretreated with 5000 IU of nonradioactive cholecalciferol 8 hours prior to the dose of 10 IU of [3H]cholecalciferol. Cellular subfractions were prepared as described by Haussler *et al.* (1969) and Tsai and Norman (1973). All purified subnuclear fractions listed were prepared from the crude nuclear fraction. Each number represents an average of 4–8 separate determinations. The ratio of absolute amount of [3H]cholecalciferol and its metabolites, 25-OH-[3H]cholecalciferol and its metabolites, or 1,25-(OH)$_2$[3H] cholecalciferol and its metabolites to [4-^{14}C]cholesterol and its metabolites in the fraction is computed from the ratio of tritium to ^{14}C and the specific activities of the parent molecules. Dilution of the [4-^{14}C]cholesterol by endogenous cholesterol is neglected. Taken from Tsai and Norman (1973), and Haussler *et al.* (1968).

[b] [3H]vitamin D$_3$ metabolites:[^{14}C]cholesterol and metabolites.

[c] 25-OH[3H]D$_3$ and metabolites:[4-^{14}C]cholesterol and metabolites.

[d] 1,25-(OH)$_2$[3H]D$_3$ and metabolites:[14-^{14}C]cholesterol and metabolites.

[e] Each chromatin fraction was washed three times with 1.0% Triton X-100 *M* Tris pH 7.5, before the radioactivity content was determined.

for 30 minutes resulted in saturation of the subsequently isolated chromatin fraction at a level of approximately 0.6 pmoles of steroid per mg DNA.

When 1,25(OH)$_2$D$_3$ was incubated with different subcellular components of the intestinal mucosa homogenates followed by isolation of the chromatin fraction (Table II), evidence was obtained for the presence of some component in the cytosol fraction which was required for the maximum localization

TABLE II
INCUBATION *in Vitro* OF 1,25-DIHYDROXY-[³H]CHOLECALCIFEROL WITH DIFFERENT
INTESTINAL MUCOSAL FRACTIONS[a]

Fraction incubated in vitro[b]	1,25-$(OH)_2$-D_3 bound to chromatin fraction (pmoles/mg DNA)	Fraction steroid bound (percent)
Homogenate	0.50	100
Crude nuclei	0.37	74
Crude nuclei washed with 0.25 *M* sucrose–TKM, 3X	0.24	48
Chromatin	0.12	24
Cytosol with 1,25-$(OH)_2$-D_3 + crude nuclei	0.62	124
Cytosol with 1,25$(OH)_2D_3$ + purified nuclei	0.63	126
Cytosol with 1,25$(OH)_2D_3$ + purified chromatin	0.59	118

[a] 1,25-Dihydroxy-[³H]cholecalciferol, 130 pmoles, was added to each incubation (15 ml) containing the indicated intestinal subcellular fraction. The incubations were carried at 0°–4°C for 30 minutes, as described. The Triton-washed chromatin fraction was prepared and the associated radioactivity determined. Each number is an average of four separate determinations. The cytosol fraction with bound 1,25-dihydroxy-cholecalciferol was prepared by incubating cytosol with 130 -moles of 1,25-dihydroxy-[³H]cholecalciferol at 0°–4°C for 30 minutes, and then adding the crude nuclear fraction for a second incubation.

[b] The abbreviations employed are defined in the legend to Fig. 1. There are approximately 25 mg of DNA per chick intestinal mucosa.

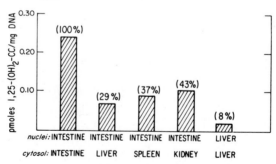

FIG. 6. Tissue specificity of cytoplasmic and chromatin binding of 1,25$(OH)_2D_3$. Cytosol protein, 60 mg, obtained from different tissues was suspended in 10 ml of 0.25 *M* sucrose–TKM (0.05 *M* Tris–HCl, pH 7.5; 0.02 *M* KCl, and 0.05 *M* $MgCl_2$) and preincubated with 65 pmoles of ³H-labeled 1,25-$(OH)_2$-D_3 at 0.0°–4°C for 30 minutes. An intestinal crude nuclear fraction was then added to the "labeled cytosol" and incubated for an additional 30 minutes at 0°–4°C. Next, the Triton X-100-washed chromatin fraction was prepared according to Tsai *et al.* (1973), and the bound radioactivity was determined.

of the $1,25(OH)_2D_3$ in the chromatin fraction. But when $1,25(OH)_2\dot{D}_3$ was incubated with purified nuclei or with the chromatin fraction alone, very little $1,25(OH)_2D_3$ was found tightly bound to the chromatin. Only when the cytosol fraction was preincubated with $1,25(OH)_2D_3$ followed by an incubation in which a crude nuclear fraction, purified nuclei, or chromatin fraction was added, followed by isolation of the chromatin fraction, was there a maximum chromatin localization of the steroid. Some localization of $1,25(OH)_2D_3$ in intestinal chromatin occurred when the crude nuclear fraction alone was incubated; this latter effect was likly due to some contamination of or inclusion in the crude nuclear fraction of enough cytoplasmic component to affect transferral of the steroid to the chromatin. When the crude nuclear fraction was washed three times with buffer, when the crude nuclear fraction was treated with Pronase, or when purified nuclei were prepared, a decreasing amount of $1,25(OH)_2D_3$ was found in the subsequently isolated chromatin. These results strongly suggest that there is an obligatory association of the steroid with the cytosol fraction prior to its subsequent localization in the chromatin (Tsai and Norman, 1973).

As shown in Fig. 6, the tissue specificity of the cytoplasmic receptor for $1,25(OH)_2D_3$ was also studied. These results indicated that the cytosol of the target tissue, the intestine, is the best mediator for the transfer of $1,25(OH)_2D_3$ to the nucleus of the intestinal mucosa. There was some localization of $1,25(OH)_2D_3$ in the intestinal chromatin, which was isolated from crude nuclear fractions which had been previously incubated with the cytoplasmic fractions obtained from the liver, kidney, or spleen. This was possibly due to the presence of a small amount of intestinal cytosol in the crude nuclear fraction of the intestinal mucosa. These results describing the *in vitro* conditions which permit the sequential binding of $1,25(OH)_2D_3$ to first a cytoplasmic and then a nuclear receptor are analogous to those reported to have occurred *in vivo* and *in vitro* for many other steroid hormones (Buller and O'Malley, 1976).

C. Evaluation of the Biochemical Properties of the Intestinal Receptor System for $1,25(OH)_2D_3$

We have undertaken to identify the chemical conditions or environment that might be utilized to dissociate the steroid–receptor complex from the chromatin. As reported by Haussler and Norman (1969), acid conditions ($0.03\ M$ citrate pH 4 or $0.15\ N\ H_2SO_4$) were not capable of significantly removing the steroid–receptor complex. This suggests that the steroid is not associated with the histone fraction. High pH conditions, on the other hand, were found to remove approximately 70% of the chromatin-bound radioactivity. When the pH 10 or pH 12 extract was treated with trichloroacetic acid (TCA), the steroid–receptor complex was precipitated. Repeated treatment of the chromatin with 1% Triton X-100 in 0.01 M Tris–HCl, pH 7.5, was incapable of removing significant amounts of the radioactive steroid. This suggests that the steroid was tightly and specifically associated with some entity of the chromatin fraction, because treatment of the subcellular fractions with this nonionic detergent had been shown to effect removal of nonspecifically bound lipids (Haussler *et al.*, 1968). By far the most gentle and effective means of solubilizing the steroid–receptor complex is treating the chromatin with moderate concentrations of KCl (see Fig. 7). The removal of the steroid–receptor complex occurs over a narrow range of ionic strengths, from 0.25 to 0.30 M KCl. We have termed the resulting supernatant fraction, after removal of the residual chromatin, the crude "receptor fraction." This extraction procedure results in a 17-fold purification over the starting intestinal mucosa homogenate.

Shown in Table III is a comparison of the chemical composition of the crude receptor fractions solubilized either by 0.30 M KCl or by 0.01 M Tris, pH 10 treatment. The KCl extraction method is used in preference to the alkaline tris extraction method because there is somewhat less total contaminating RNA and DNA. The KCl-extracted crude receptor has about 1.5% of the total homogenate protein, 1.0% of the homogenate RNA, and 0.5% of the homogenate DNA. The specific activity of the crude receptor

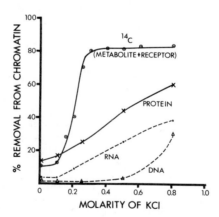

FIG. 7. Selective solubilization of the chromatin-associated "receptor" for 1,25(OH)$_2$D$_3$ with KCl. Chromatin fractions which had been previously labeled with [^{14}C]1,25(OH)$_2$D$_3$ *in vivo* were homogenized with various concentrations of KCl in 0.01 M Tris, pH 7.5 (25 ml). The residual chromatin was recovered by sedimentation of 27,000 g for 1 hour. It was then assayed for ^{14}C radioactivity (⊙———⊙, metabolite + receptor), and the supernatant was assayed for DNA (△- - -△), RNA (■- - -■), and protein (×—×—×) (Haussler and Norman, 1969).

TABLE III

CHEMICAL COMPOSITION OF RECEPTOR FRACTIONS SOLUBILIZED FROM CHROMATIN OF ONE CHICK

Type of receptor fraction	Protein		RNA		DNA		Protein RNA:DNA
	mg	% homogenate	mg	% homogenate	mg	% homogenate	
0.3 M KCl[a]	11	1.5	0.25	1.0	0.07	0.5	157:3.5:1
0.01 M Tris, pH 10	8	1.1	0.32	1.3	0.11	0.8	73:11:1

[a]Chromatin was washed with 0.01 M Tris, pH 7.5, prior to solubilization with 0.3 M KCl in 0.01 M Tris, pH 7.5.

fraction is 330 fmoles of metabolite/mg protein as compared to a specific activity for the intestinal homogenate of 7.8 fmoles/mg protein. This represents a 42-fold purification. Further attempts at purification of the crude receptor fraction via classical fractionation techniques such as DEAE cellulose chromatography have not yet been successful owing to the apparent dissociation of the steroid from the receptor complex during chromatography. It is possible to selectively precipitate the crude "receptor" with 15–30% saturated ammonium sulfate; this can then be followed by protamine sulfate precipitation. This gives a preparation with a specific activity of 1.30 pmoles/mg protein, which is equivalent to an overall purification of 167-fold.

We have also initiated efforts to evaluate the biochemical properties of the cytosol receptor protein.* The results of some of these efforts are summarized in Table IV. The mucosal cytosol which had been incubated with $1,25(OH)_2D_3$ was also treated with various enzymes such as DNase, RNase, or Pronase. The DNase or RNase treatment had no effect on the binding of $1,25(OH)_2D_3$ to the mucosal cytosol component. However, the Pronase treatment reduced the binding of $1,25(OH)_2D_3$ to the cytosol to almost a negligible level. Pretreatment of the mucosal cytosol with heat either at 60°C for 10 minutes or boiling resulted in inhibition of the binding of $1,25(OH)_2D_3$ to the cytosol component. These results collectively suggest that the cytoplasmic macromolecule (or macromolecules) which binds $1,25(OH)_2D_3$ firmly is protein in nature. When the intestinal cytosol was pretreated with sulfhydryl reagents such as N-ethylmaleimide or p-hydroxymercuribenzoate followed by incubation with $1,25(OH)_2D_3$, no effect of these compounds was observed on the amount of $1,25(OH)_2D_3$ bound to the cytosol.

We have also evaluated the chromatographic mobility of the steroid cytosol–receptor complex on long columns of Sephadex G-200. The cytosol of the intestinal mucosa was first incubated with tritiated $1,25(OH)_2D_3$, and then it was fractionated by ammonium sulfate precipitation. Most of the bound radioactivity was contained in the fraction precipitated by a 45% saturation with ammonium sulfate (Tsai and Norman, 1973). When this fraction was further studied by gel filtration on columns of Sephadex G-200, there were two major protein peaks (as shown in Fig. 8). Peak I is in the region between 65,000 and 150,000 daltons. Aldolase and bovine serum albumin were employed as molecular-weight markers. Peak II occurs at the region of less than 50,000 daltons. The radioactivity representing the migration of the steroid–receptor complex recovered from the column also showed two peaks, one of which migrated with Peak I, and one [fractions 70–100,

---

*It should be appreciated that the cytosol receptor protein may in fact be identical to the nuclear or chromatin-localized chromatin receptor. This point will become apparent upon evaluation of the sucrose-gradient centrifugation experiments presented later in Fig. 9.

TABLE IV
SOME CHARACTERISTICS OF THE CYTOPLASMIC BINDING OF
1,25-DIHYDROXY[^{3}H]CHOLECALCIFEROL[a]

Treatment	Control %
None	100
p-Hydroxymercuribenzoate	105
N-Ethylmaleimide	92
Heated 60°C, 10 minutes	58
Boiled, 10 minutes	18
$(NH_4)_2SO_4$ precipitation	100
Pronase	5
RNase	100
DNase	100

[a] The intestinal cytosol was subjected to the indicated treatment (p-hydroxymercuribenzoate, 455 μg per ml of incubation, 10 minutes at room temperature; N-ethylmaleimide, 455 μg per ml of incubation, 10 minutes at room temperature; heated at 60°C for 10 minutes; boiled for 10 minutes; Pronase, 200 μg per ml of incubation at 20°C for 18 hours; DNase, 200 μg per ml of incubation + 0.0% M Mg^{2+} at 20°C for 20 minutes or RNase, 200 gm per ml of incubation at 20°C for 20 minutes), then incubated with 65 or 130 pmoles of 1,25-dihydroxy[^{3}H]cholecalciferol. The labeled cytosol was next treated with a charcoal–dextran mixture, as described. The radioactivity remaining in the supernatant was considered to be the amount of protein-bound steroid.

Fig. 8(A)] which was shown to be free steroid. As shown in Fig. 8(B), when the intestinal cytosol–receptor fraction was treated with charcoal–dextran mixture prior to column chromatography, virtually all the radioactivity which had previously been in a "small molecule" region [Fig. 8(A)] was not present.

Shown in Fig. 9 are results of sucrose-gradient centrifugation of the intestinal steroid cytosol–receptor complex [Fig. 9(A)] and the steroid–receptor complex which had been obtained by KCl extraction of the chromatin. Both the cytosol receptor (presumably unactivated) as well as the receptor retrieved from the intestinal chromatin (which has been "activated"; see below) have identical sedimentation values of 3.5–3.7 S. On the basis of experiments of this type, it can be tentatively concluded that "activation" of the intestinal cytosol receptor for 1,25(OH)$_2$D$_3$ does not involve major modification in either the size of the shape of the receptor protein.

The present results suggest that there is a macromolecular cytoplasmic

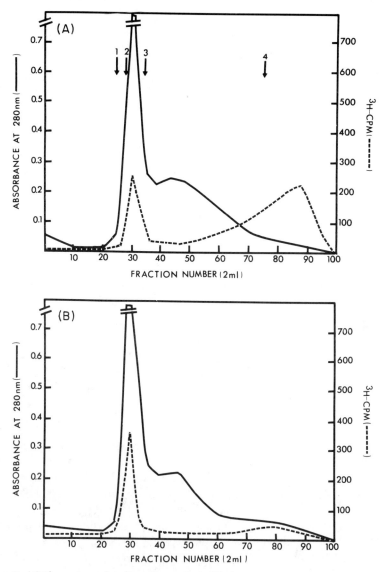

FIG. 8. (A) Chromatography of cytoplasmic-bound [³H]1,25(OH)₂D₃ on columns of Sephadex G-200. The intestinal cytosol was incubated with 520 pmoles of [³H]1,25(OH)₂D₃ at 0°C for 30 minutes in 0.01 *M* Tris, 0.015 *M* EDTA, Then ammonium sulfate was added to 45% saturation; the precipitated protein was collected via centrifugation at 8000 *g* for 10 minutes and redissolved in 0.01 *M* Tris, 0.015 *M* EDTA, pH 7.4, and chromatographed on a column of Sephadex G-200. Solid line, protein (ultraviolet absorbance at 280 nm); dotted line, tritium radioactivity. In several of the samples the molecular-weight markers, blue dextran (1), aldolase (2), bovine serum albumin (3), and ribonuclease (4), were added to the cytosol sample. (B) Sephadex G-200

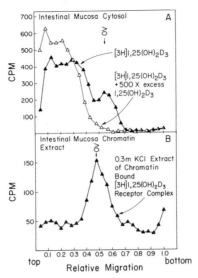

FIG. 9. (A) Sucrose-gradient analysis of intestinal cytosol and KCl-extracted intestinal mucosal chromatin after incubation with $[^3H]$-1,25$(OH)_2D_3$ in the presence ($\triangle$—$\triangle$) or absence ($\blacktriangle$—$\blacktriangle$) of 500-fold excess nonradioactive 1,25$(OH)_2D_3$ and run on 4.2 ml 5–20% sucrose gradients at 50,000 rpm for 20 hours. (B) Reconstituted chromatin and cytosol from a 40% intestinal mucosa homogenate were incubated with 14 nM $[^3H]$1,25$(OH)_2D_3$, the chromatin fraction was isolated, extracted with a 0.3 M KCl buffer, and run on 5–20% sucrose gradients, as above. $[^{14}C]$Ovalbumin was run on a parallel gradient. All gradients contained 0.3 M KCl.

receptor for 1,25$(OH)_2D_3$. The cytoplasmic receptor for 1,25$(OH)_2D_3$ in the target tissue is protein in nature, as shown by its precipitability by ammonium sulfate and its sensitivity to Pronase digestion. The size of the cytoplasmic receptor as determined by gel filtration and sucrose density-gradient centrifugation is in the range of 65,000–160,000 daltons. This is similar to the molecular-weight range of the cytoplasmic receptor for other steroid hormones (Chamness and McGuire, 1972; Puca *et al.*, 1971; Faber *et al.*, 1972; Buller and O'Malley, 1976). Our results also suggest that free sulfhydryl groups may not be required for the binding of 1,25$(OH)_2D_3$ to its cytosol–receptor protein. Neither pretreatment of the cytosol with N-ethyl-

column chromatography of dextran-coated charcoal-treated cytosol fractions. The intestinal cytosol was incubated with 520 pmoles of $[^3H]$1,25$(OH)_2D_3$ at 0°C for 30 minutes in 0.01 M Tris, 0.015 M EDTA. Then ammonium sulfate was added to 45% saturation. The precipitated protein was collected via centrifugation at 8000 g for 10 minutes and redissolved in 0.01 M Tris, 0.015 M EDTA, pH 7.5. This fraction was then treated with dextran-coated charcoal to remove unbound steroid. Charcoal-treated cytosol fraction was next chromatographed on a Sephadex G-200 column. Solid line, protein (ultraviolet absorbance at 280 nm); dotted line, tritium radioactivity.

maleimide nor p-hydroxymercuribenzoate impaired the binding of the $1,25(OH)_2D_3$ to the receptor as evaluated by a charcoal-binding assay for free steroid. This is in contrast to results previously reported for all other steroid hormones. At the current time we are undertaking further efforts to chromatographically purify the cytosol and also, separately, the chromatin–receptor complex, for $1,25(OH)_2D_3$. However, it has not been possible to employ affinity chromatography because of the complexities concerned with chemical manipulation and coupling of vitamin D metabolites to a stationary phase.

By making several simplifying assumptions, we can estimate the amount of receptor molecule that is present in the intestinal mucosa. From the saturation value of 3.25 pmoles of $1,25(OH)_2D_3$ per one chick intestinal receptor fraction and assuming a 70% yield of receptor, this can be corrected to 4.5 pmoles of metabolite per receptor from one chick intestinal mucosa (3 gm of tissue). It is known that there are 2×10^9 cells per one gram chick intestinal mucosa. Accordingly, it can be calculated that there are 460 molecules of $1,25(OH)_2D_3$ per intestinal mucosa cell, or a metabolite concentration of approximately $1.5 \times 10^{-9} M$ in the entire intestinal mucosa. This value is comparable to either the 1700 or 2500 estrogen molecules per uterine cell nucleus estimated by Maurer and Chalkley (1967) and Noteboom and Gorski (1965). Then on the assumption of a 1:1 stoichiometry of $1,25(OH)_2D_3$ binding to receptor and by employing Avogadro's number, the concentration of the receptor must also be estimated at approximately $1.5 \times 10^{-9} M$. If the receptor has a molecular weight of 100,000, then there is at most approximately 0.5 μg receptor per one chick intestinal mucosa. Because the entire mucosa from a 120-gm chick contains 675 mg of protein, this suggests that approximately a 10^6-fold purification must be obtained to isolate the receptor in homogeneous form. Obviously, the 167-fold purification thus far achieved is only a modest beginning in the isolation of the $1,25(OH)_2D_3$ receptor molecule.

III. STRUCTURE–FUNCTION STUDIES

A. Intestinal Receptor Assay for $1,25(OH)_2D_3$

It has previously been documented that under appropriate conditions saturation of a finite number of intestinal chromatin binding sites for $1,25(OH)_2D_3$ can be achieved *in vivo* or *in vitro*. It has been possible to further refine our efforts in this regard and develop a steroid-specific receptor assay for $1,25(OH)_2D_3$ which is dependent upon the two-step mechanism

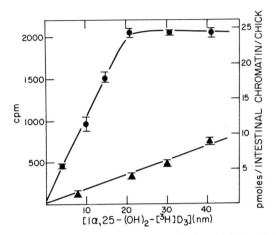

FIG. 10. Temperature dependence of the saturable binding of [³H]1,25-(OH)$_2$D$_3$ to chick intestinal mucosa chromatin. Each point represents the average of triplicate measurements ± SD.

of localization in the intestinal cytosol followed by transfer to the intestinal nucleus and its chromatin fraction. Shown in Fig. 10 is the saturation of the chromatin binding sites in the reconstituted cytosol–chromatin system. These data demonstrate that maximum binding of 1,25(OH)$_2$D$_3$ at a level of about 21–24 pmoles per chick intestinal chromatin (15 mg of DNA) occurs at a concentration of 2.0×10^{-8} M 1,25(OH)$_2$D$_3$ under our assay conditions at 25°C. When rigorous efforts are taken to maintain all incubation components at 0°C, only a much reduced amoung of 1,25(OH)$_2$D$_3$ localized in the reisolated chromatin pellet. This result is consistent with a temperature-dependent "activation" process of the cytosol receptor which is required for optimum transfer of the steroid to the chromatin. This value of 21–24 pmoles is approximately two times higher than that which occurs under conditions *in vivo* when [³H]vitamin D$_3$ is administered. However, the metabolism of 1,25(OH)D$_3$ to 1,25(OH)$_2$D$_3$ is known to be stringently regulated (Henry *et al.*, 1974), and this may account for the lower value observed *in vivo* when vitamin D$_3$ is administered. However, when radioactive 1,25(OH)$_2$D$_3$ is given to rachitic chicks *in vivo* within 2–3 hours, 20–23 pmoles of hormone per chick intestinal chromatin are maximally localized [see Fig. 4(A)], which compares favorably with the data shown in Fig. 10.

The time course for binding of 1,25(OH)$_2$D$_3$ to the intestinal chromatin is shown in Fig. 11, and indicates that saturation occurs 30 minutes after initiation of incubation of 25°C and remains at this level for at least 30 minutes longer. The results shown in Figs. 10 and 11 define the concentration of steroid (2.0×10^{-8} M), temperature (25°C), and time (45 minutes)

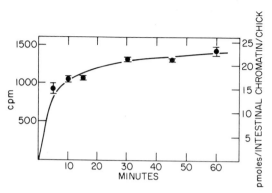

FIG. 11. Time course for the saturation of chick intestinal mucosa chromatin binding sites with $[^3H]1,25(OH)_2D_3$. Each point represents the average of triplicate measurements ± SD.

required for maximal binding of $1,25(OH)_2D_3$ to chick intestinal chromatin *in vitro* (Procsal *et al.*, 1975).

Thus it has been possible to devise a competitive binding assay for $1,25(OH)_2D_3$ which utilizes as its specific receptor the two-step cytosol–chromatin localization of this steroid. As shown in Fig. 12 (closed circles), a standard linear curve is obtained when increasing amounts of nonradioactive

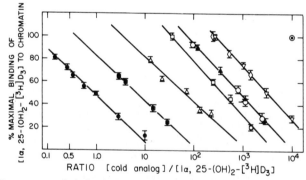

FIG. 12. Competition of cholecalciferol analogs with $1,25(OH)_2D_3$ for its chick intestinal receptor system, *in vitro*. Increasing concentrations of cold (nonradioactive) analogs were incubated for 45 minutes at 25°C with a reconstituted cytosol–chromatin receptor system in the presence of 2.0×10^{-8} M $1\alpha,25-(OH)_2-[^3H]D_3$. The percent of the maximal amount of radioactivity bound to the chromatin is plotted as a function of the relative concentrations of analog and $1,25-(OH)_2-[^3H]D_3$ present in the assay mixture. Nonradioactive compounds are denoted as follows: (●—●), $1\alpha,25-(OH)_2-D_3$; (■—■), $3-D-1\alpha,25-(OH)_2-D_3$; (△—△), 25-OH-DHT$_3$; (□—□), 25-OH-5,6-$t$-D$_3$; (○—○), 25-OH-D$_3$, (▲—▲), $1\alpha,(OH)-D_3$, (▽—▽), $24,25-(OH)_2-D_3$ (R or S); (◇—◇), $3-D-1\alpha-OH-D_3$. D$_3$, 5,6-t-D$_3$, DHT$_3$, DVH-IV, $1\alpha,25$-dihydroxycholesterol, and filipin. Each point represents the average of duplicate or triplicate determinations ± SD.

$1,25(OH)_2D_3$ are added to the radioactive $[^3H]1,25(OH)_2D_3$. The decrease in the amount of radioactive steroid bound is due to a dilution of the pool of radioactive $1,25(OH)_2D_3$ such that at a ratio of the concentration of non-radioactive steroid to radioactive steroid equal to 1.0, 50% of the maximal bound radioactivity is measured.

One important use of this assay has been to assess the structural requirements of the ligand steroid $1,25(OH)_2D_3$ for its cytosol–chromatin receptor. The results of such a study utilizing a variety of closely related vitamin D analogs are plotted in Fig. 12 and the data summarized in Figs. 13 and 14 and in Table V. Table V tabulates the relative concentrations of the various steroids required to produce half-maximal competition under these standardized assay conditions. Interpretation of these results is more complicated, however, than just an assessment of the consequences of the presence or absence of particular hydroxyls or other functional groups; equally important to consider are the geometry and conformation of the A ring of the vitamin D steroid.

By evaluation of the data presented in Figs. 13 and 14, several interesting relationships may be deduced. A basic requirement for an analog to be an effective competitor with $1,25(OH)_2D_3$ in this assay is that it be a 9,10-secosteroid. This conclusion is supported by the observation that $1,25(OH)_2$ cholesterol did not compete even at a concentration 10,000 times greater than $1,25(OH)_2D_3$. The dramatically decreased ability of 25-OH-D_3 and 1-OH-D_3 to compete with $1,25(OH)_2D_3$ in this assay (see Fig. 13) demonstrates the critical importance of both the 1α and 25-hydroxyl groups. By comparison, 3-deoxy-1,25(OH)$_2$D$_3$, which lacks a hydroxyl at the 3β position, is over 100 times more effective at competing in this assay than either 1-OH-D_3 or 25-OH-D_3. Thus, it can be concluded that in terms of the ability of $1,25(OH)_2D_3$ to interact with its chick intestinal receptor system, a 3β-hydroxyl is relatively less important than either a 25- or 1α-hydroxyl. A similar conclusion can be reached by comparison of D_3 with 3-D-1-OH-D_3. Vitamin D_3, which lacks both a 25-OH and a 1α-hydroxyl but possesses a 3β-hydroxyl, is an ineffective competitor; 3-D-1α-OH-D_3, which lacks 25- and 3β-hydroxyls but does have a 1α-hydroxyl, will interact with the receptor.

The consequence of a 180° rotation of the A ring about the 5,6-double bond to produce analogs of the 5-*cis–trans* series is illustrated in Fig. 14. A primary consequence of *cis–trans* isomerization is a change in the orientation of the C-19 methylene group. Although isomerization also moves a 3β-hydroxyl to a position sterically equivalent to the 1α-hydroxyl of steroids of the 5,6-*cis* series, this is apparently not sufficient to permit either 25-OH-5,6-*t*-D_3 or 5,6-*t*-D_3 to compete as effectively as their 5,6-*cis* counterparts 3-D-1-25-(OH)$_2$D$_3$ and 3-D-1-OH-D_3, respectively. Presumably, this dif-

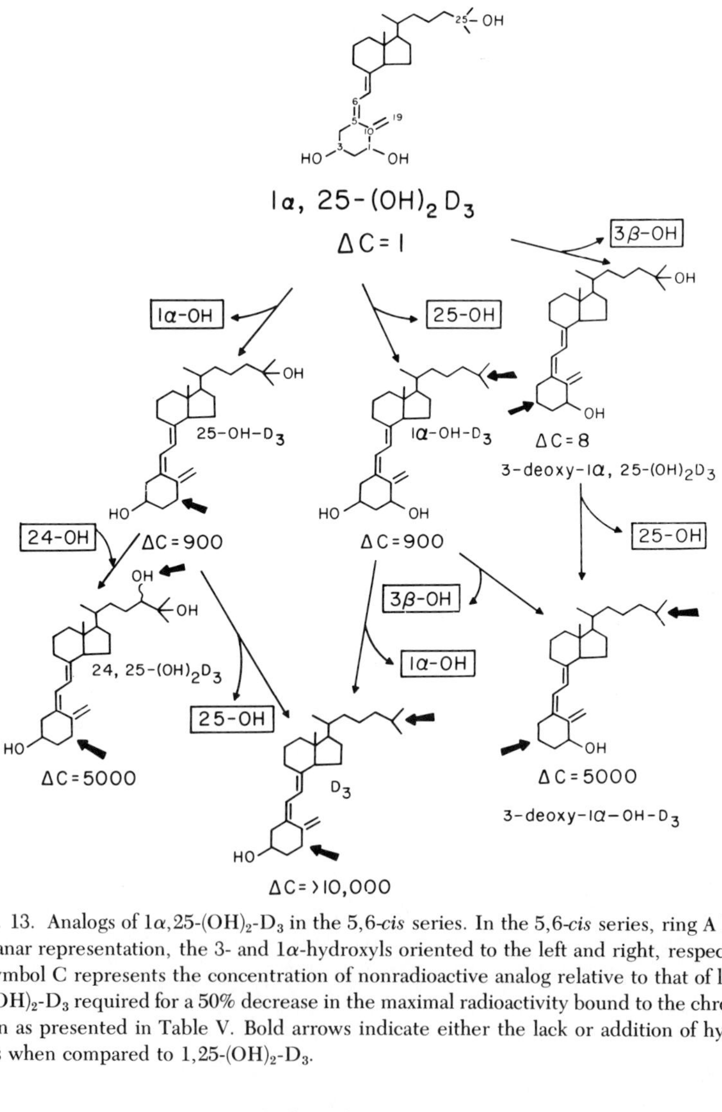

FIG. 13. Analogs of $1\alpha,25\text{-}(OH)_2\text{-}D_3$ in the 5,6-*cis* series. In the 5,6-*cis* series, ring A has, in the planar representation, the 3- and 1α-hydroxyls oriented to the left and right, respectively. The symbol C represents the concentration of nonradioactive analog relative to that of labeled $1,25\text{-}(OH)_2\text{-}D_3$ required for a 50% decrease in the maximal radioactivity bound to the chromatin fraction as presented in Table V. Bold arrows indicate either the lack or addition of hydroxyl groups when compared to $1,25\text{-}(OH)_2\text{-}D_3$.

ference is a consequence of the change in the orientation of the C-19 methylene group. This may also be the reason why DHT_3 (dihydrotachysterol$_3$) or DHV_3-IV (dihydrovitamin D_3-IV) do not compete in a receptor assay. Thus, it may be concluded that the intestinal receptor system prefers the *cis* geometry to the *trans* geometry.

Our laboratory has recently succeeded (Norman *et al.*, 1975) in introducing a hydroxyl group into the number 19 position of the 5,6-*cis* analogs, DHV_3-II and DHV_3-III, and in the 5,6-*trans* analogs, DHT_3 and DHV_3-IV. It was reasoned that the presence of a hydroxyl group at the 19 position

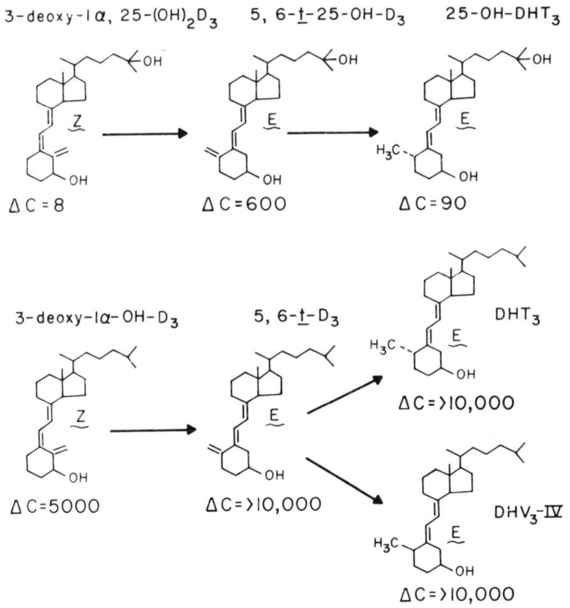

FIG. 14. Analogs of $1\alpha,25\text{-}(OH)_2\text{-}D_3$ in the 5,6-*trans* series. The 5,6-*trans* of analogs results from the rotation of the A ring 180° when compared to the 5,6-*cis* series. Thus, the 3β-hydroxyl in the 5,6-*trans* series is referred to as a pseudo-1α-hydroxyl because sterically it occupies the position equivalent to the 1α-hydroxyl of a compound in the 5,6-*cis* series. The symbols Z or E denote analogs of the 5,6-*cis* or 5,6-*trans* series, respectively. The symbol C is defined in the legend to Fig. 13.

might, to some limited degree, satisfy the requirements for a pseudo-3β-OH group in the 5,6-*trans* series or the 1-OH in the 5,6-*cis* series. However, to our surprise, no significant competition was observed for any of these compounds in our competitive binding assay. It may be that these compounds will first have to be hydroxylated in the 25 position before their relative ability to bind to the receptor can be evaluated.

As is to be expected, based upon the previous discussion of the importance of both the 1- and the 25-hydroxyl groups, 25-hydroxylation of both DHT_3 and 5,6-t-D_3 results in analogs with a superior ability to compete with $1,25(OH)_2D_3$ in this assay. Indeed, both 25-OH-DHT_3 and 25-OH-5,6-t-D_3 were more effective competitors than 25-OH-D_3, presumably by virtue of their having a pseudo-1α-hydroxyl group. Of special interest, however, is the observation that 25-OH-DHT_3 is more than six times as effective a competitor than 25-OH-5,6-t-D_3. Two possible explanations for this difference between 25-OH-5,6-t-D_3 and 25-OH-DHT_3 follows: (a) because the 5,6-*trans* is the unnatural series, a 10α-oriented C-19 methyl group could be sterically less interfering on the receptor surface where both methyl and methylene are unfavored; and/or (b) the model for optimization of biological activity based on conformational considerations may well be applicable (Okamura *et al.*, 1974). This model proposes that it is the equatorial orientation of the 1α-hydroxyl group that is necessary for optimization of biological activity. By high-resolution spectroscopy, we have determined that the A ring of 25-OH-DHT$_3$ is less biased in this orientation (69%) (Wing *et al.*, 1974; Okamura *et al.*, 1974).

It is also interesting to note that introduction of a hydroxyl group at the 24 carbon of 25-OH-D$_3$ to form either the *R* or *S* epimer of 24,25(OH)$_2$D$_3$ significantly decreases the ability of this analog to · interact with a 1,25(OH)$_2$D$_3$ intestinal receptor system. It may be that the 24-hydroxylation of a vitamin D steroid is a method of ensuring that it will not interact effectively with the intestinal receptor system. One particularly pertinent point included in Table V is the dramatic effect of shortening the side chain of 1,25(OH)$_2$D$_3$ by as little as one carbon group. The analog 24-*nor*-1,25-5,6-*t*-D$_3$ was only 1/900 as effective as 1,25(OH)$_2$D$_3$ in competing in the intestinal-receptor assay. The prefix "*nor*" here indicates loss of one carbon at the designated position. Thus, the subtle effect of shortening the side by as little as one carbon produces a quite striking effect in terms of "competability" in the intestinal-receptor assay.

In general, there is a remarkable correlation between the relative binding of analogs in the chick intestinal-receptor system and their relative ability to stimulate intestinal calcium absorption. The following conclusions may therefore be proposed with respect to the structural features required for vitamin D-like biological activity in the intestinal cell. (a) All biologically active compounds must have a 1α-hydroxyl or its geometric equivalent and a 25-hydroxyl group. (b) The presence of a hydroxyl group at a geometrically equivalent position to the 3β-hydroxyl of 1,25(OH)$_2$D$_3$ is not an absolute requirement. (c) A 5,6-*cis* geometry of the A ring is preferred to a 5,6-*trans* geometry. A comparison of the biological and binding activities of 25-OH-DHT$_3$ with those of 25-OH-5,6-*t*-D$_3$ suggests that, in compounds of the 5,6-*trans* series, a C-19 methyl is preferred over a C-19 methylene group. (d) Altering the length or modifying the side chain, including the insertion of a hydroxyl group as in 24,25-(OH)$_2$D$_3$ or 25,26-OH-$_2$D$_3$, significantly decreases the activity of a compound.

B. Consequences of Conformational Mobility of Vitamin D Secosteroids on the Intestinal Receptor System for 1,25(OH)$_2$D$_3$

As documented above, the principal focus of our structure–function studies has been an evaluation of the structure required for the interaction of

1,25-analogs to the intestinal cytosol and chromatin receptor system. Shown in Fig. 15 is the proposed two-step mode of action of 1,25(OH)₂D₃ in the intestine (left panel) as well as a postulate with regard to the consequences of the conformational mobility of the A ring of vitamin D secosteroids. It would appear that the steroid 1,25(OH)₂D₃ must first interact with a specific receptor protein present in the cytosol of the intestinal cell; then, after an "activation process" of as yet indeterminate biochemical modification, this complex is transferred to the nucleus where it associates in some specific fashion with additional binding or receptor sites unique to the intestinal nuclear–chromatin fraction. It is not known whether the actual steroid molecule is "passed on" to subsequent protein acceptors or whether the biological responses are initiated simply by virtue of the presence of the "activated-cytosol–steroid receptor complex" which was delivered to the nucleus. Clearly, the state of affairs with the steroid 1,25(OH)₂D₃ is not too dissimilar in comparison to our current detailed understanding of the interaction of classical steroid hormones with their nuclear and cytosol receptor system.

A major challenge, though, which is unique to the vitamin D steroid–receptor system, is the problem of carefully evaluating the consequences of

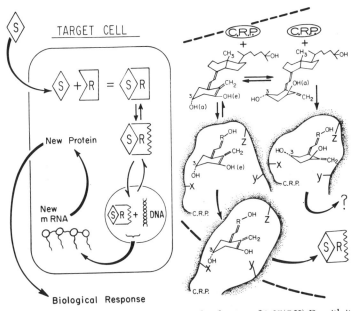

FIG. 15. Model of proposed steroid hormone made of action of 1,25(OH)₂D₃ with its intestinal receptor system. The left panel indicates the two-step movement of 1,25(OH)₂D₃ from the cytosol to the nucleus of the cell; the right panel suggests how a particular steroid conformer may preferentially interact with the cytosol receptor.

the conformational mobility of the A ring of vitamin D secosteroids and to determine unequivocally whether protein receptors (e.g., the intestinal cytosol–nuclear receptors) can distinguish between the two chair conformers. On the basis of the data presented in Table V, it would seem that the intestinal cytosol–nuclear receptor system does have a high degree of structural specificity with regard to the steroid ligand. Thus, it would seem that the receptor–ligand interaction would be potentially capable of distinguishing between the extremes of the two chair–chair conformers that the $1,25(OH)_{23}$ population of ligand molecules always presents for binding. It

TABLE V

RELATIVE EFFECTIVENESS OF STRUCTURAL ANALOGS OF VITAMIN
D IN THE $1,25(OH)_2D_3$ CHICK INTESTINAL RECEPTOR ASSAY

Compound	Relative concentration of steroid required for 50% competition[a]
$1\alpha,25(OH)_2D_2$	
5,6-*cis* (Z) series	1
$\quad$ 3-D-$1\alpha,25(OH)_2D_3$	
$\quad$ 1α-OH-D_3	8
$\quad$ $25(OH)D_3$	900
$\quad$ 3-D-1α-OH-D_3	900
$\quad$ $24R,25(OH)_2D_3$	5,000
$\quad$ $24S,25(OH)_2D_3$	5,000
$\quad$ D_3	5,000
$\quad$ 19-OH-DHV$_3$-II	>10,000
$\quad$ 10-OH-DHV$_3$-III	>10,000
5,6-*trans* (E) series	>10,000
$\quad$ 25-OH-DHT$_3$	90
$\quad$ 25-OH-5,6-t-D_3(25-OH-5E-D_3)	600
$\quad$ 5,6-t-D_3(5E-D_3)	>10,000
$\quad$ DHT$_3$	>10,000
$\quad$ DHV$_3$-IV	>10,000
$\quad$ 19-OH-DHT$_3$	>10,000
$\quad$ 19-OH-DHV$_3$-IV	>10,000
Other	
$\quad$ 1,25-dihydroxycholesterol	>10.000

[a] The data shown are the concentrations of analog required to reduce the binding of $[^3H]1,25(OH)_2D_3$ to its intestinal cytosol–chromatin receptor system by 50%. The assay was conducted as described by Procsal *et al.* (1975).

could be argued that, in the event that the protein receptors could not distinguish between the chair–chair conformers, it would be virtually impossible for the protein receptors to have structural specificity for the A-ring portion of their ligand. The differences in terms of three-dimensional architecture or topology between the pairs of chair–chair conformers for $1,25(OH)_2D_3$ (see Fig. 1) are at least as great as some of the subtle structural modifications apparent in the static representation of vitamin D analogs (Figs. 13 and 14). That is to say, the structural difference between the static representation of the analogs $25\text{-}OH\text{-}DHT_3$ and $3\text{-}D\text{-}1\alpha,25(OH)_2D_3$ is at least as great as the difference between the static representations of the pair of chair–chair conformers for $3\text{-}D\text{-}1\alpha,25(OH)_2D_3$ or $1,25(OH)_2D_3$ itself (Fig. 1).

A necessary consequence of this general model for steroid hormone action in regard to the various potential receptor–ligand interactions is that some aspect or component of the system must discriminate or have the capability of differentiating between the axial and equatorial conformers of the steroid hormone $1,25(OH)_2D_3$. Some possibilities are indicated in the right-hand panel of Fig. 15. Certainly, at the very least it would seem that the intestinal cytosol receptor is faced with a major problem—that of recognizing and "capturing" one of the two chair–chair conformers of $1,25(OH)_2D_3$ as it enters the intestinal cell. It does not seem likely that once the ligand has interacted with the intestinal receptor, continued oscillation would occur between the extremes of the two chair–chair conformers. If this postulate is accepted, then it would seem likely and perhaps obvious that one conformer might be preferentially active or preferentially receivable by the cytosol receptor as compared with the other chair–chair conformer. If this is the case, then prospects for the synthetic organic chemist are highly attractive, because it is possible to perturb the equilibrium of the chair–chair conformers by altering the nature of the functional groups on the A ring. Thus, it might be possible to either enhance or diminish the affinity or interaction between $1,25(OH)_2D_3$ analogs and the intestinal cytosol–receptor system.

It follows logically from what has been stated previously that the intracellular sequence of steroid–ligand receptor events muct contain an irreversible step(s). Otherwise, the "inactive conformer" could be reversibly transformed back to the "active conformer." Experimental support for our proposed model requires further comparison of the biological activities of a number of structural stereoisomers that differ in the relative proportion of A-ring conformers. Such studies are in progress at the present time. Because the equatorial:axial ratio of $1,25(OH)_2D_3$ is approximately 1:1, this suggests that if this equilibrium ratio could be perturbed to 9:1, it might be possible to obtain an analog with greater maximal biological activity than $1,25(OH)_2D_3$. Thus, in the terminology of Samuels and Tompkins (1970), $1,25(OH)_2D_3$ might be a "sub-optimal inducer." Samuels and Tompkins (1970) recognized in terms of their studies employing analogs of glucocorticoids (which were inducers of the liver enzyme tyrosine aminotransferase in the HTC cells in tissue culture) that there were at least three levels of response, each level being related to a structural class of the analogs. The three classes were (a) optimal inducers, i.e., those that gave the largest magnitude of response; (b) suboptimal inducers, i.e., those that generated only a fraction of the response of the optimal inducers; and (c) a class of analogs which were inactive. Samuels and Tompkins proposed that this classification resulted from the fact that the cytoplasmic glucocorticoid receptor in the HTC cells existed as two allosteric species. If, moreover, only one of the allosteric species was capable of being "activated" and transported to the nucleus to induce the biological response, then the relative magnitude of response produced by these steroids was the result of their relative affinity for the two forms of the cytoplasmic receptor. Conceivably, such a situation might also exist for the vitamin D metabolites and analogs. However, the problem is even more complicated in light of the rapid equilibration in solution of the two chair-chair conformers of these secosteroids. Each of these two conformers may have a different affinity for the two presumed allosteric forms of the cytoplasmic receptors for $1,25(OH)_2D_3$. In this connection it is interesting that the natural hormone, $1,25(OH)_2D_3$ may be a suboptimal inducer, because the analog 3-D-1-OH-D_3 can produce a greater maximum response (Norman *et al.*, 1975).

There are several reports that the target organ–cytosol receptor for steroid hormones exists in solution as an allosteric protein capable of two basic conformations (Marver *et al.*, 1972; Samuels and Tompkins, 1970). It has been suggested that only one form of the receptor protein may be capable of undergoing "activation" prior to entry of the steroid–receptor complex into the nucleus. If this is actually the case for the $1,25(OH)_2D_3$–hormone receptor system, then because of the complications induced by the unique aspects of dynamic interconversion of the A ring, it is difficult to specifically and precisely analyze the consequences of the interaction of these species with the putative allosteric forms of the cytoplasmic receptor. The conformational flexibility of the A ring of $1,25(OH)_2D_3$ is unique among steroid hormones; this singular property provides unusual challenges and problems for the experimentalist. It does follow, however, that the intracellular sequence of receptor events must contain an interreversible step. Otherwise, the "inactive conformer" could be transformed back to the "active conformer." Experimental support for our model requires further comparisons of the biological activity of a number of structural steroisomers that differ in the relative proportion of A-ring conformers.

An obvious alternative to the foregoing postulate of Okamura *et al.* (1974) and Norman *et al.* (1975, 1976) concerning possible preferential activity of one secosteroid conformer is that it is not correct. One model that is consistent with this view necessitates that the side-chain 25-hydroxyl functional group serves as a preliminary recognition group to permit "capture" and binding by the receptor of the rapidly equilibrating vitamin D ligand. Such possibilities are summarized in Fig. 16. In this set of circumstances, only one conformer is ultimately "frozen out" on the surface of the intestinal cytosol

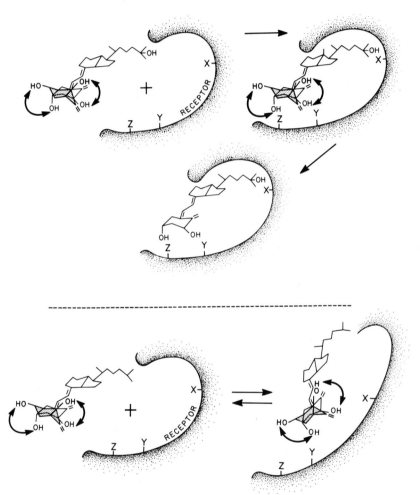

FIG. 16. Schematic model of the "steering effects" mediated by the 25-hydroxyl group of $1,25(OH)_2D_3$ as it binds to a receptor. The presence of the 25-hydroxyl group on the side chain (top panel) may orient the A ring of the secosteroid for optimum interaction with the receptor while in the absence of the 25-hydroxyl group (bottom panel) the A ring may not be "steered" for optimum binding to the receptor.

receptor. However, because of the rapid equilibration occurring between the pairs of chair–chair conformers, irrespective of the equilibrium ratio of these pairs, all possible equilibrium ratios interact with an identical association constant or affinity with the intestinal receptor system. This is possible for, as shown in Fig. 16, the 25-hydroxyl group functions as a preliminary "recognition" group to permit partial capture and interaction of the side-chain portion of the ligand to the intestinal receptor protein. Then, after interaction of the 25-hydroxyl group with appropriate functional moieties of the intestinal cytosol receptor, other favorable interactions between the receptor and the A ring of the ligand begin to occur. In the extreme and final equilibrium point, the ligand is "frozen out" in one of the two possible chair–chair conformers. Under normal circumstances this can only readily occur, i.e., with a high K_a, when the vitamin D secosteroid is preliminarily "captured" by the intestinal cytosol receptor.

One possible way to test this hypothesis is to synthesize analogs of $1,25(OH)_2D_3$ that would possess all the critical hydroxyl groups, particularly the 1α- and 25-OH groups in which the side chain is significantly shortened. Under such circumstances, one can envision that, while the initial interaction between the 25-hydroxyl group and the intesinal cytosol receptor may occur, because of the shortened side chain, the proper three-dimensional interaction of the A ring is perturbed or inhibited. Such studies are in progress in our laboratory at the present with the analog 24-*nor*-$1,25(OH)_2D_3$.

In summary, it appears that there is ample evidence to support the view that $1,25(OH)_2D_3$ is a completely legitimate steroid not only in a structural sense, but, equally as important, in a biochemical and physiological sense. It has been possible to document in great detail not only the various steps of interaction of this steroid hormone with its receptor proteins in its target cell, the intestinal mucosal cell, but to evaluate some of the biochemical properties of this receptor system in terms of the architecture of the specific binding sites for $1,25(OH)_2D_3$. It is important to realize that although $1,25(OH)_2D_3$ does qualify as a steroid hormone in the classic sense, there is an important unique aspect to this system: the conformational flexibility of the A ring of $1,25(OH)_2D_3$ is unique among all steroid hormones; clearly, this singular property provides unusual challenges and problems for the experimentalist.

REFERENCES

Adams, T. H., and Norman, A. W. (1970). *J. Biol. Chem.* **245**, 4421.

Askew, F. A., Bourdillon, R. B., Bruce, H. M., Callow, R. K. St. L., Philpot, J., and Webster, T. A. (1932). *Proc. R. Soc. London, Ser. B* **109**, 488.

Boyle, I. T., Gray, R. W., and DeLuca, H. F. (1971). *Proc. Natl. Acad. Sci. U.S.A.* **68**, 2131.
Brumbaugh, P. F., Hughes, M. R., and Haussler, M. R. (1975). *Proc. Natl. Acad. Sci. U.S.A.* **72**, 4871.
Buller, R. E., and O'Malley, B. W. (1976). *Biochem. Pharmacol.* **25**, 1.
Chamness, G. C., and McGuire, W. L. (1972). *Biochemistry* **13**, 2466.
Christakos, S., and Norman, A. W. (1978). *Fed. Proc.* Submitted for publication.
Crowfoot, D., and Dunitz, J. D. (1948). *Nature (London)* **162**, 608.
Eliel, E. N., Allinger, N. L., Angyal, N. L., and Morrison, G. A. (1965). "Conformational Analysis," Chapter 2. Wiley (Interscience), New York.
Emtage, J. S., Lawson, D. E. M., and Kodicek, E. (1973). *Nature (London), New Biol.* **246**, 100.
Faber, L. E., Sandman, M. L., and Stavely, H. E. (1972). *J. Biol. Chem.* **247**, 5648.
Fraser, D. R., and Kodicek, E. (1970). *Nature (London)* **228**, 764.
Friedlander, E. J., and Norman, A. W. (1975). *Arch. Biochem. Biophys.* **170**, 731.
Haussler, M. R., and Norman, A. W. (1967). *Arch. Biochem. Biophys.* **118**, 145.
Haussler, M. R., and Norman, A. W. (1969). *Proc. Natl. Acad. Sci. U.S.A.* **62**, 155.
Haussler, M. R., Myrtle, J. F., and Norman, A. W. (1968). *J. Biol. Chem.* **243**, 4055.
Haussler, M. R., Thomson, W. W., and Norman, A. W., (1969). *Exp. Cell. Res.* **58**, 234.
Henry, H. L., and Norman, A. W. (1975). *J. Biol. Chem.* **249**, 7529.
Henry, H. L., and Norman, A. W. (1975). *Biochem. Biophys. Res. Commun.* **62**, 781.
Henry, H. L., Midgett, R. J., and Norman, A. W. (1974). *J. Biol. Chem.* **249**, 7584.
Henry, H. L., Norman, A. W., Taylor, A. N., Hartenbower, D. L., and Coburn, J. W. (1976). *J. Nutrit.* **106**, 724.
Hodgkin, D. C., Rimmer, B. M., Dunitz, J. D., and Trueblood, K. N. (1963). *J. Chem. Soc.* p. 4945.
Holick, M. R., Schnoes, H. K., DeLuca, H. F., Suda, T., and Cousins, R. J. (1971). *Biochemistry* **10**, 2799.
Horsting, M., and DeLuca, H. F. (1968). *Biochem. Biophys. Res. Commun.* **36**, 251.
Irving, J. T. (1944). *J. Physiol. (London)* **103**, 9.
Knobler, C., Romero, C., Braun, P. B., and Hornstra, J. (1972). *Acta Crystallogr., Sect. B* **28**, 2097.
Lamar, G. D., and Budd, D. L. (1974). *J. Am. Chem. Soc.* **96**, 7317.
Larkins, R. G., MacAuley, S. J., Rapoport, A., Martin, T. J., Tulloch, B. R., Byfield, P. G. H., Matthews, E. W., and MacIntyre, I. (1974). *Clin. Sci. Mol. Med.* **46**, 569.
Lawson, D. E. M., Fraser, D. M., Kodicek, E., Morris, H. R., and Williams, D. H. (1971). *Nature (London)* **230**, 228.
Malm, O. J. (1953). *Scand. J. Clin. Lab. Invest.* **5**, 75.
Marver, D., Goodman, D. and Edelman, I. S. (1972). *Kidney Int.* **1**, 210.
Maurer, H. R. and Chalkley, G. R. (1967). *J. Mol. Biol.* **27**, 431.
Midgett, R. J., Spielvogel, A. M., Coburn, J. W., and Norman, A. W. (1973). *Clin. Endocr. Metab.* **36**, 1153.
Myrtle, J. F.. and Norman, A. W. (1971). *Science* **171**, 79.
Myrtle, J. F., Haussler, M. R., and Norman, A. W. (1970). *J. Biol. Chem.* **245**, 1190.
Nicolaysen, R. (1943). *Acta Physiol. Scand.* **5**, 201.
Norman, A. W. (1965). *Science* **149**, 184.
Norman, A. W. (1968). *Biol. Rev. Cambridge Philos. Soc.* **43**, 97.
Norman, A. W., and Henry, H. (1974a). *Clin. Orthop. Relat. Res.* **98**, 258.
Norman, A. W., and Henry, H. (1974b). *Recent Prog. Horm. Res.* **30**, 431.
Norman, A. W., Myrtle, J. F., Midgett, R. J., Nowicki, H. G., Williams, V., and Popjak, G. (1971). *Science* **173**, 51.
Norman, A. W., Mitra, M. N., Okamura, W. H., and Wing, R. M. (1975). *Science* **188**, 1013.

Norman, A. W., Johnson, R. L., Osborn, T. W., Procsal, D. A., Carey, S. C., Hammond, M. L., Mitra, M. N., Pirio, M. R., Rego, A., Wing, R. M., and Okamura, W. H. (1976). *Clin. Endocrinol.* **5**, 1215.

Noteboom, W. D. and Gorski, J. (1965). *Arch. Biochem. and Biophys.* **111**, 559.

Okamura, W. H., Norman, A. W., and Wing, R. M. (1974). *Proc. Natl. Acad. Sci. U.S.A.* **71**, 4194.

Omdahl, J. L., and DeLuca, H. F. (1973). *Phys. Rev.* **53**, 327.

Procsal, D. A., Okamura, W. H., and Norman, A. W. (1975). *J. Biol. Chem.* **250**, 8382.

Procsal, D. A., Okamura, W. H., and Norman, A. W. (1976). *Amer. J. Clin. Nutr.* **29**, 1271.

Puca, G. A., Nola, E., Sica, V., and Bresciani, F. (1971). *Biochemistry* **10**, 3769.

Samuels, H. H., and Tompkins, G. M. (1970). *J. Mol. Biol.* **52**, 57.

Tsai, H. C., and Norman, A. W. (1973). *J. Biol. Chem.* **248**, 5967.

Tsai, H. C., Midgett, R. J., and Norman, A. W. (1973). *Arch. Biochem. Biophys.* **157**, 339.

Wasserman, R. H., and Taylor, A. N. (1968). *J. Biol. Chem.* **243**, 3987.

Windaus, A., Linsert, O., Luttringhaus, A., and Weidlich, A. (1932). *Justus Liebigs Ann. Chem.* **492**, 226.

Wing, R. M., Okamura, W. H., Pirio, M. R., Sine, S. M., and Norman, A. W. (1974). *Science* **186**, 939.

Wing, R. M., Okamura, W. H., Rego, A., Pirio, M. R., and Norman, A. W. (1975). *J. Am. Chem. Soc.* **97**, 4980.

Wong, R. G., Norman, A. W., Reddy, C. R., and Coburn, J. W. (1972). *J. Clin. Invest.* **51**, 1287.

Zull, J. E., Misztal, C., and DeLuca, H. F. (1966). *Proc. Natl. Acad. Sci. U.S.A.* **55**, 177.

CHAPTER 8

The Chick Oviduct Progesterone Receptor

Wayne V. Vedeckis, William T. Schrader and Bert W. O'Malley

I. INTRODUCTION

Since their initial discovery (Toft and Gorski, 1966), steroid hormone receptor molecules have been thought to play a fundamental role in the actions of these hormones. These suspicions are supported by data demonstrating that the hormone is accumulated only in "target tissues" (Jensen and Jacobson, 1962) and that these tissues contain receptors in high abundance. Furthermore, no accumulation of radioactive steroid hormone occurs in the nucleus unless the cell contains the respective receptor. Within recent years, research in steroid hormone action has focused increasingly on hormonal induction of specific proteins in the target tissues. Studies performed on the chick oviduct have yielded an accumulation of data relating to the interaction of the progesterone receptor with its nuclear constituents and the possible mechanism whereby these molecules elicit specific gene expression. This chapter summarizes these results and attempts to correlate the molecular configuration of the progesterone receptor with the stimulation of hormone-responsive gene expression.

II. OVIDUCT PROGESTERONE RECEPTOR–HORMONE INTERACTIONS

The general characteristics of the chick oviduct progesterone receptor are similar to those of other steroid hormone receptors (see King and Mainwaring, 1974). The receptor is present in a target tissue for the hormone (oviduct) and is not detectable in nontarget tissues such as lung or spleen (Sherman *et al.*, 1970; O'Malley *et al.*, 1970).

A. HORMONE-BINDING KINETICS

The dissociation constant (K_D) has been determined by equilibrium methods for crude cytosol receptor (Sherman *et al.*, 1970; O'Malley *et al.*, 1970; Hansen *et al.*, 1976) and for the 2.6 S (mero-) receptor (Sherman *et al.*, 1974). Values obtained from this type of analysis range from $(4–50) \times 10^{-10} M$

The association rate constants (k_a) have been calculated for crude cytosol and partially purified A and B forms of the receptor (Schrader and O'Malley, 1972; Hansen *et al.*, 1976) and vary between 3×10^5 and $7.7 \times 10^5 M^{-1} \sec^{-1}$. The dissociation rate constants have also been determined for receptor in various stages of purification and molecular states. These include crude cytosol (Schrader and O'Malley, 1972; Hansen *et al.*, 1976); the A and B forms isolated from DEAE–cellulose columns (Schrader and O'Malley,

1972); affinity chromatography-purified receptor (Kuhn *et al.*, 1975); purified hen B receptor (Schrader *et al.*, 1977a); and purified A receptor (Coty *et al.*, 1978). The values obtained are $(1.6-2.4) \times 10^{-5}$ sec^{-1}. However, the dissociation rate constant from mero-receptor is somewhat larger (4.3×10^{-5} sec^{-1}; P. E. Hansen, W. T. Schrader, and B. W. O'Malley, unpublished). Table I summarizes results obtained for these kinetic parameters.

A curious dilemma is observed when determining the K_D by various methods. When the K_D is determined using the rate constants by Eq. (1),

$$K_D = k_d/k_a \tag{1}$$

it does not agree with that obtained using equilibrium methods (Table I). Particularly, the discrepancy in the values obtained by these methods varies widely as a function of temperature (Hansen *et al.*, 1976). Thus, the fundamental concept in steroid–receptor interaction, as exemplified by Eq. (2)

$$R + H \rightleftharpoons RH \tag{2}$$

where R = receptor, H = hormone, and RH = receptor–hormone complex, is still not completely understood.

The hormone-binding sites of the chick oviduct receptor are high affinity, low capacity (saturable), comprising about 0.02% of the total soluble cytosol protein or 1–2 μg receptor per gram oviduct (Sherman *et al.*, 1970). These values were confirmed in a recent study (Mešter and Baulieu, 1977) in which values of 10,000 and 40,000 receptor molecules per cell were obtained for unstimulated and DES-primed chicks, respectively.

TABLE I
HORMONE BINDING KINETICS OF THE CHICK OVIDUCT PROGESTERONE RECEPTOR[a]

	Rate constants		Equilibrium constant	
	Association $10^{-5} \times k_a$ $(M^{-1}$ sec$^{-1})$	Dissociation $10^5 \times k_d$ (sec^{-1})	From rates $10^9 \times k_d/k_a$ (M)	Scatchard $10^9 \times K_D$ (M)
Cytosol[b]	7.7	2.1	0.027	5.09
A form[c]	2.8	1.9	0.070	—
B form[c]	6.3	2.4	0.038	—
Mero-receptor	—	4.3[d]	—	0.4[e]

[a] All values for experiments performed at 0°–4°C.
[b] Hansen *et al.*, 1976.
[c] Schrader and O'Malley, 1972.
[d] P. E. Hansen, W. T. Schrader, and B. W. O'Malley, unpublished.
[e] Sherman *et al.*, 1974.

Based on the ultraviolet absorption spectrum of purified B receptor (with and without progesterone), it has been calculated that each receptor 4 S molecule binds one progesterone molecule (Kuhn *et al.*, 1977). Although this fact has been assumed for some time, this is the first empirical proof of receptor–hormone stoichiometry.

B. Steroid Specificity

The specificity of receptor binding has been studied for crude cytosol (O'Malley *et al.*, 1970; Sherman *et al.*, 1970; Smith *et al.*, 1974); ammonium-sulfate-precipitated receptor and partially purified A and B receptor (Schrader and O'Malley, 1972); affinity-chromatography-purified receptor (Kuhn *et al.*, 1975); purified hen B receptor (Schrader *et al.*, 1977a); purified A receptor (Coty *et al.*, 1978); and 2.6 S mero-receptor (Sherman *et al.*, 1974). The binding specificity correlates very well with the biological activity of the steroid as measured by the Clauberg bioassay (Smith *et al.*, 1974). In general, the relative competitive potency of these steroids when compared to progesterone are: progesterone $\geq$ deoxycorticosterone $>$ 5α-pregnane-3,20-dione $>$ dihydrotestosterone $>$ testosterone $>$ 20α-hydroxyprogesterone $>$ corticosterone $>$ estradiol-17β $>$ cortisol $>$ estrone $\geq$ androstenedione $\geq$ aldosterone. This relationship remains relatively intact throughout various stages of purification from cytosol to virtually homogeneous A and B receptor subunits.

Receptor hormone-binding activity is sensitive to pronase but not to DNase or RNase treatment (O'Malley *et al.*, 1970; Sherman *et al.*, 1970). It appears that only the polypeptide chain is necessary for receptor function.

The chick oviduct progesterone receptor, therefore, fulfills the accepted criteria for a steroid–receptor molecule: a protein with the capability of binding biologically active steroid hormone with high affinity, low capacity, and specificity.

III. ENZYMATIC AND BINDING ACTIVITIES OF THE CHICK OVIDUCT PROGESTERONE RECEPTOR

A variety of enzymatic and binding activities has been analyzed with respect to the chick oviduct progesterone receptor. Activities which fail to copurify with the progesterone receptor (Fig. 1) are DNA-dependent RNA polymerase (R. E. Buller, W. T. Schrader, and B. W. O'Malley, unpublished), cyclic AMP-dependent protein kinase (R. K. Keller, W. T. Schrader and B. W. O'Malley, unpublished), and cyclic AMP binding protein (R. K.

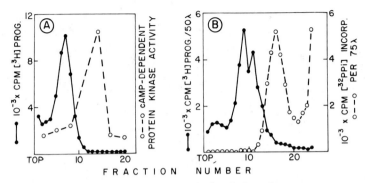

FIG. 1. Activities which do not comigrate with the chick oviduct progesterone receptor. Oviducts were removed, homogenized in Tris–EDTA–thioglycerol buffer, cytosol prepared, and labeled with [^{3}H]progesterone. Samples (200 μl) were layered on 5–20% sucrose gradients in Tris–EDTA–thioglycerol buffer containing 0.3 M KCl. Centrifugation was in a Beckman SW 50.1 rotor at 2°C for 16 hours at 45,000 rpm. Tubes were punctured, fractions collected [0.3 ml in (A); 0.2 ml in (B)], and the fractions counted for ^{3}H or assayed for enzymatic activity. Sedimentation is from left to right. (A) [^{3}H]progesterone binding activity (●—●; cyclic AMP-dependent protein kinase activity (○---○) (R. K. Keller, W. T. Schrader, and B. W. O'Malley, unpublished). (B) [^{3}H]progesterone binding activity (●—●); ATP–pyrophosphate exchange activity (○---○). From Schrader and O'Malley, (1978).

Keller, W. T. Schrader, and B. W. O'Malley, unpublished). In crude receptor preparations a contaminating polynucleotide phosphorylase activity was detected (Buller *et al.*, 1976a), but inhibition of this activity by 0.4 mM phosphate does not eliminate the effect of receptor on chromatin transcription (see Section VII,B,2).

Moudgil and Toft (1976) have reported that the chick oviduct progesterone receptor has an ATP–pyrophosphate exchange activity. The reaction is dependent on the partially purified receptor, Mn^{2+}, ATP (but not other nucleoside triphosphates), and is inhibited by *o*-phenanthroline and rifamycin AF/013, agents which inhibit binding of the receptor to nuclei (Lohmar and Toft, 1975). A recent study of this putative relationship (Schrader and O'Malley, 1978) demonstrates that the ATP–PP$_i$ exchange activity is distinct from the receptor–hormone binding activity when samples are subjected to sucrose density-gradient centrifugation in 0.3 M KCl (Fig. 1) and DEAE–cellulose gradient chromatography. In addition, the ATP–PP$_i$ exchange activity and hormone-binding activity are separable during the purification of both the A and B forms of the receptor protein. Thus, to date, no definitive enzymatic activity can be ascribed to the purified receptor.

Recently, Toft and his colleagues (Moudgil and Toft, 1975, 1977; Toft *et al.*, 1976, 1977) have suggested that ATP binding may be a property of the hen oviduct progesterone receptor. Using receptor precipitated to 35% saturated ammonium sulfate, they demonstrated that the receptor is capable of adsorbing to an ATP–Sepharose 4B column. Receptor can be eluted with a 1 M KCl step or a KCl gradient elution, with the receptor appearing as one peak between 0.5 and 0.6 M KCl. Preincubation of receptor with 1–5 mM ATP blocks subsequent adsorption to the affinity column, whereas other nucleoside triphosphates, ADP, AMP, or cyclic AMP are ineffective. Furthermore, the hormone binding activity is released with an ATP gradient (containing 0.15 M KCl), yielding one broad peak between 20 and 40 mM ATP.

Incubation of ATP with the receptor does not alter its behavior on sucrose gradients (4 S) or on polyacrylamide gel electrophoresis. Receptor eluted from the affinity column with ATP gives both the A and B forms of the receptor upon DEAE–cellulose chromatography. Conversely, DEAE cellulose-isolated A and B receptor can independently adsorb to ATP–Sepharose. Although the authors claim that ATP binding is hormone-independent and that both [^{3}H]progesterone-labeled and hormone-free receptor elute at the same KCl concentrations, they used hen oviducts which contain endogenous progesterone. Thus, it is possible that the receptor which binds to the column has endogenous unlabeled progesterone. Subsequent assay of the column fractions by incubation with [^{3}H]progesterone may have amounted to an exchange reaction with the unlabeled progesterone–receptor complex.

Interestingly, unactivated receptor (see Section VI,A,2), that is, cytosol not precipitated with ammonium sulfate, does not bind to ATP–Sepharose. However, receptor activated by heat demonstrates a time-dependent increase in both nuclear binding and ATP binding activity (Toft et al., 1976, 1977). Furthermore, salt activation of the receptor reveals a concentration-dependent increase in the amount of receptor capable of subsequent adsorption to ATP-Sepharose. Lastly, both o-phenanthroline and rifamycin AF/013, in high concentrations, are capable of inhibiting binding of ammonium-sulfate-precipitated receptor to ATP–Sepharose. Thus, ATP binding may have a potentially important role in steroid hormone receptor action. Further experiments on the effects of ATP on receptor function should illuminate this interesting problem.

IV. PROGESTERONE RECEPTOR FORMS

The chick oviduct progesterone receptor has been characterized by (a) sucrose density-gradient ultracentrifugation; (b) ion-exchange chromatography; (c) gel filtration; (d) isoelectric focusing; (e) polyacrylamide gel electrophoresis; (f) reaction with Ca^{2+} ions; (g) differential interaction with nuclear constituents; and (h) stimulation of chromatin transcription.

Although the hormone binding kinetics and specificity of the various progesterone receptor forms are virtually identical, based on these varying analyses and manipulations six forms of the progesterone receptor have been identified, some of which are components of the other forms. In low ionic strength buffers cytosol consists of two aggregate forms which sediment at 6 S and 8 S on sucrose gradients. These aggregates are composed of two separate polypeptide chains, the A and B subunits, which are both 4 S molecules. Finally, a Ca^{2+}-activated protease causes conversion of the receptor subunits to two smaller forms, form IV (3.6 S) and the mero-receptor (2.6 S). Our current belief is that the particular state of the receptor molecule is crucial in defining its physiological activity.

A. Sucrose Density-Gradient Ultracentrifugation

As has been observed in other steroid–receptor systems (Korenman and Rao, 1968), the receptor molecules display differing sedimentation characteristics when centrifuged through gradients of low or high ionic strength. In low ionic strength two major receptor forms are observed which sediment at 6 S and 8 S. When cytosol is centrifuged in high-salt sucrose gradients, one peak at 4 S is obtained (Fig. 2). Purified B receptor has a sedimentation coefficient of 4.2 S (Kuhn *et al.*, 1977), while the A form migrates at 3.6 S (Sherman *et al.*, 1976; Coty *et al.*, 1978). A mixture of these two forms would yield the observed 4 S peak for unfractionated cytosol. The 4 S peak obtained from high-salt sucrose gradients contains both A and B forms when analyzed on agarose gel filtration (Sherman *et al.*, 1970).

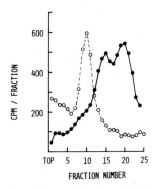

FIG. 2. Sucrose density-gradient ultracentrifugation of oviduct progesterone receptors from estrogen-primed chicks. Cytosol was prepared as in Fig. 1. Centrifugation was performed in sucrose gradients containing Tris–EDTA–thioglycerol (●———●) or the same buffer containing 0.3 M KCl (○---○). Sedimentation is from left to right. Hemoglobin (4.2 S) and aldolase (7.9 S) sediment in fractions 11 and 19, respectively. From Schrader *et al.* (1975).

B. Ion-Exchange Chromatography

As alluded to above, two separate receptor forms, termed A and B, have been purified to apparent homogeneity and have been found to each consist of a separate polypeptide chain, both capable of binding hormone (Coty *et al.*, 1978; Schrader *et al.*, 1977a). These two molecules differ significantly with respect to their interaction with ion-exchange resins, a fact which has been exploited for the purpose of purification (Schrader, 1975). A typical starting point in the characterization of these two molecules is precipitation of cytosol at 35% saturated ammonium sulfate. Under these conditions both forms are obtained in nearly equal concentrations, and no interconversion occurs.

1. Diethylaminoethyl (DEAE) Cellulose

When ammonium-sulfate-precipitated receptors are applied to DEAE–cellulose, almost all the receptor-bound radioactivity is retained [Fig. 3(A)]. A linear KCl gradient separates the receptor into two peaks, one of which elutes at 0.1–0.15 M KCl (A), and the other at 0.2 M (B). Two forms of the A receptor can be isolated independent of each other depending upon the mode of preparation (Schrader *et al.*, 1977c); one elutes at 0.1 M KCl and the other at 0.15 M KCl on DEAE–cellulose. The 0.15 M KCl form can be converted to the 0.1 M KCl form by the addition of a cytosol fraction which contains some as yet uncharacterized factor. Preliminary studies indicate that the factor is TCA-precipitable and of low molecular weight. Conversion of the 0.1 M KCl form to the 0.15 M KCl form can be accomplished by a procedure believed to remove this factor. Nondenaturing polyacrylamide gels also reveal heterogeneity in the A receptor form (see Section IV,E,1).

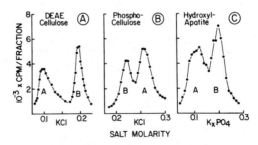

FIG. 3. Behavior of receptor forms on various ion-exchange resins. Receptor was prepared from [³H]progesterone-labeled cytosol by precipitation at 30% saturated ammonium sulfate. After dissolving the pellet in Tris–EDTA–thioglycerol buffer, receptor was applied to the columns followed by washing with the same buffer. (A) KCl gradient elution of receptor from DEAE–cellulose; (B) KCl gradient elution of receptor from PC; (C) K_xPO_4 gradient elution of receptor from HAP. From Schrader *et al.* (1977c).

2. Phosphocellulose (PC)

If the same preparation is applied to a PC column, most of the receptor adsorbs. A salt gradient again yields two peaks of hormone-binding activity [Fig. 3(B)]. The first elutes at 0.18–0.2 M KCl and corresponds to the B receptor as determined by rechromatography on DEAE–cellulose. The A receptor elutes between 0.24 and 0.28 M KCl.

3. Hydroxylapatite (HAP)

HAP has been widely used to assay receptor-bound steroid (Erdos *et al.*, 1970). Besides this application, it has also been found that the A and B progesterone receptors elute at different phosphate concentrations from HAP, A at 0.05–0.08 M phosphate and B at 0.15–0.18 M [Fig. 3(C)]. The major advantage of this column is that receptors in high salt (KCl) can be applied directly and still bind.

4. DNA–Cellulose

The B subunit does not bind to DNA–cellulose, whereas the A form does adsorb and elutes at 0.2 M KCl (Fig. 4). This property will be discussed more fully below (Section VI,C).

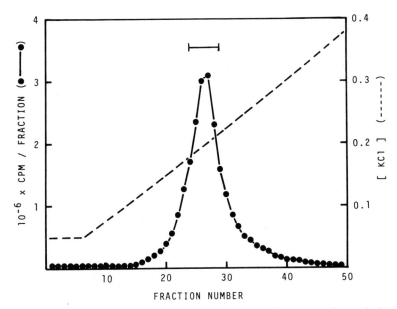

FIG. 4. DNA–cellulose chromatography of the receptor A subunit. Partially purified A protein was adsorbed to DNA–cellulose, followed by KCl gradient elution. From Coty *et al.* (1978).

C. Gel Filtration

The initial indication that more than one form of the chick oviduct progesterone receptor exists was the appearance of a double peak of binding activity when both cytosol (O'Malley *et al.*, 1969, 1970; Sherman *et al.*, 1970) and nuclear extracts (O'Malley *et al.*, 1971) were subjected to agarose A-0.5m gel filtration in 0.3 *M* KCl (Fig. 5). A more recent study (W. T. Schrader and B. W. O'Malley, unpublished) demonstrates that hormone-free cytosol or cytosol labeled very briefly (2 minutes) with progesterone yields the same two peaks when fractions are subsequently assayed for hormone-binding activity (Fig. 5). Furthermore, equivalent amounts of both forms are obtained regardless of the type of gel filtration column used or the hormonal status of the cytosol. These data argue against any interconvertibility of these two receptor forms and do not support the concept of a precursor–product relationship. The hormone-binding components, originally designated A_1 and A_2, correspond, respectively, to the B and A forms obtained upon DEAE–cellulose chromatography (Sherman *et al.*, 1976).

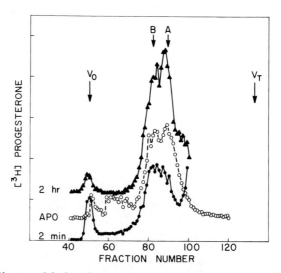

FIG. 5. Gel filtration of chick oviduct progesterone receptors. Cytosol was labeled for 2 hours (▲———▲) or 2 minutes (●———●) with [³H]progesterone and subjected to agarose A–1.5m gel filtration in Tris–EDTA–thioglycerol buffer containing 0.3 *M* KCl. Fractions were collected and counted for ³H. One sample of hormone-free cytosol (○---○) was subjected to gel filtration and the fractions labeled with [³H]progesterone. The fractions were subsequently analyzed for bound hormone using a HAP assay (Erdos *et al.*, 1970). From W. T. Schrader and B. W. O'Malley, unpublished.

D. Isoelectric Focusing

When ammonium-sulfate-precipitated receptor is subjected to isoelectric focusing, two peaks of hormone-binding activity are obtained, at pH 4.1 and 4.5. Based on the charge characteristics exhibited on DEAE–cellulose, it is presumed that these correspond to the B and A forms, respectively. Cytosol gives one peak at pH 4.8 (Sherman *et al.*, 1974), but it has been suggested that this may be caused by the coprecipitation of ovomucoids at pH 5 (Schrader and O'Malley, 1972). Precipitation of ovomucoids at pH 5 followed by focusing of the supernatant yields the same two peaks as for ammonium-sulfate-precipitated receptor. When receptor is separated from the majority of cytoplasmic proteins by sucrose gradient centrigation, however, only one peak at pH 4.8 is obtained (Sherman *et al.*, 1974). The significance of these discrepancies is unknown at this time.

E. Polyacrylamide Gel Electrophoresis

1. Nondenaturing Gels

Gel electrophoresis has been performed on progesterone receptor proteins at various stages of purification. Cytosol reveals two peaks of radioactivity which are distinctly different from chick corticosteroid binding globulin (Sherman *et al.*, 1970; Miller *et al.*, 1975). The A and B forms of the receptor have been studied in some detail and, as expected, vary significantly in electrophoretic mobility (Sherman *et al.*, 1976). Because of its high isoelectric point (pI>8), mero-receptor does not enter the gels with the system used.

The B receptor, as isolated by either gel filtration or from DEAE–cellulose filters, was identified as the fast-migrating form. By using Ferguson plots on data obtained from experiments run at different total acrylamide concentrations, this form was found to behave the same way when isolated by either method. The A form, however, migrates differently when prepared by gel filtration and DEAE–cellulose elution. This suggests that the A receptor can exist in at least two discrete forms. The heterogeneous pattern obtained for the A receptor in crude preparations analyzed by DEAE–cellulose gradient elution [Fig. 3(A)] also supports this contention (See Section IV,B,1).

When purified hen B receptor is subjected to nondenaturing polyacrylamide gel electrophoresis, the [^{3}H]progesterone binding activity comigrates with the major protein band (Fig. 6; Schrader *et al.*, 1977a). This verifies that the molecular weight assigned to the protein band observed on SDS (denaturing) gels is in fact that of the B receptor.

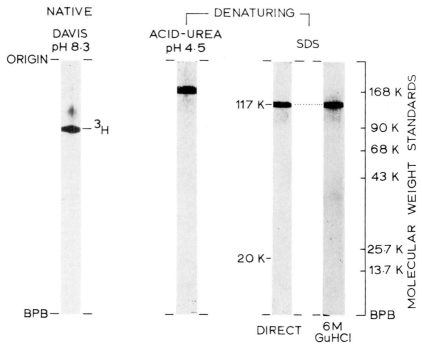

FIG. 6. Polyacrylamide gel electrophoresis of purified receptor B protein from laying hen oviducts. Labeled receptor–hormone complexes were analyzed with three different gel systems. Left-hand gel: Electrophoresis of native labeled receptor B protein on a 6.5% acrylamide gel at pH 8.3. One gel was stained for protein; a companion gel was sliced and counted for ^3H. The bar shows migration of the peak ^3H fraction and its comigration with the major protein band. Second gel from left: electrophoresis at pH 4.5 in 8.6 M urea on a 6.6% acrylamide gel. Protein was stained with amino black and destained electrophoretically. Third gel from left: SDS–polyacrylamide gel electrophoresis on 8.7% acrylamide in 1% SDS. Protein was stained with Coomassie blue and destained by diffusion. Migration of molecular-weight standards is shown on the extreme right. 20 K marker demonstrates absence of mero-receptor. Right-hand gel: SDS electrophoresis under the same conditions of a B receptor sample after it was first chromatographed by gel filtration under denaturing conditions in 6 M guanidine hydrochloride and 0.1 m β-mercaptoethanol. The sample from an agarose A–1.5m column was detected by ultraviolet absorbance at 235 nm, pooled, dialyzed into 1% SDS, and electrophoresed. From Kuhn *et al.* (1977) and Schrader *et al.* (1977a).

2. Denaturing Gels

SDS polyacrylamide gels have been used to analyze both the purity and molecular weights of progesterone receptor molecules from the chick oviduct. The B (Schrader *et al.*, 1977a) and A (Coty *et al.*, 1978) proteins have been purified to apparent homogeneity using adsorption and ion-exchange chromatography as the principal methods and migrate as single

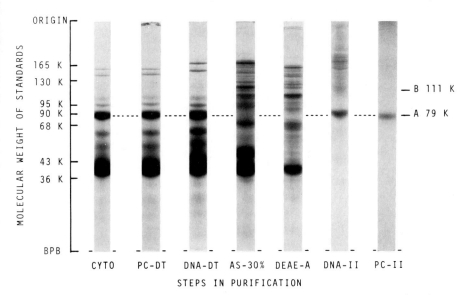

MOLECULAR WEIGHT OF STANDARDS

ORIGIN

165 K
130 K
95 K
90 K
68 K

43 K
36 K

BPB

— B 111 K

— A 79 K

CYTO PC-DT DNA-DT AS-30% DEAE-A DNA-II PC-II

STEPS IN PURIFICATION

FIG. 7. SDS–Polyacrylamide gel electrophoresis of receptor during various stages of purification of the A protein. Samples are, from left to right: cytoplasmic-soluble fraction (75 μg protein); PC dropthrough (70 μg); DNA-cellulose dropthrough (110 μg); 0–30% ammonium sulfate precipitate (70 μg); DEAE–cellulose A receptor pool (45 μg); DNA–cellulose II pool (15 μg); and final product after PC chromatography (approximately 10 μg). From Coty et al. (1978).

bands on SDS gels (Figs. 6 and 7). Both the B (Fig. 6) and A proteins have been electrophoresed on acid–urea polyacrylamide gels and comprise nearly all the protein present on these gels (Schrader et al., 1977a; Coty et al., 1978). Affinity chromatography of the intact receptor, followed by DEAE–Sephadex chromatography, yields protein bands corresponding to each of the receptor forms (Fig. 8; Kuhn et al., 1975).

F. CHARACTERISTICS OF THE PURIFIED A AND B RECEPTOR PROTEINS

Physicochemical parameters of the A and B proteins have been investigated and are listed in Table II. Both are highly asymmetric proteins, their shapes resembling that of a prolate ellipsoid (Sherman et al., 1970). The A protein has a molecular weight of 79,000 gm/mole; the B protein is found to weigh 117,000 gm/mole.

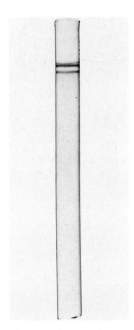

FIG. 8. SDS–Polyacrylamide gel electrophoresis of receptors obtained by affinity chromatography and DEAE–Sephadex ion exchange. The gel was 8.7% acrylamide containing 1% SDS, stained with Coomassie blue. The lower two bands correspond to the B and A subunits. From Kuhn *et al.* (1975).

G. Receptor Conversion by Treatment with Calcium

Calcium ions have been shown to promote conversion of estrogen (Rochefort and Baulieu, 1971) and aldosterone (Eldelman, 1972; Marver *et al.*, 1972) receptors to relatively small ($\sim$3 S) components. In a series of studies, Sherman and her colleagues (Sherman *et al.*, 1974, 1976; Sherman and Diaz, 1977) have demonstrated that the chick oviduct progesterone receptor can also be converted by Ca^{2+} to low-molecular-weight molecules which retain the hormone-binding site. This conversion is not a release of a subunit as originally proposed (Sherman *et al.*, 1974), but rather the result of Ca^{2+} activation of an endogenous protease. The apparent protease responsible for this conversion is not trypsin-like or a serine protease, because it has no activity toward α-N-benzoyl-DL-arginine-p-nitroanilide and is not inhibited by diisopropylfluorophosphate (Sherman *et al.*, 1974) or phenylmethylsulfonyl fluoride (W. V. Vedeckis, W. T. Schrader, and B. W. O'Malley, unpublished). A very similar activity has been extensively characterized for

TABLE II
MOLECULAR PROPERTIES OF RECEPTOR FORMS[a]

Parameter	Method	A	B
Sedimentation coefficient (S)	Sucrose gradient	3.6	4.2
Stokes radius R_s (Å)	Gel filtration	46	63
Frictional ratio (f/f_0)	S and R_s	1.74	1.9
Axial ratio (Prolate ellipsoid)	S and R_s	14	18
Partial specific volume (cm³/g)	Buoyancy in NaBr	0.73	0.73
Diffusion coefficient $10^7 \times D$ (cm²/sec)	f/f_0	3.89	3.38
Molecular weight	S and R_s	71,000	114,000
	SDS gels	79,000	117,000
	EM	—	106,000
Particle dimension (Å)	EM	—	114 × 29
Isoelectric point (pH)	Isoelectric focus	4.5	4.0
N-Terminal amino acid	Dansyl chloride	—	Lysine
Number of progesterone sites	UV Spectroscopy	—	1
Percent α-helical content	Circular dichroism	—	12%

[a]Values in this table are from the following sources: Coty *et al.*, 1978; Schrader *et al.*, 1977a; Kuhn *et al.*, 1977; Sherman *et al.*, 1970; Schrader and O'Malley, 1972.

the Ca^{2+}-activated receptor transforming factor (RTF) in the calf uterus (Puca *et al.*, 1977).

Exposure of cytosol to Ca^{2+} converts the progesterone receptor to a mero-receptor (2.6 S; Stokes radius 21 Å; molecular weight 23,000 g/mole) and form IV (3.6 S; Stokes radius 27 Å; molecular weight 43,000 g/mole). It was shown that these two forms are generated from the B and A subunits of the native receptor, respectively, and that the proteolytic activity elutes from DEAE–cellulose between 0.15 and 0.5 *M* KCl (Sherman and Diaz, 1977). However, more recent experiments (W. V. Vedeckis, W. T. Schrader, and B. W. O'Malley, unpublished) have demonstrated that, upon prolonged exposure to Ca^{2+}, all of the native cytosol receptor can be eventually converted to the mero-receptor. In addition, if [³H]A subunit is treated with Ca^{2+} in the presence of unlabeled cytosol the mero-receptor is obtained. Thus, form IV may be an intermediate in the conversion of the A subunit to the mero-receptor. Only the mero-receptor is obtained from Ca^{2+} treatment of protamine-sulfate-precipitated [Fig. 9(A)] or isoelectric-focused cytosol (Sherman *et al.*, 1974).

It was interesting to determine if this Ca^{2+}-induced fragment is of any physiological significance or if it is merely a nonspecific proteolytic product caused by the very high concentrations of Ca^{2+} used (50–100 m*M*). Heating the cytosol to 37°C in the absence of added Ca^{2+} converts the progesterone receptor to mero-receptor [Fig. 9(B); W. V. Vedeckis, W. T. Schrader, and B.

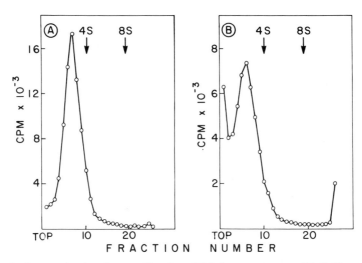

Fig. 9. Sucrose density ultracentrifugation of 2.6 S mero-receptor. (A) CaCl$_2$ generated: [^{3}H]progesterone-labeled cytosol was precipitated at 50% ammonium sulfate and applied to DEAE-cellulose. The column was washed, receptor eluted with 0.3 M KCl, and dialyzed against Tris–EDTA–thioglycerol. Receptor was precipitated with protamine sulfate, the pellet washed and treated with 0.1 M CaCl$_2$ for 1 hour at 4°C. Following dialysis, a sample (200 μl) was analyzed on sucrose gradients as in Fig. 1(B). (B) Heat-generated: [^{3}H]progesterone-labeled cytosol was heated at 37°C for 30 minutes, followed by cooling in an ice bath for 30 minutes. Sucrose density-gradient centrifugation was as in Fig. 1(b) (W. V. Vedeckis, W. T. Schrader, and B. W. O'Malley, unpublished).

W. O'Malley, unpublished]. The conversion is complete by 30 minutes at 37°C or 2 hours at 25°C (in the presence of 0.2 M KCl). The fact that the conversion occurs in the present of 0.2 M KCl suggests that the receptor need not be in the aggregate forms (6 S, 8 S); the proteolytic activity can act on the 4 S subunits. Thus, the endogenous Ca^{2+} level is apparently sufficient to activate the protease, and the large concentrations previously used simply accelerate the reaction at low temperature (4°C). At pH 7.4 in Tris–EDTA–thioglycerol buffer (Schrader and O'Malley, 1972), mero-receptor binds very weakly, if at all, to DEAE–cellulose (Schrader *et al.*, 1977b), phosphocellulose, DNA–cellulose, and hydroxylapatite (Table III). Mero-receptor generated by Ca^{2+} or heat are indistinguishable by all these criteria.

The relatively small size of the mero-receptor may facilitate studies on the interaction of the hormone with the receptor binding site and, if obtainable in sufficient quantity, may allow amino acid sequencing including the hormone binding site. A possible role for this molecule as an "off mechanism" with respect to receptor binding to the nuclear constituents is suggested below (Section VI,B,5; Section VIII).

TABLE III

ION-EXCHANGE CHROMATOGRAPHY OF MERO-RECEPTOR[a]

Resin	Ca^{2+}-mero (%)	37°C, 30 minutes-mero (%)
DEAE		
D.T.	72	78
Adsorbed	28	22
PC		
D.T.	88	97
Adsorbed	12	3
HAP		
D.T.	80	79
Adsorbed	20	21
DNA-Cellulose		
D.T.	94	96
Adsorbed	6	4

[a] All samples were applied in Tris-EDTA-thioglycerol buffer. DEAE and PC resins were eluted with a 0–0.4 M KCl gradient. HAP columns were step eluted with 0.5 M KH$_2$PO$_4$. DNA-Cellulose columns were step eluted with 0.5 M KCl. D.T. = dropthrough fraction.

V. CHARACTERISTICS OF RECEPTOR AGGREGATE FORMS

As mentioned above, cytosol which is sedimented through low-ionic-strength sucrose gradients reveals two aggregate forms, 6 S and 8 S (Sherman *et al.*, 1970; O'Malley *et al.*, 1970; Toft and O'Malley, 1972; Schrader *et al.*, 1975). Cytosol receptor aggregates extracted from unstimulated chick oviduct are comprised of the 4 S and 6 S forms, whereas estrogen-primed oviduct contains about equal quantities of 6 S and 8 S receptor forms (Toft and O'Malley, 1972; Schrader *et al.*, 1975). Recently, attention has been drawn to these aggregate receptor forms, with the hope of determining if any functional significance is attributable to them.

A. Ion-Exchange Chromatography

Cytosol prepared in low-ionic-strength buffers differs significantly from ammonium-sulfate-precipitated receptors with respect to their behavior on ion-exchange resins.

1. DEAE–Cellulose

Whereas 4 S receptor forms (35% ammonium sulfate precipitate) yield two equal peaks when chromatographed on DEAE–cellulose [see Fig. 3(A)], cytosol displays a doublet of bound progesterone eluting at 0.2 and 0.23 M KCl (Schrader *et al.*, 1975, 1977c). Isolation of the 6 S and 8 S aggregates from low-salt sucrose gradients followed by DEAE–cellulose demonstrates that the 6 S receptor elutes at 0.2 M KCl, while the 8 S form elutes at 0.23 M.

2. Phosphocellulose (PC)

Crude cytosol or 6 S and 8 S receptors isolated from sucrose gradients do not adsorb to PC columns. Furthermore, if cytosol is diluted 5- to 10-fold and then applied to PC, the dropthrough fraction contains mostly 6 S receptor. If the dropthrough is then warmed to 25°C or exposed to 0.3 M KCl for 30 minutes and then applied to PC, both the A and B forms appear in approximately equal amounts (Schrader *et al.*, 1975). Similarly, 6 S material which is collected from sucrose gradients, treated with 0.3 M KCl, diluted, and chromatographed on PC, exhibits an equal amount of the A and B forms (M. Birnbaumer, W. T. Schrader, and B. W. O'Malley, unpublished). These experiments led us to conclude that the 6 S form is a dimer consisting of one A subunit and one B subunit. This hypothesis is further supported by the fact that approximately equal amounts of the A and B forms are obtained by gel filtration of cytosol in high-salt buffers and after ammonium sulfate precipitation (Schrader and O'Malley, 1972).

In spite of the data supporting the dimer model, some experiments are difficult to explain when placed in this framework. When 6 S receptors isolated from sucrose gradients are treated with 0.3 M KCl, diluted, and applied to DEAE–cellulose, only one peak of hormone binding activity (at 0.2 M KCl) is obtained. As mentioned above, equal amounts of the A and B forms are obtained when the same preparation is analyzed on PC. One explanation for these findings is that the A and B subunits "snap back" on DEAE but not on PC.

Although there is no solid evidence to support it, an alternative model which includes a conversion (proteolytic?) of the B protein to the A form can be constructed. In addition, an inhibitory activity which, in most cases, stops the reaction at 50% would be necessary to account for the equivalent quantities of the A and B proteins obtained in the experiments outlined above. In one experiment (W. V. Vedeckis, W. T. Schrader, and B. W. O'Malley, unpublished) cytosol was applied to DEAE–cellulose and step eluted with 0.15 and 0.3 M KCl. The material eluting at 0.3 M KCl was diluted, reapplied to DEAE, and the step elutions repeated. Eventually, 75% of the radioactive receptors were converted to a form which eluted at 0.15 M KCl (A), while 25% continued to elute at 0.3 M KCl (B) throughout the experiment. In spite of this, it is quite clear that purified receptors undergo no such conversion. Nonetheless, the fact that both the A and B proteins display the same hormone binding kinetics and the same response to competition by various steroids (Section II) suggests that both proteins are closely related polypeptide chains.

3. DNA–Cellulose

Cytosol at low ionic strength, as well as 6 S receptor, binds poorly to DNA–cellulose (see Fig. 11). This property has been utilized for the purification of the A (DNA-binding) receptor (Coty *et al.*, 1978).

B. Reconstitution of the 6 S Receptor

It has not yet been possible to reconstitute the 6 S receptor from homogeneous A and B receptor proteins. However, if partially purified A receptor is mixed with cytosol blocked with unlabeled progesterone, a 6 S receptor aggregate is obtained upon low-salt sucrose gradient centrifugation (Schrader *et al.*, 1975). The reciprocal experiment, utilizing labeled B receptor, does not yield a 6 S aggregate but rather a 4 S peak on sucrose gradients, as if it were centrifuged alone. An A-B dimer may not be formed when B is used because an essential factor (associated with the A subunit) is purified away during the B preparation, or because some relationship between the A and B proteins exists which has not yet been elucidated.

In an attempt to obtain receptor in a form which is active in the stimulation of RNA synthesis-initiation sites (see Sections VII,A,3 and VII,B,2), Buller *et al.* (1976b) partially purified the chick oviduct progesterone receptor using a series of step elutions from various ion-exchange columns.

After some initial purification steps, receptor is adsorbed to a PC column, followed by thorough washing of the column with low-salt buffer. As mentioned above, only the 4 S forms of the receptor (A and B) adsorb to PC, while aggregate forms (6 S, 8 S) drop through this column. Following step elution of this column, the receptor is applied to HAP, the column washed, and the receptor step eluted with phosphate. The last step is desalting on a G-75 column.

Sucrose density-gradient centrifugation of this material yields the following distribution of radioactivity: 4 S = 54%; 6 S = 34%; large aggregates (tube bottom) = 12%. Thus, a significant proportion of receptor which had previously bound to PC (4 S) subsequently appears as 6 S aggregate. This represents an apparent reconstitution of the 6 S dimer from 4 S subunits. DEAE–cellulose chromatography reveals that most of the receptor elutes at 0.22 M KCl, while PC chromatography of salt-treated receptor gives both A and B forms in approximately equal amounts. Therefore, the preparation obtained in this study demonstrates the same properties ascribed to the native 6 S dimer: (a) migration at 6 S on sucrose gradients, (b) elution as a single peak at approximately 0.2 M KCl on DEAE–cellulose; and (c) the presence of approximately equal amounts of the A and B forms on PC after salt treatment. Dissociation of the subunits during sucrose gradient centrifugation could explain the lower level (34%) of 6 S receptor obtained as compared to the apparent 6 S dimer peak on DEAE–cellulose (90%). The apparent reconstitution of a 6 S dimer from 4 S subunits could be due to the retention of some essential factor by step elution of these columns which is lost during the gradient elutions used to prepare homogeneous A and B receptor forms. In addition, an increase in the concentration of receptor subunits obtained by the HAP step may facilitate reconstitution.

An interesting observation is that, at physiological ionic strength (0.15–0.2 M KCl), the 6 S receptor is metastable, that is, conversion to the 4 S form is approximately 50% complete (Schrader *et al.*, 1975, 1977b). Thus, a 6 S A-B dimer would be capable of dissociation into monomers at physiological ionic strength.

C. Conclusions

In spite of inconsistencies in some experiments which cannot yet be explained, the best interpretation at present for the majority of the existing data obtained is that the 6 S receptor is a dimer of one A and one B subunit. The 8 S form, although not extensively studied thus far, is believed to be a nonspecific aggregate of 4 S components because it is unstable to dilution and dialysis. The postulated conversion of the receptor B to A forms or the existence of a precursor to both is unlikely but remains a possibility until immunological studies can be performed and, ultimately, until the amino acid sequence of the A and B proteins is known.

VI. PROGESTERONE RECEPTOR INTERACTION WITH NUCLEAR COMPONENTS

A. NUCLEI

After *in vivo* injection of radioactive estrogen or progesterone, autoradiography of target tissues such as the uterus reveals accumulation of hormone in the cell nucleus (King *et al.*, 1965; Jensen *et al.*, 1968; Stumpf, 1968; Stumpf and Sar, 1973). Using cell fractionation, nuclear accumulation of progesterone in the chick oviduct is also demonstrable after *in vivo* hormone administration or incubation of tissue slices with progesterone (O'Malley *et al.*, 1969, 1970, 1971), as well as after incubation of [³H]progesterone-labeled cytosol with nuclei *in vitro* (O'Malley *et al.*, 1971; Buller *et al.*, 1975a). In view of the striking effects steroid hormones have on the synthesis of specific proteins, extensive information has been collected on the interaction of the progesterone receptor protein with the nucleus.

1. Cytoplasmic Depletion of Receptor

After *in vivo* injection of [³H]progesterone, a time-dependent depletion of receptor occurs in the cytoplasmic compartment, followed by an accumulation of receptor in the nucleus (O'Malley *et al.*, 1971). The concomitant stoichiometric loss of cytoplasmic receptor during nuclear uptake supports the notion that the cytoplasmic receptor enters the nucleus (O'Malley *et al.*, 1970, 1971; Buller *et al.*, 1975a). Measurement of receptor concentrations by the exchange assay (Anderson *et al.*, 1972) demonstrates that rat uterine cytoplasmic estrogen receptor is driven into the nucleus by estrogen injection and is accompanied by a stoichiometric increase in the nuclear receptor content (see Clark *et al.*, 1976a). This is the most convincing evidence that the nuclear receptor is derived from the cytoplasmic receptor, because prior to hormone injection no receptor can be detected in the nucleus. Thus, it is difficult to envision an acceptable alternative for steroid uptake into the nucleus. The results described for the chick oviduct progesterone receptor in the following three sections support nuclear uptake of the cytoplasmic receptor.

2. Nuclear Translocation and Receptor Activation

As has been observed for other receptors (see King and Mainwaring, 1974), transfer of radioactive progesterone from the cytoplasm to the nucleus is a temperature- and time-dependent process. Incubation of oviduct tissue slices with hormone *in vitro* at 0°C results in a very slow nuclear accumulation of radioactivity, whereas elevation to 37°C causes rapid uptake (O'Malley *et al.*, 1970, 1971). Progesterone appears predominantly in the cytosol fraction at very short incubation times, while nuclear levels increase only after longer periods. Similarly, *in vitro* incubation of [^{3}H]progesterone-labeled cytosol with purified nuclei at 0°C results in very little nuclear uptake, while at 23°–25°C a rapid nuclear uptake of hormone occurs coincident with depletion of hormone–receptor complex from the cytosol (O'Malley *et al.*, 1971; Buller *et al.*, 1975a; Pikler *et al.*, 1976). The progesterone receptor is essential for the process of hormone uptake because lung, liver, and spleen cytosol or buffer alone containing [^{3}H]progesterone do not facilitate nuclear uptake.

These observations could be explained by either a simple acceleration of steroid–receptor complex diffusion into and retention in the nucleus, or by a temperature-dependent active transport mechanism. Observations with the estrogen receptor (Jensen *et al.*, 1972) support the argument that active transport is not the case. These investigators discovered that merely warming the cytosol, followed by incubation at 0°C with nuclei, enhances the uptake process. The temperature-dependent modification of the receptor which allows nuclear uptake at low temperature is termed "activation." In this, and in studies described below, it is important to bear in mind that "activation" is studied in isolated cytosol, in which receptors may be exposed to proteins that they do not encounter *in vivo*. Association of the receptor with these proteins upon homogenization could result in the formation of an "inactive" receptor. Warming might then simply cause a dissociation of receptor from contaminants, resulting in a return to a more physiological state. Thus, the *in vivo* significance of *in vitro* activation remains to be established.

A detailed study has demonstrated that receptor activation also occurs for the chick oviduct progesterone receptor (Buller *et al.*, 1975a). Treatment of cytosol at 25°C for 30 minutes results in a doubling of nuclear uptake upon subsequent incubation with nuclei at 0°C when compared to unheated cytosol. Similar heat pretreatment of nuclei alone does not increase the amount of uptake and indicates that receptor activation is the limiting factor in nuclear translocation. Nevertheless, when the uptake experiment is performed at 25°C (with activated or unactivated receptor), the level is increased another 2-fold over those obtained using activated receptor and nuclei at 0°C. Furthermore, there is no change in the K_D of receptor binding to nuclei ($K_D = 1.5 \times 10^{-8} M$; Buller *et al.*, 1975b). Thus, temperature both causes receptor activation and accelerates the rate of uptake by a separate mechanism.

As has been reported for other steroid receptors (DeSombre *et al.*, 1972; Higgins *et al.*, 1973), high ionic strength can also induce progesterone receptor activation (Buller *et al.*, 1975a; Jaffe *et al.*, 1975; Pikler *et al.*, 1976). Precipitation of cytosol with 30% saturated ammonium sulfate activates the progesterone receptor, and heat treatment of ammonium-sulfate-activated receptor does not further augment nuclear uptake.

3. Hormonal Requirement for Receptor Activation and Nuclear Retention

Temperature-induced activation of the chick oviduct progesterone receptor requires the presence of a preformed progesterone–receptor complex (Buller *et al.*, 1975a). Treatment of hormone-free receptor at 25°C for 30 minutes, followed by hormone binding at 0°C, results in nuclear uptake levels characteristic of unactivated receptor. If the same experiment is performed using ammonium-sulfate-activated receptor, however, nuclear uptake resembles that of hormone–receptor complex activated by the salt treatment. Most importantly, ammonium-sulfate-activated receptor without bound hormone is not translocated into the nucleus (Buller *et al.*, 1975a). Therefore, although receptor can be "activated" by salt exposure alone, nuclear retention manifests an absolute requirement for the presence of a steroid–receptor complex.

Finally, the dissociation of 6 S receptor by salt was studied in the absence and presence of [³H]progesterone (Schrader *et al.*, 1977b). At physiological ionic strength the 6 S receptor–hormone complex is metastable, and dissociation into the 4 S form is virtually complete at 0.25 M KCl. On the contrary, when hormone-free receptor is centrifuged on sucrose gradients of varying ionic strengths, and fractions assayed afterward for hormone binding activity, most of the receptor remains as a 6 S aggregate. Thus, hormone destabilizes the 6 S form, making it more readily dissociable by salt.

4. Effect of Nucleotides on Receptor Activation

Recent studies implicate nucleotides as putative regulatory agents in the process of receptor activation (Toft *et al.*, 1977). At low concentrations of nucleotides activation is inhibited, whereas high concentrations cause an apparent increase in activation Both these effects are presumably on the rate of the activation process because upon prolonged incubation, both control and experimental values can attain the same level. This, along with the ATP-binding data mentioned above (Section III), requires that the effect of nucleotides on the chick oviduct progesterone receptor be examined further.

5. Molecular Nature of the Nuclear Receptor

High-salt buffers extract receptor–hormone complexes from the nucleus. When these extracts are subsequently analyzed on sucrose gradients, a single peak at 4 S is observed which is indistinguishable from that obtained for the cytosol receptor (O'Malley et al., 1970, 1971; Schrader et al., 1972; Buller et al., 1975a). Similarly, if cytosol receptor is activated by temperature, a single 4 S peak is obtained on high-salt sucrose gradients (Buller et al., 1975a). Extraction of either crude or highly purified nuclei yields only a 4 S peak (O'Malley et al., 1971). Thus, there is no discernible "transformation" of the receptor as is evidenced by the 4 S → 5 S conversion reported in studies on the uterine estrogen receptor (see Jensen et al., 1974).

When oviduct tissue slices are incubated in vitro with [³H]progesterone, the high-salt nuclear extracts contain both the A and B forms in approximately equal amounts when analyzed by gel filtration (O'Malley et al., 1971) or DEAE–cellulose chromatography (Schrader et al., 1972). Likewise, if DEAE-purified A and B components are incubated with purified nuclei in vitro, both are capable of binding to nuclei. However, only one time point was investigated in these studies. It would be advantageous to undertake a kinetic analysis of receptor uptake into the nucleus in order to determine if the A and B subunits enter at the same rate. If so, this would support the notion that the subunits are translocated into the nucleus as a 6 S dimer.

6. Tissue Specificity of Nuclear Binding

The chick oviduct progesterone receptor demonstrates tissue specificity for binding to nuclei. If oviduct, lung, liver, spleen, heart, and erythrocyte nuclei are incubated in vitro with chick oviduct cytosol, high-salt extraction of the nuclei reveals more 4 S receptor from oviduct nuclei than from the others (O'Malley et al., 1971; Buller et al., 1975a,b). This led O'Malley and his co-workers (1971) to postulate the presence of specific "acceptor" sites in the target-cell nucleus which are responsible for the increased uptake and retention of the steroid hormone–receptor complex. The acceptor sites for receptor are present in a higher concentration in target tissue than in nontarget tissue nuclei.

7. Saturability and Multiplicity of Nuclear Binding Sites

An ongoing controversy in the field of steroid–receptor interaction with the nucleus is the question of saturability. Recent reports (Chamness et al., 1974; Simons et al., 1976) suggest that the apparent saturability of nuclear binding which occurs during *in vitro* incubations with cytosol may be due to the variations in total protein content or the presence of an inhibitor of nuclear binding. While it is not our goal to present a detailed analysis of this problem, studies done on the chick oviduct system may emphasize the parameters responsible for yielding conflicting results in various laboratories.

Detailed studies have been carried out on the kinetics of progesterone receptor binding to the nucleus (Buller *et al.*, 1975b; Spelsberg *et al.*, 1975, 1976a; Pikler *et al.*, 1976; Spelsberg, 1976). The interaction of the progesterone receptor with the nucleus is dependent upon time, temperature, protein concentration, ionic strength, and the method used to purify the nuclei.

Buller *et al.* (1975b) observed that ionic strength has a dramatic effect on the number of nuclear binding sites for receptor, while it does not affect the affinity of the receptor for these sites. At low ionic strength at 25°C, a large number of binding sites is observed ($\sim$80,000 sites/nucleus) with an apparent K_D of approximately $0.8 \times 10^{-8}\ M;$ a smaller class of sites ($\sim$2,000 sites/nucleus) with a higher affinity ($\sim 3 \times 10^{-11}\ M$) is also present. As the ionic strength of the incubation buffer is raised, the number of binding sites decreases to about 8000 sites/nucleus at $0.25\ M$ KCl (using ammonium-sulfate-activated receptor at 0°C). Further experiments were done at $0.15\ M$ KCl (a presumptive physiological salt concentration) at which 20,000 sites/nucleus were found.

Under the specific conditions chosen for the assays, it was found that nuclear binding is saturable at both 0°C and 25°C in the presence of a constant protein concentration but is inhibited by high concentrations of protein. The source of the protein (hormone-free oviduct cytosol, oviduct cytosol containing unlabeled progesterone, heart or colon cytosol, bovine serum albumin) does not alter the extent of inhibition. Receptor binding to nontarget tissue (colon, erythrocyte) nuclei is also a saturable phenomenon, but these nuclei bind less total hormone–receptor complex. Finally, the number of binding sites is dependent upon incubation temperature because the value doubles at 25°C as compared to 0°C.

An extensive study has been undertaken by Spelsberg (1976) to resolve the questions of saturability and specificity of nuclear binding of the chick oviduct progesterone receptor. By injecting various doses of labeled progesterone, it was discovered that more than one type of binding site may be present in oviduct nuclei. The first class saturates at 50–75 μg of injected progesterone ($\sim$ 1000–10,000 sites/nucleus), while a second saturates at 500–1000 μg of hormone ($\sim$100,000 sites/nucleus). Using multiple doses of progesterone, three classes of nuclear binding sites are detectable at levels of 1000, 10,000, and 100,000 sites/nucleus. Analysis of RNA polymerase activi-

ties demonstrates that saturation of the highest-affinity class (1000 sites/
nucleus) depresses RNA polymerase II activity without affecting RNA
polymerase I. Saturation of the second class of binding sites further depresses RNA polymerase II and stimulates RNA polymerase I activities.
RNA polymerase I activity is depressed when the third class of sites is
saturated. Progesterone doses which result in physiological serum levels of
the hormone are capable of saturating only the highest-affinity nuclear sites.
To further complicate matters, the method for preparing nuclei influences
the amount of bound progesterone measured.

An *in vitro* study, using ammonium-sulfate-precipitated receptor, emphasizes that one of the most crucial parameters to analyze with respect to
nuclear binding (number of sites, saturability, tissue specificity) is the ionic
strength (Pikler *et al.*, 1976). In the absence of KCl no saturation is observed. As the ionic strength is increased, saturation is obtained along with a
lower degree of total binding. Titration of nuclei with receptor at varying
ionic strengths reveals the presence of multiple classes of nuclear binding
sites, supporting the *in vivo* studies discussed above. At low ionic strength
(0.05 M KCl) hen oviduct nuclei display three classes of binding sites: (a)
highest affinity—$K_D = 1.2 \times 10^{-9} M$, 5300 sites/nucleus; (b) intermediate
affinity—$K_D = 1.3 \times 10^{-8} M$, 20,600 sites/nucleus; and (c) lowest affinity—K_D
$= 3.9 \times 10^{-8} M$, 34,800 sites/nucleus. When the binding reaction is done at
physiological ionic strength (0.15 M), only the highest-affinity class of nuclear
binding sites is observed. If the same type of analysis is performed using
nontarget tissue nuclei and low-ionic-strength buffer, no high-affinity sites
are observed for these nuclei, although lower-affinity classes of sites are
present. In high-ionic-strength buffer (0.15 M KCl), no high-affinity sites are
evidenced for spleen or liver nuclei, but nuclei of erythrocyte and lung
display some of these sites, albeit at a lower level than that found in oviduct
nuclei.

The conclusion drawn from these two studies is that only the high-affinity
class of nuclear binding sites is important for the physiological response of
the cell to progesterone, for only this class is occupied and saturated at the
physiological ionic conditions and hormone levels found in the cell. Other
studies demonstrating nonsaturable, nonspecific nuclear binding may have
only been detecting the lower-affinity binding sites. It is also evident from
these studies that small increments of receptor concentration should be used
for nuclear binding experiments because a large range of concentration may
detect a few points in each binding class, yielding data consistent with nonsaturable binding.

8. KCl-Resistant Nuclear Receptor

Mešter and Baulieu (1977) have observed that a portion of the nuclear
receptor is resistant to extraction with 0.5 M KCl. If the nuclei are not

exposed to increased temperature prior to extraction, 75% of the receptor is extractable with salt, whereas after a 1-hour incubation at 30°C only 12% is extractable. Irrespective of temperature treatment, 12% of the radioactive hormone is nonextractable, even with 2 M NaCl–5 M urea. A time-dependent increase has also been observed for KCl-resistant nuclear receptor levels during incubation of oviduct slices with [³H]progesterone at 25°C and 37°C (W. V. Vedeckis, W. T. Schrader, and B. W. O'Malley, unpublished).

Studies on the rat uterine estrogen receptor suggest that the KCl-resistant nuclear-bound receptors may be those which are responsible for true uterine growth (Clark and Peck, 1976; Clark *et al.*, 1976b). The lowest effective dose of estradiol which can promote the uterine response to hormone results in the formation of the same number of KCl-resistant nuclear sites as higher doses; larger amounts of hormone cause an increase only in the KCl-extractable sites. Thus, it is suggested that the highest-affinity, physiologically significant sites are those which are resistant to extraction with KCl (1500–3000 sites/nucleus).

9. Binding of Purified Receptors to Nuclei

Chick oviduct progesterone receptor purified by affinity chromatography (Kuhn *et al.*, 1975) and labeled hen B receptor purified to apparent homogeneity (Kuhn *et al.*, 1977) bind to oviduct nuclei in a saturable fashion and display binding kinetics very similar to those obtained using crude cytosol or ammonium-sulfate-precipitated receptor. This demonstrates that the receptor is responsible for the nuclear binding observed using crude preparations, and that saturation is due to the receptor itself, not to inhibition by contaminating proteins (Simons *et al.*, 1976).

10. Inhibition of Nuclear Binding

It has been shown that both *o*-phenanthroline and rifamycin AF/013 inhibit binding of ammonium-sulfate-precipitated receptor to oviduct nuclei (Lohmar and Toft, 1975). The effect of these agents is apparently on the receptor and not the nuclei, although neither the progesterone binding activity nor sedimentation coefficient of the receptor is drastically altered. In view of the inhibitory effects of these agents on RNA polymerases and the zinc binding ability of *o*-phenanthroline, this study raises interesting possibilities with respect to the mechanism of receptor binding to nuclei. Furthermore, both these components inhibit the ATP–pyrophosphate exchange activity alluded to earlier (Moudgil and Toft, 1976; see Section III), which suggests a role for this activity in the process of receptor uptake into the nucleus. However, the concentration of rifamycin AF/013 needed for inhibition of the enzyme activity is very high (80–300 μg/ml), so that much more information is needed before any plausible explanation for these results is feasible.

11. Molecular Nature of the Nuclear Binding Site for the Progesterone Receptor

Using pancreatic DNase (type I), Buller *et al.* (1975a) digested up to 60% of the nuclear DNA prior to incubation with progesterone receptor. This treatment results in a decrease of only 10–15% in the nuclear bound receptor, suggesting that if DNA is important in the nuclear binding of the receptor, it is located in relatively DNase-resistant regions in the chromatin.

12. Conclusions

In spite of the effects of differing experimental parameters on the results obtained, studies on the interaction of the chick oviduct progesterone receptor with the nucleus have been most informative. After binding hormone, the cytosol receptor undergoes an activation step, followed by uptake into the nucleus. The receptor binds to the nucleus in a saturable fashion with high affinity, and saturation is not due to inhibition by a cytoplasmic contaminant. Both 4 S forms (A and B) appear in the nucleus. At physiological ionic strength, the receptor binds to target-cell nuclei to a much greater extent than to nontarget tissue nuclei. Finally, DNA involved in the nuclear acceptor sites resides in relatively DNase-resistant regions.

B. CHROMATIN

The studies performed on nuclei described above have been further extended utilizing preparations of chromatin. As observed with nuclei, temperature and ionic strength have profound effects on the type and extent of binding observed. Likewise, the tissue specificity evidenced for nuclei is preserved in the chromatins from various tissues. Significantly, the absence of intact membranes and nucleoplasmic proteins as well as chromatin reconstitution has allowed considerable progress in the identification of the "acceptor sites" present in nuclei and chromatin, leading to an increased understanding of the chemical composition of these sites. By switching the chromatin components (DNA, histones, nonhistone proteins), it has been determined that a combination of nonhistone proteins and DNA, but not histones, is important for the construction of functional acceptor sites. The salient features of these studies are summarized below.

1. Receptor Forms Binding to Chromatin

The following preparations of chick oviduct progesterone receptor have been investigated with respect to chromatin binding: crude cytosol (Steggles *et al.*, 1971,a,b; Spelsberg *et al.*, 1971a,b, 1972; Jaffe *et al.*, 1975); ammonium-sulfate-precipitated receptor (Schrader *et al.*, 1974; Jaffe *et al.*, 1975; Spelsberg *et al.*, 1975, 1976a,b,c, 1977; Webster *et al.*, 1976); 6 S receptor prepared by phosphocellulose exclusion (Schrader *et al.*, 1977b); A and B receptor isolated from DEAE–cellulose (Schrader *et al.*, 1972; Jaffe *et al.*, 1975); affinity-chromatography-purified receptor (Jaffe *et al.*, 1975; Kuhn *et al.*, 1975); and homogeneous B protein (Kuhn *et al.*, 1977). When determined for these substantially different preparations, the K_D and number of sites per cell are found to be remarkably similar, varying between $(1.5–7.8) \times 10^{-9} M$ and 3380–5500, respectively. Saturable binding is observed in all cases. The A receptor protein does not bind at all to chromatin (Schrader *et al.*, 1972), a fact which proves important in assigning functional relationships to the various receptor forms (see Section VIII).

To determine if the progesterone receptor is altered after interacting with chromatin the following experiments have been performed. Oviduct tissue slices were incubated *in vitro* with [³H]progesterone and chromatin prepared. Extraction of receptor from this chromatin followed by high-salt sucrose density-gradient centrifugation yields one peak of macromolecular-bound radioactivity identical to that originally found in the cytosol (Palmiter *et al.*, 1973). Likewise, cytosol was incubated *in vitro* with chick oviduct chromatin. After the binding reaction, both the cytosol and a 0.3 M KCl extract of the chromatin demonstrate 4 S peaks on high-salt sucrose gradients (Spelsberg *et al.*, 1971a). Thus, there is no change in the sedimentation behavior of the progesterone receptor after binding to target-tissue chromatin.

2. Tissue Specificity

Experiments similar to those done with nuclei were performed using homologous and heterologous cytosols and chromatins (Spelsberg *et al.*, 1971a,b; Steggles *et al.*, 1971a,b; Webster *et al.*, 1976). In all cases, the oviduct cytosol labeled with [³H]progesterone binds to a larger extent to oviduct chromatin than to nontarget tissue chromatins such as spleen, liver, erythrocyte, and heart. Cytosols of these nontarget tissues, as well as chick serum or buffer alone, are ineffective in promoting [³H]progesterone binding to oviduct chromatin. When spleen and erythrocyte chromatins are used with ammonium-sulfate-precipitated oviduct progesterone receptor, the same K_D is obtained as with oviduct chromatin [$(4–5) \times 10^{-9} M$], but the number of sites is reduced, being 2200 and 850 sites/cell, respectively, compared to 3360 sites/cell for oviduct chromatin (Jaffe *et al*, 1975). Thus, as is the case for nuclear binding, both the target-tissue receptor and chromatin acceptor are necessary for maximal binding of the hormone to chromatin.

3. Parameters Affecting Chromatin Binding

a. Ionic Strength. As expected, the ionic strength of the receptor–chromatin incubation has a dramatic effect on the extent of binding observed (Spelsberg *et al.*, 1971a; Jaffe *et al.*, 1975; Webster *et al.*, 1976). A poignant illustration of this is an observed 2-fold increase in the total protein content of chromatin incubated with cytosol at low ionic strength (Spelsberg *et al.*, 1971a). This large nonspecific adsorption of protein could easily obliterate any specific interaction of the receptor and chromatin. As the ionic strength of the incubation mixture is raised, there is a progressive decrease in the amount of bound progesterone for both oviduct and spleen chromatins (Jaffe *et al.*, 1975; Webster *et al.*, 1976). Based upon the physiological conditions of the cell and the nature of the binding sites observed, it appears that 0.15 *M* KCl is a reasonable ionic strength at which to perform the binding reaction.

b. Temperature. Temperature influences both the receptor and the acceptor with respect to chromatin binding. When chromatin is titrated with crude cytosol at 22°–24°C, a much higher level of binding is observed than at 4°C (Fig. 10; Jaffe *et al.*, 1975; Webster *et al.*, 1976). In addition, preincubation of the cytosol at 25°C followed by chromatin binding at 4°C yields higher binding than if the cytosol is not pretreated, provided the binding reaction is performed at low ionic strength (Jaffe *et al.*, 1975). On the contrary, if binding is done at high ionic strength (0.15 *M*), preincubation of the cytosol at 25°C does not enhance subsequent binding to chromatin at 4°C (Fig. 10). This suggests that the high salt present in the incubation may "activate" the receptor, obviating the need for a temperature-induced activation. This suspicion was confirmed by preincubating cytosol in 0.15 *M* KCl for up to 2 hours, diluting to a low salt concentration, and then assaying chromatin binding at 4°C. The receptor undergoes a time-dependent salt-induced activation which reaches completion at about 2 hours. Ammonium sulfate precipitation also activates receptor such that equivalent levels of chromatin binding are obtained at 4°C or 24°C (Webster *et al.*, 1976).

In addition to the activation of receptor, elevated temperature has an effect on the number of acceptor sites exposed in chromatin. Thus, when binding is done in high salt, more binding is observed when the reaction is carried out at 22°C than at 4°C (Fig. 10). The K_D is unchanged at this higher temperature (4.4×10^{-9} *M*), but the number of sites is increased (8800 sites/cell).

c. Cofactors. Because low molecular weight components are removed during the preparation of chromatin and ammonium-sulfate-precipitated receptor, Jaffe *et al.* (1975) analyzed the effects of some small molecules on chromatin binding of the oviduct progesterone receptor.

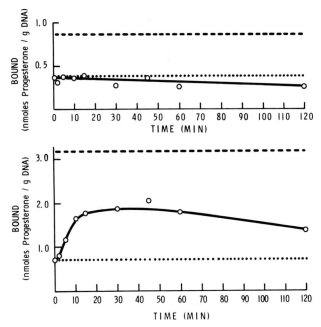

FIG. 10. Effect of cytosol preincubation at 25°C on binding of the progesterone–receptor complex to oviduct chromatin. Cytosol was labeled with [³H]progesterone at 4°C. Portions of the cytosol were then incubated at 25°C for the amount of time listed on the abscissa. The cytosol (final receptor concentration, 1.46 n*M*) was then incubated with chromatin for 2 hours at 4°C in 0.15 *M* KCl (upper panel) or 0.025 *M* KCl (lower panel) (O———O). The bottom line (····) represents the binding level obtained with cytosol which was kept at 4°C. The top line (---) represents the binding level obtained when cytosol was preincubated for 2 hours at 4°C and the binding to chromatin performed for 2 hours at 22°C. From Jaffe *et al.* (1975).

Neither the type of monovalent cation (NaCl, KCl, or NH₄Cl, all at 0.15 *M*) nor 10 m*M* β-mercaptoethanol significantly alters chromatin binding. However, either MgCl₂ or CaCl₂ (at 5 mM) reduces binding substantially, as does 5–10 mM EDTA alone. These results are interpreted as follows: Divalent cations alone probably cause chromatin aggregation, effectively removing acceptor sites from solution, while EDTA alone may remove some component from chromatin necessary for optimal binding of the progesterone–receptor complex. A likely candidate is low concentrations of Mg²⁺, for it can partially reverse EDTA inhibition. Scatchard analysis of binding in the presence of EDTA demonstrates that its effect is on chromatin and not the receptor because the K_D is unaffected (3.3×10^{-9} *M*), while the number of sites is reduced (1600 sites/cell). The inhibitory effects of these agents seem general, as they were observed with both oviduct and nontarget spleen chromatin.

4. Multiple Binding Sites

The same multiple binding sites for receptor observed in nuclei (Pikler *et al.*, 1976; Spelsberg *et al.*, 1976a) were found in experiments utilizing chromatin (Webster *et al.*, 1976). At low ionic strength (0.05 *M* KCl), oviduct chromatin displays several classes of binding sites. Spleen chromatin also binds oviduct progesterone receptor, but the highest-affinity class observed in oviduct chromatin is absent in spleen. At physiological salt concentration (0.15 *M*) the only class of sites detectable in oviduct chromatin is that of highest affinity (K_D = 6 × 10^{-9} *M*, 5500 sites/cell). In addition, the same number of high-affinity sites is obtained when progesterone is injected *in vivo* or when hormone–receptor complexes are bound to nuclei or chromatin *in vitro* (Spelsberg *et al.*, 1976c, 1977).

These studies complement those performed on nuclei and demonstrate that the highest-affinity class of binding sites, considered to be of biological relevance, is target-tissue specific. Earlier studies showing tissue specificity (see Section VI,B,2) were carried out at 0.15 *M* KCl.

5. Progesterone–Receptor Complex Dissociation from Chromatin

Analysis of the dissociation of [³H]progesterone–receptor complex from specific chromatin-acceptor sites reveals that it is a first-order process (Jaffe *et al.*, 1975). At 22°C, the half-life for dissociation of progesterone from the receptor is shorter (26 minutes) than the half-life of dissociation of progesterone which is complexed to chromatin-bound receptors (107 minutes). Equations (3) and (4) offer two mechanisms which could explain these data.

$$\text{Chromatin–receptor–progesterone} \rightarrow \text{chromatin} + \text{progesterone–receptor} \qquad (3)$$
$$\text{Chromatin–receptor–progesterone} \rightarrow \text{chromatin–receptor} + \text{progesterone} \qquad (4)$$

Using a HAP assay, it was determined that Eq. (4) is more likely to be correct, because released radioactivity appears initially as free hormone. At that time, however, the temperature-dependent generation of mero-receptor was unknown, and because mero-receptor does not bind well to HAP, it would be detected as free hormone. In view of the fact that mero-receptor does not bind at all to DNA–cellulose, this receptor form is a potential intermediate in the mechanism of progesterone–receptor dissociation from chromatin.

6. Molecular Nature of the Chromatin Acceptor Sites

By far the most important information obtained from chromatin binding experiments using the chick oviduct system is that concerning the molecular makeup of the acceptor site. The work of Spelsberg and his colleagues has contributed greatly to our understanding in this area.

a. DNA. Experiments have been performed to determine the contribution of DNA in chromatin toward binding of the progesterone receptor (Jaffe *et al.*, 1975). Chromatin preincubated with antibodies against either single- or double-stranded DNA shows levels of progesterone receptor binding equivalent to those in untreated chromatin. At the dilutions used (1:50–1:10,000), both these antibodies are capable of blocking transcription of their respective antigenic (DNA) template by *E. coli* RNA polymerase, but neither antibody inhibits transcription of chromatin (Towle *et al.*, 1976). Likewise, use of a single-stranded DNA-specific enzyme (mung bean nuclease) does not affect progesterone receptor binding to chromatin, nor does it inhibit transcription of native DNA or chromatin, although transcription of denatured DNA is severely reduced. Thus, it appears that regions of naked single- or double-stranded DNA are not essential for the interaction of the progesterone receptor with chromatin acceptor sites.

b. Histones. For these studies and those done with nonhistone proteins, chromatin reconstitution has been the primary tool used to dissect the acceptor sites. In all the experiments described below, control reconstitutions have been performed using entirely homologous components, all of which demonstrate that reconstituted chromatin faithfully resembles native chromatin with respect to (a) chemical composition, (b) binding of the oviduct progesterone–receptor complex, and (c) template activity (Steggles *et al.*, 1971a,b; Spelsberg *et al.*, 1971a, 1972).

Reconstitution of pure chick DNA with histones in a histone:DNA ratio which approximates native chromatin causes a reduction in the amount of progesterone receptor binding when compared to native chick oviduct chromatin (Steggles *et al.*, 1971a; Spelsberg *et al.*, 1971a). Thus, the oviduct histone fraction does not bestow acceptor activity on the chromatin. Reconstitution of dehistonized oviduct chromatin with either calf thymus or chick spleen histones does not alter the amount of binding observed in native chick oviduct chromatin; a loss of binding activity would have been expected if oviduct histones were important in the binding of the receptor. Furthermore, dehistonized spleen chromatin does not gain acceptor activity when reconstituted with oviduct histones. Therefore, histones do not appear to play a positive role in binding the chick oviduct progesterone receptor to oviduct chromatin. It is now well established that histones, by virtue of their arrangement into nucleosomes, are largely responsible for chromatin structure (Olins and Olins, 1974; Kornberg, 1974; Weintraub *et al.*, 1976).

c. Nonhistone (Acidic) Proteins. Because naked DNA and histones are apparently not the major determinants of chromatin-acceptor-site activity, the nonhistone proteins have been analyzed in great detail with intriguing results.

If total histones and nonhistone proteins from chick oviduct are reconstituted with DNA from chick heart or erythrocyte, the hybrid chromatins bind the progesterone receptor as well as native chick oviduct chromatin (Spelsberg et al., 1972). Conversely, when histones and nonhistone proteins from these nontarget tissues are reconstituted with pure oviduct DNA, the resultant hybrid chromatin binds receptor at a level which is similar to that observed for native nontarget tissue chromatin. Therefore, there is nothing unique about oviduct DNA which confers receptor binding activity to oviduct chromatin. On the contrary, the nonhistone protein fraction from the target tissue dictates the extent of acceptor activity present in a particular chromatin. Following a sequential extraction of histones and nonhistone proteins from oviduct chromatin, progesterone receptor binding was assayed on chromatins containing differing nonhistone protein fractions (Spelsberg et al., 1972). One nonhistone protein fraction (AP_3), which comprises approximately 40–50% of the total nonhistone protein, was found to contain the acceptor activity. Reconstituted chromatins lacking the AP_3 fraction bind only one-fourth as much progesterone–receptor complex as native oviduct chromatin and resemble chromatins from nontarget tissue in their acceptor activity. No other nonhistone protein fraction enhances the level of receptor-binding activity. Although the AP_3 fraction specifies the acceptor activity, it must be associated with DNA to elicit progesterone receptor binding; AP_3 alone is incapable of binding the chick oviduct progesterone–receptor complex (Spelsberg, 1974).

Thus, the chromatin acceptor ability for the oviduct progesterone receptor resides in a specific fraction of the chromatin nonhistone proteins, which must be complexed to DNA to be active in receptor binding.

7. Masked Acceptor Sites

Recently, a renewal of interest has occurred in the study of chick oviduct chromatin-acceptor sites. Because of the development of such new techniques as chromatin–cellulose complexes and streptomycin precipitation of soluble chromatin fractions (Pikler et al., 1976; Webster et al., 1976), simple, rapid assays were made available to measure acceptor activity.

During sequential removal of histones, $AP_1 + AP_2$, and AP_3, the number of acceptor sites was analyzed by receptor titration (Spelsberg et al., 1976b,c; Webster et al., 1976). Removal of histones, AP_1, and AP_2, yields a fraction termed by the authors nucleo-acidic protein (NAP), which includes AP_3, AP_4, and DNA. Production of NAP results in a large increase in the acceptor activity when compared to that obtained using native oviduct chromatin. In addition, because these assays are done at low receptor concentrations and high salt, the acceptor sites generated are of the highest-affinity class. Using NAP as 100%, it was calculated that the amount of total acceptor sites exposed in native oviduct chromatin and dehistonized oviduct chromatin is 29% and 37%, respectively. Even more striking is the fact that preparation of NAP from spleen chromatin results in the appearance of acceptor sites equivalent in number to those present in chick oviduct NAP, the total number present in both being approximately 20,000 sites/cell. The sites exposed in spleen NAP are also of the highest-affinity type which, as mentioned previously, are detectable in native oviduct, but not in native spleen, chromatin. Based on spleen total NAP (100%), only 6% of the total acceptor sites are exposed in native spleen chromatin. Thus, it appears that the same number of acceptor sites is present in target and nontarget tissue chromatin, but that target tissues have more sites exposed (unmasked) which are available to interact with the receptor. The majority of the acceptor sites are apparently masked by nonhistone proteins (AP_1 and AP_2), because dehistonized oviduct chromatin contains only 8% more sites than native oviduct chromatin. It is interesting to note that an increase in acceptor sites was observed in an earlier study (Spelsberg et al., 1971a) when dehistonized spleen and oviduct chromatins were assayed for progesterone receptor binding. In the earlier chromatin fractionation protocol, the AP_1 fraction (10–15% of total nonhistone proteins) was removed with the histones.

A method has been developed for purification of chromatin-acceptor sites (Spelsberg et al., 1975) using a high-capacity chromatin–cellulose column. Chromatin proteins are dissociated using a guanidine hydrochloride (GuHCl) gradient (0–8 M) or step elution, in the presence of 0.1 M β-mercaptoethanol. Multiple peaks of protein are obtained during gradient elution, with most of the protein eluting by 4 M GuHCl; however, no unmasking of acceptor sites is observed at this concentration, although all the histones and most nonhistone proteins are removed. Titration of chromatin with receptor reveals a 10- to 20-fold increase in acceptor sites when chromatin–cellulose is treated with 4–6 M GuHCl (unmasking) followed by a decrease at 7 M GuHCl (acceptor elution from the column). Using this method, Spelsberg and his colleagues have purified the acceptor protein(s) 100-fold over native chromatin.

Finally, recent studies report the possible purification of the chromatin nonhistone acceptor proteins to homogeneity (Spelsberg et al., 1976c, 1977). Fractions containing acceptor activity are isolated from either chromatin–cellulose or chromatin–hydroxylapatite using a GuHCl gradient. Further purification is achieved using sequential gel filtration columns (agarose or Bio-Gel) of differing exclusion limits under denaturing conditions. When active fractions from these columns are analyzed by SDS–polyacrylamide gel electrophoresis two major protein bands are obtained with molecular weights between 13,000 and 17,000 gm/mole. Proteins of high molecular weights are occasionally present in the preparation, so that it is not certain whether the low molecular weight proteins are the actual acceptor proteins or breakdown products of a larger molecule. The generation of acceptor activity by this highly purified preparation requires annealing to DNA and is Pronase-sensitive.

8. Hormonal Effects on Acceptor Site Concentration

The concentration of acceptor sites increases with daily estrogen administration to immature chicks and reaches a maximum at 7 days of treatment. The level falls to that found in two-year-old hens after 20 days of estrogenic stimulation (Spelsberg *et al.*, 1971b, 1976c, 1977). However, pretreatment with estrogen is not essential for progesterone receptor binding to chromatin, as immature oviduct chromatin still binds receptor to a greater extent than spleen (nontarget tissue) chromatin.

9. Nonhistone Proteins, Transcription, and Gene Expression

The functional importance of nonhistone (acidic) proteins has been emphasized by recent experiments. Using reconstituted homologous and heterologous chromatins from estrogen-stimulated (chronic) and hormone-withdrawn chicks, it was found that the extractable nonhistone protein fraction determines the amount of ovalbumin mRNA (as measured using a $[^3H]$cDNA probe to ovalbumin mRNA) synthesized *in vitro* from reconstituted chromatin (S. Y. Tsai *et al.*, 1976a). Reconstituted chromatin containing DNA–tight binding nonhistone protein (DNA–TBp) and histones from estrogen-stimulated chicks produces low levels of $mRNA_{ov}$ when the nonhistone proteins are removed and replaced with those from hormone-withdrawn chromatin. On the other hand, relatively large amounts of $mRNA_{ov}$ are synthesized from hybrid chromatins containing DNA–TBp and histones from withdrawn chick oviduct chromatin, but nonhistone proteins from hormone-stimulated chromatin. Similarly, transcriptional properties of the chromatins analyzed using the rifampicin challenge assay for RNA chain-initiation sites (see Section VII,A,3) clearly show that the number of initiation sites is dependent upon the source of the nonhistone protein fraction present in the chromatin. A subsequent study (S. Y. Tsai *et al.*, 1976b) demonstrates that expression of the ovalbumin gene by the hybrid chromatins is under a positive regulatory control by the nonhistone protein fraction of hormone-stimulated chromatins rather than under negative control by the nonhistone proteins present in hormone-withdrawn chromatins. Finally, preliminary experiments (S. Y. Tsai, M.-J. Tsai, and B. W. O'Malley, unpublished) show that the nonhistone proteins can be partially purified into a number of different fractions, some of which can greatly facilitate transcription of the ovalbumin gene in chromatin *in vitro*. In light of these studies, it would be interesting to know what relationships exist between the chromatin nonhistone proteins responsible for steroid hormone–receptor binding and those controlling expression of the ovalbumin gene.

C. DNA

The interaction of chick oviduct progesterone receptors with DNA has been analyzed by a number of different methods. When the A and B receptors are incubated with DNA and subsequently centrifuged on sucrose gradients, the B receptor sediments at 4 S, whereas the A protein shows radioactivity complexed with DNA and dispersed throughout the bottom one-third of the tube. Thus, of the two 4 S forms of the receptor, only the A receptor appears to be capable of binding to DNA.

When using DNA–cellulose to assay for DNA binding, it is found that 6 S receptor (prepared by phosphocellulose exclusion) and B receptor (from DEAE–cellulose) do not bind to DNA, whereas A receptor isolated from DEAE binds tightly to DNA (Fig. 11; Coty *et al.*, 1978; Schrader *et al.*, 1977b). Identical results are obtained when purified B protein is analyzed

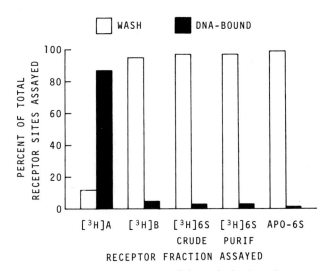

FIG. 11. Binding of receptor forms to DNA–cellulose. The binding of progesterone receptor forms to DNA–cellulose was determined by chromatography of receptor samples on 1.2 × 1.6 cm DNA–cellulose columns. Receptor samples were applied in Tris–EDTA–thioglycerol buffer containing 0.05 *M* KCl and 0.5 mg/ml bovine albumin, and the columns washed with the same buffer. Receptor was eluted with the same buffer containing 0.25 *M* KCl. Receptor bound to DNA–cellulose is expressed as percent of radioactivity recovered; recoveries of [^{3}H]progesterone were greater than 90%. From Coty *et al.* (1978).

(Kuhn *et al.*, 1977). As was mentioned previously, mero-receptor is also inactive in DNA binding. Thus, the only receptor form capable of binding to DNA is the A protein.

A recently developed method (Coty *et al.*, 1978) permits the purification of the A receptor to homogeneity and in sufficient yield to perform sensitive equilibrium DNA-binding studies using the Millipore filter binding assay (Jones and Berg, 1966; Riggs *et al.*, 1970). Although binding can be detected using this assay, no saturability or specificity for the source of DNA is demonstrable. All binding studies are done at 0.09 *M* KCl.

Because the only chick oviduct progesterone receptor form capable of binding to DNA is the A protein, any model of hormone action needs to rely heavily on this fact, and incorporate the relationship of this DNA-binding protein and the other receptor forms (see Section VIII).

VII. EFFECTS OF THE CHICK OVIDUCT PROGESTERONE RECEPTOR ON TRANSCRIPTION

Steroid hormones have a profound effect on RNA transcription and the stimulation of synthesis of specific proteins. Our goal here is not to review the extensive literature concerning these effects; this subject has been reviewed elsewhere, and the reader is directed to these other sources for detailed treatments of the effects of steroid hormones on gene expression and protein synthesis in the chick oviduct system (O'Malley and Means, 1974, 1976; Rosen and O'Malley, 1975; Woo and O'Malley, 1975; Palmiter *et al.*, 1976; Towle *et al.*, 1976; M.-J. Tsai and O'Malley, 1977). However, some recent studies have been directed toward an analysis of the effects of the chick oviduct progesterone receptor on transcription and gene expression, and an understanding of a number of *in vivo* experiments is crucial in interpreting the *in vitro* studies.

A. *In Vivo* Correlations

1. *RNA Polymerase and Template Activities*

Estrogen treatment of immature chicks results in an increased template capacity for endogenous nuclear RNA synthesis for both RNA polymerase I and II within 2 hours after estradiol injection (Cox *et al.*, 1974). Estrogen likewise stimulates the initial rate and total amount of endogenous RNA synthesis from chromatin *in vitro*, with increases detectable 30 minutes after hormone administration. Finally, chromatin isolated from estrogen-treated chicks is a more efficient template for exogenously added hen oviduct polymerase II. Thus, estrogen is capable of rapidly mobilizing a number of components in the target-cell transcriptional apparatus.

Recently, similar experiments have been conducted on hormone-withdrawn chicks given secondary stimulations with estrogen, progesterone, and estrogen plus progesterone, with basically the same results (Spelsberg and Cox, 1976). It is important to note that either estrogen or progesterone is capable of inducing specific egg white proteins upon secondary stimulation of estrogen-withdrawn chicks (Fig. 12; Palmiter *et al.*, 1970). Although antagonistic activities are noted for estrogen and progesterone with respect to RNA polymerase I activity, RNA polymerase II activity is stimulated within 15 minutes after DES or estrogen injection, and at less than 1 hour after progesterone treatment. Thus, early events in the synthesis of new non-ribosomal RNA are similarly responsive to estrogen or progesterone.

2. Ovalbumin Messenger RNA

The synthesis of DNA complementary to ovalbumin messenger RNA ($cDNA_{ov}$) has allowed sensitive hybridization studies for the analysis of gene expression in the chick oviduct system (Sullivan *et al.*, 1973; Cox *et al.*, 1974; Harris *et al.*, 1975; Monahan *et al.*, 1976). Using this probe, it has been

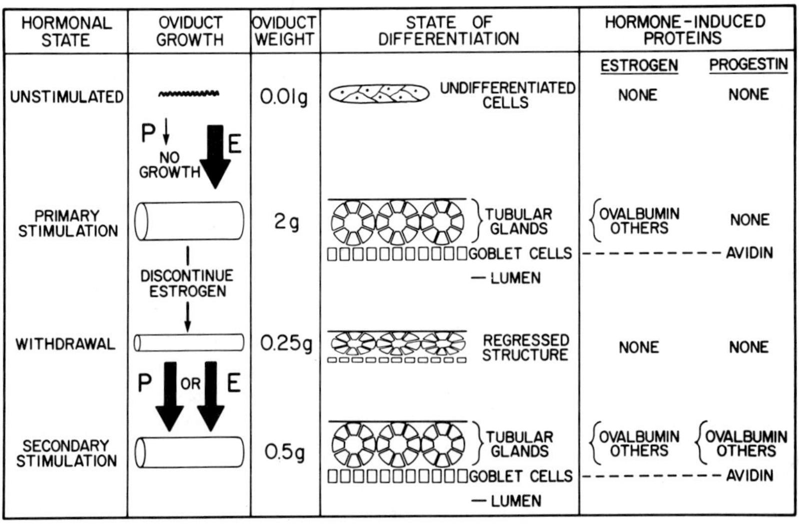

FIG. 12. Schematic diagram of the hormonal events in the immature chick oviduct. The degree of growth and cell types produced are shown as a function of the hormonal regimen utilized. Cell-specific marker proteins produced under the influence of these hormones are indicated on the right. Note the induction of ovalbumin by both estrogen and progesterone during secondary stimulation.

determined that estrogen (primary stimulation) and estrogen or progesterone (secondary stimulation) induce the synthesis of new mRNA transcripts for ovalbumin (Cox *et al.*, 1974; Harris *et al.*, 1975; McKnight *et al.*,
1975; Spelsberg and Cox, 1976). Thus, *in vivo* these hormones act primarily
at the transcriptional level. When chromatin is isolated from estrogen-
stimulated chick oviduct and allowed to code for the synthesis of RNA *in
vitro*, substantial amounts of $mRNA_{ov}$ are made, whereas unstimulated or
withdrawn oviduct chromatins produce very little $mRNA_{ov}$ (Harris *et al.*,
1976). These data support the hypothesis that steroid hormones act primarily
by gene activation.

3. *Molecular Mechanism of Steroid Hormone Stimulation of RNA Synthesis*

Although the synthesis of new messenger RNA is the principal point of
steroid hormone action, the transcription process itself is complicated and
contains a number of subreactions. Among these, any of the following are
candidates for control by steroid hormones: (a) polymerase interaction with
chromosomal proteins; (b) polymerase binding to nonspecific regions of
DNA; (c) polymerase binding to specific regions of DNA; (d) formation of a
stable RNA polymerase–DNA preinitiation complex; (e) rate of initiation
(initial phosphodiester bond formation); (f) rate of chain elongation; (g) chain
termination; (h) reinitiation; (i) endogenously bound RNA polymerase activity; and (j) endogenous RNase activity. A series of studies has been carried
out recently to determine at exactly what step(s) the steroid hormone exerts
its effect on RNA synthesis (M.-J. Tsai *et al.*, 1975; Schwartz *et al.*, 1975;
Hirose *et al.*, 1976).

Using an adaptation of the rifampicin challenge assay developed for prokaryotic systems, the substeps in the transcription cycle can either be eliminated or controlled (for details and original references, see M.-J. Tsai *et al.*,
1975; Towle *et al.*, 1976; M.-J. Tsai and O'Malley, 1977). In short, chromatin
is incubated with *E. coli* RNA polymerase and allowed to form stable binary
(rapid-start) complexes in the absence of nucleotides. To commence RNA
synthesis, the four nucleoside triphosphates (one of which is radioactive) and
the drug rifampicin are added. Those polymerase molecules free in solution
or associated weakly with the template are attacked and inhibited by the
drug, while those in the most stable preinitiation complexes are more resistant to rifampicin attack. These latter polymerase molecules synthesize only
one RNA chain, for once the chain terminates, the polymerase is released
from the template and reinitiation is prevented by rifampicin attack on the
released polymerase. RNase activity is prevented by inclusion of heparin in
the reaction mixture, and the low endogenous RNA polymerase activity is
monitored by controls containing no exogenously added *E. coli* RNA

polymerase. The RNA chains synthesized are analyzed on sucrose gradients to determine the number average chain length, and short incubation times are used to estimate the rate of chain elongation.

When immature, hormone-withdrawn, or restimulated chick oviduct chromatins are compared, no differences are found in the rate of chain propagation or in chain length (Schwartz *et al.*, 1975). Furthermore, in oviduct chromatin from unstimulated chicks or those injected with DES for 2, 4, or 6 days, the endogenous RNA polymerase activity accounts for less than 1% of the RNA synthesis obtained using exogenously added *E. coli* RNA polymerase. However, in all these experiments, chromatin isolated from chicks stimulated for varying times with DES show a time-dependent increase in the total amount of RNA synthesized *in vitro* and in the chromatin template activity. The hormone-induced increase in RNA synthesis is due to an increase in the number of initiation sites available for RNA polymerase. Thus, more *E. coli* RNA polymerase is needed to saturate the available initiation sites of chromatins prepared from DES-stimulated animals. Another independent assay for RNA chain initiation using the incorporation of $[\gamma\text{-}^{32}P]GTP$ into the 5' ends of rifampicin-resistant RNA chains confirms these results. Therefore, it appears that *in vivo*, the steroid hormone acts by increasing the number of available RNA polymerase binding and initiation sites available in chick oviduct chromatin (Schwartz *et al.*, 1975).

4. Nuclear Receptor Levels, Initiation Sites, and mRNA$_{ov}$

Experiments have been performed with the purpose of correlating the level of nuclear estrogen and progesterone receptor, the number of RNA initiation sites, and the concentration of messenger RNA for ovalbumin (S. Y. Tsai *et al.*, 1975; Kalimi *et al.*, 1976). After withdrawal from DES, the level of nuclear estrogen receptor decreases with the same time course observed for RNA chain initiation. Likewise, both oviduct nuclear estrogen levels and RNA initiation sites demonstrate similar responses to various doses of injected DES. Secondary stimulation with DES elicits an increase of nuclear receptor levels at 15–20 minutes (Kalimi *et al.*, 1976; Spelsberg and Cox, 1976). RNA polymerase II activity is enhanced at 15 minutes and peaks at 1 hour after DES. The concentration of RNA initiation sites is significantly elevated at 30 minutes after DES injection, and an increase of ovalbumin mRNA is noted 60 minutes after treatment. Thus, temporally the first noticeable effect of steroid hormone administration is the appearance of receptor in the nucleus. This is rapidly followed by an increase in the number of initiation sites for RNA transcription and, finally, by the appearance of mRNA$_{ov}$ (Fig. 13). The appearance of nuclear progesterone receptor also precedes an increase in RNA polymerase II activity and is also followed by a rise in mRNA$_{ov}$ (Spelsberg and Cox, 1976). Although these studies do

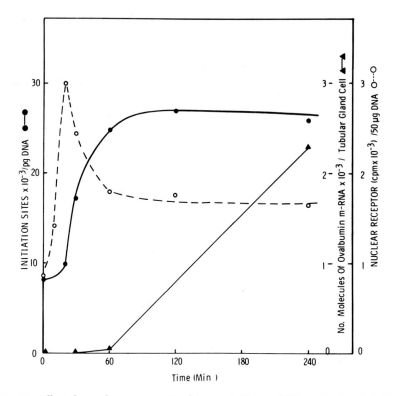

FIG. 13. Effect of secondary estrogen stimulation on initiation of RNA synthesis and the level of nuclear receptors for estrogen. The level of nuclear receptors (O---O) was determined by exchange assay, the number of initiation sites (●———●) by the rifampicin challenge assay, and the number of mRNA$_{ov}$ molecules (▲———▲) by hybridization with cDNA$_{ov}$. From S. Y. Tsai et al. (1975) and Harris et al. (1975).

not prove that these observed sequential events are functionally linked, they at least demonstrate that such a relationship is not temporally prohibited.

B. IN VITRO STIMULATION OF RNA SYNTHESIS BY THE CHICK OVIDUCT PROGESTERONE RECEPTOR

1. Affinity-Chromatography-Purified Receptor

Although the synthesis of egg white proteins is stimulated similarly by estrogen and progesterone (Palmiter et al., 1970), it is important to verify that the RNA initiation sites respond equivalently to these two hormones upon secondary stimulation (Schwartz et al., 1975). Time-course studies

·TABLE IV

EFFECT OF COMBINED ADMINISTRATION OF PROGESTERONE AND DIETHYLSTILBESTROL
ON INITIATION SITES FOR RNA SYNTHESIS IN OVIDUCT CHROMATIN[a]

Dose of hormone	RNA chains initiated (pmoles)/5 μg DNA	Initiation sites/pg DNA
Control	0.076	9,150
0.25 mg progesterone	0.135	16,260
1.25 mg progesterone	0.187	22,530
2.0 mg progesterone	0.196	23,610
1.25 mg diethylstilbestrol	0.191	23,010
1.25 mg progesterone + 1.25 mg diethylstilbestrol	0.180	21,680

[a]From Schwartz *et al.* (1976)

show that progesterone and estrogen are equally effective in causing an increase in the number of initiation sites for RNA synthesis. Furthermore, injection of both DES and progesterone together, at concentrations capable of maximally stimulating initiation site levels when injected singly, does not yield an additive level (Table IV). It appears that both hormones, during secondary stimulation, exert their effects on the same initiation sites.

Progesterone-receptor complexes isolated by affinity chromatography were added to chromatin *in vitro* followed, after 30 minutes, by the addition of *E. coli* RNA polymerase. After a second preincubation, nucleoside triphosphates and rifampicin were added and the number of initiation sites calculated as usual. Figure 14 shows that there is a concentration-dependent increase in

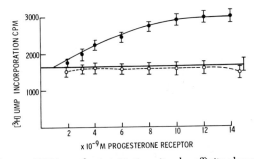

FIG. 14. Stimulation of RNA synthesis initiation sites by affinity-chromatography-purified receptor. Crude ammonium-sulfate-precipitated cytosol was divided into two parts. Progesterone was added to one half (O---O), while the other half remained untreated (●———●). Both fractions were separately incubated with deoxycorticosterone–bovine serum albumin affinity resin. After elution, receptor was incubated with withdrawn oviduct chromatin. The rifampicin initiation site assay was used to monitor RNA synthesis. The straight line represents untreated chromatin values. From Schwartz *et al.* (1976).

TABLE V

REQUIREMENTS FOR RECEPTOR STIMULATION OF CHROMATIN RNA INITIATION SITES[a]

Components added to assay	[³H]UMP Incorporated (cpm)	Percent activity
Background:		
RNA polymerase only (15μg)	230	8
Polymerase + progesterone–receptor complex (10^{-8} M)	400	14
Chromatin alone (5 μg as DNA)	200	7
Control:		
Chromatin + RNA polymerase	2730	100
Chromatin + boiled receptor + polymerase	2860	105
Chromatin + 10^{-8} M free progesterone + polymerase	2430	89
Experimental:		
Chromatin + polymerase + 10^{-8} M receptor complexes	4100	150
+ α-amanitin (10 μg)	3740	137
+ actinomycin D (10 μg)	320	12

[a] From Schwartz *et al.* (1976).

the number of available RNA initiation sites as increasing levels of progesterone receptor are added. Control experiments using receptor blocked with progesterone prior to affinity chromatography demonstrate the absence of a nonreceptor contaminant which might be isolated by this method and be responsible for the observed stimulation. The receptor interaction with the chromatin is time dependent and 30 minutes of preincubation appears to be optimal (Schwartz *et al.*, 1976; Buller *et al.*, 1976b). The time of preincubation and the amount of receptor–hormone complex required for half-maximal stimulation (5×10^{-9} M) are virtually identical to the optima observed for chromatin binding of the receptor *in vitro*.

Control experiments reveal that the stimulation of RNA-chain initiation is both template and receptor dependent (Table V). Also, the receptor preparation does not cause nicking of the DNA and has no detectable proteolytic activity as analyzed by F_1 histone integrity or an azoalbumin hydrolysis assay. The observed increase in RNA synthesis is not due to increase in chain elongation rate or chain size, but rather to an increase the total number of initiation sites available for RNA polymerase. Using incorporation of [γ-^{32}P]GTP into 5′-termini, it was confirmed that the number of RNA chains initiated is increased by the addition of receptor to the incubation. Finally, the progesterone receptor is not capable of stimulating the number of initiation sites in chromatin of such nontarget tissue as liver and erythrocyte (Fig. 15).

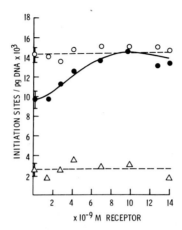

FIG. 15. Tissue specificity for the effect of the progesterone receptor on RNA initiation sites. Chromatin from oviduct (●———●), erythrocyte (△---△), and liver (○---○) was incubated with increasing doses of purified progesterone receptor. Data are expressed as initiation sites per pg of chromatin DNA. From Schwartz *et al.* (1976).

2. *Receptor Forms and Chromatin Transcription*

Studies have been performed to determine what functional relationship might exist between the various receptor forms and transcriptional events (Buller *et al.*, 1976b). Receptor which possesses properties ascribed to the 6 S A-B dimer was prepared by step elutions of various ion-exchange columns, total purification being 200- to 1000-fold (see Section V,B). When this preparation is tested using the rifampicin challenge assay for the initiation of RNA synthesis, a concentration-dependent increase is observed, with half-maximal stimulation at 5×10^{-9} *M*. The A and B forms purified independently and to apparent homogeneity (Coty *et al.*, 1978; Schrader *et al.*, 1977a) do not elicit an increase in chromatin transcription when analyzed either alone or mixed together. As seen in Fig. 16, the B subunit alone in high concentration may actually inhibit transcription. Half-maximal stimulation by the A subunit occurs at a concentration approximately 10-fold higher than that for the 6 S receptor form. These results suggest that the functional receptor form is the 6 S A-B dimer.

VIII. MOLECULAR MODEL OF STEROID HORMONE ACTION

Based on the information available on the chick oviduct progesterone receptor which is summarized in this chapter, a hypothetical model for steroid

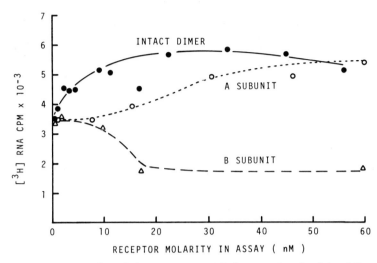

FIG. 16. Comparison of purified intact receptor A-B dimers with isolated A and B proteins. Increasing quantities of the various receptor forms were incubated with withdrawn chick oviduct chromatin (10 µg DNA) and RNA synthesis measured using the rifampicin challenge assay. From Schrader *et al.* (1977c).

hormone action can be proposed (Fig. 17). This model attempts to integrate the various structural and functional properties known at this time for the progesterone receptor.

Progesterone, which is bound to a serum-binding protein in the blood, enters the oviduct cell, probably by diffusion. The hormone then binds to the 6 S A-B receptor dimer followed by receptor activation and subsequent nuclear translocation. Because only the B subunit has a chromatin binding site, it searches the chromatin until it finds the appropriate acceptor protein(s), to which it binds with high affinity. Thus, the B subunit fulfills the role of a "specifier" protein, for it is postulated that the acceptor proteins are located adjacent to hormone-responsive genes. The A subunit, whose DNA-binding site has up to this point been occluded, dissociates from the 6 S complex. As it is the only DNA-binding form of the progesterone receptor, it alone would be capable of binding to the DNA at some regulatory (effector) site. This process may then facilitate binding of RNA polymerase to an initiation site for RNA synthesis (promoter?), followed by transcription of the hormone-responsive gene. This train of events explains the results obtained in the transcription experiments. The B subunit itself, because it does not bind to DNA, is ineffective in stimulating transcription. The A subunit, because it doesn't bind to the nonhistone protein acceptor sites, is not able to

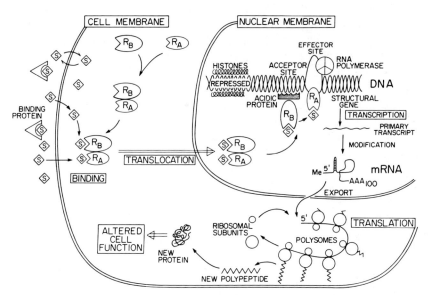

FIG. 17. Proposed model for steroid hormone effects on gene expression. The details are described in Section VIII; based on studies performed using the chick oviduct progesterone receptor. R_B, receptor B subunit; R_A, receptor A subunit; S, steroid. From Buller *et al.* (1976b).

make its way efficiently to the effector site. Thus, in the absence of the B subunit, a much higher concentration of the A subunit is needed to ensure that an efficient interaction with the effector site will occur. The final step in the interaction of the receptor with the genome most likely involves dissociation of the hormone from the receptor when the cellular concentration of free hormone falls. This event results in dissociation of the receptor from the chromatin, or a conversion of the receptor to a form which doesn't bind to the genome (mero-receptor?).

Although this model is tentative, the data available at this time are fit best into the framework presented. For the sake of argument, the B to A conversion scheme mentioned previously (see Section V,A,2) would not seriously alter the functional aspects of this model. Thus, one could postulate that the B receptor (or a B-B dimer), with an associated protease, is translocated into the nucleus where it binds to the chromatin acceptor site. This activates the protease which clips off the chromatin binding site, yielding the A receptor with its previously occluded DNA-binding site now exposed. The DNA, by virtue of its affinity for the A receptor, removes it from the protease. If the A receptor or some other factor were inhibiting the hydrolysis of a second B protein, this might now no longer be the case and a second A protein would be produced from the original B-B dimer. In any event, the remainder of the process responsible for the stimulation of transcription would be identical.

IX. FUTURE DIRECTIONS

Future experiments on the chick oviduct progesterone receptor (and others) will undoubtedly focus increasingly on the physicochemical properties of the receptor and its interaction with the genetic material of the cell.

Structurally, it would be advantageous to analyze the hormone, chromatin, and DNA-binding sites. This will require large quantities of pure receptor, and this is now feasible for the chick oviduct progesterone receptor (Schrader et al., 1977a). An ultimate goal would be the determination of the entire amino acid sequence of these proteins, as well as their structure. A powerful technique recently applied successfully to human cortiscosteroid-binding globulin (Marver et al., 1976) is photoaffinity labeling of the steroid binding site. The convalent coupling of a photoaffinity label to the hormone binding site of steroid receptors would further our understanding of the interaction of the ligand with the receptor at the molecular level.

The relationships among the various receptor forms are of paramount importance in finally clarifying the structure–function relationships of the receptor. Immunological studies should elucidate any homology between the B and A receptor forms, so that we can determine if there is sufficient reason to further entertain a precursor–product relationship. The exact composition of the native 6 S receptor has recently been studied using an innovative application of a method used to cross-link ribosomal proteins (M. Birnbaumer, W. T. Schrader, and B. W. O'Malley, unpublished). Using bifunctional cross-linking reagents, it has been possible to generate receptor aggregates which are stable at high ionic strength, a condition under which the 6 S and 8 S receptor forms are notoriously unstable and yield 4 S molecules. Purification of a cross-linked 6 S receptor should finally resolve all doubts as to whether the 6 S form is indeed a dimer consisting of A and B subunits.

Finally, the exact molecular nature of receptor interaction with the genome is an ultimate goal. What is the composition of the chromatin and DNA-binding sites on the receptor? The role of DNA in rendering the acceptor proteins competent for receptor binding is also a pressing question. Perhaps, most important of all, it would be exciting to understand the exact physicochemical events which facilitate the transcription of a hormone-responsive gene. How does the receptor interact with the chromosomal proteins and DNA to allow transcription by RNA polymerase? Does the A protein act as a "melt-out" or "unwinding" protein capable of lowering the activation energy of RNA polymerase for formation of a stable preinitiation (RS) complex?

The above considerations raise intriguing questions which must be addressed in the future. The chick oviduct system offers certain advantages in the analysis of the mechanism of steroid hormone action in terms of its biochemical specificity. Future studies using this model system and other steroid hormone systems should eventually culminate in a detailed molecular knowledge of the modulation of gene expression by steroid hormone receptors.

REFERENCES

Anderson, J., Clark, J. H., and Peck, E. J., Jr. (1972). *Biochem. J.* **126**, 561.

Buller, R. E., Toft, D. O., Schrader, W. T., and O'Malley, B. W. (1975a). *J. Biol. Chem.* **250**, 801.

Buller, R. E., Schrader, W. T., and O'Malley, B. W. (1975b). *J. Biol. Chem.* **250**, 809.

Buller, R. E., Schwartz, R. J., and O'Malley, B. W. (1976a). *Biochem. Biophys. Res. Commun.* **69**, 106.

Buller, R. E., Schwartz, R. J., Schrader, W. T., and O'Malley, B. W. (1976b). *J. Biol. Chem.* **251**, 5178.

Chamness, G. C., Jennings, A. W., and McGuire, W. L. (1974). *Biochemistry* **13**, 327.

Clark, J. H., and Peck, E. J., Jr. (1976). *Nature (London)* **260**, 635.

Clark, J. H., Peck, E. J., Jr., Schrader, W. T., and O'Malley, B. W. (1976a). *Methods Cancer Res.* **12**, 367–417.

Clark, J. H., Eriksson, H. A., and Hardin, J. W. (1976b). *J. Steroid Biochem.* **7**, 1039.

Coty, W. A., Schrader, W. T., and O'Malley, B. W. (1978). *J. Steroid Biochem.* (in press).

Cox, R. F., Haines, M. E., and Emtage, J. S. (1974). *Eur. J. Biochem.* **49**, 225.

DeSombre, E. R., Mohla, S., and Jensen, E. V. (1972). *Biochem. Biophys. Res. Commun.* **48**, 1601.

Edelman, I. S. (1972). *J. Steroid Biochem.* **3**, 167.

Erdos, T., Best-Belpomme, M., and Bessada, R. (1970). *Anal. Biochem.* **37**, 244.

Hansen, P. E., Johnson, A., Schrader, W. T., and O'Malley, B. W. (1976). *J. Steroid Biochem.* **7**, 723.

Harris, S. E., Rosen, J. M., Means, A. R., and O'Malley, B. W. (1975). *Biochemistry* **14**, 2072.

Harris, S. E., Schwartz, R. J., Tsai, M.-J., O'Malley, B. W., and Roy, A. K. (1976). *J. Biol. Chem.* **251**, 524.

Higgins, S. J., Rousseau, G. G., Baxter, J. D., and Tomkins, G. M. (1973). *J. Biol. Chem.* **248**, 5866.

Hirose, M., Tsai, M.-J., and O'Malley, B. W. (1976). *J. Biol. Chem.* **251**, 1137.

Jaffe, R. C., Socher, S. H., and O'Malley, B. W. (1975). *Biochim. Biophys. Acta* **399**, 403.

Jensen, E. V., and Jacobson, H. I. (1962). *Recent Prog. Horm. Res.* **18**, 387.

Jensen, E. V., Suzuki, T., Kawashima, T., Stumpf, W. E., Jungblut, P. W., and DeSombre, E. R. (1968). *Proc. Natl. Acad. Sci. U.S.A.* **59**, 632.

Jensen, E. V., Mohla, S., Gorell, T., Tanaka, S., and DeSombre, E. R. (1972). *J. Steroid Biochem.* **3**, 445.

Jensen, E. V., Brecher, P. I., Mohla, S., and DeSombre, E. (1974). *Acta Endocrinol. (Copenhagen), Suppl.* **191**, 159.

Jones, O. W., and Berg, P. (1966). *J. Mol. Biol.* **22**, 199.

Kalimi, M., Tsai, S. Y., Tsai, M.-J., Clark, J. H., and O'Malley, B. W. (1976). *J. Biol. Chem.* **251**, 516.

King, R. J. B., and Mainwaring, W. I. P. (1974). "Steroid-Cell Interactions." Univ. Park Press, Baltimore, Maryland.

King, R. J. B., Gordon, J., and Inman, D. R. (1965). *J. Endocrinol.* **32**, 9.

Korenman, S. G., and Rao, B. R. (1968). *Proc. Natl. Acad. Sci. U.S.A.* **61**, 1028.

Kornberg, R. D. (1974). *Science* **184**, 868.

Kuhn, R. W., Schrader, W. T., Smith, R. G., and O'Malley, B. W. (1975). *J. Biol. Chem.* **250**, 4220.

Kuhn, R. W., Schrader, W. T., Coty, W. A., Conn, P. M., and O'Malley, B. W. (1977). *J. Biol. Chem.* **252**, 308.

Lohmar, P. H., and Toft, D. O. (1975). *Biochem. Biophys. Res. Commun.* **67**, 8.

McKnight, G. S., Pennequin, P., and Schimke, R. T. (1975). *J. Biol. Chem.* **250**, 8105.

Marver, D., Goodman, D., and Edelman, I. S. (1972). *Kidney Int.* **1**, 210.

Marver, D., Chiu, W.-H., Wolff, M. E., and Edelman, I. S. (1976). *Proc. Natl. Acad. Sci. U.S.A.* **73**, 4462.

Mešter, J., and Baulieu, E.-E. (1977). *Eur. J. Biochem.* **72**, 405.

Miller, L. K., Diaz, S. C., and Sherman, M. R. (1975). *Biochemistry* **14**, 4433.

Monahan, J. J., Harris, S. E., Woo, S. L. C., Robberson, D. L., and O'Malley, B. W. (1976). *Biochemistry* **15**, 223.

Moudgil, V. K., and Toft, D. O. (1975). *Proc. Natl. Acad. Sci. U.S.A.* **72**, 901.

Moudgil, V. K., and Toft, D. O. (1976). *Proc. Natl. Acad. Sci. U.S.A.* **73**, 3443.

Moudgil, V. K., and Toft, D. O. (1977). *Biochim. Biophys. Acta* **490**, 477.

Olins, A. L., and Olins, D. E. (1974). *Science* **183**, 330.

O'Malley, B. W., and Means, A. R. (1974). *Science* **183**, 610.

O'Malley, B. W., and Means, A. R. (1976). *Prog. Nucleic Acid Res. Mol. Biol.* **19**, 403–419.

O'Malley, B. W., McGuire, W. L., Kohler, P. O., and Korenman, S. G. (1969). *Recent Prog. Horm. Res.* **25**, 105.

O'Malley, B. W., Sherman, M. R., and Toft, D. O. (1970). *Proc. Natl. Acad. Sci. U.S.A.* **67**, 501.

O'Malley, B. W., Toft, D. O., and Sherman, M. R. (1971). *J. Biol. Chem.* **246**, 1117.

Palmiter, R. D., Christensen, A. K., and Schimke, R. T. (1970). *J. Biol. Chem.* **245**, 833.

Palmiter, R. D., Catlin, G. H., and Cox, R. F. (1973). *Cell Differ.* **2**, 163.

Palmiter, R. D., Moore, P. B., Mulvihill, E. R., and Emtage, S. (1976). *Cell* **8**, 557.

Pikler, G. M., Webster, R. A., and Spelsberg, T. C. (1976). *Biochem. J.* **156**, 399.

Puca, G. A., Nola, E., Sica, V., and Bresciani, F. (1977). *J. Biol. Chem.* **252**, 1358.

Riggs, A. D., Suzuki, H., and Bourgeois, S. (1970). *J. Mol. Biol.* **48**, 67.

Rochefort, H., and Baulieu, E.-E. (1971). *Biochimie* **53**, 893.

Rosen, J. M., and O'Malley, B. W. (1975). In "Biochemical Actions of Hormones" (G. Litwack, ed.), Vol. 3, pp. 271–315. Academic Press, New York.

Schrader, W. T. (1975). In "Methods in Enzymology" (B. W. O'Malley and J. G. Hardman, eds.), Vol. 36, pp. 187–211. Academic Press, New York.

Schrader, W. T., and O'Malley, B. W. (1972). *J. Biol. Chem.* **247**, 51.

Schrader, W. T., and O'Malley, B. W. (1978). *Biochem. Biophys. Res. Commun.* (in press).

Schrader, W. T., Toft, D. O., and O'Malley, B. W. (1972). *J. Biol. Chem.* **247**, 2401.

Schrader, W. T., Buller, R. E., Kuhn, R. W., and O'Malley, B. W. (1974). *J. Steroid Biochem.* **5**, 989.

Schrader, W. T., Heuer, S. S., and O'Malley, B. W. (1975). *Biol. Reprod.* **12**, 134.

Schrader, W. T., Kuhn, R. W., and O'Malley, B. W. (1977a). *J. Biol. Chem.* **252**, 299.

Schrader, W. T., Coty, W. A., Smith, R. G., and O'Malley, B. W. (1977b). *Ann. N.Y. Acad. Sci.* **286**, 64.

Schrader, W. T., Kuhn, R. W., Buller, R. E., Schwartz, R. T., and O'Malley, B. W. (1977c). *In* "Receptors in Pharmacology" (J. R. Smythies, ed.). Dekker, New York (in press).

Schwartz, R. J., Tsai, M.-J., Tsai, S. Y., and O'Malley, B. W. (1975). *J. Biol. Chem.* **250**, 5175.

Schwartz, R. J., Kuhn, R. W., Buller, R. E., Schrader, W. T., and O'Malley, B. W. (1976). *J. Biol. Chem.* **251**, 5166.

Sherman, M. R., and Diaz, S. C. (1977). *Ann. N.Y. Acad. Sci.* **286**, 81.

Sherman, M. R., Corvol, P. L., and O'Malley, B. W. (1970). *J. Biol. Chem.* **245**, 6085.

Sherman, M. R., Atienza, S. B. P., Shansky, J. R., and Hoffman, L. M. (1974). *J. Biol. Chem.* **249**, 5351.

Sherman, M. R., Tuazon, F. B., Diaz, S. C., and Miller, L. K. (1976). *Biochemistry* **15**, 980.

Simons, S. S., Jr., Martinez, H. M., Garcea, R. L., Baxter, J. D., and Tomkins, G. M. (1976). *J. Biol. Chem.* **251**, 334.

Smith, H. E., Smith, R. G., Toft, D. O., Neergaard, J. R., Burrows, E. P., and O'Malley, B. W. (1974). *J. Biol. Chem.* **249**, 5924.

Spelsberg, T. C. (1974). *In* "Acidic Proteins of the Nucleus" (I. L. Cameron and J. R. Jeter, Jr., eds.), pp. 247–296. Academic Press, New York.

Spelsberg, T. C. (1976). *Biochem. J.* **156**, 391.

Spelsberg, T. C., and Cox, R. F. (1976). *Biochim. Biophys. Acta* **435**, 376.

Spelsberg, T. C., Steggles, A. W., and O'Malley, B. W. (1971a). *J. Biol. Chem.* **246**, 4188.

Spelsberg, T. C., Steggles, A. W., and O'Malley, B. W. (1971b). *Biochim. Biophys. Acta* **254**, 129.

Spelsberg, T. C., Steggles, A. W., Chytil, F., and O'Malley, B. W. (1972). *J. Biol. Chem.* **247**, 1368.

Spelsberg, T. C., Webster, R., and Pikler, G. M. (1975). *In* "Chromosomal Proteins and Their Role in the Regulation of Gene Expression" (G. S. Stein and L. J. Kleinsmith, eds.), pp. 153–186. Academic Press, New York.

Spelsberg, T. C., Pikler, G. M., and Webster, R. A. (1976a). *Science* **194**, 197.

Spelsberg, T. C., Webster, R. A., and Pikler, G. M. (1976b). *Nature (London)* **262**, 65.

Spelsberg, T. C., Webster, R., Pikler, G., Thrall, C., and Wells, D. (1976c). *J. Steroid Biochem.* **7**, 1091.

Spelsberg, T. C., Webster, R., Pikler, G., Thrall, C., and Wells, D. (1977). *Ann. N.Y. Acad. Sci.* **286**, 43.

Steggles, A. W., Spelsberg, T. C., and O'Malley, B. W. (1971a). *Biochem. Biophys. Res. Commun.* **43**, 20.

Steggles, A. W., Spelsberg, T. C., Glasser, S. R., and O'Malley, B. W. (1971b). *Proc. Natl. Acad. Sci. U.S.A.* **68**, 1479.

Stumpf, W. E. (1968). *Endocrinology* **83**, 777.

Stumpf, W. E., and Sar, M. (1973). *J. Steroid Biochem.* **4**, 477.

Sullivan, D., Palacios, R., Stavnezer, J., Taylor, J. M., Faras, A. J., Kiely, M. L., Summers, N. M., Bishop, J. M., and Schimke, R. T. (1973). *J. Biol. Chem.* **248**, 7530.

Toft, D. O., and Gorski, J. (1966). *Proc. Natl. Acad. Sci. U.S.A.* **55**, 1574.

Toft, D. O., and O'Malley, B. W. (1972). *Endocrinology* **90**, 1041.

Toft, D. O., Lohmar, P., Miller, J., and Moudgil, V. (1976). *J. Steroid Biochem.* **7**, 1053.

Toft, D. O., Moudgil, V., Lohmar, P., and Miller, J. (1977). *Ann. N.Y. Acad. Sci.* **286**, 29.

Towle, H. C., Tsai, M.-J., Hirose, M., Tsai, S. Y., Schwartz, R. J., Parker, M. G., and O'Malley, B. W. (1976). *In* "The Molecular Biology of Hormone Action" (J. Papaconstantinou, ed.), pp. 107–136. Academic Press, New York.

Tsai, M.-J., and O'Malley, B. W. (1977). *In* "Chromatin and Chromosome Structure" (H. J. Li and R. A. Eckhardt, eds.), pp. 255–298. Academic Press, New York.

Tsai, M.-J., Schwartz, R. J., Tsai, S. Y., and O'Malley, B. W. (1975). *J. Biol. Chem.* **250**, 5165.

Tsai, S. Y., Tsai, M.-J., Schwartz, R., Kalimi, M., Clark, J. H., and O'Malley, B. W. (1975). *Proc. Natl. Acad. Sci. U.S.A.* **72**, 4228.

Tsai, S. Y., Harris, S. E., Tsai, M.-J., and O'Malley, B. W. (1976a). *J. Biol. Chem.* **251**, 4713.

Tsai, S. Y., Tsai, M.-J., Harris, S. E, and O'Malley, B. W. (1976b). *J. Biol. Chem.* **251**, 6475.

Webster, R. A., Pikler, G. M., and Spelsberg, T. C. (1976). *Biochem. J.* **156**, 409.

Weintraub, H., Worcel, A., and Alberts, B. (1976). *Cell* **9**, 409.

Woo, S. L. C., and O'Malley, B. W. (1975). *Life Sci.* **17**, 1039.

CHAPTER 9

Integrated Mammary Tumor Virus Genes: Transcriptional Regulation by Glucocorticoids and Specific Effects on Host Gene Expression

Keith R. Yamamoto, Robert D. Ivarie, Janet Ring, Gordon M. Ringold, and Michael R. Stallcup

I. MAMMARY TUMOR VIRUS DNA AS A SPECIFIC GENETIC PROBE

Steroid receptor proteins are likely to act by associating with some component(s) on the chromosome, thereby triggering biochemical events leading to an alteration in gene expression. In this view, the hormone–receptor interaction can be considered an allosteric reaction which increases the affinity of the receptor for the nuclear sites. Steroids display a high degree of biological selectivity, with direct effects on only a few genes (Ashburner *et al.*, 1973; Yamamoto and Alberts, 1976; Ivarie and O'Farrell, 1977). In a

373

number of cases, it is clear that steroids mediate an increase in the intracellular accumulation of specific RNA's (Harris et al., 1974; McKnight et al., 1975; Parks et al., 1975; Ringold et al., 1975a,b; Feigelson et al., 1975; Palmiter et al., 1976; Tata, 1976). Thus, it is tempting to conclude that steroid receptors are analogous to the well-characterized prokaryotic regulatory proteins (e.g., cyclic AMP-binding protein) (Majors, 1975; Dickson et al., 1975) that function by specific interactions with the genome.

On the other hand, the interaction of the receptor with nuclei in vivo (Williams and Gorski, 1972) and with nuclear components in vitro (Chamness et al., 1974; Yamamoto and Alberts, 1975; Simons et al., 1976) appears to be predominantly nonspecific and of low affinity. It has been proposed that a few specific, high-affinity receptor-binding sites might exist, but that the vast excess of nonspecific binding renders the specific sites undetectable by conventional binding studies (Yamamoto and Alberts, 1974, 1975); a direct test of this idea has not yet been devised.

Taken together, these observations define some of the major problems that must be resolved in order to understand the mode of action of this class of hormones. For example, one long-range goal is to determine how biological selectivity is maintained against a high background of apparent biochemical nonselectivity. Another basic question relates to the organization of the specific genes that respond to the hormonal stimulus, and the mechanisms by which a given hormone elicits different responses in different tissues. A third central issue is to define the actual biochemical reactions underlying the hormonal response. It seems likely that some novel experimental approaches will be needed to ultimately unravel some of these complex problems.

In our laboratory, we have recently begun to examine the physical and biological properties of the genes that specify mouse mammary tumor virus (MTV). Normal mouse cells contain multiple copies of MTV DNA covalently integrated into the genome (Varmus et al., 1972); these copies most likely represent endogenous viral genes, transmitted through the germ line as part of the normal mouse gene complement. The virus particle itself contains an RNA genome; when MTV infects cells, the incoming viral RNA is thought to replicate via a double-stranded DNA intermediate synthesized by the virion-associated RNA-directed DNA polymerase ("reverse transcriptase") (Temin and Baltimore, 1972). During infection, some viral DNA intermediates become covalently integrated into the host genome (Ringold et al., 1977a; Yamamoto and Ringold, 1977). In most mammary tumors producing MTV particles, the tumor cells contain somewhat elevated levels of integrated viral DNA, presumably acquired via infection (Morris et al., 1977). Thus, uninfected nonmurine cells contain no detectable MTV genes, whereas normal mouse tissues carry endogenous viral DNA, and mouse mammary tumor cells may contain additional exogenously derived copies.

Surprisingly, the expression of MTV genes integrated into the genomes of cultured cell lines derived from murine mammary tumors (Parks *et al.*, 1974, 1975; Ringold *et al.*, 1975a,b), rat hepatoma (Ringold *et al.*, 1977a), mink lung (Vaidya *et al.*, 1976), or cat kidney (Vaidya *et al.*, 1976) is strongly regulated by glucocorticoids. Using the viral reverse transcriptase to synthesize DNA complementary to the MTV genomes (MTV cDNA), molecular hybridization reagents for the specific and direct quantification of the hormone-inducible transcript (Parks *et al.*, 1974, 1975; Ringold *et al.*, 1975a,b) are readily prepared. Thus, this system has the technical advantage of bypassing the often difficult step of mRNA isolation and purification, yet still allowing direct cDNA hybridization measurements.

There is now strong evidence from pulse-labeling studies in whole cells that the dexamethasone-stimulated accumulation of MTV RNA can be accounted for by a specific increase in the rate of transcription of the viral genes (Young *et al.*, 1977; Ringold *et al.*, 1977c). In this report we describe a series of preliminary experiments aimed at characterizing RNA synthesis in isolated nuclei. It is conceivable that such a system can eventually be extended to yield new information about the mechanisms by which steroid receptors modulate the efficiency of eukaryotic gene transcription.

At the cell-biological level, it is especially intriguing that MTV genes, which are endogenous only to the mouse, retain hormone responsiveness even when they become integrated into the genome of an entirely different species. In addition, we show here that MTV infection of rat hepatoma (HTC) cells may affect the dexamethasone responsiveness of certain host genes, as well as the expression of a small subset of hormonally nonresponsive host genes.

These biochemical and biological data are considered in terms of a speculative model which proposes that MTV genes might exert their effects in a direct manner dependent on their site and orientation of integration into the host genome; moreover, functionally analogous transposable genetic elements could determine the nature and specificity of hormone responsiveness during normal development.

II. RNA SYNTHESIS IN ISOLATED GR CELL NUCLEI

In GR cells, the stimulation of viral RNA accumulation by dexamethasone is rapid, becoming detectable within 30 minutes and half-maximal by 2.5 hours (Ringold *et al.*, 1975b). Based on assays measuring the kinetics of molecular hybridization of cellular RNA to [³H]MTV cDNA, MTV RNA comprises about 0.02% of the steady-state concentration of cell RNA in the absence of dexamethasone, and about 0.5% in its presence (Ringold *et al.*, 1975a,b). To determine whether the increase in viral RNA concentration is due to a specific increase in its rate of synthesis, a hybridization assay was employed that vastly reduces hybridization backgrounds, thereby enabling specific detection of low levels of labeled RNA (Stavnezer and Bishop, 1978). Using this method to measure the fraction of pulse-labeled cell RNA which is viral specific, we found that dexamethasone causes a 10-fold increase in the rate of MTV RNA synthesis, and that the change in rate is complete within the shortest period examined, 0–15 minutes (Ringold et al., 1977c). The overall rate of cellular RNA synthesis was not appreciably affected in these experiments. Young et al. (1977), using a different cell line and assay procedure, have reached similar conclusions.

The direct demonstration that dexamethasone rapidly and selectively stimulates the rate of transcription of MTV genes provides a biological correlate for monitoring the biochemical nature of the primary effect of glucocorticoids. Using this measurement of the whole-cell response as an assay, we have now begun to investigate RNA synthesis in isolated GR cell nuclei. In these initial experiments, our goal has been to establish conditions under which nuclei from hormone-treated and untreated cells synthesize viral RNA at rates characteristic of hormone-treated and untreated cells, respectively. Our studies have been greatly facilitated by the work of other investigators, particularly P. Feigelson and R. C. C. Huang and their co-workers (Ernest et al., 1976; Marzluff et al., 1973), who have examined cell-free RNA synthesis in other systems.

When GR cell nuclei are isolated and incubated at 25°C in the presence of [^{3}H]CTP under the conditions described in the legend to Fig. 1, radioactivity accumulates into trichloracetic-acid-insoluble material at a measurable but steadily declining rate for about an hour (Fig. 1). Several lines of evidence support the idea that the incorporation observed represents DNA-directed synthesis of RNA mediated by the endogenous cellular RNA polymerases. First, incorporation is dependent on the presence of ribonucleoside triphosphates, and the TCA-insolubility of the product is abolished by ribonuclease, but not by deoxyribonuclease or by Pronase (data not shown). Second, incorporation is inhibited ~90% by actinomycin D (data not shown); this is an important control in view of recent findings that artifactual reactions occur under some conditions, resulting in DNA-independent (and actinomycin D-insensitive) RNA synthesis (G. Schutz, personal communication; Zasloff and Felsenfeld, 1977). Finally, the pattern of inhibition of the incorporation by α-amanitin (Schwartz et al., 1974) implies that all three nuclear RNA polymerases (Roeder and Rutter, 1970) are active under our conditions (Fig. 2).

In order to estimate what fraction of the RNA synthesized in this cell-free system is MTV specific, we used a modification of the hybridization assay of Stavnezer and Bishop (1978) as described in detail by Ringold et al. (1977c).

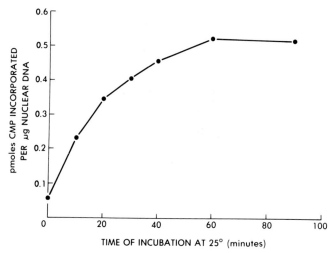

FIG. 1. Time course of [³H]CMP incorporation in isolated GR cell nuclei. Confluent GR cell cultures were removed from culture flasks by scraping. Nuclei were prepared using methods similar to those described by Marzluff *et al.* (1973) and Ernest *et al.* (1976). The cells were swollen in a hypotonic buffer, disrupted with a Dounce homogenizer in the presence of 0.1% NP40, and the nuclei pelleted and resuspended in 1 M sucrose, 15 mM Tris–Cl (pH 8.0), 7.5 mM MgCl, 0.5 mM dithriothreitol. The nuclei were centrifuged through a 2 M sucrose pad containing the same buffer and resuspended in 25% glycerol, 50 mM HEPES, 5 mM Mg(OAc)$_2$, 0.5 mM dithiothreitol, and 1% crystalline bovine serum albumin. Light microscopic examination revealed that the final preparation is free from contamination by cytoplasmic debris and whole cells. Conditions for cell-free RNA synthesis were essentially those of Ernest *et al.* (1976) except that nuclei were used at a concentration of 1 mg nuclear DNA/ml and RNA was labeled with 60 μM [³H]CTP (1 Ci/mmole). Unlabeled ATP, UTP, and GTP were present at concentrations of 1 mM each in a buffer containing 50 mM HEPES (pH 8.0), 5 mM Mg(OAc)$_2$, 0.5 mM MnCl$_2$, 2.5 mM dithiothreitol, 150 mM NH$_4$Cl, 10% glycerol, 1% bovine serum albumin. The reactions were carried out in 50 μl at 25°C, and were monitored by measuring radioactivity insoluble in 10% trichloracetic acid.

Briefly, the procedure utilizes unlabeled partially duplex molecules of viral DNA which contain double-stranded regions and single-stranded "tails" complementary to the viral RNA; this "tailed duplex" DNA is the product of the endogenous viral reverse transcriptase (Ringold *et al.*, 1976). When labeled viral RNA is annealed to the single-stranded regions of tailed duplex DNA, it can be selectively retained on hydroxylapatite using a special buffer which allows only double-stranded DNA to bind to the column matrix (Stavnezer and Bishop, 1978); the nonviral radioactive RNA passes through the column.

Table I summarizes the results of experiments in which nuclei were prepared from untreated GR cells and from cells treated for 30 minutes with

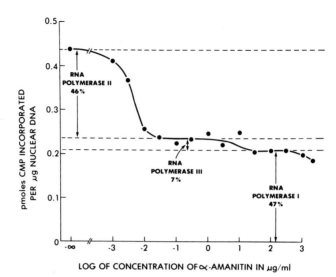

LOG OF CONCENTRATION OF α-AMANITIN IN μg/ml

Fig. 2. Inhibition of cell-free RNA synthesis by α-amanitin. RNA synthesis was carried out for 60 minutes at 25°C as described in Fig. 1, except that varying concentrations of α-amanitin were included in the reaction mix. Schwartz *et al.* (1974) have studied in detail the inhibition of mammalian RNA polymerases by α-amanitin and find the general pattern of sensitivity to be II > III > I.

TABLE I
RELATIVE RATES OF SYNTHESIS OF MTV RNA[a]

	$\left(\dfrac{\text{MTV-Specific [}^3\text{H]RNA}}{\text{Total [}^3\text{H]RNA}}\right) \times 100$		
	$-$Dex	$+$Dex	$+/-$Dex
In isolated nuclei	0.025	0.430	17
	(0.017–0.030)	(0.408–0.450)	
In whole cells	0.036	0.444	12
	(0.027–0.050)	(0.240–0.530)	

[a] Nuclei were isolated as described in Fig. 1 either from untreated cells, or from cultures which had been exposed to 10^{-6} M dexamethasone (Dex) for 30 minutes at 37°C. RNA was tritium labeled for 60 minutes at 25°C under the cell-free conditions described in Fig. 1, and total RNA was phenol extracted and purified. The tritium-labeled MTV-specific RNA was measured using the hybridization procedure of Stavnezer *et al.* (1977), as described briefly in the text, and in detail by Ringold *et al.* (1977c). Typical whole-cell labeling data are included for comparison, and represent incorporation of [³H]uridine into total and viral RNA in a 15-minute pulse at 37°C; the whole-cell data are taken from Ringold *et al.* (1977c).

10^{-6} M dexamethasone; the nuclei were incubated for 60 minutes in a reaction mixture containing [^{3}H]CTP. Total RNA was extracted and purified, and labeled viral RNA measured as described above. It can be seen that nuclei from cells exposed to dexamethasone for 30 minutes synthesize about 20-fold more MTV RNA than nuclei from untreated controls. Moreover, of the total RNA that is synthesized in the cell-free system by nuclei from hormone-treated and untreated cultures, the fraction that is viral specific is similar to the levels seen in comparably treated whole cells; the results of typical [^{3}H]uridine pulse-labeling experiments with whole cells (Ringold *et al.*, 1977c) are given in Table I for comparison.

There is strong biochemical and genetic evidence that cellular mRNA is transcribed by RNA polymerase II, the enzyme that displays the greatest sensitivity to inhibition by α-amanitin (Lindell *et al.*, 1970; Somers *et al.*, 1975). Furthermore, RNA synthesis from integrated avian C-type viral genes is also mediated by this enzyme (Rymo *et al.*, 1974; Jacquet *et al.*, 1974). Thus, it was of interest to examine the α-amanitin sensitivity of the synthesis of MTV RNA in isolated nuclei. For these experiments, cell-free RNA synthesis was performed in the absence of α-amanitin, or in the presence of 0.3 or 300 μg/ml of the toxin. These concentrations are sufficient to inhibit, respectively, RNA polymerase II alone, or RNA polymerases II and III in these nuclei (Fig. 2). The results reveal that virtually all ($\sim$97%) of the MTV RNA synthesis in isolated nuclei is blocked by the lower concentration of α-amanitin (Fig. 3), suggesting that RNA polymerase II is responsible for its synthesis.

It remains to be seen whether a system employing intact nuclei can be extended to experiments in which the rate of synthesis of viral RNA can be altered by addition of the appropriate regulatory components. It is likely that at the minimum, such an approach will require long-term synthesis beginning at the correct initiation sites. In systems utilizing endogenous RNA polymerase II, the observed synthesis probably exclusively reflects the completion of chains initiated *in vivo* (Cox, 1973; Ferencz and Seifart, 1975). Moreover, there are as yet no reports that exogenously added enzymes are able to initiate correctly at sequences normally transcribed by RNA polymerase II. Nevertheless, it appears that our conditions for nuclear isolation and subsequent RNA synthesis are able to maintain, at least for a short time, the patterns of transcription that had been established in the whole cell. It is conceivable that this noninitiating system, if otherwise faithful, might help to determine the patterns of transcription of the viral genes; the primary products of MTV DNA transcription, and the effects of dexamethasone on them are currently unknown (Varmus *et al.*, 1977). Of course, we shall also attempt to define conditions that support faithful initiation of transcription in this system.

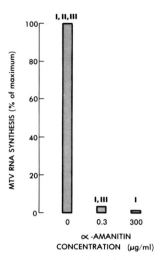

FIG. 3. Inhibition of cell-free MTV RNA synthesis by α-amanitin. Cell-free RNA synthesis was carried-out for 60 minutes as described in Fig. 1, but in the presence of 0, 0.3, or 300 μg/ml α-amanitin, conditions that are permissive for the activity of RNA polymerase I + II + III, I + III, or I, respectively (Fig. 2). Total RNA was then isolated, and the labeled viral RNA measured by molecular hybridization as described in Table I.

III. RESPONSIVENESS OF MTV GENES IN INFECTED HTC CELLS

It is apparent that all mouse mammary tumor cell lines that produce MTV contain viral genes that respond to dexamethasone in a fashion similar to the GR cells described here (Dickson *et al.*, 1974; Fine *et al.*, 1974; Parks *et al.*, 1974; L. Young *et al.*, 1975). On the other hand, some nonmammary mouse cells that express MTV genes do so in a hormone-independent manner (see below). Some insight into the relationship of glucocorticoid regulation to cellular differentiation state and viral gene integration state has been gained by examining nonmurine cells that have been infected by MTV. When populations of cultured mink lung, feline kidney (Vaidya *et al.*, 1976), and rat hepatoma (Ringold *et al.*, 1977a) cells are exposed to MTV, viral DNA becomes stably integrated into the cellular genomes, and transcription of the newly acquired viral genes is strongly stimulated by dexamethasone.

These results have several interesting implications. They suggest that if the glucocorticoid receptor alters MTV gene expression by interacting directly with a viral DNA sequence, then the receptors from these four highly diverged species are still able to recognize the mouse-specific sequence. Alternatively, if the viral genome integrates into host DNA in a site-specific manner such that it is adjacent to a receptor-binding site, then the integration site for all four species must have been conserved during evolution of these species. Finally, the ability of viral genes to respond in all these cultured cell types rules out the possibility that glucocorticoid responsiveness is strictly limited to mammary cells.

To begin to examine these effects in more detail, we have isolated a large number of independent clones from populations of infected HTC cells. The amount of integrated MTV DNA per cell, and the level of expression of these genes, have been determined in the separate homogenous clonal lines. Figure 4 shows the kinetics of association of nuclear DNA from two MTV-infected clones with [³H]MTV cDNA. When the extent of hybridization at various values of C_0t (the product of DNA concentration × time in mole second liter^{-1} for each clone is compared with the reassociation rate of ^{14}C-labeled rat DNA representing only unique sequences, the number of copies of viral DNA per haploid cell genome can be directly estimated.

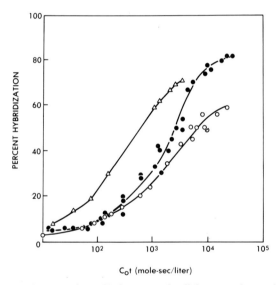

FIG. 4. Association kinetics of MTV[³H]cDNA and cellular DNA from infected HTC cells. Cellular DNA was extracted and purified as described (Ringold *et al.*, 1977a), and was fragmented and denatured in alkali (0.3 N NaOH, 90°C for 60 minutes). Annealing was carried out at 68°C in 0.6 M NaCl using ~10³ cpm MTV [³H]cDNA, as described by Morris *et al.* (1977), and was monitored by pattern of elution of trichloroacetic-acid-insoluble radioactivity from hydroxyapatite columns. Viral genome copy number is estimated by comparison of $C_0t_{1/2}$ values (C_0t at 50% of maximum hybridization) with the reassociation rate of ^{14}C-labeled rat unique sequence DNA (●————●, $C_0t_{1/2}$ = 1750) prepared as described by Morris *et al.* (1977). $C_0t_{1/2}$ values for MTV-infected HTC cell clones J2.15 (○————○) and M1.7 (△————△) are 1500 and 260, respectively.

Thus, clone J2.15 contains one viral DNA equivalent per haploid cell, whereas M1.7 contains seven copies of MTV DNA per haploid cell (Fig. 4). Concentration of intracellular viral RNA is determined in an analogous fashion, measuring the kinetics of hybridization between cellular RNA and [^{3}H]MTV cDNA as described for the uncloned infected cells (Ringold et al., 1977a).

Table IIA summarizes the results of viral DNA and RNA assays in a series of infected clones that contain between 1 and 10 integrated viral genomes per haploid cell. It appears that clones containing many copies of viral genes produce more viral RNA in the presence of dexamethasone than clones

TABLE II

	A. MTV DNA and RNA in infected HTC cells[a]			B. TAT and GS in infected HTC cells[b]			
				Relative enzyme activity			
		MTV RNA (copies/cell)		TAT		GS	
Clone	MTV DNA (copies/haploid genome)	−Dex	+Dex	−Dex	+Dex	−Dex	+Dex
HTC4.1	0	0	0	1	15 (11–19)	1	8 (5–11)
J2.15	1	0	0	1	15	1.5	6
J2.31	1	0	0	0.8	13.5	1	8
J2.17	1	<1	700	0.9	12	1	7
J0.1	1–2	<1	1000				
J1.3	2	<0.05	5				
M1.7	4–7	3	3000	1	1.5	1	1.7
M1.20	5–8	65	8000	1	12	1	4.6
M1.54	3–6	160	18000	0.3	1.5	1	2
M1.60	10	130	6500	1	5	1	2.3

[a] MTV sequences integrated into cellular DNA were measured by C_0t analysis as described in Fig. 4, except M1.20 and M1.60, which were measured by calibration-curve analysis (Yamamoto and Ringold, 1977). Intracellular MTV RNA was measured by molecular hybridization as described by Ringold et al. (1977a); the number of viral RNA copies per cell are based on a $C_0t_{1/2} = 2 \times 10^{-2}$ mole sec liter^{-1} for pure viral RNA (Varmus et al., 1973).

[b] Cells [(1–3) $\times$ 10^7] were removed from culture dishes in 10 mM Tris, pH 8.0, 1 mM EDTA, 0.25 M sucrose, and were lysed by freezing and thawing. Cell debris was removed by low-speed centrifugation, and enzymatic activities were determined on aliquots of the extract, using essentially the methods of Diamondstone (1966) and Kulka et al. (1972) for TAT and GS, respectively. Results are presented relative to basal activities in uninfected control (HTC4.1) cells. Range given for dexamethasone-induced activities in uninfected cells represents the extent of clonal variability seen in subclones of HTC4.1 (Yamamoto and Ringold, 1977). Dexamethasone was used at 10^{-6}M in all experiments.

containing few MTV DNA copies. However, it is clear from these data, as well as from other studies comparing levels of MTV RNA in clones, that all contain similar numbers of viral genes (Yamamoto and Ringold, 1977; J. Ring and K. R. Yamamoto, unpublished), that this correlation is not a strict one. Moreover, Table IIA also shows that the extent of MTV RNA induction by dexamethasone varies greatly from clone to clone (ranging from 50- to 1000-fold) in a manner which has no apparent relationship to the number of integrated viral genes. It may be significant to note that every clone examined which contains more than 2 copies of MTV DNA per haploid cell produces MTV RNA (we have examined ~25 such clones), while clones which appear to carry only 1–2 copies of MTV DNA per haploid cell often contain no detectable viral RNA. Finally, of the clones examined, all those that produce basal levels of MTV RNA are stimulated to produce increased quantities by dexamethasone.

The fact that basal expression and glucocorticoid responsiveness of the viral genes are not related in a simple manner to viral gene dosage is consistent with the idea that not all the integrated MTV genomes are being transcribed to an equivalent extent in the absence of hormone, and that not all of them are stimulated to an equivalent extent in its presence. Thus, one interpretation is that the site of integration of the viral DNA is a critical determinant affecting its activity.

IV. ALTERED HOST GENE EXPRESSION IN INFECTED HTC CELLS

Glucocorticoids affect the activity of a restricted and defined set of genes in HTC cells (Ivarie and O'Farrell, 1977). The response of HTC4, the parent clone used in this study, includes two dexamethasone-inducible enzymatic activities: tyrosine aminotransferase (Thompson *et al.*, 1966) and glutamine synthetase (Kulka *et al.*, 1972). Experimentally, these enzymes are useful as internal markers for hormone responsiveness in the infected cells. However, it seemed conceivable that if hormone responsiveness of the viral genes is related to their sites of integration, infection might selectively affect the expression of responsive host genes. If this were the case, the endogenous glucocorticoid-sensitive genes might also serve as highly sensitive monitors of the effect on the host cell of acquiring exogenous hormone-responsive genes.

Table IIB summarizes the relative enzyme activities, in the presence and absence of dexamethasone, of tyrosine aminotransferase (TAT) and glutamine synthetase (GS) in some of the clones of infected HTC cells examined for viral RNA and DNA in Table IIA. The activities are presented relative to the basal levels detected in uninfected subclone HTC4.1; it should be noted that the dexamethasone-induced activities of these enzymes are somewhat variable, even among different subclones of HTC4, fluctuating over a 60–140% range for GS and a 75–125% range for TAT (Yamamoto and Ringold, 1977; see also Aviv and Thompson, 1972). Nevertheless, the average magnitude of the dexamethasone effect in uninfected cells (~15-fold for TAT; ~8-fold for GS) is sufficient for comparison with the infected clones.

Several of the infected clones described in Table IIB display altered host gene inducibility by dexamethasone. It is interesting that in cases where inducibility of one enzyme is abnormal, the other also appears to be affected. For example, dexamethasone brings about an increase in TAT activity that is less than 2-fold in clone M1.7, yielding a fully induced enzyme level only 10% of that seen in unifected cells. Induction of GS is also reduced in M1.7, reaching <25% of the activity of HTC4.1. In some cases, it appears that both the basal and induced levels of expression can be affected; M1.54, for example, expresses TAT at a level 3-fold below HTC4.1 in the absence of dexamethasone, and 10-fold below HTC4.1 in its presence. The observed changes in the induction pattern in these infected clones appear not to be due to alterations in the receptor protein, because dose–response analyses suggest that receptor activity in these clones is indistinguishable from uninfected cells (Yamamoto et al., 1977).

Nearly all our analyses of this type have been carried out with "multiple-copy" clones, i.e., those containing three or more genome equivalents of the viral DNA per haploid cell. Well over half the clones of this type that we have examined (about 20) seem to differ from HTC4.1 in TAT and GS inducibility, although most of the differences are not as striking as those seen with M1.7 or M1.54 (see, e.g., M1.60). Enzyme induction in lines containing just 1–2 copies of MTV DNA per haploid cell has been measured in only a few cases. We have not yet detected any significant differences in TAT and GS activities in these so-called "single-copy" clones relative to HTC4.1 (Table IIB). Whether the single-copy clones actually represent a separate class, in which integration of 1–2 viral genomes does not generally affect host-gene inducibility, is an open question awaiting further analysis.

In order to determine if MTV infection is general or specific in its effects on host-cell gene expression, we have examined the rate of synthesis of a large number of cell proteins, separating [^{35}S]methionine pulse-labeled total-cell extracts by high-resolution two-dimensional gel electrophoresis (O'Farrell, 1975). Autoradiographs of gels from HTC4.1 cells labeled in the absence and presence of dexamethasone (Fig. 5) reveal that the hormone brings about only a small number of detectable changes in the pattern of gene expression. The major changes are seen as inductions, i.e., increased rates of synthesis of specific proteins; some of these are marked in the lower panel of Fig. 5. Ivarie and O'Farrell (1978) have examined the phenotypic

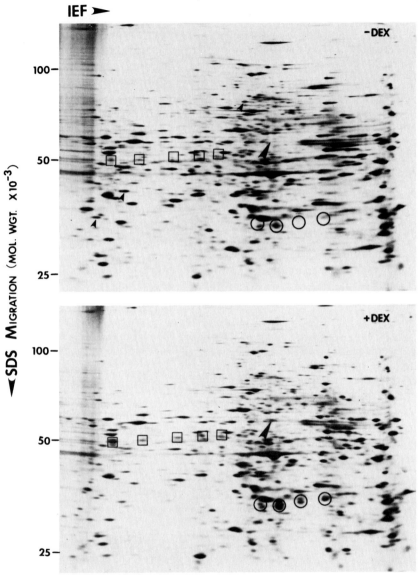

FIG. 5. Two-dimensional gel autoradiograms from untreated (upper panel) and 10^{-6} M dexamethasone-treated (lower panel) HTC4.1 cells. Cells were grown and labeled for 30 minutes with 250 μc/ml [^{35}S]methionine, as described by Ivarie and O'Farrell (1977). Samples were prepared, electrophoresed, and autoradiographed as described by O'Farrell (1975). Spots marked in the upper panel by small arrows denote proteins that are absent in MTV-infected clones (see Fig. 8); spots marked by squares and circles denote some of the major changes mediated by dexamethasone; the large arrow identifies TAT (Ivarie and O'Farrell, 1978).

effects of dexamethasone on HTC cells in detail, and conclude that specific changes are detectable in fewer than 1% of the resolved protein spots: Using protein purification and immunoprecipitation techniques, these workers have identified TAT on these gels as a somewhat diffuse dexamethasone-induced spot migrating in the SDS dimension with an apparent molecular weight of 56,000 (see arrow, lower panel of Fig. 5). A spot corresponding to glutamine synthetase activity has not been identified; this enzyme may migrate outside of the pI range ($\sim$7.0–4.5) of these gels (Crook, 1976).

Figure 6 shows details of the three regions of the gels that contain major dexamethasone-induced proteins and examines the effect of progesterone on their synthesis. There is some evidence that the five induced spots detected in the region denoted "Belt I" may be derived from a single gene product which undergoes a discrete series of posttranslational modifications (Ivarie and O'Farrell, 1977). Similarly, the spots in the region denoted "Belt II" may also represent various stages of modification of a single protein. In any case, Fig. 6 reveals that progesterone does not affect TAT synthesis but does increase the rate of synthesis of the Belt I and Belt II spots.

Progesterone is an "antiglucocorticoid" that acts as a competitive inhibitor of dexamethasone action; it appears to associate with the dexamethasone-binding site on the receptor without bringing about the allosteric alteration that results in subsequent association of the receptor with nuclear sites (Samuels and Tomkins, 1970). The apparent affinity of the glucocorticoid receptor for progesterone is relatively low; thus, high concentrations (comparable to those used here) are required to inhibit TAT induction in the presence of dexamethasone (data not shown). These results confirm previous biochemical experiments showing that TAT enzyme activity is not induced

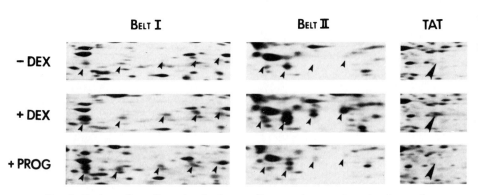

FIG. 6. Regions of two-dimensional gel autoradiograms that contain major dexamethasone-induced proteins: comparison of effects of $2 \times 10^{-7} M$ dexamethasone and $5 \times 10^{-5} M$ progesterone.

by progesterone alone or by dexamethasone in the presence of excess progesterone (Samuels and Tomkins, 1970).

The fact that high concentrations of progesterone induce the Belt I and Belt II spots is consistent with the possibility that the dexamethasone effect on the synthesis of these proteins is not mediated by the glucocorticoid receptor. Alternatively, it is conceivable that the progesterone effect reflects a previously undetected "cytoplasmic" activity of steroid-complexed glucocorticoid receptor. It may be significant in this regard that high concentrations of estradiol or epicortisol, neither of which interacts with the glucocorticoid receptor, do not induce the Belt I and Belt II spots (R. D. Ivarie, P. H. O'Farrell, and K. R. Yamamoto, unpublished). Whichever the case may be, progesterone appears to divide into two classes the dexamethasone response in these cells, one which accompanies nuclear binding of the receptor (TAT induction), and another which seems to occur independent of nuclear binding (Belt I and Belt II induction).

Figure 7 shows the same regions of the gels, comparing the proteins labeled in HTC4.1 and M1.7 in the presence of dexamethasone. Clone M1.7, in which TAT and GS activities are induced by the hormone to levels far below those found in uninfected cells (Table II B), seems to synthesize the Belt I and Belt II proteins at rates similar to the uninfected cells, whereas the TAT spot is undetectable. Analogous results have been obtained with other "multiple-copy" infected clones (data not shown), i.e., the intensity of the TAT spot is proportional to the magnitude of the TAT activity in each clone, while induction of the Belt I and Belt II spots appears to be unaffected by infection. Taken at face value, these results are consistent with the idea that MTV infection of HTC cells affects the dexamethasone responsiveness of only those proteins whose induction is mediated by receptor action at the nuclear level.

Infection of HTC cells by MTV may also be accompanied by a small number of specific changes in the expression of genes not regulated by dexamethasone. The upper panel of Fig. 5 identifies three spots (marked

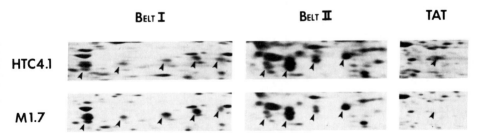

FIG. 7. Regions of two-dimensional gel autoradiograms that contain major dexamethasone-induced proteins: comparison of uninfected (HTC4.1) and MTV-infected (M1.7) cells.

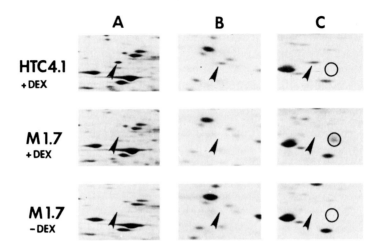

FIG. 8. Regions of two-dimensional gel autoradiograms that contain changes accompanying MTV infection. See text for details.

with small arrows) that are consistently undetectable in the independently isolated infected clones we have examined thus far. Figure 8 shows details of the regions of gels containing these proteins, comparing HTC4.1 and M1.7 in the presence and absence of dexamethasone. In each cell type, the presence or absence of these three spots is unchanged by the hormone.

Also shown in Fig. 8 is a diffuse spot circled in "region C" that is synthesized in the presence of dexamethasone in M1.7 but not in its absence; the uninfected HTC4.1 cells apparently lack this polypeptide. This hormone-induced protein has been detected in six other MTV-infected cells (data not shown). It is conceivable that it represents a viral protein, made in increased amounts in response to the increased viral RNA production brought about by dexamethasone; this possibility has not yet been directly tested. Progesterone, which inhibits MTV RNA inductin by dexamethasone in these cells (Ringold *et al.*, 1975b; H. Young *et al.*, 1975), also prevents induction of this protein (data not shown).

In sum, our results indicate the integration of MTV DNA into the HTC genome is associated with specific rather than general changes in the pattern of gene expression; in clones containing multiple copies of viral DNA, hormone responsiveness of host genes is often altered.

V. MTV AND TRANSPOSABLE GENETIC ELEMENTS

The so-called endogenous MTV sequences, present in relatively constant numbers (~5–10 per cell) in all normal mouse cells examined (Morris *et al.*,

1977), seem to be transcribed at high levels only in lactating mammary tissue (Varmus *et al.*, 1973). This apparent specificity is analogous to that seen for the expression of the major glycoprotein (gp 70) of endogenous C-type viral genomes, in which this gene product is detected only in certain differentiated cell types (Stockert *et al.*, 1971; DelVillano *et al.*, 1975); interestingly, it appears that the integrated viral genome that expresses gp 70 in one tissue is distinct from that which expresses it in another (Elder *et al.*, 1977).

In mouse mammary tumors and mammary tumor cell lines, additional integrated MTV sequences are generally acquired (Morris *et al.*, 1977); at least some of the viral genomes in these cells are expressed and regulated by glucocorticoids. In addition, MTV genes have been found to be transcribed at a high level in a mouse Leydig cell tumor (Varmus *et al.*, 1973) and in a cell line derived from mouse lymphosarcoma (Ringold *et al.*, 1975b). Hormone responsiveness has not been examined in the case of the Leydig cell tumor, but viral RNA production in lymphosarcoma cells is unaffected by dexamethasone (Ringold *et al.*, 1975a, 1977c). It is interesting that MTV genes can also be transcribed and responsive to glucocorticoids when integrated into the genomes of continuous cell lines derived from liver, lung, and kidney of nonmurine origin (Vaidya *et al.*, 1976; Ringold *et al.*, 1977a).

These observations, together with the specific alterations detected in host-gene expression in MTV infected cells, can be explained by assuming that the chromosomal locus at which an MTV genome is located determines its phenotypic effects. Accordingly, the site of integration might affect both determinative responsiveness (i.e., whether a given sequence will be transcribed in a given differentiated tissue) and modulatory responsiveness (i.e., ligand-mediated induction or repression of the level of transcription of that sequence in differentiated cells). Thus, one interpretation consistent with these data is that (a) endogenous MTV sequences are integrated at loci which are normally expressed only in lactating mammary epithelia; (b) expression of endogenous MTV sequences can be activated accompanying neoplastic growth of certain nonmammary tissues, but in general is not glucocorticoid regulated; (c) exogenously introduced MTV sequences are preferentially integrated at common specific loci in a wide variety of tissue types and species; in each case, some of these preferred sites are subject to glucocorticoid regulation; and (d) integration of viral DNA can selectively alter the expression of contiguous host sequences.

In effect, the MTV genome can be regarded as a mobile, or transposable, genetic element whose biological effects depend on position within the host genome. Such a notion has numerous experimental precedents in other systems, and it is worth briefly reviewing some of their features. In bacteria, it has been clearly established that certain specific segments of DNA can move from place to place on the chromosome, and that these transposable elements alter the pattern of expression of nearby genes (Bukhari *et al.*,

1977). Transposable elements were first directly detected in *E. coli* as short segments of DNA that could insert into a coordinately controlled set of genes (operon), and thereby exert a strong polar effect, i.e., reduce expression of distal genes in the operon (Hirsch *et al.*, 1972; Saedler *et al.*, 1972). Four distinct elements ("insertion sequences") of this type have been characterized (Hirsch *et al.*, 1972; Fiandt *et al.*, 1972). Termed *IS*1, *IS*2, *IS*3, and *IS*4, they range in size from 750 to 1400 base pairs, and appear unrelated in primary sequence.

Multiple "endogenous" copies of *IS* sequences are present in the *E. coli* chromosome. For example, Saedler and Heiss (1973) showed that about 8 copies of *IS*1 and 5 copies of *IS*2 are found in each of 4 separate strains examined. Thus, while insertion sequences move to new loci, their total number remains roughly constant. It seems likely that other transposable elements exist undetected on bacterial DNA. Other segments of DNA exhibiting the characteristics of nonrandom integration and polar effects on gene expression have been characterized in various plasmid and viral DNA's (Heffron *et al.*, 1975a; Berg *et al.*, 1975). Thus, there are mechanisms for transmission of transposable elements to new host cells. Heffron *et al.* (1975b) have shown that such sequences can be efficiently passed between many different species.

In addition to their strong polar effects on adjacent gene expression, at least some *IS* elements can occasionally display the opposite biological effect, actually promoting gene expression. In an elegant analysis of a set of insertions affecting expression of the *E. coli* galactose operon, Saedler *et al.* (1974) found that *IS*2 exerts a polar effect when integrated in one orientation, but activates genes when oriented in the opposite direction. The mechanism of the promotor effect is not yet understood. However, it appears that the property of polarity results from recognition of a sequence in the *IS* element by rho, a transcription termination protein in *E. coli* (DeCrombrugghe *et al.*, 1973; Wetekam and Ehring, 1973).

The biochemical characterization of transposable elements in eukaryotes has not approached this level of sophistication. Nevertheless, one of the first indications of their existence originated with McClintock's elegant genetic studies of mutable loci in *Zea mays*, in which she suggested that "controlling elements" regulate gene expression during plant development (see McClintock, 1967, for review). She concluded that when a controlling element is present and active, it affects the activity of adjacent genes in a defined manner dependent on the state of the element. In addition, an unlinked second component can interact with the controlling element, thereby affecting its activity. "Presetting" the activities of the controlling element and modulating the activity of the second component could then produce a complex regulated sequence of events governed by only two genetic regions. A straightforward analogy can be made between the actions of bacterial episomes and maize-controlling elements (Peterson, 1970); Fincham and Sastry (1974) have developed in detail the notion that controlling elements are specific transposable sequences.

Mutable loci have now been characterized in many systems (McClintock, 1967), and it is not unreasonable to speculate that they might represent the actions of transposable elements. In *Drosophila*, Green (1969a,b; 1976) has examined a number of these loci, especially those operating on the white locus. It has been established that the mutability property maps adjacent to the affected genes (Green, 1969a), and that transposition of this element to other chromosomes is accompanied by retention of the mutability property at the new integration site (Green, 1969b). Green concludes that these changes are most easily explained by the integration of a "viruslike agent" into the *Drosophila* genome. Evidence for different transposable controlling elements in *Drosophila* has been documented by others (Judd, 1969; Green, 1973; Ising and Ramel, 1976).

If the effects of MTV infection of HTC cells are mechanistically related to the actions of known transposable elements in prokaryotes and those inferred in eukaryotes, then several predictions can be made which suggest the direction of future experiments. First, effects on host-gene expression should require integration of viral DNA into host sequences, and should act in *cis*. Second, the integration sites should be contiguous to genes whose activity is altered, assuming that the alterations that are monitored are direct effects of integration. Third, infection of these cells by other viruses that are not responsive to dexamethasone (or infection by the appropriate MTV variants, if they can be selected) are likely to display a different set of biological effects, at least with respect to hormone-regulated host genes. Fourth, specific integration sites, or a hierarchy of preferred integration sites, should exist in the host genome.

The potential for analyzing integration sites of viral genes within the host genome is now becoming available. In the case of the mammalian DNA virus SV40, the viral genome itself has been extensively mapped with respect to sites of cleavage by a large number of restriction endonucleases (see Tooze, 1973, for references). Starting with this information, Botchan *et al.* (1976) and Ketner and Kelly (1976) have cleaved cellular DNA from cloned SV40-transformed cultures with restriction enzymes, separated the cleavage products by agarose gel electrophoresis, and identified fragments containing viral sequences by a sensitive hybridization procedure (Southern, 1975). They were unable to detect any indication that SV40 integrates nonrandomly; i.e., each transformed clone yields a different pattern of viral DNA-containing fragments. On the other hand, Battula and Temin (1977) have shown that the integration site for infectious DNA specifying spleen necrosis virus, an RNA virus, appears to be highly nonrandom and perhaps specific.

Although mouse mammary tumor cells appear to lack unintegrated MTV DNA sequences (Ringold *et al.*, 1978), the infected HTC cells contain both closed circular and linear forms of unintegrated double-stranded viral DNA (Ringold *et al.*, 1977b). The metabolism and physical properties of these molecules are consistent with the idea that they are products of reverse transcription of MTV RNA (Ringold *et al.*, 1978), analogous to the viral DNA molecules detected during acute infection by avian and murine C-type viruses (Guntaka *et al.*, 1975, 1976; Gianni *et al.*, 1975). Analysis of unintegrated MTV DNA by restriction enzymes has been carried out (Shank *et al.*, 1978); we now hope to be able to compare integration sites of MTV-infected clones displaying different biological characteristics, although preliminary results suggest that this approach will be complex (P. R. Shank and G. M. Ringold, unpublished data).

In general, the initial predictions stemming from the idea that MTV is a transposable controlling element are directly testable. Beyond this point, it is interesting to speculate about the evolutionary process that resulted in regulation of these viral genes by glucocorticoids. Perhaps some of the so-called viral functions originally evolved as host genes important for some hormone-dependent phenomenon. Alternatively, viruses per se may be important as transmissible genetic elements at specific stages in differentiation and development (Huebner *et al.*, 1970); in this view, only under aberrant conditions will virus particles affect cell transformation. Finally, the suggestion that this genetic element might alter specific gene responsiveness to a hormonal signal could be a hint that hormone responsiveness is determined during normal tissue differentiation by insertion of functionally analogous sequences into regions near potentially responsive genes. It is conceivable that these intriguing questions might eventually be approached in systems similar to this one.

ACKNOWLEDGMENTS

We thank Harold Varmus for valuable discussions throughout the course of this work and Edward Stavnezer and J. Michael Bishop for use of their hybridization assay prior to publication. This work was supported by National Cancer Institute Grant CA 20535-01, the Cancer Research Coordinating Committee, and the Committee on Research of the Academic Senate of the University of California. M.R.S. was supported by a postdoctoral fellowship from the American Cancer Society, G.M.R. by a Damon Runyon–Walter Winchell Cancer Fund fellowship, and R. D. I. by the National Institute of General Medical Sciences.

REFERENCES

Ashburner, M., Chihara, C., Meltzer, P., and Richards, G. (1973). *Cold Spring Harbor Symp. Quant. Biol.* **38**, 655.

Aviv, D., and Thompson, E. B. (1972). *Science* **177**, 1201.

Battula, N., and Temin, H. M. (1977). *Proc. Natl. Acad. Sci. U.S.A.* **74**, 281.

Berg, D. E., Davies, J., Allet, B., and Rochaix, J.-D. (1975). *Proc. Natl. Acad. Sci. U.S.A.* **72**, 3628.

Botchan, M., Topp, W., and Sambrook, J. (1976). *Cell* **9**, 269.

Bukhari, A. I., Shapiro, J. A., and Adhya, S., eds. (1977). "DNA Insertion Elements, Plasmids and Episomes." Cold Spring Harbor Lab., Cold Spring Harbor, New York.

Chamness, G. C., Jennings, A. W., and McGuire, W. L. (1974). *Biochemistry* **13**, 327.

Cox, R. F. (1973). *Eur. J. Biochem.* **39**, 49.

Crook, R. B. (1976). Ph.D. Dissertation, University of California, San Francisco.

DeCrombrugghe, B., Adhya, S., Gottesman, M., and Pastan, I. (1973). *Nature (London) New Biol.* **241**, 260.

DelVillano, B. C., Nave, B., Croker, B. P., Lerner, R. A., and Dixon, F. J. (1975). *J. Exp. Med.* **141**, 172.

Diamondstone, T. I. (1966). *Anal. Biochem.* **16**, 395.

Dickson, C., Haslam, S., and Nandi, S. (1974). *Virology* **62**, 242.

Dickson, R., Abelson, J., Barnes, W., and Reznikoff, W. (1975). *Science* **187** 27.

Elder, J. H., Jensen, F. C., Bryant, M. L., and Lerner, R. A. (1977). *Nature* **267**, 23.

Ernest, M. J., Shutz, G., and Feigelson, P. (1976). *Biochemistry* **15**, 824.

Feigelson, P., Beato, M., Colman, P., Kalimi, M., Killewich, L., and Schutz, G. (1975). *Recent Prog. Horm. Res.* **31**, 213.

Ferencz, A., and Seifart, K. H. (1975). *Eur. J. Biochem.* **53**, 605.

Fiandt, M., Szybalski, W., and Malamy, M. H., (1972). *Mol. Gen. Genet.* **119**, 223.

Fincham, J. R. S., and Sastry, G. R. K. (1974). *Annu. Rev. Genet.* **8**, 15.

Fine, D. L., Plowman, J. K., Kelley, S. P., Arthur, L. O., and Hillman, E. A. (1974). *J. Natl. Cancer Inst.* **52**, 1881.

Gianni, A. M., Smotkin, D., and Weinberg, R. A. (1975). *Proc. Natl. Acad. Sci. U.S.A.* **72**, 447.

Green, M. M. (1969a). *Genetics* **61**, 423.

Green, M. M. (1969b). *Genetics* **61**, 429.

Green, M. M. (1973). *Genetics* **73**, Suppl. 187.

Green, M. M. (1976). *In* "The Genetics and Biology of Drosophila" (M. Ashburner and E. Novitski, eds.), Vol. 1B, pp. 929–946. Academic Press, New York.

Guntaka, R. V., Mahy, B. W. J., Bishop, J. M., and Varmus, H. E. (1975). *Nature (London)* **253**, 507.

Guntaka, R. V., Richards, O. C., Shank, P. R., Kung, H. J., Davidson, N., Fritsch, E., Bishop, J. M., and Varmus, H. E. (1976). *J. Mol. Biol.* **106**, 337.

Harris, S. E., Rosen, J. M., Means, A. R., and O'Malley, B. W. (1974). *J. Steroid Biochem.* **5**, 341 (abstr.).

Heffron, F., Rubens, C., and Falkow, S. (1975a). *Proc. Natl. Acad. Sci. U.S.A.* **72**, 3623.

Heffron, F., Sublett, R., Hedges, R. W., Jacob, A., and Falkow, S. (1975b). *J. Bacteriol.* **122**, 250.

Hirsch, H. J., Saedler, H., and Starlinger, P. (1972). *Mol. Gen. Genet.* **115**, 266.

Huebner, R. J., Kelloff, G. J., Sarma, P. S., Lane, W. T., Turner, H. C., Gilden, R. V., Oroszlan, S., Meier, H., Myers, D. D., and Peters, R. L. (1970). *Proc. Natl. Acad. Sci. U.S.A.* **67**, 366.

Ising, G., and Ramel, C. (1976). *In* "The Genetics and Biology of Drosophila" (M. Ashburner and E. Novitski, eds.), Vol. 1B, pp. 947–954. Academic Press, New York.

Ivarie, R. D., and O'Farrell, P. H. (1978). *Cell* **13**, 41.

Jacquet, M., Groner, Y., Monroy, G., and Hurwitz, J. (1974). *Proc. Natl. Acad. Sci. U.S.A.* **71**, 3045.

Judd, B. H. (1969). *Genetics* **62**, s29.

Ketner, G., and Kelly, T. J., Jr. (1976). *Proc. Natl. Acad. Sci. U.S.A.* **73**, 1102.

Kulka, R. G., Tomkins, G. M., and Crook, R. B. (1972). *J. Cell Biol.* **54**, 175.

Lindell, T. J., Weinberg, F., Morris, P. W., Roeder, R. G., and Rutter, W. J. (1970). *Science* **170**, 447.

McClintock, B. (1967). *Dev. Biol., Suppl.* **1**, 84.

McKnight, G. S., Pennequin, P., and Schimke, R. T. (1975). *J. Biol. Chem.* **250**, 8105.

Majors, J. (1975). *Nature (London)* **256**, 672.

Marzluff, W. F., Jr., Murphy, E. C., Jr., and Huang, R. C. C. (1973). *Biochemistry* **12**, 3440.

Morris, V. L., Medeiros, E., Ringold, G. M., Bishop, J. M., and Varmus, H. E. (1977). *J. Mol. Biol.* **114**, 93.

O'Farrell, P. H. (1975). *J. Biol. Chem.* **250**, 4007.

Palmiter, R. D., Moore, P. B., Mulvihill, E. R., and Emtage, S. (1976). *Cell* **8**, 557.

Parks, W. P., Scolnick, E. M., and Kozikowski, E. H. (1974). *Science* **184**, 158.

Parks, W. P., Ransom, J. C., Young, H. A., and Scolnick, E. M. (1975). *J. Biol. Chem.* **250**, 3330.

Peterson, P. A. (1970). *Theor. Appl. Genet.* **40**, 367.

Ringold, G. M., Shank, P. R., and Yamamoto, K. R. (1978). *J. Virol.* (in press).

Ringold, G. M., Lasafargues, E. Y., Bishop, J. M., and Varmus, H. E. (1975a). *Virology* **65**, 135.

Ringold, G. M., Yamamoto, K. R., Tomkins, G. M., Bishop, J. M., and Varmus, H. E. (1975b). *Cell* **6**, 299.

Ringold, G. M., Blair, P. B., Bishop, J. M., and Varmus, H. E. (1976). *Virology* **70**, 550.

Ringold, G. M., Cardiff, R. D., Varmus, H. E., and Yamamoto, K. R. (1977a). *Cell* **10**, 11.

Ringold, G. M., Yamamoto, K. R., Shank, P. R., and Varmus, H. E. (1977b). *Cell* **10**, 19.

Ringold, G. M., Yamamoto, K. R., Bishop, J. M., and Varmus, H. E. (1977c). *Proc. Natl. Acad. Sci. U.S.A.* **74**, 2879.

Roeder, R. G., and Rutter, W. J. (1970). *Proc. Natl. Acad. Sci. U.S.A.* **65**, 675.

Rymo, L., Parsons, J. T., Coffin, J. M., and Weissmann, C. (1974). *Proc. Natl. Acad. Sci. U.S.A.* **71**, 2782.

Saedler, H., and Heiss, B. (1973). *Mol. Gen. Genet.* **122**, 267.

Saedler, H., Besemer, J., Kemper, B., Rosenwirth, B., and Starlinger, P. (1972). *Mol. Gen. Genet.* **115**, 258.

Saedler, H., Reif, H. J., Hu, S., and Davidson, N. (1974). *Mol. Gen. Genet.* **132**, 265.

Samuels, H. H., and Tomkins, G. M. (1970). *J. Mol. Biol.* **52**, 57.

Schwartz, L. B., Sklar, V. E. F., Jaehning, J. A., Weinmann, R., and Roeder, R. G. (1974). *J. Biol. Chem.* **249**, 5889.

Shank, P. R., Cohen, J. C., Varmus, H. E., Yamamoto, K. R., and Ringold, G. M. (1978). Submitted for publication.

Simons, S. S., Jr., Martinez, H. M., Garcea, R. L., Baxter, J. D., and Tomkins, G. M. (1976). *J. Biol. Chem.* **251**, 334.

Somers, D. G., Pearson, M. L., and Ingles, C. J. (1975), *J. Biol. Chem.* **250**, 4825.

Southern, E. M. (1975). *J. Mol. Biol.* **98**, 503.

Stavnezer, E., and Bishop, J. M. (1978). In preparation.

Stockert, E., Old, L. J., and Boyse, E. A. (1971). *J. Exp. Med.* **133**, 1334.

Tata, J. R. (1976). *Cell* **9**, 1.

Temin, H., and Baltimore, D. (1972). *Adv. Virus Res.* **17**, 129–186.

Thompson, E. B., Tomkins, G. M., and Curran, J. (1966). *Proc. Natl. Acad. Sci. U.S.A.* **56**, 296.

Tooze, J. (1973). "The Molecular Biology of Tumour Viruses." Cold Spring Harbor Lab., Cold Spring Harbor, New York.

Vaidya, A. B., Lasfargues, E. Y., Heubel, G., Lasfargues, J. C., and Moore, D. H. (1976). *J. Virol.* **18**, 911.

Varmus, H. E., Bishop, J. M., Nowinski, R. C., and Sarkar, N. H. (1972). *Nature (London) New Biol.* **238**, 189.

Varmus, H. E., Quintrell, N., Medeiros, E., Bishop, J. M., Nowinski, R. C., and Sarkar, N. H. (1973). *J. Mol. Biol.* **79**, 663.

Varmus, H. E., Ringold, G. M., and Yamamoto, K. R. (1978). *In* "Mechanisms of Glucocorticoid Action" (J. D. Baxter and G. G. Rousseau, eds.). Springer-Verlag, Heidelberg (in press).

Wetekam, W., and Ehring, R. (1973). *Mol. Gen. Genet.* **124**, 345.

Williams, D., and Gorski, J. (1972). *Proc. Natl. Acad. Sci. U.S.A.* **69**, 3464.

Yamamoto, K. R., and Alberts, B. (1974). *J. Biol. Chem.* **249**, 7076.

Yamamoto, K. R., and Alberts, B. M. (1975). *Cell* **4**, 301.

Yamamoto, K. R., and Alberts, B. M. (1976). *Annu. Rev. Biochem.* **45**, 721.

Yamamoto, K. R., and Ringold, G. M. (1977). *In* "Receptors and Hormone Action" (B. W. O'Malley and L. Birnbaumer, eds.), Vol. 2, pp. 297–322. Academic Press, New York.

Yamamoto, K. R., Stallcup, M. R., Ring, J. and Ringold, G. M. (1978). *Cold Spring Harbor Symp. Quart. Biol.* (in press).

Young, H. A., Scolnick, E. M., and Parks, W. P. (1975). *J. Biol. Chem.* **250**, 3337.

Young, H. A., Shih, T. Y., Scolnick, E. M., and Parks, W. P. (1977). *J. Virol.* **21**, 139.

Young, L. J. T., Cardiff, R. D., and Ashley, R. L. (1975). *J. Natl. Cancer Inst.* **54**, 1215.

Zasloff, M., and Felsenfield, G. (1977). *Biochem. Biophys. Res. Commun.* **75**, 598.

CHAPTER 10

Induction and Regulation of Vitellogenin Synthesis by Estrogen

J. R. Tata

I. INTRODUCTION

Developmental hormones have already proved to be very valuable tools in triggering the expression of a genetic program in already committed but immature cells. The recent successes with ecdysone in unraveling gene transcription during insect polytenic chromosomal puffs (Edström and Lambert, 1975) and the activation by estrogen of the ovalbumin gene in chick oviduct (O'Malley and Means, 1974; Schimke *et al.*, 1973) are good examples of the way in which hormones can be exploited as tools for exploring differentiative processes. There are, however, major drawbacks in assembling a composite picture from too many different developmental systems. Ideally, a single hormone-induced system should allow one to integrate multiple molecular and cell-biological processes involved in differentiation.

In this chapter I shall discuss work on the induction of egg-yolk protein by estradiol in order to illustrate how a single developmental system can be exploited to study very diverse aspects of gene expression. The following are the major issues that will be considered:

1. The physiology of the activation of a gene that would normally not be fully expressed by a cell in its lifetime, i.e., the activation of liver cells from male animals to synthesize egg-yolk proteins which are normally only made by the female.

2. The induction *in vivo* and in tissue culture of liver of the large multicomponent polypeptide vitellogenin, which is cleaved into different egg proteins in the ovary.

3. The distribution in the cytoplasm and the translation of the messenger RNA for the precursor, particularly with a view to exploring a possible specific translational control.

4. Posttranslation processing of the precursor polypeptide in liver and its ultimate cleavage in the ovary.

GENE EXPRESSION

In the earlier literature one finds that "gene expression" meant the ultimate consequence of the presence of a functional gene or a group of genes, i.e., the color of eyes, the ability to form urea from nitrogen, etc. (Moore, 1972). However, more recently it has often come to denote the transcription of sequences encoded by the DNA of a specific gene into RNA, not necessarily even messenger RNA. This is based on the assumption that in higher organisms, genes are either "on" or "off" and therefore the "switching on" of a gene by the transcriptional machinery would in itself constitute the expression of the gene. However, there is no definite evidence yet to believe that there exists an all-or-none distinction at the level of transcription between active and dormant genes. It may well turn out that in differentiation, one is dealing with the modulation or preferential transcription of a given gene from a large number of "slightly leaky" genes.

It is now quite well established that in eukaryotes a large number of DNA transcripts do not leave the nucleus and that there is extensive posttranscriptional regulation of the initial gene products (Britten and Davidson, 1969; Davidson and Britten, 1973; Darnell *et al.*, 1973; Lewin, 1975). In the context of the ultimate expression of the vitellogenin gene, i.e., the deposition of the correct proteins in the yolk of the egg, one has not only to contend with transcription, but also posttranscriptional modifications, possible translational regulation of the messenger, its distribution in the cytoplasm and extensive posttranslational modifications, secretion and cleavage of the polypeptide before the final components are deposited in their correct location. It is from this viewpoint of integration of diverse molecular processes into a cellular perspective that the expression of the vitellogenin gene will be considered below.

II. VITELLOGENIN

A. The Nature of Vitellogenin

Although egg-yolk proteins, particularly phosvitin and lipovitellin, have been intensively studied over the last 40 years and chemically well characterized, it is only recently that we have known that these are not individually synthesized but derived from a common precursor. This precursor is called vitellogenin, following the introduction of the generic term "vitellogenins," first used for insect-yolk proteins, to refer to all the plasma precursors of egg-yolk proteins (Pan *et al.*, 1969). It is synthesized in the liver of all egg-laying animals and transported in the blood to the ovary, where it is cleaved to the final egg-yolk proteins and is best characterized in the chicken and *Xenopus*. Table I lists some of the properties of *Xenopus* vitellogenin as recovered from blood and compares them with those of its products, phosvitin and lipovitellin, as derived from eggs. Further accounts of the nature of chicken and *Xenopus* vitellogenin can be found in some recent reviews and original papers (Wallace, 1963, 1970; Redshaw and Follet, 1971; Ansari *et al.*, 1971; Follet and Redshaw, 1974; Clemens, 1974; Tata, 1976). There is still some doubt about the exact size of the native protein as found in *Xenopus* blood [$(4.9–6.0) \times 10^5$ daltons], but its single subunit seems to have a molecular weight of $(2.1–2.2) \times 10^5$ daltons, as judged by polyacrylamide gel electrophoresis under denaturing conditions (Clemens, 1974; Bergink and Wallace, 1974; Clemens *et al.*, 1975; Tata, 1976; Berridge *et al.*, 1976). A similar large protein [subunit of $(2.7–2.8) \times 10^5$ daltons which would be the

TABLE I
Properties of *Xenopus* Phosvitin, Lipovitellin, and Vitellogenin[a]

Component	Mol. wt. (10³ daltons)	% P	Serine (% residues)	Methionine	Lipid %	Carbohydrate %
Phosvitin	55 (35,30)	10.0	56	−	0.5	10.0
Lipovitellin	290 (110,30)	0.7	4	+	20.0	0.3
Vitellogenin	500	1.3	12	+	11.2	1.6

[a] Figures in parenthesis give the molecular weights of individual subunits. Data combined from Wallace (1963), Redshaw and Follet (1971), Ansari *et al.* (1971), Clemens (1974), and Follet and Redshaw (1974).

precursor of yolk proteins] has been reported in chicken blood (Jost and Pehling, 1976; Gruber *et al.*, 1976; Deeley *et al.*, 1975; Wetekam *et al.*, 1975; Christmann *et al.*, 1977). Besides its large size, an interesting feature of vitellogenin is the presence of phorphorus, calcium, lipid, and sugar, which are extremely unevenly distributed along the large polypeptide. For example, almost all the phosphoprotein phosphorus is in the phosvitin moiety (MW of 32,000) in which 56% of amino acid residues are serine, more than 70% of which are phosphorylated (Redshaw and Follett, 1971). Similarly, almost all the lipid associated with vitellogenin is accounted for by that in lipovitellin. An interesting question that arises when considering the quantitative problem of products derived from vitellogenin is that the molecular weight of the precursor is greater than the sum of those of phosvitin and lipovitellin. There is a discrepancy corresponding to a protein of about 30,000 daltons (see Table I). Could it be that vitellogenin comprises an as yet unidentified egg-yolk protein or that there could be two phosvitin residues in each vitellogenin subunit, as recently suggested (Christmann *et al.*, 1977)?. Another explanation may lie in the heterogeneity of lipovitellin which is known to occur, both in birds and in amphibia, in a large and a small form. Whatever the exact composition of the yolk, another interesting feature is that the major components (i.e., phosvitin and lipovitellins), when cleaved from the precursor, can interact to produce very insoluble crystalline complexes, as shown in Fig. 1 for the yolk platelet structure in *Rana pipiens* (Karasaki, 1963).

B. Advantages of Vitellogenesis as an Experimental System

It is a unique development system which allows one to study most, if not all, of the diverse facets of the cell biology of induction of a well-defined gene product. Its major advantages are as follows:

FIG. 1. High magnification of the small-yolk platelet indicated by an asterisk (*). The entire main body displays a hexagonal array of dots approximately 45 Å in diameter with an average center-to-center distance of approximately 80 Å between dots. The superficial layer consists of fine particles or fibrils (arrows) (average diameter 50 Å), which are much smaller than the cytoplasmic ribonucleoprotein particles (average diameter 200 Å). × 200,000. (From Karasaki, 1963.)

1. Reversible inducibility of an easily characterizable, stable protein with a single chemically defined stimulus.

2. Virtually no cell proliferation or hypertrophy which usually vitiates studies on transcription and translation in most other developmental systems, particularly those that are hormone-induced (Tata, 1970).

3. Cessation of induced protein formation upon withdrawal of the stimulus and maintenance of competence for reinduction.

4. The feasibility of reproducing reversible induction directly in tissue culture.

5. The multicomponent nature of vitellogenin makes it an ideal protein to study posttranslational modifications and processing. These include phosphorylation, lipidation, glycosylation, and proteolytic cleavage.

6. Finally, the induced formation of a "female" protein in cells of male animals, which normally would not produce it, makes it easier to study the early cellular events in the action of growth and developmental hormones, particularly the role of estradiol receptors.

III. PHYSIOLOGY OF VITELLOGENESIS

A. Obligatory Hormonal Control

The formation of all egg proteins is under the control of estrogenic hormones (Follett and Redshaw, 1974; Clemens, 1974; Bergink *et al.*, 1974). Figure 2 summarizes the major hormone-dependent processes involved in the formation of egg-yolk proteins (Tata, 1976). The salient features concerning this regulation in the whole animal are the following:

1. The initial stimulus for a series of responses comes from the environment (temperature, length of daylight) and is transmitted via the neuroendocrine hypothalamopituitary complex to the ovary, which then secretes the hormones estrogen and progesterone.

2. Egg-yolk proteins are synthesized in the liver, whereas the egg-white or jelly proteins are made in the oviductal cells so that the maturation of the egg is achieved by a high level of coordination at the level of the whole organism by hormonal regulation.

3. The administration of a single injection of estrogen to male animals results in the formation and secretion into the blood stream of substantial amounts of vitellogenin (Wallace and Jared, 1968a), thus offering an experimental control of "zero" background.

4. In *Xenopus*, chronic exposure to estradiol will result in vitellogenin

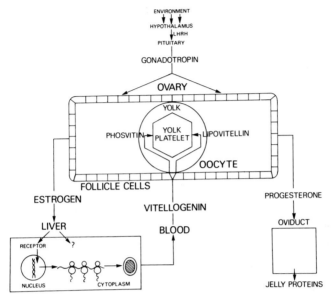

FIG. 2. Scheme summarizing the physiology of vitellogenesis in *Xenopus*. See text for details. From Tata (1976).

almost totally replacing all the normal serum proteins, including albumin (Follett and Redshaw, 1968; Redshaw and Follett, 1971). This is to some extent due to the very long life of vitellogenin in male amphibian blood ($t_{1/2}$ >40 days) relative to that in females ($t_{1/2}$ < 2 days), the latter arising from the rapid uptake, cleavage, and platelet formation in the ovary (Wallace and Jared, 1968a).

5. Although vitellogenin as such was not identified, Wallace and Jared (1969), were able to demonstrate that a lipophosphoprotein, secreted into the blood of the female *Xenopus*, is selectively taken up by the ovary where it was converted into crystalline yolk platelet proteins. Later work from the same laboratory (Bergink and Wallace, 1974) conclusively established this precursor–product relationship and showed that the ovary contains a specific enzyme to cleave vitellogenin to yield phosvitin and lipovitellin. These workers had also established that the oocyte itself does not synthesize yolk proteins, for which the circulating vitellogenin is the only source (Wallace and Jared, 1969; Wallace *et al.*, 1972; Bergink and Wallace, 1974).

6. It was felt for a number of years that other hormones or factors, particularly of pituitary origin or insulin, may play a "permissive" role (see Follett and Redshaw, 1974; Clemens, 1974). However, as mentioned below, vitellogenin synthesis can be induced directly by the hormone in *Xenopus*

liver tissue cultures, thus establishing that estrogen alone is responsible for vitellogenin synthesis in both male and female animals (Wangh and Knowland, 1975; Green and Tata, 1976).

B. PRIMARY VERSUS SECONDARY INDUCTION

A general feature of the action of most growth and developmental hormones is a lag period preceding the onset of hormonal action which is typical for a given hormone and its target tissue (see Tata, 1970). This latent period, which is important in explaining the early events underlying hormone action, can vary according to whether or not the target has been previously primed by the hormone. In the liver of a male *Xenopus* exposed for the first time to estrogen, there is a lag period before the appearance of vitellogenin (see Fig. 3). A shorter lag period has been reported for birds (Gruber *et al.*, 1976). The length of the latent period for such a primary induction in absolute terms is a function of the sensitivity of the assay used for detecting vitellogenin and would vary according to whether vitellogenin is induced *in*

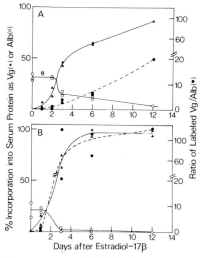

FIG. 3. Immunological determination of labeled vitellogenin and albumin in the serum of male *Xenopus* as a function of time during the onset of primary and secondary responses to estradiol. Twenty-four hours before drawing blood, each frog was injected with 200 μCi of [35S]methionine. The radioactivity into total serum protein at different times after hormone treatment is given in Table I. ○, Albumin; ▲, vitellogenin; ●, ratio of incorporation into vitellogenin to that into albumin. (A) Primary response; (B) secondary response (a second injection of 1 mg of estradiol given to frogs treated with the same dose 41 days earlier). From Farmer *et al.* (unpublished).

vivo or in tissue culture, or according to whether one is trying to measure the level of the protein in the tissue or after it is secreted into blood or the culture medium, etc. (Dolphin *et al.*, 1971; Clemens *et al.*, 1975; Green and Tata, 1976; Berridge *et al.*, 1976; Farmer *et al.*, 1977). The highly sensitive technique of fluorographic detection of radioactive vitellogenin, used by Wangh and Knowland (1975), combined with radioimmunoassay, is the most sensitive and specific technique for detecting the first appearance of vitellogenin.

Upon removal of the primary hormonal stimulus, the production of this protein gradually returns to zero levels. If a second dose of estrogen is given, the lag period is virtually abolished and the synthesis of the respective proteins is rapidly established at a maximal rate, which is termed the secondary response. A similar enhancement of secondary response coupled with a shorter lag period has been observed in the induction by estradiol of chicken-blood phosvitin and other phosphoproteins (Beuving and Gruber, 1971; Jailkhani and Talwar, 1972a) as well as that of ovalbumin in the chick oviduct (Palmiter, 1975). A comparison in tissue culture of the lag period in primary and secondary stimulations makes it possible to better establish the primary events associated with the induction process as well as study some aspects of the utilization of mRNA for vitellogenin, as will be discussed later (Section III,C). As will be seen later, the different lag periods preceding the primary and secondary responses have been important in designing experiments for studying specific translational control (see Section IV).

C. Direct Induction of Vitellogenin Synthesis in Tissue Culture

Several questions concerning the mechanism of hormonal induction of proteins, especially the early events, can be better examined in cultured cells or organs than in the whole animal. Furthermore, tissue-culture studies allow us to better analyze questions of the dynamics of hormone distribution and receptor interaction, the role of obligatory DNA synthesis in induction, the requirement for "permissive" hormones or factors, etc. For a long time, all attempts to elicit the full physiological response of a normal adult tissue to a developmental hormone *in vitro* have ended in failure. Most of the successful attempts concern cell lines or organ cultures of neoplastic tissues, often abnormal in their function and eliciting an unphysiological response. It is therefore most significant that it is now possible to obtain a full vitellogenic response to estradiol added *in vitro* to organ cultures of male *Xenopus* liver (Wangh and Knowland, 1975; Green and Tata, 1976).

Direct induction of vitellogenin *in vitro* has already settled some outstanding issues concerning its induction. Thus, estrogen is now shown to be the sole inducer, and it has been demonstrated that the process does not require other steroids, insulin, or pituitary hormones to play a "permissive" role, as had previously been suggested (see Follett and Redshaw, 1974). Not only does estrogen trigger the initial induction of vitellogenin, but its continuous presence is required during the lag period for the maintenance of vitellogenin synthesis (Green and Tata, 1976). The cessation of vitellogenin synthesis upon withdrawal of the hormone in tissue culture is compatible with the response *in vivo*, and the reversibility of the phenomenon is useful in designing experiments on control of translation of mRNA, in a manner analogous to those used for estrogen-induced ovalbumin synthesis in chick oviduct (Palmiter and Carey, 1974; Palmiter, 1975).

Induction of vitellogenin in organ cultures has also established that an obligatory round of DNA synthesis is not essential for the initial stages of induction, contrary to the conclusions drawn from earlier studies *in vivo* in rooster liver (Jailkhani and Talwar, 1972b; see also Jost *et al.*, 1973). However, it is quite likely that an uninterrupted DNA synthesis may be essential for the long-term maintenance or amplification of response to the hormone.

Tissue-culture studies also facilitate a more accurate analysis of the difference between primary and secondary responses to the hormone than is possible *in vivo*. Figure 4 is a typical result showing the induction of vitellogenin, as well as the deinduction of albumin, in cultured tissues as determined by radioammunoassay of the two proteins. The lag period for the appearance of vitellogenin in the culture medium for the secondary response is half that observed for the primary response, but, as already mentioned, the absolute value for the lag period depends on the sensitivity of the assay method used for detecting vitellogenin. The mechanism of the deinduction of albumin in cultured tissue is not understood, nor is it clear whether or not it is related to the virtual disappearance from blood of albumin and other serum proteins synthesized by the liver following exposure to estradiol *in vivo* (Follett and Redshaw, 1968; Wallace and Jared, 1968b; Redshaw and Follett, 1971). Deinduction of albumin synthesis *in vivo* is also observed, but to a lesser extent, following a single injection of the hormone (Clemens *et al.*, 1975). As seen in Fig. 3, the effect of a single injection of estradiol for the first time does not lower the absolute rate of albumin synthesis but only the fraction of total protein synthesized as albumin. However, secondary induction of vitellogenin synthesis is accompanied by a rapid inhibition of albumin synthesis (Farmer *et al.*, unpublished). Again, the mechanism of the differential primary and secondary responses is unknown. From the dose–response curves of induction *in vitro*, the response was detectable at 10^{-10} *M* estradiol being maximal at around 10^{-8} *M* (Wangh and Knowland, 1975; Green and Tata, 1976), which is surprisingly low in comparision with the high levels of 1

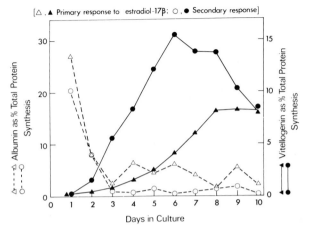

FIG. 4. Rates of synthesis of vitellogenin and albumin by male *Xenopus* liver maintained in organ culture during primary and secondary response to estradiol added directly to the culture medium. Liver explants from untreated males (primary) and from males treated with 1 mg estradiol-17β 35 days earlier (secondary) were cultured for the times indicated. The rates of incorporation of [^{35}S]methionine into vitellogenin and albumin were determined immunologically each day between 18 and 24 hours after addition of 5 μCi of [^{35}S]methionine to culture dishes containing 10^{-6} M estradiol. ▲, Vitellogenin in primary induction; ●, vitellogenin in secondary induction; △, albumin (primary); ○, albumin (secondary). Data assembled from Green and Tata (1976).

mg per 100 gm body weight needed for full induction *in vivo* (Clemens, 1974). The estradiol dose–response curve *in vitro*, and the relative potency of other steroids tested, are compatible with the properties of estradiol receptor found in the chick oviduct and other mammalian target tissues (O'Malley and Means, 1974; Jensen and De Sombre, 1973; King and Mainwaring, 1974). Thus, the establishment of a culture system for directly inducing vitellogenin synthesis *in vitro* opens the way for further studies on several aspects of the induction process which cannot be easily studied *in vivo*. The validity of the tissue-culture system also rests on the fact that the only difference between induction *in vitro* and *in vivo* seems to be a quantitative one.

IV. PROTEIN SYNTHESIS IN THE LIVER DURING VITELLOGENIN INDUCTION

Considering the relatively long history of work on egg-yolk proteins and the advantages of studying the regulation of their induction, analysis of protein synthetic mechanisms underlying the process are only now beginning to receive attention. Two major reasons may account for this lapse.

First, it has only been relatively recently realized that the primary translation product in the liver is the precursor vitellogenin and not the individual protein fragments (phosvitin and lipovitellin) present in the egg. Second, it has been very difficult to obtain in an undegraded state the large polyribosomes from avian and amphibian tissues engaged in the synthesis of a polypeptide of molecular weight > 210,000.

The first studies on male frog and chicken liver showed that the overall protein synthetic capacity of the tissue was markedly enhanced following the administration of estrogen and that the stimulation preceded the appearance of egg-yolk protein in the blood (Wittliff and Kenney, 1972a; see Follett and Redshaw, 1974; Clemens, 1974). Clemens *et al.* (1975) found that the same was true for total protein synthesis as opposed to vitellogenin secreted into culture medium when studying *Xenopus* liver explants at different times after hormonal treatment of male *Xenopus in vivo*. When protein synthesis was studied in cell-free systems, the capacity of *Xenopus* liver ribosomes to incorporate amino acid into protein was found to be enhanced by estrogen administration *in vivo* (Clemens and Tata, 1973). This stimulation was in addition to that caused by the accumulation of vitellogenin mRNA in the ribosomal preparations used *in vitro*, because it was also detectable for the poly(U)-directed synthesis of polyphenylalanine. At the same time, the stimulation was selective according to the amino acid studied. The incorporation of serine relative to that of phenylalanine in preparation from estrogen-stimulated animals was twice as high as that noted for control preparations (Table II). This finding suggests that the ribosomes were synthesizing a serine-rich protein, which is significant, because the serine: phenylalanine ratio of vitellogenin is about three times the average for total liver proteins. An interesting observation also emerging from the same study was that the maximum effect of hormonal treatment could only be observed if ribosomes from treated animals were incubated with cell sap also derived from treated animals (see Table II). It would be important if one is to understand translational control to learn more about the cell sap factor(s) responsible for this cooperative effect between ribosomes and cell sap (Clemens and Tata, 1972, 1973). Whatever the explanation for the requirement of homologous cell sap, it is clear that an uninterrupted RNA synthesis is also important for obtaining the full hormonal stimulation of protein synthesis. The first studies in the chicken had shown that inhibition of RNA synthesis with actinomycin D at, or soon after, the administration of estradiol blocked the subsequent appearance of phosvitin (Greengard *et al.*, 1964), although there has been some controversy regarding the effect of inhibiting RNA synthesis on the secondary response to the hormone (Beuving and Gruber, 1971; Jost *et al.*, 1973). In the *Xenopus* also, actinomycin D will block the rise in synthesis of vitellogenin. Clemens *et al.* (1975) used this drug to

TABLE II

COMBINED EFFECT OF ESTRADIOL ON RIBOSOMAL AND CELL SAP FRACTIONS OF MALE
Xenopus LIVER AS SEEN BY A PREFERENTIAL SYNTHESIS OF A SERINE-RICH PROTEIN[a]

| | | Incorporation into protein (pmoles/μg RNA) | | Ratio of Ser:Phe |
Ribosomes	Cell sap	[^{14}C]Phe	[^{14}C]Ser	incorporated
Control	Control	0.042	0.073	1.72
Control	Treated	0.062	0.140	2.24
Treated	Control	0.061	0.181	2.96
Treated	Treated	0.093	0.302	3.24

[a] The shift to the synthesis of a serine-rich protein is taken to indicate the induction of vitellogenin. Treated animals were injected with estradiol 5 days before the experiment. Details of the experiment will be found in Clemens and Tata (1973).

estimate the stability of messenger RNA for vitellogenin by adding actinomycin D at different times to cultured explants of liver taken from male frogs previously injected with estradiol. The mRNA for *Xenopus* and chicken vitellogenin has a half-life of 40–48 hours (Greengard *et al.*, 1964; Beuving and Gruber, 1971; Gruber *et al.*, 1976).

The stability of vitellogenin mRNA means that a massive accumulation of the mRNA would be expected in estrogenized animals. Indeed, several workers have reported that vitellogenin mRNA and vitellogenin-synthesizing polysomes are the most abundant species in the liver of male frogs and chickens. The actual estimates of the values vary from 15 to 50% of the total and depend on the precision of the method used for determining mRNA or the nascent proteins, according to whether the induction is *in vivo* or in culture or if it is primary or secondary induction (Clemens, 1974; Gruber *et al.*, 1976; Berridge *et al.*, 1976; Green and Tata, 1976; Wahli *et al.*, 1976; Ryffel *et al.*, 1977; Mullinix *et al.*, 1976). Whatever the absolute values, considering that the liver is perhaps the tissue most active in RNA and protein synthesis, one is dealing with a very substantial activational machinery of the hormonal target cell.

A. TRANSCRIPTION AND POSTTRANSCRIPTIONAL MODIFICATIONS

The induction of vitellogenesis by estradiol is characterized by a massive increase in total liver RNA (Schjeide and Lai, 1970; Wittliff and Kenney, 1972b; Jost *et al.*, 1973; Tata and Baker, 1975; Lewis *et al.*, 1976). Much of the extra RNA synthesized is found to be ribosomal RNA if cytoplasmic or total liver RNA is determined at the height of the vitellogenic response (Wittliff and Kenney, 1972b; Lewis *et al.*, 1976). However, a more complex picture emerges if one measures RNA synthesis in the nucleus during the lag period preceding the onset of vitellogenin synthesis. Thus, it is not surprising that simtulation of both RNA polymerase I and II activities was observed in liver nuclei at 24 hours after the injection of estradiol into male chickens (Weckler and Gschwendt, 1976). At the early stages of estradiol action, a significant increase in the rate of nuclear RNA synthesis *in vivo* can be observed within 3 hours after the injection of estradiol to the male *Xenopus*, reaching a maximum elevation of 8-fold the control values by 11 hours (Tata and Baker, 1975). Much of the newly made hormone-induced RNA made at 3–6 hours after the administration of the hormone is nonribosomal, with an increasing proportion of ribosomal RNA being synthesized after 11 hours (Wittliff and Kenney, 1972b; Tata and Baker, 1975). It is quite possible that vitellogenin mRNA synthesis begins very soon after hormone administration; analysis of nuclear RNA by hybridization to complementary DNA made against cytoplasmic mRNA, in the same way as has been done for estrogen-induced mRNA for ovalbumin in chick oviduct (Schimke *et al.*, 1973; O'Malley and Means, 1974), should be able to confirm this possibility. Hybridization studies would also establish whether or not uninduced male *Xenopus* liver nuclei do or do not contain any vitellogenin mRNA sequences. Synthesis and processing of RNA is known to be compartmentalized within the nucleus and can be easily observed upon nuclear fractionation (Tata and Baker, 1974). Nuclei were fractionated into their structurally different components, and additional newly labeled RNA in hormone-treated animals was recovered in all the major subnuclear fractions (Tata and Baker, 1975). However, quite marked differences were noted in the nature and metobolism of RNA associated with the different nuclear fractions from treated and untreated animals. Polyadenylation, "capping," cleavage, and degradation of HnRNA precursor for messenger RNA are the most important posttranscriptional processing steps in the nucleus (Darnell *et al.*, 1973; Lewin, 1975). A 2- to 10-fold increase in the poly(A) content of male *Xenopus* liver nuclear RNA accompanied the estrogen-induced increase in the total amount of newly synthesized RNA, much of the increase being associated with the euchromatin fraction (Table III). The differential subnuclear distribution of newly synthesized poly(A)-containing RNA was further emphasized in the size distribution of RNA in the different subnuclear fractions. A large proportion of the poly(A)-rich RNA found in the nuclear sap was of low molecular weight, presumably reflecting intranuclear degradation and turnover, whereas most of the total or polyadenylated RNA associated with the euchromatin fraction was of high molecular weight when analyzed by

TABLE III

EFFECT OF ESTRADIOL ADMINISTRATION TO MALE *Xenopus* ON THE SYNTHESIS OF RAPIDLY
LABELED LIVER NUCLEAR RNA AND POLY(A) CONTENT OF RNA RECOVERED IN DIFFERENT
SUBNUCLEAR FRACTIONS[a]

Subnuclear fraction	Total [³H]RNA recovered (cpm)		Specific activity of [³H]RNA (cpm/µg)		Poly(A) content of RNA (%)	
	C	T	C	T	C	T
Nuclear sap	1830	30,865	68	957	0.27	0.80
Euchromatin	5153	69,200	36	185	0.04	0.73
Nucleoli	5470	30,418	41	122	0.03	0.21
Heterochromatin, nucleoli, + RNP particles	3630	46,336	45	416	0.24	0.39

[a] C, Control uninjected animals; T, male *Xenopus* injected with estradiol 11 hours before death.
RNA was labeled with 100 µCi of [³H]uridine injected 60 minutes before killing the animals.
Poly(A) content was measured by hybridization of unlabeled RNA to [³H]poly(U) (from Tata and
Baker, 1975).

SDS(or formamide)-polyacrylamide gel electrophoresis (Tata and Baker,
1975; Fig. 5). Besides, a marked increase in high molecular weight RNA
fraction, presumably corresponding to HnRNA (>50 S), induction of
vitellogenin in male frogs was characterized by the appearance of polyadenylated high molecular weight (32–36 S) RNA of approximately 2.2
× 10⁶ daltons, i.e., close to the calculated minimum size of cytoplasmic
mRNA for vitellogenin. If cDNA hybridization studies eventually show that
vitellogenin mRNA sequences are indeed enriched in this fraction, then it
can be concluded that the most stable form of putative nuclear RNA containing vitellogenin sequences is only slightly larger than the cytoplasmic mRNA
and that this form is closely associated with the transcriptionally active fraction of the nucleus.

Because of the extraordinarily high serine content (56%) of phosvitin,
possible differences in seryl-tRNA species in vitellogenin and nonvitel-
logenic animals would be expected. It is therefore of some interest that the
pattern of seryl-tRNA's was found to be altered during estrogen-induced
vitellogenesis, including the appearance of two new tRNA isoacceptor
species (Mäenpää and Bernfield, 1969; Mäenpää, 1972). Unfortunately,
these observations have not been followed up, either in birds or in amphibia.
Perhaps the cell-sap effect noted for *Xenopus* liver (Table II) may reflect a
change in seryl-tRNA pattern which may also underlie a specific mechanism
of translational control of vitellogenin mRNA.

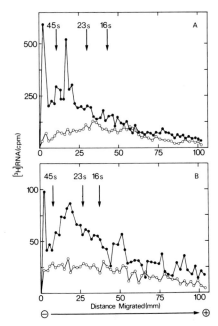

FIG. 5. Sodium dodecyl sulfate (SDS)–polyacrylamide gel electrophoresis of total and poly(A)-rich nuclear RNA from liver of control and estradiol-treated male *Xenopus*. RNA was labeled with 400 μCi of [³H]orotic acid injected 1.6 hours before death into two groups of 3 frogs, each of which served as control ($\bigcirc$) and the other had been treated with 1 mg of estradiol 11 hours before death ($\bullet$). RNA was extracted from nuclei and then resolved into poly(A)-poor and poly(A)-rich RNA by chromatography on oligo(dT)–cellulose. Electrophoresis was carried out on 2.3% polyacrylamide–SDS gels and the radioactivity measured in 2-mm slices. (A) Total nuclear RNA; (B) poly(A)-rich nuclear RNA. "X" denotes the migration of a major nuclear RNA component found in estrogen-treated male *Xenopus*. From Tata and Baker (1975).

B. Polyribosomes and Translation of Vitellogenin and Albumin Messenger RNA's

The identity of serine-rich protein synthesized *in vitro* as vitellogenin has only been recently established by electrophoretic and immunological analysis of the product of polyribosomal synthesis (Clemens *et al.*, 1975; Lewis *et al.*, 1976; Berridge *et al.*, 1976; Wetekam *et al.*, 1975; Roskam *et al.*, 1976b). Until recently, attempts to identify and isolate intact vitellogenin-synthesizing polysomes have ended in failure because of the large size of the messenger RNA and the high level of ribonuclease in avian and amphibian livers. This technical difficulty has now been overcome by lowering the ribonuclease activity with high pH (8.5) or heparin. Figure 6 shows profiles of polysomes from estrogenized male and female *Xenopus*

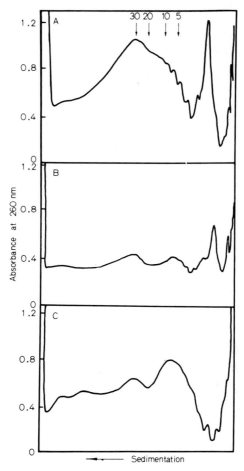

FIG. 6. Size of liver polysomes from male and female *Xenopus* after treatment with estrogen. Polysomes were prepared from estrogen-treated *Xenopus* by the pH 8.5 procedure and analyzed on linear 20–50% sucrose gradients. Polysome size, determined by extrapolation of the log–linear relationship between ribosome monomeric units and distance of migration in sucrose gradients, is shown at the top of (A). (A) Polysomes from female *Xenopus* liver; (B) polysomes from male *Xenopus* liver; (C) polysomes from *Xenopus* tadpole tails. From Berridge *et al.* (1976).

liver in which the large 30–40 ribosome aggreagtes are retained. Control male *Xenopus* liver do not have polysomes of more than 20 monomeric units (Berridge *et al.*, 1976). Berridge *et al.* thus characterized *Xenopus* vitellogenin- and albumin-syntheiszing polyribosomes by radioammunoassay and by immunoprecipitation, using double-antibody techniques analogous to those so successfully used for identifying ovalbumin-synthesizing polysomes in chick-oviductal cells (Palmiter, 1975). Jost and Pehling (1976), Roskam *et al.* (1976a,b), and Bast *et al.* (1977) have also described similar polysomes induced in rooster by estradiol treatment. Polysomes of about 30–40 monomeric units have been found to be engaged in the synthesis of vitellogenin. Not unexpectedly, smaller polyribosomes were found to be engaged in synthesizing albumin. In order to characterize the messengers for the two proteins, RNA has been extracted from livers of estradiol-treated male *Xenopus* or from polyribosomes immunoprecipitated with antivitellogenin or antialbumin antibodies, and assayed in a rabbit reticulocyte or wheat-germ cell-free translational system (Berridge *et al.*, 1976; Shapiro *et al.*, 1976; Wahli *et al.*, 1976). As can be seen from Fig. 7, RNA fractions from estrogen-treated *Xenopus* were found to code for immunoprecipitable polypeptides of 210,000 daltons (vitellogenin), and a large number of smaller immunospecific polypeptides were also present in the reticulocyte lysate after incubation. These fragments are thought to arise from a combination of nonspecific proteolysis of the completed vitellogenin polypeptide and the translation of partially degraded vitellogenin mRNA (Berridge *et al.*, 1976).

The large size of mRNA of vitellogenin is an advantage in its purification and consequently in the synthesis of a complementary DNA. Wahli *et al.* (1976) and Shapiro and Baker (1977) have recently prepared cDNA to *Xenopus* vitellogenin, and Shapiro has prepared a full-length copy of the message. This now offers a powerful probe to extend studies on the kinetics of mRNA accumulation (see below) as well as to study the nature and kinetics of synthesis of the primary nuclear transcripts of the vitellogenin gene.

C. TRANSLATION OF MESSENGER RNA's FOR *XENOPUS* VITELLOGENIN AND ALBUMIN IN *XENOPUS* OOCYTES

We have already noted from work from Wallace's laboratory that the *Xenopus* ovary or the oocyte does not synthesize the egg-yolk platelet proteins (phosvitin and lipovitellin), which are entirely derived from circulating vitellogenin. Although *in vivo*, circulating vitellogenin is converted into phosvitin and lipovitellin in the ovary, it is degraded when injected into oocytes (Wallace and Jared, 1969; Wallace *et al.*, 1972; Dehn and Wallace, 1973). Berridge and Lane (1976) have recently demonstrated that *Xenopus* liver mRNA for vitellogenin, when microinjected into *Xenopus* oocytes, is not only translated but that the nascent vitellogenin is correctly cleaved into platelet phosvitin and lipovitellin. Lanclos and Hamilton (1975) also detected newly synthesized lipovitellin in oocytes after injection of total liver polyribosomes obtained from estradiol-treated frogs.

The oocyte system has already proved to be a valuable living cell system for characterizing a number of eukayrotic messenger RNA's and for elucidat-

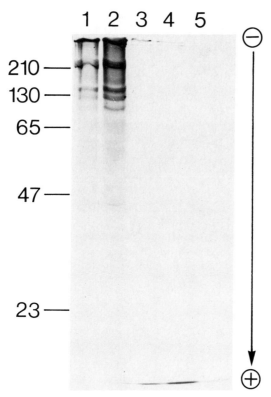

FIG. 7. Autoradiogram of SDS–polyacrylamide gel electrophoresis of the vitellogenin-specific immunoprecipitation of the translated product of rabbit-reticulocyte lysate programmed with liver RNA from untreated (slots 3–5) and estradiol-treated (slots 1, 2) male *Xenopus*. Fifty μg of total postnuclear RNA were added to a reticulocyte cell-free system incorporating [^{35}S]methionine into protein. The latter was treated with rabbit antivitellogenin antibody and the immunoprecipitate analyzed on 10% SDS–polyacrylamide gels, as described previously. Numbers on left represent molecular-weight markers; that of 210,000 is for the vitellogenin subunit. From Farmer *et al.* (unpublished).

ing the posttranslational modifications of their products (Lane and Knowland, 1975). A general feature that has emerged from work on a dozen foreign mRNA's injected into *Xenopus* oocytes is the extraordinary stability of these messages and their continued translation at maximal rates for long periods of time. For this reason too, it is significant that Berridge and Lane (1976) found that the kinetics of the translation of *Xenopus* vitellogenin mRNA, but not of *Xenopus* albumin mRNA, did not correspond to this general pattern of continued stability. As shown in Fig. 8, the rate of translation of vitellogenin was found to increase over a period of 5 days after which it declined relatively rapidly, whereas those of *Xenopus* albumin and rabbit

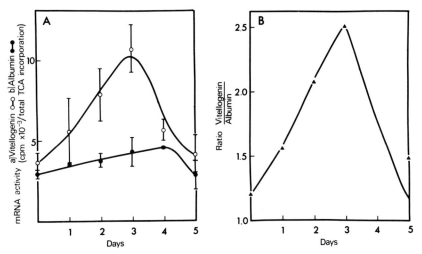

FIG. 8. The functional stability and rate of establishment of *Xenopus* liver messengers injected into oocytes. (A) and (B) show the functional stability of vitellogenin and albumin messengers. Each of a batch of about 200 oocytes was injected with total liver RNA, and at various times duplicate batches of 10 oocytes were labeled for 22 hours with [^{35}S]methionine (100 μCi). TCA-insoluble vitellogenin (O———O) and albumin (●———●) radioactivity were measured; values obtained directly by counting gel bands were checked by densitometry of autoradiograms. Vertical bars show the range of values present in the duplicate batches of oocytes. (B) shows variation in the ratio (▲———▲) of vitellogenin to albumin radioactivity with incubation time. From Berridge and Lane (1976).

globin mRNA's reached a relatively stable, maximum level very rapidly. Whether or not the potentiation of vitellogenin mRNA translation is due to a relatively slow diffusion of an unusually large RNA is not known, but the phenomenon emphasizes the importance of accumulation and activation of mRNA's when considering kinetics of induction of proteins, which may be particularly critical during development.

V. TRANSLATIONAL CONTROL AND POSTTRANSLATIONAL MODIFICATIONS OF VITELLOGENIN

A. Messenger RNA and Polysomes during Primary and Secondary Induction

The possibility of stored, inactive mRNA in the cytoplasm which can be mobilized into active polyribosomes following a developmental or nutritional signal has often been considered but direct evidence has been difficult to obtain (Tomkins and Gelherter, 1972; Heywood *et al.*, 1975). The ease with which synthesis of massive amounts of a new protein can be induced in already differentiated and virtually nondividing cells makes estradiol-induced vitellogenin a system of choice for investigating this question of specific translational control. In our laboratory, the question of a possible, selective control of translation of vitellogenin mRNA in the liver has been tackled by investigating the difference between the kinetics of accumulation of translatable mRNA and the synthesis of the protein during primary and secondary induction of vitellogenin (S. R. Farmer, E. C. Henshaw, M. V. Berridge, and J. R. Tata, unpublished). As already mentioned (Fig. 3), the characteristic lag between the administration of estradiol to male animals and the detection of vitellogenin during primary induction is much reduced in animals exposed to the hormone for a second time. The magnitude of the secondary response was greater but often shorter-lived than that of the primary response. When the rate of accumulation of mRNA, as calculated in a reticulocyte cell-free translational system (see Table IV), was compared with the appearance of immunoprecipitable polysomes actively engaged in synthesizing vitellogenin, an interesting difference between the two responses came to light. As shown in Fig. 9, translatable vitellogenin mRNA appeared in the liver relatively rapidly and at about the same rate for both the primary and secondary responses. The kinetics of mRNA appearance did

TABLE IV
DETERMINATION OF mRNA CODING FOR VITELLOGENIN IN A
RABBIT-RETICULOCYTE LYSATE[a]

Input RNA (μg)	Total incorporation (cpm $\times 10^{-3}$)	Antivitellogenin immunoprecipitable incorporation (cpm $\times 10^{-3}$)
0	3600	0
5	4680	16.25
12.5	5280	56.25
25	4980	97.50
50	4800	150.00
100	3870	127.50

[a] Optimal input of total postnuclear RNA prepared from male *Xenopus* liver at the height of the primary response to estrogen was determined in a rabbit-reticulocyte lysate cell-free translation system. Increasing amounts of postnuclear RNA extracted from livers of male *Xenopus* 12 days after the first injection of 1 mg estradiol-17β were translated in a rabbit-reticulocyte lysate cell-free system. Incorporation of [^{35}S]methionine into trichloroacetic-acid-insoluble and antivitellogenin-specific products was determined as described by Berridge *et al.* (1976). From Farmer *et al.* (1977).

418   J. R. Tata

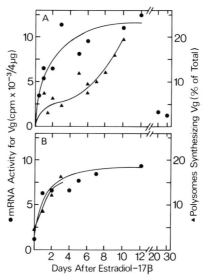

FIG. 9. Changes in levels of vitellogenin mRNA and of polysomes engaged in its translation in liver of male *Xenopus* at different stages during primary and secondary responses to estradiol *in vivo*. Forty μg total postnuclear RNA obtained at different stages of primary and secondary responses were assayed in a reticulocyte cell-free system for vitellogenin mRNA activity by immunoprecipitation of [^{35}S]methionine-labeled translation product, with antivitellogenin antibodies. Polysomes were labeled for 24 hours with 200 μCi of [^{3}H]orotic acid before removing the liver. Approximately four A_{260} units of polysomes obtained at each stage of response to estradiol were immunoprecipitated with antibody to calculate the fraction engaged in the synthesis of vitellogenin. (A) Primary response; (B) secondary response (a second injection of 1 mg of estradiol given to frogs treated with the same dose 35 days earlier). ●, Level of vitellogenin mRNA; ▲, polysomes synthesizing vitellogenin. From Farmer *et al.* (1977).

not match at later times during the primary and secondary responses, but it is the initial period of onset of the responses that is important. At this stage, one notices a marked discrepancy in the coupling of mRNA synthesis to polysome formation during the two sets of responses. The difference between primary and secondary stimulation can thus be explained by the rates at which polyribosomes engaged in synthesizing vitellogenin became functional. During primary stimulation, there was a temporal gap between the accumulation of mRNA and immunoprecipitable polysomes, whose duration is compatible with the physiological latent period. However, when the tissue resumed vitellogenin synthesis for the second time, the rate of appearance of vitellogenin was primarily a function of the rate at which mRNA appeared in the cytoplasm.

An interesting point to note in Fig. 9 is that, at 35–40 days after the first injection of estradiol when the synthesis of vitellogenin has ceased *in vivo*

(Fig. 3), there is virtually no (<4% of the maximum) mRNA in the cytoplasm. Thus, both the primary and secondary induction of vitellogenin are dependent on *de novo* transcription of the vitellogenin gene. Ryffel *et al.* (1977), using the more powerful probe of hybridization to cDNA, have come to the same conclusion for male *Xenopus* responding to primary and secondary hormonal stimuli. However, in the male chicken, Mullinix *et al.* (1976), using the heterologous cell-free translation assay, come to a different conclusion. These workers find that substantial amounts of vitellogenin mRNA, to the extent of 20% of the maximum levels during primary response, persisted at the onset of secondary response when vitellogenin synthesis had ceased. Thus, in the chicken, the initiation of secondary response may be due to the mobilization of inactive mRNA, presumably stored as mRNP particles, into active polysomes. It would be interesting to see for how long such inactive mRNA molecules persist after each single estrogenic stimulus.

The correlation between mRNA levels and active polysomes synthesizing vitellogenin during secondary induction in the *Xenopus* is analogous to the secondary induction by estrogen of ovalbumin synthesis in chick-oviduct cells (Palmiter, 1975). Because of the technical difficulties inherent in working with oviducts in immature chicks, it has not been possible to detect a similar temporal dissociation between mRNA accumulation and its translation during primary stimulation. It should, however, be noted that the oviduct cell population is drastically altered following primary stimulation (Socher and O'Malley, 1973; O'Malley and Means, 1974), whereas this is not so for vitellogenin induction in the liver.

Our studies on *Xenopus* show that some rate-limiting mechanism or factors essential for specific translation of vitellogenin messenger must be established during the latent period preceding primary induction. Such a factor has to be relatively permanently "imprinted" so that secondary stimulation then involves only a replenishment of the mRNA formed during primary stimulation and subsequently degraded. What component(s) of the translational machinery is involved is not certain, but from our other observations it may be a combination of more than one of the following: (a) The requirement of some specific initiation or elongation factor(s) (see Table II). (b) The requirement for special tRNA's, especially in view of the high serine content of the phosvitin moiety (Mäenpää, 1972). Mäenpää and Bernfield (1975) now show a preferential increase in a seryl-tRNA (AGU·AGC) in the nucleus and rough endoplasmic reticulum following estradiol injection in the rooster. (c) Our recent ultrastructural observations (Lewis *et al.*, 1976; C. D. Green, unpublished) suggest that it may be necessary to establish a stable system of endoplasmic reticulum to preferentially facilitate both translation of vitellogenin mRNA and posttranslational modification of the nascent protein (see below).

The specificity of the regulation of vitellogenin mRNA synthesis and polysome accumulation in *Xenopus* became clear when the same parameters
were examined for albumin in the same samples of tissue and subcellular fractions as for vitellogenin (S. R. Farmer, E. C. Henshaw, M. V. Berridge, and
J. R. Tata, unpublished). Figure 10 shows that estrogen administration did
not significantly affect either the levels of mRNA for albumin or the fraction
of total polysomes engaged in its synthesis. The wide variation in the values of
albumin mRNA and polysomes does not enable us to draw a firm relationship
between the downward trend in values and the lower rate of albumin synthesis *in vivo* during both the primary and secondary inductions. We have no
explanation for the scatter, but the range of 4–10% of total liver polysomes
engaged in albumin synthesis compares well with values obtained elsewhere
by different approaches (Clemens *et al.*, 1975; Green and Tata, 1976).

In our laboratory, we are now extending the above studies on the correlation between the formation and translation of mRNA to the converse
situation—that of deinduction of albumin synthesis accompanying the induction of vitellogenin, both in the whole animal and in culture (see Figs. 2 and
3). The notion of translational control for hormone-induced protein synthesis

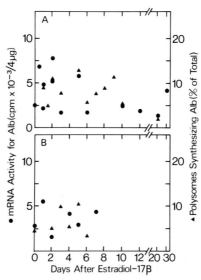

FIG. 10. Changes in levels of albumin mRNA and of polysomes engaged in its translation in
Xenopus liver at different stages of primary and secondary responses to estradiol. The same
samples of liver as those used in the experiments depicted in Fig. 9 were used, except that
antialbumin antibodies replaced those directed against vitellogenin. All experimental conditions
were the same as those in Fig. 9. ●, Albumin mRNA; ▲, albumin-synthesizing polysomes.
From Farmer *et al.* (unpublished).

or during development has been advanced for some time, particularly by Tomkins (Tomkins and Gelherter, 1972; Heywood *et al.*, 1975), and there have been some recent examples to support this idea (Young *et al.*, 1975; Zahringer *et al.*, 1976; see Humphreys, 1973; Lodish, 1976). However, in general, the inability to isolate and identify specific messenger molecules and polysomes engaged in their translation, or the failure to induce a reversible induction in a stable population of cells, has been largely responsible until now for the failure to establish well-defined requirements for specific translational control. The obvious advantages of estrogen-induced vitellogenesis, as judged by the results presented above, make it a system of choice to establish the nature and limits of translational control mechanisms.

B. Cytoplasmic Distribution of Vitellogenin Messenger RNA and Polyribosomes

In common with all secretory proteins (Palade, 1975; Rolleston, 1974), vitellogenin is synthesized on membrane-bound ribosomes (Lewis *et al.*, 1976). As shown in Fig. 11, a characteristic feature of induction of vitellogenesis is the parallel increase in the amount of ribosomal or polyribosomal populations of *Xenopus* and chicken hepatocytes (Clemens, 1974; Berridge *et al.*, 1976; Lewis *et al.*, 1976; Bast *et al.*, 1977). The build-up of additional ribosomes is coordinated with the proliferation of the membranes of the endoplasmic reticulum to which these ribosomes are bound, as established both by electron microscopy and biochemical analysis (Lewis *et al.*, 1976). A coordinated proliferation of ribosomes and the membranes to which they are bound is not a peculiar feature of vitellogenesis, but it is a phenomenon common to all cells undergoing rapid growth and development, whether hormone-induced or not (see Tata, 1973). A question that is seldom considered is whether or not there would be any significance to the synthesis of induced proteins on membrane-bound ribosomes, besides that of secretion. Two other functions briefly discussed below are the segregation of polyribosomes and posttranslational modification of nascent protein. These two features have been considered in detail elsewhere (Shore and Tata, 1977a).

The concept of segregation on membranes of populations of polyribosomes engaged in the synthesis of different classes of proteins is less easy to establish than is the role of attachment to membranes of ribosomes engaged in synthesizing secretory proteins. For the latter, it suffices to separate membrane-bound from free polysomes and to demonstrate that secretory proteins were synthesized on bound but not on free ribosomes (Tata, 1973; Rolleston, 1974). A minimum requirement for the demonstration of topological segregation is to obtain two or more distinguishable subclasses of membrane-

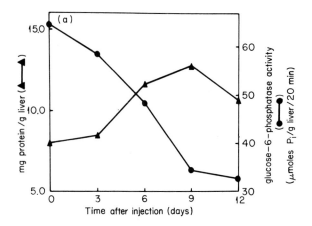

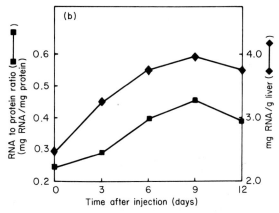

FIG. 11. Time course of changes in RNA and protein content and glucose-6-phosphatase activity (as an index of microsomal membrane proliferation) after estradiol-17β treatment. Groups of three male *Xenopus* each were injected with 1 mg of estradiol-17β at various times before death. Subnuclear fractionation of the livers was carried out as described by Lewis *et al.* (1976). The fractions (homogenate, smooth and rough microsomes, and total microsomes) were assayed for protein and RNA content and glucose-6-phosphatase activity. The total microsomal protein content has been corrected for losses to low-speed pellets using the microsomal specific activity and the amount of total activity recovered in the 640 g and 6000 g pellets (correction factor varied between 2.2 and 2.6). (a) Changes in total liver glucose-6-phosphatase activity (●————●) and in total microsomal protein (▲————▲); (b) Changes in total RNA content of liver (◆————◆) and in rough microsomal RNA:protein ratio (■————■). A lowering in specific activity of glucose-6-phosphatase indicates proliferation of endoplasmic reticulum. From Lewis *et al.* (1976).

bound ribosomes. Lewis and Tata (1973) have described a procedure based on rate sedimentation through discontinuous sucrose gradients which resolves the total membrane-bound population of polysomes into two operational subclasses of endoplasmic reticulum ("rapidly sedimenting" and "buoyant"). Using this procedure, we have recently found that in rat liver there is an 8-fold difference between the "rapidly-sedimenting" and "buoyant" fractions of membrane-bound ribosomes in the relative distribution of translatable mRNA coding for albumin and for those mitochondrial proteins that are synthesized on cytoplasmic ribosomes (Shore and Tata, 1977b). Although by itself this does not constitute definitive evidence for a topological segregation, it strongly suggests an unequal distribution of polysomes on membranes which would not be incompatible with a possible topological segregation *in vivo*.

When the above types of experiments were extended to *Xenopus* vitellogenin and albumin (both secreted proteins), a rather complex pattern of distribution of mRNA and functional membrane-bound polysomes was observed (S. R. Farmer and J. R. Tata, unpublished). At the onset of induction of vitellogenin in male *Xenopus* liver by estradiol (2–3 days), the distribution of immunoprecipable nascent chains showed that the polysomes coding for the two proteins were almost equally distributed in the two subfractions of membrane-bound ribosomes. However, as the proportion of vitellogenin-synthesizing polysomes reached their maximum level (at 6 days after hormone injection), a differential distribution of the mRNA for the two proteins became apparent. The majority of immunoprecipable vitellogenin-synthesizing polysomes was at this stage recovered in the "buoyant" fraction. On the other hand, the distribution of extracted mRNA, as revealed by translation in rabbit-reticulocyte lysate, was the same in all the subfractions of membrane-bound ribosomes for messages coding for vitellogenin and albumin.

If the above results still do not constitute definitive proof of a topological segregation of polysomes on membranes of the endoplasmic reticulum, the possibility that some function(s) other than secretion must also be served by a membrane–ribosome interaction is strengthened by the following correlations: (a) the widespread presence of membrane-bound polysomes in developing nonsecretory cells, i.e., brain, muscle, oocytes, etc.; (b) the enhanced proliferation of membrane-polysome complex in secretory cells switching to synthesis of intracellular proteins, as during growth or regeneration (see Tata, 1973). That one of these nonsecretory functions is to achieve a topological segregation can eventually only be convincingly shown by a combination of techniques of molecular biology and cell biology, e.g., by combining cDNA probes for mRNA distribution and immunohistochemical localization of the corresponding polypeptide product. The ribosome–membrane interaction may also involve some other function, compatible with topological segregation, such as posttranslational modifications of the nascent polypeptide chain, which is briefly discussed below.

C. Posttranslational Modifications

Vitellogenin is extensively modified soon after its synthesis and before it is secreted into the blood. The major modifications are the extensive phosphorylation of the 56% seryl residues of the phosvitin moiety and its glycosylation and lipidation of the lipovitellin moiety. The intracellular site for the extensive posttranslational modifications of vitellogenin may be the membranes of the endoplasmic reticulum (see Clemens, 1974; Tata, 1976).

In the scheme shown in Fig. 12, it is suggested that the enzymes and substrates for phosphorylation, glycosylation, and lipidation are available only at the membrane site, so that modification of the polypeptide would begin during and immediately after translation on the rough endoplasmic reticulum. This process would continue throughout the vectorial movement and packaging of the protein in the Golgi apparatus prior to secretion. It could thus be argued that a coordinated proliferation of polyribosomes and membranes to which these are attached (Lewis *et al.*, 1976) following hormonal induction would ensure the rapid and correct modification of the newly synthesized vitellogenin. The final physiological process of cleavage of vitellogenin to yolk-platelet proteins occurs in the oocyte; although the role of follicular cells is not clear (Wallace and Dumont, 1968; Wallace *et al.*, 1972), the recent findings of Berridge and Lane (1976) on the translation of vitellogenin mRNA injected into oocytes (see Section IV,C) are of considerable interest. These workers followed the fate of labeled vitellogenin synthesized on the injected messenger template by carrying out "chase" experiments over 3 days. Both labeled phosvitin and lipovitellin were recovered from yolk platelets in the oocyte, thus demonstrating that nascent vitellogenin, although not normally made in the oocyte, can be correctly cleaved by the oocyte if it is present as nascent protein made on injected mRNA. In view of the earlier discussion of topological segregation of mRNA or polysomes (see Section IV,B), recent studies have indicated that the injected vitellogenin mRNA is distributed, and vitellogenin synthesized, on membrane-bound ribosomes (Zehavi-Willner and Lane, 1977). It will be interesting to determine whether or not there is a differential distribution of vitellogenin mRNA with respect to some other mRNA, say that coding for *Xenopus* albumin. In any event, even if the handling of vitellogenin in the oocyte of the animal is not the same as that following mRNA injection into the oocyte, the

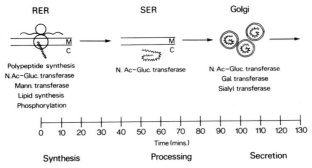

FIG. 12. Schematic representation of vectorial movement of vitellogenin synthesized on membrane-bound ribosomes through the smooth endoplasmic reticulum and the Golgi bodies before secretion into *Xenopus* blood. The location of enzymes involved in posttranslational modifications (phosphorylation, glycosylation, lipidation) in the different membrane components are indicated. The whole sequence is from synthesis of unmodified vitellogenin to the secretion of the fully processed protein is estimated to take 2 hours. RER: rough endoplasmic reticulum; SER: smooth endoplasmic reticulum; M: membrane; C: cisternal space of the endoplasmic reticulum; N.Ac–Gluc: *N*-acetylglucosamine; Mann: mannose; Gal: galactose. From Tata (1976).

capacity of the oocyte to phosphorylate, lipidate (perhaps also glycosylate), and then correctly cleave nascent protein made under direction of injected mRNA extends the usefulness of the oocyte microinjection system to the study of posttranslational modifications.

Posttranslational modifications of vitellogenin are not merely a peculiarity of egg-yolk proteins but have wider implications in cell biology. It is known that the enzymes or processes for posttranslational modifications of other proteins synthesized on membrane-bound ribosomes are also located in membranes of the endoplasmic reticulum, as e.g., the enzymes in the thyroid gland for iodination of nascent thyroglobulin, the enzyme responsible for the disulfide interchange in the maturation of ribonuclease, and the hydroxylation of proline in newly synthesized collagen (see Shore and Tata, 1977a). It is indeed surprising that this aspect of the location in membranes of modification enzymes at the site of synthesis of proteins, particularly those destined for secretion, has received scant attention. Because most, if not all, secreted proteins are modified after translation, the location of the posttranslational machinery in membranes may be the most important reason governing the synthesis of secreted proteins on membrane-bound ribosomes.

The derivation of yolk proteins from a larger precursor protein is also relevant to the current interest generated by findings that several important proteins, many of them hormones, are formed from larger precursors by proteolytic cleavage. These include insulin, parathyroid hormone, albumin, and collagen (Steiner *et al.*, 1972; Habener, 1976; Quinn *et al.*, 1975; Gallop and Paz, 1975). Specific proteolytic enzyme(s) that cleave off the hydrophobic "signal" extension at the N-terminus may also reside in the membrane component of rough microsomes (Blobel and Dobberstein, 1975). What is unique about vitellogenin in this respect is that it is itself the precursor for two (or more) totally different proteins. It may well happen that more such multicomponent protein precursors will be discovered in the future. For example the pituitary hormones adrenocorticotropic hormone (ACTH), melanocyte-stimulating hormone (MSH), and lipotropic hormone (LPH) may be synthesized on a common polypeptide precursor. Whether or not this idea is too speculative at the moment, vitellogenin represents the first example of an animal multicomponent precursor studied in such great detail.

VI. ESTRADIOL RECEPTORS AND THE EXPRESSION OF THE VITELLOGENIN GENE

It is generally accepted that all steroid hormones initiate their action by a "two-step" process by which the hormone first binds to a receptor in the target cell's cytoplasm and the hormone–receptor complex is then translocated into the nucleus to combine with "acceptor" sites on the chromatin (Jensen and De Sombre, 1973; O'Malley and Means, 1974). Although the initial event leading to vitellogenesis must be triggered by an interaction between estradiol and a receptor in the liver, extremely little is known about the nature of the receptor in bird or amphibian liver. One of the reasons for the paucity of information is that, unlike the estradiol receptor found in tissues like the rat uterus or chick oviduct, the putative receptor in chicken or frog liver is extremely labile.

Arias and Warren (1971) described a cytosol receptor for estradiol in chicken liver, but Mester and Baulieu (1972) and Lebeau *et al.* (1973) suggested that the hormone interacted directly with the nucleus without necessarily first binding to a cytosol component. In more recent studies, Gschwendt has found that estradiol binds directly to rooster liver chromatin with a high affinity ($K_d \sim 10^{-9}$ M), whereas its interaction with cytosol proteins is weak ($K_d \sim 10^{-8}$ M) (Gschwendt and Kittstein, 1974; Gschwendt, 1975). For *Xenopus* liver the information is even more scarce. A recent report has described the presence in *Xenopus* liver of a protein of low molecular weight ($\sim 20,000$ daltons), as determined by electrophoresis on polyacrylamide gels, which binds both estradiol and testosterone (Bergink and Wittliff, 1975). However, much work has still to be done before establishing a cytoplasm-to-nucleus translocation of hormone receptor as a prerequisite for the initiation of the chain of events leading to the full expression of the vitellogenin gene.

VII. CONCLUSIONS

Figure 13 summarizes the major features of the induction of vitellogenesis and also highlights the major problems that still have to be solved in order to integrate the different molecular responses of the hepatocyte stimulated by estradiol. A major problem to be resolved now is the characterization of the elements in the target cell that initially interact with the hormone in order to transmit the signal for a major developmental response, i.e., the receptors. Eventually it will be necessary to link such receptor interaction and a possible cytoplasm-to-nuclear movement of the hormone–receptor complex with the activation of the vitellogenin gene. The possibility of inducing the whole physiological process directly *in vitro* now makes it easier to attack this problem. Wangh *et al.* (1976) have proposed that it should be possible to directly test the hormone–receptor interaction by microinjection of the two

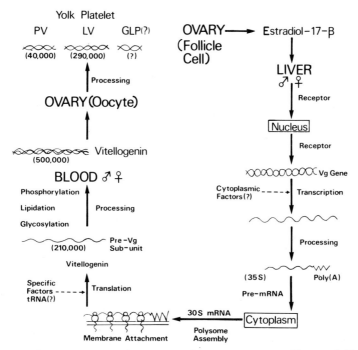

FIG. 13. Scheme summarizing the sequence of major events triggered by estradiol leading to the secretion of vitellogenin into the blood of male or female *Xenopus* and the deposition of phosvitin (PV) and lipovitellin (LV) in egg-yolk platelets. Values in parentheses refer to nominal size of RNA or protein. GLP refers to another yolk protein derived from vitellogenin and which may be phosvitin. See text for further details. GLP refers to a polypeptide derived from vitellogenin which may be a second phosvitin residue or an as yet inknown component which may be glycosylated, phosphorylated, or lipidated. From Tata (1976).

components into the oocyte in which vitellogenin should be induced if the hormone-receptor complex activates the vitellogenin gene. Our knowledge of transcriptional events is also relatively superficial. No doubt, the availability of cDNA to vitellogenin mRNA will help greatly in clarifying several questions concerning the activation of the vitellogenin gene, in the same way it has been possible to elucidate that concerning the ovalbumin gene in avian oviduct. In particular, it would be important to verify whether the vitellogenin gene is completely "shut off" in the liver of an unstimulated male frog or chicken or whether the gene is always transcribed at a low rate but that the protein it codes for is not made. The large size of the vitellogenin mRNA is particularly suited to following the dynamics of synthesis and processing of the primary transcript bearing the pre-mRNA sequences. The availability of cDNA would also help in the study of possible cytoplasmic factor(s) that may preferentially regulate the transcription of vitellogenin gene in isolated nuclei or subnuclear preparations.

Now that vitellogenin mRNA and polyribosomes engaged in the synthesis of the induced protein have been immunologically identified and extracted, an important question that can be tackled is to determine whether or not this messenger is selectively subjected to translational control. Two different lines of evidence presented above suggest that it is (a) the preferential stimulation by cell sap of estrogenized male *Xenopus* liver of the synthesis of a vitellogeninlike protein by isolated polysomes (Table II); (b) the temporal dissociation between the rate of accumulation of vitellogenin message and the active polysomes engaged in synthesizing vitellogenin (Fig. 8). Could there be a common mechanism underlying these two phenomena? An obvious explanation would be an "imprinting" of a different pattern of tRNA's (particularly seryl-tRNA) or initiation factors occurring at the onset of primary induction but which would be permanent or long lasting so as not to be rate-limiting for the translation of new mRNA produced during secondary stimulation. This question can be directly tackled by analyzing liver-cell sap for its ability to support vitellogenin translation at different stages of primary and secondary induction. Although mechanisms of specific translational control during development or adaptation have been previously proposed for other proteins (particularly for the initiation of synthesis of tyrosine aminotransferase, myosin, ferritin, and hemoglobin), vitellogenesis is particularly well suited for finding a solution to this intriguing question. Its advantages over the other systems lie principally in (a) the ease of reversible induction and deinduction, (b) an unusual gene product made in differentiated cells that would normally not express it, and (c) the ease of characterization of its messenger and polyribosomes.

Being a secreted protein, vitellogenin is synthesized on membrane-bound ribosomes, which in itself is not unusual. But the fact that the extensive and diverse posttranslational modifications of vitellogenin (phosphorylation, glycosylation, lipidation) occur in the membranes of the rough endoplasmic reticulum and Golgi apparatus may mean that posttranslational modifications are a key determining factor for protein synthesis taking place on membrane-bound ribosomes. Much interest has also been generated around the posttranslational proteolytic cleavage of larger precursors of many secreted proteins. What is unique about vitellogenin is that its cleavage does not occur in the cell in which it is synthesized but that phosvitin and lipovitellin are produced in a remote tissue, the ovary. Vitellogenin is also the first example of the synthesis of distinct animal proteins synthesized as a single multicomponent precursor. These considerations of posttranslational modifications makes it imperative that we learn more about the chemistry of vitellogenin. For example, does it have one or two phosvitin residues? Or is there another egg-yolk component besides phosvitin and lipovitellin derived from vitellogenin? Which of these fragments if at N- and C-terminus of the precursor? What confers on vitellogenin special substrate specificity for the ovarian protease?

REFERENCES

Ansari, A. Q., Dolphin, P. J., Lazier, C. B., Munday, K., and Akhtar, M. (1971). *Biochem. J.* **122**, 107–113.

Arias, F., and Warren, J. C. (1971). *Biochim. Biophys. Acta* **230**, 550–559.

Bast, R. E., Garfield, S. A., Gehrke, L., and Ilan, J. (1977). *Proc. Natl. Acad. Sci. U.S.A.* **74**, 3133–3137.

Bergink, E. W., and Wallace, R. A. (1974). *J. Biol. Chem.* **249**, 2897–2903.

Bergink, E. W., and Wittliff, J. L. (1975). *Biochemistry* **14**, 3115–3121.

Bergink, E. W., Wallace, R. A., Van der Berg, J. A., Bos, E. S., Gruber, M., and AB, G. (1974). *Am. Zool.* **14**, 1177–1193.

Berridge, M. V., and Lane, C. D. (1976). *Cell* **8**, 283–297.

Berridge, M. V., Farmer, S. R., Green, C. D., Henshaw, E. C., and Tata, J. R. (1976). *Eur. J. Biochem.* **62**, 161–171.

Beuving, G., and Gruber, M. (1971). *Biochim. Biophys. Acta* **232**, 529–536.

Blobel, G., and Dobberstein, B. (1975). *J. Cell Biol.* **67**, 835–851.

Britten, R. J., and Davidson, E. H. (1969). *Science* **165**, 349–358.

Christmann, J. L., Grayson, M. J., and Huang, R. C. C. (1977). *Biochemistry* **16**, 3250–3256.

Clemens, M. J. (1974). *Prog. Biophys. Mol. Biol.* **28**, 71–107.

Clemens, M. J., and Tata, J. R. (1972). *Biochim. Biophys. Acta* **269**, 130–140.

Clemens, M. J., Lofthouse, R., and Tata, J. R. (1975). *Biochem. J.* **250**, 2213–2218.

Darnell, J. E., Jelinek, W. R., and Molloy, G. R. (1973). *Science* **181**, 1215–1221.

Davidson, E. H., and Britten, R. J. (1973). *Q. Rev. Biol.* **48**, 565–613.

Deeley, R. G., Mullinix, K. P., Wetekam, W., Kroneberg, H. M., Myers, M., Eldridge, J. D., and Goldberger, R. F. (1975). *J. Biol. Chem.* **250**, 9060–9066.

Dehn, P. F., and Wallace, R. A. (1973). *J. Cell Biol.* **58**, 721–724.

Edström, J. E., and Lambert, B. (1975). *Prog. Biophys. Mol. Biol.* **30**, 57–82.

Farmer, S. R., Henshaw, E. C., Berridge, M. V., and Tata, J. R. (unpublished).

Follett, B. K., and Redshaw, M. R. (1968). *Endocrinology* **40**, 439–456.

Follett, B. K., and Redshaw, M. R. (1974). In "Physiology of the Amphibia" (B. Lofts, ed.), Vol. 2, pp. 219–308. Academic Press, New York.

Gallop, P. M., and Paz, M. A. (1975). *Physiol Rev.* **55**, 418–487.

Green, C. D., and Tata, J. R. (1976). *Cell* **7**, 131–139.

Greengard, O., Gordon, M., Smith, M. A., and Acs, G. (1964). *J. Biol. Chem.* **239**, 2079–2082.

Gruber, M., Bos, E. S., and AB, G. (1976). *Mol. Cell. Endocrinol.* **5**, 41–50.

Gschwendt, M. (1975). *Hoppe-Seyler's Z. Physiol. Chem.* **356**, 157–165.

Gschwendt, M., and Kittstein, W. (1974). *Biochim. Biophys. Acta* **361**, 84–96.

Habener, J. F. (1976). *Polypep. Horm.: Mol. Cell. Aspects, Ciba Found. Symp.* Excerpt Med. Found. Int. Compr. Ser. No. 41, pp. 197–219.

Heywood, S. M., Kennedy, D. S., and Bester, A. J. (1975). *Eur. J. Biochem.* **58**, 587–593.

Humphreys, T. (1973). In "Developmental Regulation: Aspects of Cell Differentiation" (S. J. Coward, ed.), pp. 1–22. Academic Press, New York.

Jailkhani, B. L., and Talwar, G. P. (1972a). *Nature (London) New Biol.* **236**, 239–240.

Jailkhani, B. L., and Talwar, G. P. (1972b). *Nature (London), New Biol.* **239**, 240–241.

Jensen, E. V., and DeSombre, E. R. (1973). *Science* **182**, 126–134.

Jost, J. P., and Pehling, G. (1976). *Eur. J. Biochem.* **62**, 299–306.

Jost, J. P., Keller, R., and Dierks-Ventling, C. (1973). *J. Biol. Chem.* **248**, 5262–5266.

Karasaki, S. (1963). *J. Cell Biol.* **18**, 135–151.

King, R. J. B., and Mainwaring, W. I. P. (1974). "Steroid Cell Interactions." Butterworth, London.

Lanclos, K. D., and Hamilton, T. H. (1975). *Proc. Natl. Acad. Sci. U.S.A.* **72**, 3934–3938.

Lane, C. D., and Knowland, J. S. K. (1975). In "The Biochemistry of Animal Development" (R. Weber, ed.), Vol. 3, pp. 145–181. Academic Press, New York.

Lebeau, M. C., Mossol, N., and Baulieu, E. E. (1973). *Eur. J. Biochem.* **36**, 294–300.

Lewin, B. (1975). *Cell* **4**, 11–20.

Lewis, J. A., and Tata, J. R. (1973). *J. Cell Sci.* **13**, 447–459.

Lewis, J. A., Clemens, M. J., and Tata, J. R. (1976). *Mol. Cell. Endocrinol.* **4**, 311–329.

Lodish, H. F. (1976). *Annu. Rev. Biochem.* **45**, 39–72.

Mäenpää, P. H. (1972). *Biochem. Biophys. Res. Commun.* **47**, 971–974.

Mäenpää, P. H., and Bernfield, M. R. (1969). *Biochemistry* **8**, 4926–4935.

Mäenpää, P. H., and Bernfield, M. R. (1975). *Biochemistry* **14**, 4820–4826.

Mester, J., and Baulieu, E. E. (1972). *Biochim, Biophys. Acta* **261**, 236–244.

Moore, J. A. (1972). "Readings in Heredity and Development." Oxford Univ. Press, London and New York.

Mullinix, K. P., Wetekam, W., Deeley, R. G., Gordon, J. J., Meyers, M., Kent, K. A., and Goldberger, R. F. (1976). *Proc. Natl. Acad. Sci. U.S.A.* **73**, 1442–1446.

O'Malley, B. W., and Means, A. R. (1974). *Science* **183**, 610–620.

Palade, G. E. (1975). *Science* **189**, 347–358.

Palmiter, R. D. (1975). *Cell* **4**, 189–197.

Palmiter, R. D., and Carey, N. H. (1974). *Proc. Natl. Acad. Sci. U.S.A.* **71**, 2357–2361.

Pan, M. L., Bell, W. J., and Telfer, W. H. (1969). *Science* **165**, 393–394.

Quinn, P. S., Gamble, M., and Judah, J. D. (1975). *Biochem. J.* **146**, 389–393.

Redshaw, M. R., and Follett, B. K. (1971). *Biochem. J.* **124**, 759–766.

Rolleston, F. S. (1974). *Biochemistry* **3**, 91–117.

Roskam, W. G., Tichelaar, W., Schirm, J., Gruber, M., and AB, B. G. (1976a). *Biochim. Biophys. Acta* **435**, 82–90.

Roskam, W. G., Gruber, M., and AB, B. G. (1976b). *Biochim. Biophys. Acta* **435**, 91–94.

Ryffel, G., Wahli, W., and Weber, R. (1977). *Cell* 11, 213–221.

Schimke, R. T., Rhoads, R. E., Palacios, R., and Sullivan, D. (1973). *Karolinska Symp.* 6, 357–379.

Schjeide, O. A., and Lai, G. C. B. (1970). *In* "Cell Differentiation" (O. A. Schjeide and J. de Vellis, eds.), pp. 447–475. Van Nostrand-Reinhold, Princeton, New Jersey.

Shapiro, D. J., and Baker, H. J. (1977). *J. Biol. Chem.* 252, 5244–5250.

Shapiro, D. J., Baker, H. J., and Stitt, D. T. (1976). *J. Biol. Chem.* 251, 3105–3111.

Shore, G. C., and Tata, J. R. (1977a). *Biochim. Biophys. Acta* 472, 197–236.

Shore, G. C., and Tata, J. R. (1977b). *J. Cell Biol.* 72, 726–743.

Socher, S. H., and O'Malley, B. W. (1973). *Dev. Biol.* 30, 411–417.

Steiner, D. F., Kemmler, W., Clark, J. L., Oyer, P. E., and Rubenstein, A. H. (1972). *Handb. Physiol., Sect. 7: Endocrinol.* 1, 175–198.

Tata, J. R. (1970). *In* "Biochemical Actions of Hormones" (G. Litwack, ed.), Vol. 1, pp. 89–133. Academic Press, New York.

Tata, J. R. (1973). *Acta Endocrinol. (Copenhagen), Suppl.* 180, 192–224.

Tata, J. R. (1976). *Cell* 9, 1–14.

Tata, J. R., and Baker, B. (1974). *Exp. Cell Res.* 83, 125–138.

Tata, J. R., and Baker, B. (1975). *Biochem. J.* 150, 345–355.

Tomkins, G. M., and Gelherter, T. D. (1972). *In* "Biochemical Actions of Hormones" (G. Litwack, ed.), Vol. 2, pp. 1–20. Academic Press, New York.

Wachsmuth, E. D., and Jost, J. P. (1976). *Biochim. Biophys. Acta* 437, 454–461.

Wahli, W., Wyler, T., Weber, R., and Ryffel, G. U. (1976). *Eur. J. Biochem.* 66, 457–465.

Wallace, R. A. (1963). *Biochim. Biophys. Acta* 74, 505–518.

Wallace, R. A. (1970). *Biochim. Biophys. Acta* 215, 176–183.

Wallace, R. A., and Dumont, J. M. (1968). *J. Cell. Physiol.* 72, Suppl. 1, 73–89.

Wallace, R. A., and Jared, D. W. (1968a). *Can. J. Biochem.* 46, 953–959.

Wallace, R. A., and Jared, D. W. (1968b). *Science* 160, 91–92.

Wallace, R. A., and Jared, D. W. (1969). *Dev. Biol.* 19, 498–526.

Wallace, R. A., Nickol, J. M., Ho, T., and Jared, D. W. (1972). *Dev. Biol.* 29, 255–272.

Wangh, L. J., and Knowland, J. (1975). *Proc. Natl. Acad. Sci. U.S.A.* 72, 3172–3175.

Wangh, L. J., Longthorne, R. F., and Knowland, J. (1976). *Symp. Soc. Dev. Biol.* 34, 151–169.

Weckler, C., and Gschwendt, M. (1976). *FEBS Lett.* 65, 220–224.

Wetekam, W., Mullinix, K. P., Deeley, R. G., Kroneberg, H. M., Eldridge, J. D., Meyers, M., and Goldberger, R. F. (1975). *Proc. Natl. Acad. Sci. U.S.A.* 72, 3364–3368.

Wittliff, J. L., and Kenney, F. T. (1972a). *Biochim. Biophys. Acta* 269, 485–492.

Wittliff, J. L., and Kenney, F. T. (1972b). *Biochim. Biophys. Acta* 269, 493–504.

Young, R. B., Goll, D. E., and Stromer, M. H. (1975). *Dev. Biol.* 47, 123–135.

Zahringer, J., Baliga, B. S., and Munro, H. N. (1976). *Proc. Natl. Acad. Sci. U.S.A.* 73, 857–861.

Zehavi-Willner, T., and Lane, C. D. (1977). *Cell* 11, 683–694.

CHAPTER 11

Multihormonal Control of the Messenger RNA for the Hepatic Protein α_{2u} Globulin

David T. Kurtz and Philip Feigelson

I. INTRODUCTION

The complex biochemical processes that determine the pattern of protein synthesis in a given cell, and the processes involved when an alteration of this pattern occurs (e.g., during normal development, hormonal induction, or neoplastic transformation) have been the focus of much of modern molecular biology. Hormones have long been known to have both quantitative and qualitative effects on the proteins being synthesized in the hormone's target cell. The subtle molecular mechanisms underlying these effects have been the focus of our attention in this laboratory for several years. An overall scheme of macromolecular metabolism in eukaryotes is shown in Figure 1. Selected regions of the genome are transcribed by RNA

433

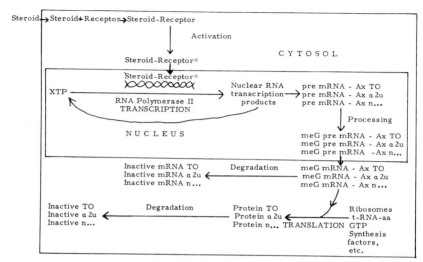

FIG. 1. Overall scheme of macromolecular metabolism.

polymerase II into the RNA precursors of cytoplasmic messenger RNA's. These nuclear RNA's undergo 5′-end modification, hydrolytic cleavage, and 3′-polyadenylation, and are then transported to the cytoplasm. There, the mRNA's combine with the ribosomes, tRNA's, and numerous factors necessary for protein synthesis to produce functional protein. The steady-state level of a given protein could be modulated at several of the stages depicted in Fig. 1: changes in the level of transcription of a given gene by RNA polymerase; selective effects on nuclear modification of specific pre-mRNA's; selective transport of specific mRNA's to the cytoplasm; increases or decreases in nuclease activity in the cytoplasm, which may act selectively to stabilize or degrade a given mRNA; changes in the translational efficiency of a specific mRNA; or, finally, alterations of the degradative half-life of the protein itself caused by changes in protease activity. Control at any of these stages could affect the level of a given protein, and, indeed, for the induction of specific proteins by steroid hormones, control at several of these levels has been postulated (Tompkins *et al.*, 1969; Chan *et al.*, 1976; Schutz *et al.*, 1973; Palmiter and Carey, 1974; Killewich *et al.*, 1975; Sharma and Borek, 1976). However, the studies done in this and several other laboratories in recent years have strongly indicated that the hormonal control of the synthesis of a given protein occurs via the modulation of the level of the messenger RNA coding for that protein, i.e., the control is pretranslational, and *may* be transcriptional.

II. α_{2u} GLOBULIN

Much of our recent work has focused on the rat hepatic protein, α_{2u} globulin. This a protein with a molecular weight of 20,000 daltons which was first described by Roy and Neuhaus (1966a) to be excreted in the urine of mature male rats and absent from the urine of female rats. It was first thought to be a prostatic secretion, but liver perfusion, immunofluorescence studies, and *in vivo* labeling have demonstrated that α_{2u} globulin is synthesized in the liver, secreted into the serum, and excreted in the urine (Roy and Neuhaus, 1966b; Roy and Raber, 1972; Kurtz *et al.*, 1976a). The function of this protein is unknown; however, it has recently been suggested that α_{2u} globulin can prevent estrogen-mediated damage to spermatogenesis in male rats (Roy *et al.*, 1976).

Because α_{2u} globulin has no known enzymatic activity, the level of this protein in liver cytosol, serum, and urine can be measured using a radial immunodiffusion assay. α_{2u} globulin can easily be purified to homogeneity from male rat urine (Kurtz *et al.*, 1976a). The purified protein is then used to prepare monospecific rabbit anti-α_{2u} globulin by repeated intracutaneous injections of α_{2u} globulin in Freund's complete adjuvant. The anti-α_{2u} globulin is then used to determine α_{2u} globulin: a solution of anti-α_{2u} globulin is mixed with an equal volume of 2% agar at 50°–54°C, and the mixture is immediately poured into a Petri dish. The agar is allowed to harden and 2-mm diameter wells are cut with a tubular cutter. Ten μl of standard concentrations of purified α_{2u} globulin are placed in several of the wells and 10 μl of the unknown samples in the rest. The plates are left at room temperature for 12–14 hours, and the diameters of the resulting precipitin rings around the wells are proportional to log α_{2u} (Fig. 2). By varying the

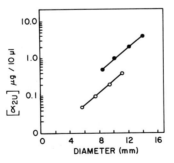

FIG. 2. Radial immunodiffusion assay for α_{2u} globulin. Diameters of precipitin rings were measured after 12 hours at room temperature. Plates contained 12.5 mg of anti-α_{2u} IgG (●) or 5.0 mg of anti-α_{2u}IgG (○) in 15 ml of 1% buffered agar. From Kurtz *et al.* (1976a).

amount of anti-α_{2u} in the agar, different ranges of α_{2u} globulin concentrations can be measured. This technique can be used to measure α_{2u} globulin concentrations in a range of 5.0–800 μg/ml.

Alternatively, the rate of hepatic α_{2u} globulin biosynthesis can be measured using an *in vivo* labeling technique: rats are given a single intravenous injection (tail vein) of [^{3}H]leucine (0.5 mCi/100 gm body weight). From 12 to 15 minutes later, the rats are sacrificed and a liver cytosol fraction is prepared. [Short incorporation times are necessary to prevent labeled hepatic proteins from being secreted into the serum (Schreiber *et al.*, 1969).] The α_{2u} globulin content of the cytosol is determined using the immunodiffusion assay, and anti-α_{2u} globulin is added to give antigen–antibody equivalence. The resultant immunoprecipitate is collected, washed thoroughly, and subjected to SDS–polyacrylamide gel electrophoresis. The counts incorporated into α_{2u} globulin *in vivo* are then compared with the counts incorporated into total S100 protein (Fig. 3). Using this technique, it has been found that α_{2u}

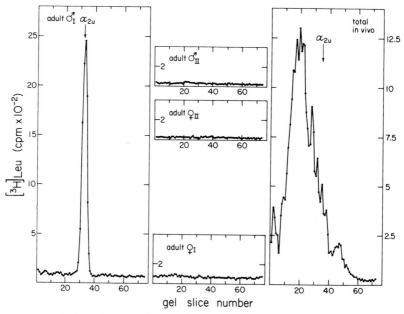

FIG. 3. SDS–Polyacrylamide gel electrophoretic profile of total S100 proteins and immunoprecipitated α_{2u} globulin synthesized in rat liver *in vivo*. Male and female rats received injections of [^{3}H]leucine. Right, electrophoretic pattern of 25 μl total S100 protein; left, α_{2u} globulin immunoprecipated from 1 ml of the labeled S100 derived from male liver; bottom center, immunoprecipitate derived from 1 ml of labeled S100 from female liver. The two top center panels verify that no labeled α_{2u} globulin could be found with a second round of immunoprecipitation. Arrows, position of authentic α_{2u} globulin. From Sippel *et al.* (1976).

globulin represents approximately 1% of total hepatic protein synthesis in a mature male rat (Sippel *et al.*, 1976), and that no detectable synthesis of this protein occurs in females.

Our interest in α_{2u} globulin is based on the fact that the hepatic synthesis of this protein is under complex hormonal control (Table I): androgens, glucocorticoids, thyroid hormones, and pituitary growth hormone are necessary to maintain normal levels of α_{2u} globulin synthesis in male rats, and estrogens administered to males repress the synthesis of this protein *in vivo* (Roy, 1973; Sippel *et al.*, 1975; Kurtz *et al.*, 1976a,b). α_{2u} globulin synthesis can be induced in ovariectomized female rats by treatment with androgens (Sippel *et al.*, 1975) (Table I). This multihormonal control of hepatic α_{2u}

TABLE I

MULTIHORMONAL CONTROL OF α_{2u} GLOBULIN BIOSYNTHESIS AND ITS MESSENGER RNA

Endocrine state	α_{2u} globulin (% of control males)			α_{2u} globulin mRNA	Ref.
	Serum	Liver cytosol	Urine		
Thyroidectomized	0	0	—	0	Kurtz *et al.*, 1976a
Thyroidectomized + 4 days T4	20	7.5	—	20.1	Kurtz *et al.*, 1976a
Thyroidectomized + 10 days T4	92.1	97.5	—	105	Kurtz *et al.*, 1976a
Thyroidectomized + androgens	0	0	—	0	Kurtz *et al.*, 1976a
Intact male + 4 days estrogens	—	35	17	34	Kurtz *et al.*, 1976b
Intact male + 8 days estrogens	—	0	0	0	Kurtz *et al.*, 1976b
Castrated male	11	—	13	12	Kurtz *et al.*, 1976b
Castrated male + 4 days androgens	37	45	36	35	
Castrated male + 8 days androgens	70	73	78	72	Kurtz *et al.*, 1976b
Adrenalectomized male	—	—	5	20	Sippel *et al.*, 1975
Adrenalectomized male + 10 days glucocorticoids	—	—	26	32	Sippel *et al.*, 1975
Hypophysectomized male	—	0	0	0	
Hypophysectomized[a] male + growth hormone + androgens + glucocorticoids	—	102	—	95	

[a] Hypophysectomized male rats (Carworth Ltd., Boston, Mass.) given rat growth hormone (1 mg/kg body weight), T4 (100 μg/kg), hydrocortisone (3 mg/kg), and/or dihydrotestosterone (500 μg/kg), daily for 10 days.

globulin biosynthesis offers a unique opportunity to study the mechanisms by which these different hormones exert their effects on their target tissues, and particularly, to probe into the molecular mechanisms by which several hormones may act coordinately to control the expression of a single structural gene. Thus, we were led to explore the effects of these hormones on the level of the messenger RNA coding for α_{2u} globulin, in order to determine whether the hormonal control of the synthesis of this protein involves effects on transcriptional, translational, or posttranslational events.

The functional level of a specific mRNA can be measured using an mRNA-dependent cell-free translational system. This technique involves the following steps:

(1) Extraction of RNA from total tissue or polysomes and isolation of the poly(A)-containing mRNA by affinity chromatography using oligo(dT)cellulose, poly(U)–Sepharose, poly(U)–mica, or untreated cellulose. The poly(A)-containing RNA usually represents 1–2% of total tissue RNA.

(2) Incubation of this mRNA in a heterologous cell-free translational system, containing ribosomes, tRNA, the initiation and elongation factors necessary for protein synthesis, and the amino acids, at least one of which is radioactive. Cell-free translational systems commonly employed include rabbit reticulocyte lysate, Krebs II ascites cell S30, or wheat germ S30.

(3) Removal of the polysomes from the cell-free system by centrifugation to obtain the released (labeled) proteins which have been coded by the exogenous mRNA.

(4) Isolation, from this released protein fraction, of the specific protein under study, usually by immunoprecipitation with monospecific antibody, but occasionally by processing the labeled released proteins in a manner analogous to the purification scheme used for that particular protein.

(5) Quantification of the amount of label incorporated into the particular protein, using SDS–polyacrylamide gel electrophoresis, slicing and counting, or fluorography on a slab gel. The counts incorporated into the particular protein are then compared with the counts incorporated into total proteins in the cell-free system. It should be pointed out than in a cell-free system, such a percentage, i.e., (cpm in a given protein)/(cpm in total proteins), is *not* an accurate reflection of the percentage of a given mRNA in the total RNA population. Cell-free systems translate smaller RNA's much more efficiently than larger ones. However, the translational systems can be used to compare an array of mRNA's for their relative content of a given mRNA (i.e., the results must always be presented as "percent of control").

For the study of α_{2u} globulin mRNA, we have found a wheat germ extract to be most suitable (Kurtz *et al.*, 1976a). This S30 is quite easy to prepare and requires no exogenous initiation factors or tRNA for maximum activity. If rat hepatic poly(A)-containing mRNA is added to the wheat germ system, the

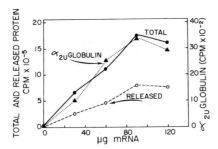

FIG. 4. Dependence of *in vitro* protein synthesis on exogenous mRNA. [³H]Leucine incorporation into total (●) and released chain (○) TCA-precipitable counts after 60-minute incubation at 30°C. Incorporation of [³H]leucine into α_{2u} globulin (▲) immunoprecipitated from 400 μl of the released polypeptide chain fraction. From Kurtz *et al.* (1976a).

extent of leucine incorporation into total protein and into released polypeptide chains is a linear function of the amount of mRNA added (Fig. 4). If monospecific anti-α_{2u} globulin is added to the released chain fraction, along with unlabeled α_{2u} globulin carrier, the immunoprecipitate contains a labeled protein which comigrates with authentic α_{2u} globulin on SDS–polyacrylamide gels (Fig. 5). [³H]Leucine incorporation into α_{2u} globulin is a

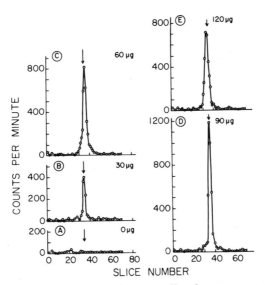

FIG. 5. SDS–Polyacrylamide gel electrophoretic profiles of immunoprecipitated α_{2u} globulin synthesized *in vitro*. α_{2u} globulin immunoprecipitated from 400 μl of released polypeptide chain fraction of the WG S30 system containing: (A) 0, (B) 30, (C) 60, (D) 90, and (E) 120 μg of male rat liver mRNA. Arrows mark position of authentic α_{2u} globulin. From Kurtz *et al.* (1976a).

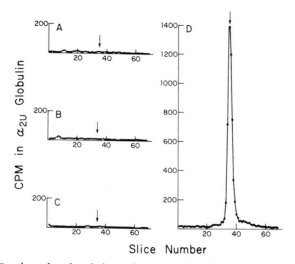

FIG. 6. SDS–polyacrylamide gel electrophoretic profiles of α_{2u} globulin synthesized in vitro by mRNA from male rat liver, female rat liver, and male rat kidney. α_{2u} globulin immunoprecipated from 400 μl of released chain fraction of the WG S30 system containing: (A) no exogenous mRNA, or 100 μg of mRNA from (B) female liver, (C) male kidney, and (D) male liver. From Kurtz *et al.* (1976a).

function of the amount of hepatic mRNA added, and parallel saturation of [³H]leucine incorporation into protein occurs with respect to α_{2u} globulin and total protein synthesis (Fig. 4). Messenger RNA isolated from female rat liver or male rat kidney did not direct the synthesis of any immunologically identifiable α_{2u} globulin (Fig. 6), although these mRNA's could direct [³H]leucine incorporation into total protein at levels comparable to that directed by male liver mRNA. Thus, the wheat germ S30 system can be used to determine the functional level of hepatic α_{2u} globulin mRNA in rats in the various endocrine states.

III. EFFECT OF THYROID HORMONES ON α_{2u} GLOBULIN SYNTHESIS AND α_{2u} GLOBULIN mRNA

It was first reported by Roy (1973) that thyroidectomy depresses the urinary output of α_{2u} globulin. We have also found that thyroidectomized males have no detectable α_{2u} globulin in liver cytosol or serum (Table I). Furthermore, thyroidectomized males showed no incorporation of [³H]leucine into α_{2u} globulin *in vivo* (Fig. 7). Treatment of these tyroidectomized males

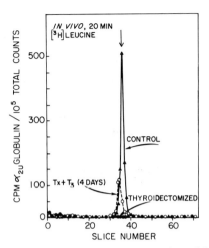

FIG. 7. SDS–polyacrylamide gel electrophoretic profiles of α_{2u} globulin synthesized *in vivo* by control, thyroidectomized, and thyroid-hormone-treated males. α_{2u} globulin immunoprecipated from livers of control males (▲), thyroidectomized males (●), and thyroidectomized males after 4 days' treatment with T3 (○). Arrow marks position of authentic α_{2u} globulin marker. From Kurtz *et al.* (1976a).

with thyroxine (T4) or triiodothyronine (T3) induced α_{2u} globulin synthesis, as measured in serum and liver cytosol, and *in vivo* incorporation of [³H]leucine into α_{2u} globulin (Fig. 7).

To determine if this modulation of α_{2u} globulin synthesis by thyroid hormones is the result of control of the functional level of its mRNA, the poly(A)-containing mRNA was extracted from the livers of these thyroidectomized and hormone-treated males, and translated in the wheat germ system. Thyroidectomized males had no detectable α_{2u} globulin mRNA (Fig. 8). Administration of T3 or T4 resulted in the production of functional mRNA for α_{2u} globulin (Fig. 8, Table I). The time course of the induction of the mRNA by thyroid hormones paralleled the appearance of the protein in the liver cytosol and serum.

The multihormonal control of α_{2u} globulin biosynthesis introduces a complication in interpreting these data obtained with thyroid hormones, because it is difficult to prove *in vivo* that the thyroid hormones are acting directly on the liver to modulate α_{2u} globulin synthesis. It was reported by Hellman *et al.* (1959) that the level of thyroid hormones greatly influences the production of androgens in male rats. Because androgens play a primary role in the regulation of α_{2u} globulin synthesis, the possibility existed that the observed effects of thyroid hormones on α_{2u} globulin synthesis in thyroidectomized males was the result of a decrease in androgen production following

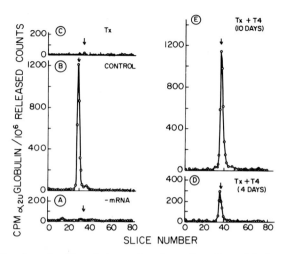

FIG. 8. SDS–polyacrylamide gel electrophoretic profiles of α_{2u} globulin synthesis *in vitro* directed by liver mRNA from control, thyroidectomized, and thyroid-hormone-treated males. α_{2u} Globulin immunoprecipitated from 400 μl of the released chain fraction of the WG S30 system containing: (A) no exogenous mRNA, or 100 μg of mRNA from the livers of (B) control males, (C) thyroidectomized males, (D) thyroidectomized males after 4 days' treatment with T4, and (E) thyroidectomized males after 10 days' treatment with T4. Arrows mark position of authentic α_{2u} globulin marker. From Kurtz *et al.* (1976a).

thyroidectomy and a subsequent reinduction of androgens by thyroid hormones. However, treatment of thyroidectomized males with a variety of androgens failed to stimulate any detectable α_{2u} globulin synthesis (Table I). It would appear, therefore, that the effect of thyroid hormones on α_{2u} globulin synthesis is not a result of modulation of androgen levels. It has recently been reported (Hervas *et al.*, 1975) that thyroidectomy greatly reduces the circulating levels of growth hormone, which is also necessary for hepatic α_{2u} globulin synthesis. However, our preliminary experiments indicate that administration of growth hormone to thyroidectomized males does not induce α_{2u} globulin biosynthesis.

These results indicate that thyroid hormones influence the synthesis of a specific protein, α_{2u} globulin, by inducing its mRNA, and may possibly be acting at the level of transcription. This is consistent with the recent reports of specific hepatic nuclear binding sites for thyroid hormones (Surks *et al.*, 1973), and the reports of increased RNA synthesis caused by thyroid hormones (Griswold and Cohen, 1973), and in contrast to earlier suggestions which postulated direct effects of thyroid hormones on cytoplasmic organelles (Litwack, 1964). As mentioned above, this induction of functional mRNA levels is compatible with, but does not provide direct evidence for, transcriptional control of α_{2u} globulin synthesis.

IV. EFFECTS OF SEX HORMONES ON α_{2u} GLOBULIN SYNTHESIS AND mRNA

Administration of estradiol-17β to an adult male rat gradually depresses the hepatic synthesis of α_{2u} globulin (Fig. 9). After 4 days of estrogen treatment (0.5 mg/kg/day), the α_{2u} globulin content of the liver S100 fell to approximately 30% of the control value, and the urinary output of α_{2u} globulin was similarly decreased. After 8 days of estrogen treatment, no α_{2u} globulin was detectible in the liver S100 or urine. Figure 10 shows the effects of increasing doses of estradiol-17β on α_{2u} globulin synthesis in intact males. Inhibition was apparent at the lowest dose used (0.25 mg/kg/day), and increasing doses of estradiol-17β brought about a greater depression of α_{2u} globulin synthesis.

To determine if this estrogen-mediated depression of α_{2u} globulin synthesis was due to a depression of the level of the hepatic mRNA coding for this protein, the poly(A)-containing RNA was extracted from the livers of these

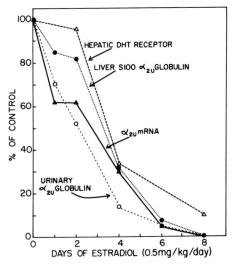

FIG. 9. Effect of estradiol-17β on a α_{2u} globulin synthesis, α_{2u} globulin mRNA, and hepatic androgen receptor (intact male). (O), Urinary α_{2u} globulin; ($\bullet$), liver S100 α_{2u} globulin; ($\blacktriangle$), α_{2u} globulin mRNA; ($\triangle$), hepatic dihydrotestosterone receptor, following estradiol-17β administration. From Kurtz *et al.* (1976b).

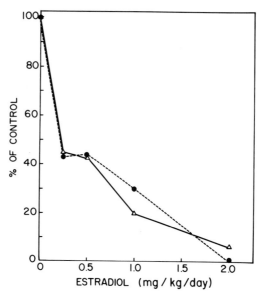

Fig. 10. Dose response of estradiol-mediated inhibition of α_{2u} globulin synthesis. (●), Liver S100 α_{2u} globulin; (△), α_{2u} globulin mRNA following estrogen administration. From Kurtz *et al.* (1976b).

estrogen-treated males and translated in the wheat germ system, and the amount of *in vitro* α_{2u} globulin synthesis directed by these mRNA's was determined. It was found that hepatic mRNA from estrogen-treated males contained diminished α_{2u} globulin mRNA activity (Fig. 11). The time course of this depression of the level of the mRNA closely paralleled the decrease of the level of the protein in liver S100 and urine (Fig. 9). After 8 days of estrogen treatment, no α_{2u} globulin mRNA was detectable. Increasing doses of estradiol were increasingly effective in diminishing the level of α_{2u} globulin mRNA, and the decreased mRNA levels correlated well with the decreased levels of the protein in liver S100 (Fig. 10).

Castration of male rats diminishes hepatic α_{2u} globulin synthesis. Fifteen days following castration, α_{2u} globulin levels in urine, serum, and liver S100 were approximately 10% of control values (Table I). This low but detectable level of α_{2u} globulin synthesis following castration seems to be maintained indefinitely. α_{2u} globulin synthesis could be induced in castrated males by administration of dihydrotestosterone (Fig. 12). An increase in α_{2u} globulin synthesis could be seen after 1 day of androgen treatment, and the levels of this protein in urine and serum reached 75–80% of control values after 8 days of treatment with dihydrotestosterone. Androstenedione and androsterone, both weakly androgenic, could also induce α_{2u} globulin synthesis in castrated

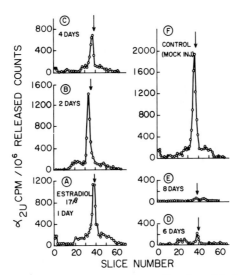

FIG. 11. SDS–polyacrylamide gel electrophoretic profiles of α_{2u} globulin synthesized *in vitro* by hepatic RNA from male rats treated with estradiol-17β. α_{2u} globulin immunoprecipitated from 400 μl of the released chain fraction of the WG S30 system containing 100 μg of mRNA from livers of male rats treated with estradiol-17β (0.5/mg/kg/day) for: (A) 1, (B) 2, (C) 4, (D) 6, or (E) 8 days, or (F) 8 days mock injected. Arrows mark position of authentic α_{2u} globulin. From Kurtz *et al.* (1976b).

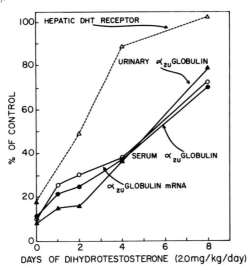

FIG. 12. Effect of castration and dihydrotestosterone treatment on α_{2u} globulin synthesis, α_{2u} globulin mRNA, and hepatic dihydrotestosterone receptor. (▲), Urinary α_{2u} globulin; (●), serum α_{2u} globulin; (○), α_{2u} globulin mRNA; (△), hepatic dihydrotestosterone receptor following administration of dihydrotestosterone to castrated males. From Kurtz *et al.* (1976b).

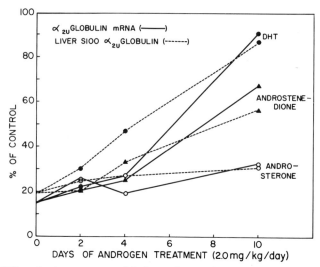

FIG. 13. Effect of androgens on α_{2u} globulin synthesis and mRNA in castrated males. Dashed lines, liver S100 α_{2u} globulin; solid lines, α_{2u} globulin mRNA induced in castrated males by (●), dihydrotestosterone; (▲), androstenedione; and (○), androsterone. From Kurtz *et al.* (1976b).

males (Fig. 13), but to a lesser extent than could dihydrotestosterone. To determine if this induction of α_{2u} globulin synthesis by androgens occurred via an induction of its hepatic mRNA, the α_{2u} globulin mRNA content of livers from castrated and androgen-treated males was measured using the *in vitro* translation assay. Livers from castrated males contained α_{2u} globulin mRNA at a level which was approximately 10% of the level in control males (Fig. 14). Administration of dihydrotestosterone to castrated males resulted in an increase in the level of translatable α_{2u} globulin mRNA (Fig. 14). The time course of induction of the message paralleled the appearance of the protein in liver, serum, and urine (Fig. 12). Androstenedione and andros-terone could also induce α_{2u} globulin mRNA, but to a lesser extent than could dihydrotestosterone, and the induction of this mRNA by these weaker androgens also paralleled the induction of the protein in liver S100 (Fig. 13).

It was reported by Roy *et al.* (1974) that sex hormones affect the level of the hepatic cytosol dihydrotestosterone receptor. Those studies determined the amount of labeled dihydrotestosterone bound to the 3.5 S protein peak in a linear sucrose gradient. Using a charcoal–dextran assay for steroid recep-tors (Beato *et al.*, 1974), we found that male rat cytosol contained a protein with high affinity for [³H]dihydrotestosterone (Table II). Livers from cas-trated males contained this protein, the putative androgen receptor, at a level approximately 20% that of control livers. Administration of dihydrotes-

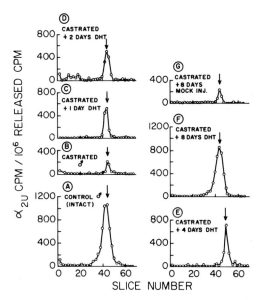

FIG. 14. SDS–polyacrylamide gel electrophoretic profiles of α_{2u} globulin synthesized *in vitro* by hepatic mRNA from castrated males treated with 2mg/kg dihydrotestosterone. α_{2u} globulin immunoprecipitated from 400 μl of the released chain fraction of the WG S30 system containing 100 μg of mRNA from livers of: (A) control males; (B) castrated males; and castrated males treated with dihydrotestosterone for (C) 1, (D) 2, (E) 4, or (F) 8 days, or (G) castrated male 8 days mock injected. From Kurtz *et al.* (1976b).

TABLE II

[³H]DIHYDROTESTOSTERONE BINDING TO RAT LIVER
CYTOSOL RECEPTOR[a]

Additions	fmoles dihydrotestosterone specifically bound per mg cytosol protein
None	44.0
50 nM estradiol-17β	47.5
10,000 nM estradiol-17β	40.8
20 nM cyproterone acetate	26.4
50 nM cyproterone acetate	11.6

[a] Two hundred μl of steroid-free cytosol were incubated at 0°C for one hour with 20 nM [³H]dihydrotestosterone together with the indicated additions. One hundred μl of a suspension of activated charcoal–dextran were then added, and the solution was kept at 0°C for 10 minutes to remove unbound steroids. The charcoal was removed by centrifugation, and the supernatants were collected and counted. Specific binding of [³H]dihydrotestosterone was taken as the difference between the cpm bound in the absence and in the presence of a 1000-fold excess of unlabeled dihydrotestosterone. From Kurtz *et al.* (1976b).

447

tosterone to castrated males increased the level of this dihydrotestosterone "receptor" in liver cytosol (Fig. 12). The level of this androgen-binding protein reached control values after 8 days of treatment with dihydrotestosterone.

It was also found that administration of estradiol-17β to male rats resulted in a decrease in the level of the hepatic dihydrotestosterone "receptor" (Fig. 9). After 8 days of estrogen treatment, the level of the hepatic dihydrotestosterone "receptor" fell to approximately 10% of the control value. Estradiol-17β does not bind to the dihydrotestosterone-binding site on the receptor, for unlabeled excess estradiol-17β could not compete with [^{3}H]dihydrotestosterone binding (Table II). Unlabeled cyproterone acetate, an antiandrogen known to compete with dihydrotestosterone for prostate receptor (Liao *et al.*, 1974), was effective in competing with labeled dihydrotestosterone for receptor in liver cytosol (Table II).

α_{2u} globulin synthesis can be induced in spayed female rats by administration of androgens (Sippel *et al.*, 1975). Hepatic mRNA from these induced females was found to contain functional α_{2u} globulin mRNA (Fig. 15). (These

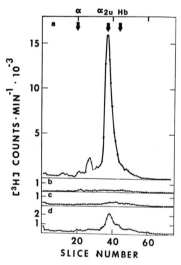

FIG. 15. SDS–polyacrylamide gel electrophoretic pattern of immunologically precipitated α_{2u} globulin synthesized *in vitro* by liver mRNA from normal male and ovariectomized female rats. (a) synthesis directed by 17.5 μg male liver mRNA; (b) synthesis directed by the cell-free system without addition of exogenous mRNA; (c) synthesis directed by 17.5 μg liver mRNA from ovariectomized females; (d) synthesis directed by 17.5 μg liver mRNA from ovariectomized females treated for 10 days with dihydrotestosterone (50 μg/100 gm body weight). From Sippel *et al.* (1975).

earlier studies were done using a Krebs II ascites translational system rather than the wheat germ S30).

These findings indicate that sex hormones affect the synthesis of α_{2u} globulin by modulating the level of its mRNA, with good correlation in all instances between the α_{2u} globulin mRNA level and the tissue level of this protein. This precludes translational control as a major mechanism in the control of α_{2u} globulin biosynthesis by sex hormones.

An early effect of dihydrotestosterone on the livers of castrated males seems to be the induction of its own "receptor." This receptor is presumably required for the steroid to exert its effects on RNA and protein synthesis. This is analogous to the action of glucocorticoids administered to adrenalectomized animals: the glucocorticoid receptor level in liver falls gradually following adrenalectomy, and an early effect of glucocorticoid hormones is the reinduction of the receptor for these hormones (Beato *et al.*, 1974).

Androgens are required to maintain normal levels of α_{2u} globulin synthesis in liver. The antagonistic effect of estradiol-17β on the synthesis of this protein in males could, therefore, be the result of indirect processes which result in a decrease in circulating androgen levels following estrogen administration. Estrogens are known to act on the pituitary gland and reduce circulating levels of luteinizing hormone (Gay and Bogdanove, 1969) which is required for the synthesis of androgens in the Leydig cells. It has also been shown (Yanaihara and Troen, 1972) that estradiol-17β can prevent the synthesis of testosterone from its precursors in testicular tissue. Either of these effects would reduce the circulating levels of androgens. The observed depression in the level of the hepatic dihydrotestosterone receptor following estrogen administration could thus be explained, because maintenance of normal dihydrotestosterone receptor levels seems to require dihydrotestosterone. By lowering circulating androgen levels, estradiol-17β would gradually decrease α_{2u} globulin synthesis.

However, it has been proposed that estrogen interferes with the uptake of androgens by hepatocytes and interferes in an unspecified manner with the receptor mechanism (Roy *et al.*, 1974). Also, estrogen administered simultaneously with androgens to spayed females reportedly prevented the induction of α_{2u} globulin in these animals. So estrogens may, in fact, be acting directly on the liver to decrease α_{2u} globulin biosynthesis.

V. EFFECTS OF OTHER HORMONES ON α_{2u} GLOBULIN SYNTHESIS AND mRNA

Studies on α_{2u} globulin mRNA levels on adrenalectomized males and hypophysectomized males also indicated that glucocorticoids can modulate

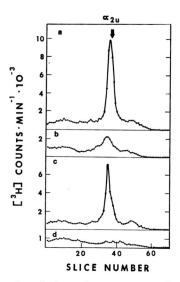

FIG. 16. SDS–polyacrylamide gel electrophoretic pattern of immunologically precipitated α_{2u} globulin synthesized *in vitro* by the liver mRNA from normal and adrenalectomized male rats. The arrow indicates the position of authentic α_{2u} globulin in the gel. Protein synthesis directed by 17.5 μg of liver mRNA from: (a) normal adult males; (b) adrenalectomized males; (c) adrenalectomized males treated for 10 days with corticosterone (3.0 mg/100 gm body weight); and (d) synthesis directed by the cell-free system without addition of exogenous mRNA. From Sippel *et al.* (1975).

the level of α_{2u} globulin mRNA (Fig. 16, Table I), and that growth hormone is required to maintain normal α_{2u} globulin levels (Table I).

Thus the multihormonal control of hepatic α_{2u} globulin biosynthesis is the result of modulation of the functional level of the messenger RNA coding for this protein. Translational control may exist as a "fine-tuning" mechanism but does not seem to be an important factor in the control of α_{2u} globulin synthesis by steroids and thyroid hormones.

VI. α_{2u} GLOBULIN SYNTHESIS IN ISOLATED HEPATOCYTE SUSPENSIONS

As mentioned above, the multihormonal control of α_{2u} globulin synthesis introduces a complication in interpreting the data concerning hormonal control of specific mRNA's, in that, it is difficult, using *in vivo* studies, to preclude the possibility that a given hormone, rather than acting directly on the liver, is actually modulating the level of another hormone, and thus indirectly affecting α_{2u} globulin biosynthesis.

Such problems would be circumvented by using an *in vitro* hormone-responsive α_{2u} globulin-synthesizing system. By perfusing rat liver *in situ* with collagenase and soybean trypsin inhibitor (Berry and Friend, 1969; Seglen, 1973; Crane and Miller, 1974), we have prepared isolated hepatocyte suspensions that synthesize and secrete hepatic proteins, and that remain viable for 36 hours. Incorporation of [³H]leucine into total hepatic protein appears almost linear for more than 30 hours of incubation. Newly synthesized protein is secreted into the medium and, by 12 hours, represents approximately 60% of the total newly synthesized protein. That this protein which appears in the medium is not due to cell leakage is shown by the fact that 10 μM colchicine, a drug known to inhibit protein secretion by binding to microtubules, completely abolishes the appearance of ³H-labeled protein in the medium. By immunoprecipitation of the medium and S100 with anti-α_{2u} globulin, it can be seen (Fig. 17) that α_{2u} globulin synthesis remains linear for almost 36 hours, and that, as *in vivo*, 90% of the newly synthesized α_{2u} globulin is secreted into the medium. Only a very small steady-state level of α_{2u} globulin is present within the cells. α_{2u} globulin synthesis in these hepatocyte suspensions is found to represent 1–2% of the

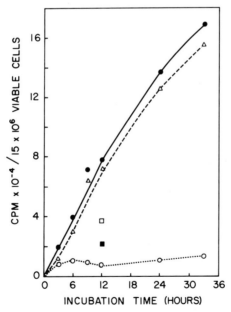

FIG. 17. α_{2u} globulin synthesis and secretion in hepatocyte suspensions. α_{2u} Globulin was immunoprecipitated from the medium and S100 derived from hepatocytes incubated with [³H]leucine. (●), Total α_{2u} globulin; (△), medium α_{2u} globulin; (○), S100 α_{2u} globulin. α_{2u} globulin in the medium (■) and S100 (□) from cells incubated with 30 μM colchicine.

total newly synthesized protein, a figure comparable to that found *in vivo*. Thus, we have an *in vitro* α_{2u} globulin-synthesizing system. Preliminary results indicate that these hepatocyte suspensions are responsive to dexamethasone for the induction of tryptophan oxygenase, tyrosine aminotransferase, and α_{2u} globulin and its mRNA.

By preparing hepatocyte suspensions from rats in the various endocrine states, and incubating these cells with each individual hormone and in combinations, it will be possible to ascertain which of the hormones are acting directly on the liver to induce the messenger RNA for α_{2u} globulin.

VII. α_{2u} GLOBULIN SYNTHESIS IN HEPATOMAS

The cytogenic alterations which occur during and after the process of transformation of normal cells to a neoplastic state lead to a change in the pattern of cellular proteins being synthesized. Certain neoplastic cells develop the capability of synthesizing carcinofetal antigens (Coggin *et al.*, 1971), or new isozymic species (Weinhouse, 1972). Alternatively, certain transformed cells lose the ability to synthesize certain tissue-specific proteins (Pitot *et al.*, 1964). We have found that α_{2u} globulin synthesis is absent in Morris minimal-deviation hepatomas 5123D and 7793 (Sippel *et al.*, 1976). Hepatoma-bearing males were given injections of [³H]leucine as outlined above, and cytosol fractions were prepared from liver and hepatoma. Immunoprecipitation with anti-α_{2u} globulin demonstrated that the host liver synthesizes α_{2u} globulin at a normal rate, while no α_{2u} globulin synthesis was detectable in the hepatoma (Table III). In order to determine if the deletion of this protein in hepatoma tissue was due to the absence of its mRNA, the Krebs II ascites system was used to measure the functional level of α_{2u} globulin mRNA in host liver and hepatoma. It was found that host liver contained normal levels of α_{2u} globulin mRNA, while the hepatoma contained no detectable mRNA coding for this protein (Fig. 18, Table III).

It was also found (Ramanaranayan-Murthy *et al.*, 1976) that the hepatoma cells contained normal levels of cytoplasmic glucocortocoid receptors that could bind glucocorticoids, undergo "activation," and translocate to both normal and neoplastic nuclei. Thus, the lack of α_{2u} globulin synthesis in hepatomas is not due to the loss or inactivation of steroid receptor during transformation. Nor is the lack of this protein in hepatoma due to some gross changes in the endocrine state of the animal bearing the tumor, because host liver synthesizes α_{2u} globulin at normal levels. The Morris hepatomas 5123D and 7793 synthesize no α_{2u} globulin because they lack the mRNA coding for this protein, suggesting that the responsible genes have become silent, or, less probably, deleted.

TABLE III
α_{2u} GLOBULIN SYNTHESIS *in Vivo* AND α_{2u} GLOBULIN MESSENGER RNA ACTIVITY
IN HEPATOMA AND HOST LIVER

| | | [³H]Leucine incorporation | | | |
| | | *In vivo*[a] | | *In vitro*[b] | |
Tissue		cpm	%	pmoles	%
Male host liver	Total	406,000	100	111.1	100
	α_{2u} globulin	4100	1.02	1.92	1.7
Hepatoma 5123D	Total	146,000	100	106.7	100
	α_{2u} globulin	0	0	0	0

[a] Values derived from 1 ml of S100 prepared from host liver and hepatoma from rats given [³H]leucine *in vivo*.
[b] Values derived from 250 μl of the released chain fraction of the Krebs II ascites translational system. From Sippel *et al.* (1976).

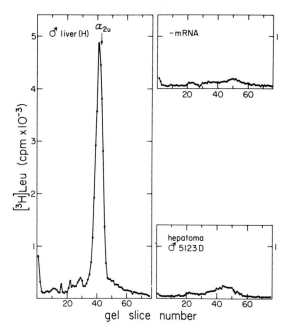

Fig. 18. SDS–polyacrylamide gel electrophoretic profiles of α_{2u} globulin synthesis *in vitro* directed by mRNA from hepatoma 5123D and host liver. Left, α_{2u} globulin synthesized *in vitro* from host liver mRNA. Bottom right, hepatoma mRNA added to the *in vitro* system. Top right, no exogenous RNA added. From Sippel *et al.* (1976).

VIII. CONCLUSIONS

The scheme depicted in Fig. 1 for the hormonal modulation of the steady-state level of a given protein shows that there are several possible sites where the hormone could be exerting its effects. We have found that, for the hormonal induction of the hepatic protein α_{2u} globulin, the control occurs through modulation of the functional level of the mRNA coding for this protein. Good correlation was found, in all the endocrine states, between the tissue level of the protein and the functional level of its messenger RNA. It has been difficult to ascertain *in vivo* which of the various hormones are acting directly on the liver to modulate α_{2u} globulin biosynthesis, but the use of the isolated hepatocyte suspensions will now enable us to explore and hopefully resolve this question.

Pretranslational control by steroid hormones has also been found in this laboratory for the hepatic protein tryptophan oxygenase (Schutz *et al.*, 1973; Killewich *et al.*, 1975). It is tempting to consider that these hormones are exerting their effects at the level of gene transcription. However, these measurements of the functional level of a specific mRNA cannot distinguish between control of transcription and modulation of nuclear processing and transport mechanisms. Such questions can most easily be approached through the purification of the specific mRNA under study. The purified mRNA may serve as a template to synthesize a complementary DNA, which can be used to identify and quantitate messenger and gene sequences for the protein under study. We have recently developed (Schutz *et al.*, 1977) a technique for the purification of specific messenger RNA's from polysomes, using a variation of the double-antibody technique. Preliminary results indicate that this technique can be used to prepare a homogeneous preparation of α_{2u} globulin cDNA. Using this probe, we will now be able to explore at a deeper level the genetic mechanisms underlying the hormonal control of the synthesis of specific proteins, and attempt to elucidate why gene expression and its control mechanisms become aberrant following neoplastic transformation.

REFERENCES

Beato, M., Kalimi, M., Beato, W., and Feigelson, P. (1974). *Endocrinology* **94**, 377.
Berry, M. N., and Friend, D. S. (1969). *J. Cell Biol.* **43**, 506.
Chan, L., Means, A. R., and O'Malley, B. W. (1973). *Proc. Natl. Acad. Sci. U.S.A.* **70**, 1870.
Coggin, J. H., Jr., Ambrose, K. R., and Anderson, N. G. (1971). *In* "Embryonic and Fetal Antigens in Cancer" (N. G. Anderson and J. H. Coggin, Jr., eds.), Vol. 1, pp. 185–202. Dept. of Commerce, Springfield, Virginia.
Crane, L. J., and Miller, D. L. (1974). *Biochem. Biophys. Res. Commun.* **60**, 1269.

Gay, L. V., and Bogdanove, E. N. (1969). *Endocrinology* **84**, 1132.

Griswold, M. D., and Cohen, P. P. (1973). *J. Biol. Chem.* **248**, 5854.

Hellman, L., Bradlow, H. L., Zumoff, B., Fukushima, D. K., and Gallagher, T. F. (1959). *J. Clin. Endocrinol. Metab.* **19**, 936.

Hervas, F., Morreale de Escobar, G., and Escobar del Rey, F. (1975). *Endocrinology* **97**, 91.

Killewich, L., Schutz, G., and Feigelson, P. (1975). *Proc. Natl. Acad. Sci. U.S.A.* **72**, 4285.

— Kurtz, D. T., Sippel, A. E., and Feigelson, P. (1976a). *Biochemistry* **15**, 103.

— Kurtz, D. T., Sippel, A. E., Ansah-Yiadom, R., and Feigelson, P. (1976b). *J. Biol. Chem.* **251**, 3594.

Liao, S., Howell, D. K., and Chang, T. (1974). *Endocrinology* **94**, 1205.

Litwack, G. (1964). *In* "Actions of Hormones on Molecular Process" (G. Litwack and D. Kritchevsky, eds.), pp. 132–153. Wiley, New York.

Palmiter, R. D., and Carey, N. H. (1974). *Proc. Natl. Acad. Sci. U.S.A.* **71**, 2357.

Pitot, H. C., Peraino, C., Morse, P. A., and Potter, V. (1964). *Natl. Cancer Inst., Monogr.* **13**, 229.

Ramanaranayan-Murthy, L., Colman, P., Morris, H. P., and Feigelson, P. (1976). *Cancer Res.* **36**, 3594.

Roy, A. K. (1973). *J. Endocrinol.* **56**, 295.

Roy, A. K., and Neuhaus, O. W. (1966a). *Proc. Soc. Exp. Biol. Med.* **121**, 894.

Roy, A. K., and Neuhaus, O. W. (1966b). *Biochim. Biophys. Acta* **127**, 82.

Roy, A. K., and Raber, D. L. (1972). *J. Histochem. Cytochem.* **20**, 89.

Roy, A. K., Milin, B. S., and McMinn, D. (1974). *Biochim. Biophys. Acta* **354**, 213.

Roy, A. K., Byrd, J. G., Biswas, N. M., and Chardhury, A. Y. (1976). *Nature (London)* **260**, 719–720.

Schreiber, G., Rottermund, H. M., Maeno, H., Weigand, Y., and Lesch, R. (1969). *Eur. J. Biochem.* **10**, 355–361.

Schutz, G., Kiilewich, L., Chen, G., and Feigelson, P. (1973). *Proc. Natl. Acad. Sci. U.S.A.* **70**, 1218–1222.

Schutz, G., Kieval, S., Groner, B., Sippel, A. E., Kurtz, D. T., and Feigelson, P. (1977). *Nucleic Acids Res.* **4**, 71.

Seglen, P. O. (1973). *Exp. Cell Res.* **82**, 391.

Sharma, O. K., and Borek, E. (1976). *Cancer Res.* **36**, 4320.

— Sippel, A. E., Feigelson, P., and Roy, A. K. (1975). *Biochemistry* **14**, 825.

Sippel, A. E., Kurtz, D. T., Morris, H. P., and Feigelson, P. (1976). *Cancer Res.* **36**, 3588.

Surks, M. I., Koerner, D., and Dillman, W. (1973). *J. Biol. Chem.* **248**, 7066.

Tompkins, G. M., Gelehrter, T. D., Granner, D., Martin, D., Jr., Samuels, H. H., and Thompson, E. B. (1969). *Science* **166**, 1474.

Weinhouse, S. (1972). *Cancer Res.* **32**, 2007.

Yanaihara, T., and Troen, P. (1972). *J. Clin. Endocrinol. Metab.* **34**, 968.

Index